THE FRANK[LIN]
The Insider's Gui[de]

www.franklinreport.com

Los Angeles
Second Edition

❖ ❖ ❖

Allgood Press
New York

AN ALLGOOD PRESS PUBLICATION

EDITOR-IN-CHIEF
Elizabeth Franklin

MAIN CONTRIBUTORS
Emily Max Bodine, Liza Bulos, Beverly Hevron, Chase Palmer

TECHNOLOGY TEAM
Michael Brennan, Charles "Skip" Schloss

PROJECT EDITORS
Joy Goodwin, Luke O'Hara

COVER CONCEPT AND ILLUSTRATION
J.C. Suares, Chesley McLaren

ARCHITECTURE ON FRONT COVER
KAA Design Group Inc.

SPECIAL THANKS TO
Pete Mueller, Jeffrey Sechrest

ISBN 0-9705780-7-5

Printed in the United States of America

Second Edition

1 2 3 4 5 6 7 8 9 10

To purchase books directly from The Franklin Report,
call our toll free number, 1-866-990-9100

Library of Congress Cataloging-in-Publication Data
Please check directly with the Library of Congress for The Franklin Report
cataloging data, which was not available at the time of initial publication.

Allgood Press
New York

TABLE OF CONTENTS

THE FRANKLIN REPORT.
The Insider's Guide to Home Services

INTRODUCTION

Welcome to the second edition of *The Franklin Report (Los Angeles)*, the regional edition of a national series of guides. *The Franklin Report* is a comprehensive survey of the city's top home service providers, based on client reviews. Some of these companies and individuals have been profiled in national magazines, and others are well-kept secrets or rising stars, but all reportedly excel in their fields. Since the firms are the "best of class," the quality ratings are consistently high. Remember, a "3" rating in quality is still "very strong," and for most people is all the quality that is necessary for most jobs.

In this guide, you will find factual information and opinions about service providers from architects and interior designers to electricians and millworkers. We invite you to use this guide and participate in our project. To submit reports on providers you have used, please visit our website at www.franklinreport.com or use the postcard or reference forms provided at the end of this book. We are committed to keeping all reviews absolutely anonymous.

Our mission is to simplify the task of choosing a home service provider by codifying the "word-of-mouth" approach. We do the homework for you with detailed fact checking, research and extensive interviews of both service providers and clients. We then give you and the community a chance to contribute to this ongoing dialogue. We hope you will join us.

Understanding The Franklin Report

The evaluations and reports on the service providers in *The Franklin Report* are based on factual information from the providers themselves, publicly available information, industry experts and thousands of in-depth customer interviews and surveys submitted through our website and by e-mail, fax, telephone and in person. The Summary, Specific Comments and Ratings that make up each entry are based on these sources and do not reflect the opinion of The Franklin Report. You can always visit our website www.franklinreport.com for the latest information on these service providers.

We have gone to great lengths to ensure that our information originates from verifiable and reliable sources, and have conducted follow-up interviews when any questions arose. In addition, it is our policy to disregard any unsubstantiated information or surveys that differ markedly from the consensus view.

Each service category opens with a brief, informative introduction to the specific home service industry. These summaries provide facts and valuable insights on how to choose a service provider, including realistic expectations and cost considerations. Armed with this information, you'll be well prepared to speak to service providers listed in *The Franklin Report* and make your best choice. In addition, the following section, "What You Should Know About Hiring a Service Provider," covers general issues that apply to all the home service categories, from interior design to air conditioning.

Each listing contains the following components:

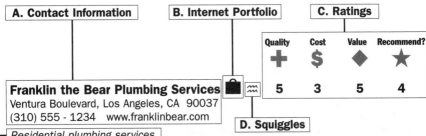

| A. Contact Information | B. Internet Portfolio | C. Ratings |

	Quality	Cost	Value	Recommend?
Franklin the Bear Plumbing Services	5	3	5	4

Ventura Boulevard, Los Angeles, CA 90037
(310) 555 - 1234   www.franklinbear.com

D. Squiggles

Residential plumbing services

References roar with praise for Franklin the Bear. We hear that principal Franklin and his band of service "cubs" ably attend to the plumbing needs at some of Los Angeles's top treehouses. Available 24 hours for emergencies, clients tell us that Franklin and his crew actually work better at night, especially in the summer months. One note of caution, however—getting service in the dead of winter seems to be quite difficult, and clients note that Franklin's cheerfulness fades a bit as the days grow shorter.

Franklin the Bear has been a family-owned and operated business for generations. The firm undertakes full plumbing renovations as well as maintenance work.

"Frankly, my dear, the Bear is the best!" "Great service. Just try to avoid January."

| E. Services and Specialties | F. Summary and Specific Comments |

A. Contact Information: Service providers are listed alphabetically by the first word in the name of the company (Alexander Zed Designs comes before Elizabeth Anderson Designs). Some vendors provide multiple home services and are listed in more than one category.

B. Internet Portfolio: The Vendors with portfolios are listed at the front of their respective sections. Visit The Franklin Report website at www.franklinreport.com to see a portfolio of online images of this company's work and a description of their philosophy and latest projects.

C. Ratings: Providers are rated in four columns—Quality, Cost, Value and Recommend?—on a 5-point scale, with 5 as the highest rating. **Keep in mind that because we only include the firms that received the most positive reviews, a 3 in Quality is still an excellent score: the ratings differentiate the top providers.**

Note also that while a high rating is generally better, a higher Cost rating means that company is more expensive. Reading the introductory section of each home service category will help you understand the specific pricing structure in each profession. Value is determined by the relationship between Quality and Cost. Recommend? indicates whether the customer would use the provider again or recommend the firm to a friend.

Quality
5 – Highest Imaginable
4 – Outstanding
3 – Strong
2 – Moderate
1 – Adequate

Cost
5 – Over the Top
4 – Expensive
3 – Reasonable
2 – Moderate
1 – Inexpensive

Value
5 – Extraordinary Value, Worth Every Penny
4 – Good Value
3 – Mediocre Value
2 – Poor Value
1 – Horrible Value

Recommend?
5 – My First and Only Choice
4 – On My Short List, Would Recommend to a Friend
3 – Very Satisfied, Might Hire Again
2 – Have Reservations
1 – Not Pleased, Would Not Hire Again

 Open folders indicate that while we did not feel we had enough information to issue a rating, we've heard good things about this firm. If you have worked with any of the firms with open folders, please fill out reference reports on these providers on our website or on the forms provided in this book.

D. Squiggles: The graphic of two squiggly lines indicates a significant number of mixed reviews about a provider.

E. Services and Specialties: This describes the main services the company provides.

F. Summary and Specific Comments: *The Franklin Report* editors distilled information from all sources to write a summary profiling each service provider that reflects the consensus view. In select categories, where appropriate, we use several abbreviations to indicate certain special recognitions the firm has received:

AD 100, 2002: listed in *Architectural Digest*'s top 100 in that year
HB Top Designers, 2005: listed in *House Beautiful*'s annual compendium
ID Hall of Fame: Interior Design's Hall of Fame Award

A number of schools are mentioned throughout this section, with the indicated abbreviations: California Polytechnic State University, Pamona (Cal Poly/Pamona), California Polytechnic State University, Obispo (Cal Poly/San Luis Obispo), Southern California Institute of Architecture (SCI-Arc), and The University of California at Los Angeles (UCLA).

In Specific Comments, clients, peers and industry experts describe the process of working with the service provider—and the end results—in their own words.

WHAT YOU SHOULD KNOW ABOUT
HIRING A SERVICE PROVIDER

Hiring a service provider to work in your home is not a task to be taken lightly. In addition to issues of quality, cost and scheduling, keep in mind that these professionals and their team may become an integral, albeit temporary, part of your life. The following nine-step process will help you make the best choice.

1. DETERMINE YOUR NEEDS

First, you need to think about the nature and scope of your project. The service provider that may be perfect for a full-scale renovation may be unresponsive and unnecessarily costly for repair or maintenance work. Are you looking for simple built-in bookcases or an integrated, elaborate library? Next, weigh your priorities. Is it crucial that the project is done by the holidays? Or is it more important to get a particular style? Is budget a driving factor? Evaluating your requirements will make it easier to decide upon a vendor, because you will know where you can compromise and where you can't. Your requirements may evolve as you learn more about what is in the marketplace, but it's a good idea not to stray too far from your original intent.

2. IDENTIFY POSSIBLE CANDIDATES

To find the best professional for the job, start by asking for recommendations from friends, colleagues, neighbors, your building superintendent or related service providers you trust. *The Franklin Report* will help you evaluate those candidates and identify others by offering insight into their competitive strengths and weaknesses.

3. CHECK PUBLIC RECORDS

To make most efficient use of your time, first do quick background checks of the candidates to eliminate those with questionable records. For each specific category, city or state licenses may be required or professional associations may offer additional information (check *The Franklin Report* overviews for specifics on each category). If you are investigating *The Franklin Report* service providers, you will be informed of past client satisfaction in this book and on our regularly updated website, www.franklinreport.com.

4. INTERVIEW SERVICE PROVIDERS

While it may not be necessary to conduct a face-to-face interview with a provider who is going to do a one- or two-day project, phone interviews are recommended before they show up. And for even the smallest job, such as window washing, it is good to get an estimate up front. For larger projects, it is wise to meet with the potential providers to learn all you possibly can about process, expectations, quality and price, and to judge your potential compatibility. Don't be shy. Personality and style "fit" are extremely important for longer-term projects that will involve design decisions or complicated ongoing dialogues, but are less critical when seeking a professional steam cleaner.

The following are general interview questions that will help you make the most of discussions with potential vendors. More specific questions that apply to each specific profession may be found in the category overviews.

- ✧ How long have you been in the business?
- ✧ What are your areas of expertise?
- ✧ Have you recently completed similar jobs? Can I speak with these clients for a reference?
- ✧ Who will be my primary day-to-day contact? What percentage of time will they spend on site?
- ✧ What sections of the job will be done by your employees and what sections will be subcontracted?
- ✧ Are you licensed, registered and insured? What about the subcontractors? (It is crucial to verify that all workers are covered by workman's compensation—otherwise, you may be liable for any job-site injuries.)
- ✧ How long will the project take to complete? Any concerns or qualifications?
- ✧ Do you offer warranties? Do you provide written contracts? Will the contract have an arbitration clause?
- ✧ Are you a member of any national or local professional associations? (While not essential, this can show dedication to the profession.)
- ✧ How will we communicate with each other? Will we have regular meetings?

Other things to consider:
- ✧ How long it took them to return your initial phone call.
- ✧ Whether or not the firm's principal attended the initial meeting.
- ✧ How receptive they were to your ideas.
- ✧ How thoughtful and flexible they were in pricing, budgeting and scheduling.
- ✧ Personality/fit and how interested they were in your project.

Licenses, registrations, insurance, bonding and permits are key parts of the equation, but are category dependent (again, check the category overviews). Any suspicious activity on this front, like a contractor who asks you to get the permits yourself or can't seem to find his proof of insurance, is a red-flag event. Similarly, anyone who refuses to give you references, asks for all the money up front or who tells you what a great deal you can have if you sign today should be eliminated from your list.

5. SPEAK WITH PAST CLIENTS

In discussions with references provided by the potential candidates, be aware that these clients should be their greatest fans. For a more balanced view, review their *Franklin Report* write-up.

Suggested questions for client references:
- ✧ What was the scope of your project?
- ✧ Were you happy with both the process and quality of the result?
- ✧ How involved were you in the process?
- ✧ Were they responsive to your concerns?

✧ Were work crews timely and courteous, and did they leave the job site clean?
✧ Did they stick to schedule and budget?
✧ Were they worth the cost?
✧ Were they communicative and professional about any issues or changes?
✧ Were they available for any necessary follow-up?
✧ Would you use this firm again?

6. Ask About Cost

Each service category works differently in terms of pricing structure. Projects may be priced on a flat fee, estimated or actual time, a percentage over materials, a percent of the total job (if other contractors are involved) and a host of other variations. What appears difficult and costly to some providers may be routine for others. Many providers will be responsive to working with you on price (and it is always worth a try). However, under strong economic conditions, the service provider may only be pushed so far—they may actually be interviewing you during your call. For more specific details and recommendations, see the pricing discussions in each of *The Franklin Report* category overviews.

7. Evaluate the Bids and Make Your Choice

Narrow your list and ask for at least three bids for substantial jobs. Describe your project clearly and thoroughly, including any timing constraints. Once received, do your best to compare the bids on an "apples to apples" basis. Ask each provider to break down their bids so you can see whether some include more services or higher quality specifications (processes and materials) than others. Don't be afraid to keep asking questions until you fully understand the differences between the bids.

Cheaper is not always better, as a bid might be lower because the workers are less skilled or the materials are of lower quality. Compare samples where possible. If speed is important, you may be willing to pay more for the person who can start next week instead of six months from now and who checked out to be more reliable on timing.

8. Negotiate a Contract

Just as with pricing, you will need to understand what the acceptable business practices are within each industry and negotiate a contract, if appropriate. Most service professionals have standard contracts that they prefer.

SMALLER JOBS: For one-time-only situations that you will be supervising (rug cleaning, window washing, etc.) a full-blown contract approved by your lawyer hardly seems necessary. Just ask for a written estimate after you thoroughly discuss the job with the provider.

LARGER JOBS: For larger projects, like a general contracting job that will cost multiple thousands of dollars and will involve many people and lots of materials, a detailed contract is essential. Don't be afraid to ask about anything that is unclear to you. This is all part of the communication process, and you don't want to be working with a service provider who intimidates you into accepting anything that you don't understand.

The contract should clearly spell out, in plain English, the following:
✧ The scope of the project in specific, sequential stages.
✧ A detailed list of all required building materials, including quality specifications. They should meet minimum code standards, unless otherwise specified.

❖ Completion schedule. Don't be too harsh here, since much may be contingent upon building conditions or supply deliveries. Some, but very few providers are open to a bonus/penalty system in meeting specific timing deadlines.

❖ A payment schedule.

❖ Permit issues and responsibilities if applicable.

❖ A description of how any scope changes ("change orders") will be processed and priced.

❖ The specific tasks and accountability of the service provider, noting exactly what they will and will not do.

Once the contract is written, you may want an attorney to review and identify any potential issues. While most homeowners do not take this step, it could save you from costly and frustrating complications further down the road.

9. Overseeing the Job

No matter how professional your team of service providers may be, they need your input and direction to satisfactorily complete the job. Be specific as to who will supervise on-site and who will be the overall project manager (responsible for the interaction between service providers and, ultimately, the dreaded punch lists). This task will fall to you unless you assign it away.

On larger projects, generally the architect (usually within their standard fee contract) or the interior designer (usually for an additional fee) will fulfill the project manager role. You should be available and encourage periodic meetings to ensure that there are no surprises in design, timing or budget. Whether or not you have a project manager, stay on top of the process (but do not get in the way), as this will be your home long after the dust settles and these professionals move on to the next project.

The Franklin Report website—a virtual companion to this reference book—is updated regularly with new vendor commentaries and other helpful material about home repair, maintenance and renovation. With expert, accessible information guiding you through the process and dedicated professionals on the job, every stage of your home project will move smoothly toward completion. Knowledge is power, regardless of whether you're engaging a plumber for a plugged sink or a general contractor for a new custom home. The Franklin Report is your companion in this process, with current, insightful home service information.

Hiring an Air Conditioning & Heating Service Provider

Known in the trades as Heating, Ventilation and Air Conditioning (HVAC), this home service industry keeps your climate controlled and your family comfortable. It is also often responsible for custom sheet-metal work, such as kitchen hoods and copper window dressing. An HVAC system means central air, central heat and central convenience, and when it's expertly installed and maintained, that means you can keep pretending global warming doesn't exist. At least until the next rolling blackout.

An HVAC Primer

All air conditioning (AC) systems operate on the same principle: a fan sucks in your home's warm air, sends it across coils that contain a refrigerant (freon), and the cooled air is then blown into the room. Central AC operates with two principal components: a condensing unit and an evaporator coil. The condenser pressurizes the refrigerant to cool it. Heat is released in the process, so the condenser must be located outside the home or with an opening to the outside. The cooled refrigerant is then pushed to the evaporator coil, where it cools and dehumidifies the warm air collected from your plenum (the dead space above the ceiling). Finally, this cool air is directed via ductwork back into the rooms. And you thought an air conditioner just contained a fan and a block of dry ice!

Heating is supplied in one of three ways: forced air, hydronic or steam. In the forced-air system, air is heated by your furnace or a heat pump, and a blower pushes it through the heat source, then into your home. While a furnace heats the air by burning natural gas, oil, wood or coal, a heat pump functions like an air conditioner with the refrigerant cycle reversed. Chill is captured by the condenser and warm air is produced with the evaporator coil. The air is further heated through electric heating coils at the blower. In the hydronic system, water is heated via gas or electricity in a boiler and distributed to radiators. The steam system works similarly to the hydronic with steam, rather than water, distributed directly to radiators.

How Much Do You Need?

Believe it or not, it's not the air that makes your room a delightful temperature. It's math. By understanding the following, your eyes will not glaze over when your HVAC man starts spouting acronyms such as BTU, SEER and CFM. All of this has to do with the efficiency of your system. Heating is measured in BTUs (British Thermal Units). Cooling is measured in tons. The capacities of furnaces, boilers, heat pumps and air conditioners are determined by how many tons or BTUs they carry. One ton equals 12,000 BTUs. The standard for an 800 square foot area is 30,000 BTUs of heat and one ton of air conditioning. Obviously, the bigger the space, the more capacity you will need.

The SEER, or Seasonal Energy Efficiency Rating, measures the relationship between space and the energy needed to properly condition its climate. The minimum SEER in California is ten. Equipment with higher SEERs will properly condition more space with less capacity. The higher the SEER, the higher the quality (and cost) of the equipment and the lower your energy bills. Ducts are a significant aspect of HVAC system efficiency. Obviously, you want to have as direct a path as possible between the heat/cool source and the space it's meant to condition. If the ductwork is too small, the distance from the source too far, or if there are too many bends and jogs, the airflow will suffer. Designers specify the amount of CFMs (Cubic Feet per Minute—the measurement of the airflow through your ductwork) necessary to properly condition a space. If this isn't met, the efficiency of your system is compromised because your equipment has to work harder than it should for a given space.

On Cost and Contracts

As in any other trade, you'll be charged for labor, materials and a ten- to twenty-percent markup for overhead, profit and tax. Demand a flat fee for equipment and installation of new systems. Make sure the estimate specifies any other associated work—electrical, plumbing, plaster—that may be necessary for the installation. All makes and models of equipment should be spelled out on the bid proposal. It's okay to sign off on the bid proposal to execute the work, but it should refer to drawings (best generated by an engineer as opposed to a sketch on the back of a napkin) and they should be attached. Clean-up, transportation, commencement and completion dates, payment schedule, change-order procedure, licensing and insurance information should all be included in the contract if not on the bid proposal. The technician should be responsible for the cost and time of obtaining permits. If your HVAC professional is fishing for a service agreement to cover the gaps in the warranty, see if you can get him to discount his price.

On Service

There are a lot of variables in HVAC, so warranties count. One year for parts and labor is typical. You should get your mechanical contractor to do a check-up once a year. Many offer early-bird spring maintenance specials before the busy AC season of summer begins, when pinning down a date with a technician is about as easy as getting Steven Spielberg on the phone. Diagnostic fees run from about $50 to $75.

Treat HVAC like oral hygiene—you wouldn't neglect to brush your teeth between check-ups, and you shouldn't neglect your filters between visits from the HVAC guy. Change them once a month in the summer—dirty filters will degrade the system's efficiency. It's easy to do—just get a lesson before the installer leaves. Also know where the gauges and valves are and learn how to read them. And try to maintain a good relationship with your mechanical man after the job. You don't want to have to pay someone else to become familiar with your custom-designed, intricate home system.

What Should I Look For in an HVAC Professional?

Your HVAC service provider is essentially putting the lungs into your house, and you don't pick your surgeon based on a nudge and a wink. Talk to general contractors and ask who they recommend. Know that HVAC invariably involves plumbing and electrical work. You want to know whether the person you hire can handle the work necessary to make the system function, or if you'll have to bring in other trades to assist. If there is going to be work in and around your existing space, find out how clean and careful he is.

Choose the service provider and system best suited to your project. For renovations in tight spaces, such as condos or historic bungalows where ceiling height is precious, high-pressure air conditioning systems that utilize small-diameter ducts permit retrofitting with little disruption to the surrounding structure. Large estates often demand computerized multiple-zoning systems, which allow for regulating different temperatures in different parts of the house. When renovating around steam, many HVAC professionals will recommend switching to hydronic. For the green-minded, an ozone-friendly refrigerant, while a little more expensive, should be an option given by every high-end mechanical pro. Your research into a good HVAC person will be more effective if you learn a few things about how these systems work. There's more to HVAC than thermostats.

CREDENTIALS, PLEASE

HVAC is a complicated field. With all the inter-trade coordination, mechanical-speak and math involved, your mechanical contractor should be backed up with the required licensing and insurance. This includes coverage for general liability, workman's compensation and property damage. Manufacturers and distributors are a great source for recommending mechanical contractors, and often distinguish the best with awards. The EPA requires anyone working with refrigerant to be licensed. For more information, check out the Air Conditioning Contractors of America website at www.acca.org.

QUESTIONS YOUR HVAC CONTRACTOR WILL ASK

❖ Where is the interior unit going to go? Large utility room? A closet?
❖ Do you have permission to place a condenser outside? From the co-op? The city?
❖ Is there enough ceiling height to add ductwork?
❖ Where do you want the controls? How many zones?

AIR CONDITIONING & HEATING

💼 FIRMS WITH PORTFOLIOS 💼

D.A. Engel Heating & Air Specialist 💼   4   3   5   5
19425 Soledad Canyon Road, Suite 341, Santa Clarita, CA 91351
(661) 268 - 1209
HVAC installation and service

Dave Engel considers all the angles in installing a heating and cooling system—for example, he likes to check the angle at which the sun hits the house. Engel's comprehensive approach has won him clients from Santa Barbara to San Diego, for whom he performs both new installations and remodeling jobs. Projects range from small studios to mansions, with maintenance service available after completion. The firm is big on air purification, encourages the use of ozone-friendly refrigerant and is a dealer for Lennox.

Engel has been in the industry since 1979, but it wasn't until 2005 that he opened D.A. Engel Heating & Air Specialist. Customers appreciate that Engel always gives two or three options on system packages and pricing, and explains the pros and cons of each in an up-front, clear manner. The firm's main clientele are contractors and business managers. We hear that Engel really takes the time to talk and listen when he visits a job. His technicians all follow Engel's lead, providing a level of product and service that makes clients call the firm "an excellent value for the money."

"High level of integrity and loyalty." "Dave has made sure at every step that we are satisfied." "When the supplier failed to deliver a special UV filter at the last minute, Dave called around the entire area, located a filter that was a two-hour drive away, and went himself to pick it up." "Super job."

FIRMS WITHOUT PORTFOLIOS

Air Design   5   4   5   5
12306 Hatteras Street, West Hollywood, CA 91607
(818) 980 - 7342
Expert HVAC installation and service

Air Design owner Joe Camky is highly skilled, knowledgeable and ethical—no wonder he's busy. But clients say they'd rather wait for his services than call anyone else. Camky and Air Design offer high-end residential HVAC design/build, complex systems with multi-zoned thermostats and air filtration in historic renovations and massive new homes. The firm is well versed in meeting the demands of high-caliber customers. Service is limited to past clients, or to those who sign up for Air Design's maintenance program.

Camky, who has been honing his craft since the 1970s, is known as an innovator who's helped to formulate new industry practices. Clients rave about his attention to detail and his hands-on approach. With only three employees, Camky does the design and installation himself. He and his men interact well with clients, who describe them as being "extremely fair," "prompt," "professional" and "always tidy." While Camky's costs ride high on the charts, customers say his value is off the map.

"It's rare to find someone who knows his craft so well." "Great sense of humor, always a pleasure to be around." "Hasn't disappointed us in twenty years." "He was there when he said he'd be there." "Our system works perfectly." "I like details, and unlike other contractors I've dealt with, Joe was always polite and thorough in explaining what he planned to do and why." "Joe is honest beyond compare." "Joe's true genius is his ability to mastermind any complicated air conditioning design."

AZ Air Conditioning and Heating   3.5   3.5   4   4.5

18627 Topham Street, Reseda, CA 91335
(818) 705 - 8892   www.amstd-dealer.com/dis_34/5387/home.htm

HVAC installation and service

Customers looking for A to Z service on their HVAC systems find it at AZ Air Conditioning and Heating. Whether you're building a home or just cooling down your existing digs, we hear this firm spells "success" the first time. AZ prides itself on timeliness and reports say their installers "appear as if by magic" at the appointed hour. Founded in 1984, AZ designs, installs and services indoor and outdoor air conditioners, gas furnaces and heat pumps.

AZ is a member of American Standard Customer Care, which imposes a rigid vendor-training program in service. Reports say this training pays dividends in the maintenance and service programs, where friendly technicians are on a first name basis. AZ employs a team of twenty technicians and also has a toll-free number for client emergencies 24 hours a day.

"My gut was right on the money. Your crew was just as professional, courteous and responsive as you, and the job was completed without a glitch." "Your workers were professional, organized, neat and clean, and the job was completed in only two days!"

Broadway Air Conditioning & Heating   4   4   4   4

1748 21st Street, Santa Monica, CA 90404
(310) 829 - 3416

HVAC installation and service

Established in 1926, this third generation company stands behind its work, going above and beyond the industry-standard one-year warranty to offer two whole years. The firm's Air Conditioning & Heating division performs custom installations of central HVAC systems for the residential market, including some *Architectural Digest*-worthy homes. The division also crafts light fixtures, skylights and mailboxes from high-end architectural sheet metals, such as copper and brass. Broadway Industries, the company's service arm, works with homeowners and also performs maintenance for the finished properties of some of Santa Monica's top contractors.

Owner Alexander Merzel oversees 30 highly trained technicians. Merzel's investment in his men is evident in the firm's outstanding quality and reliable, prompt service: phone calls are returned immediately.

"For AC emergencies, I absolutely recommend them." "Alexander and his crew stayed until all my questions were answered."

Certified Services
309 West Verdugo Avenue, Burbank, CA 91502
(800) 266 - 2301   Sales@csihvac.com

4.5   4   4.5   4.5

HVAC installation and service

Insiders promise that this family owned and operated firm is certifiably brilliant. Certified doesn't just work around clients' heating and cooling energy needs—it also makes every effort to accommodate their busy schedules. The company designs/builds systems that improve indoor air quality and energy efficiency. Projects range from small residential remodeling jobs to new custom construction. A well-regarded maintenance and service department keeps the customer satisfied. Noise-sensitive A/V facilities turn to the firm for sound attenuation, while designers tap it for architectural sheet-metal work, such as its stylish registers made from polished nickel or brass. The firm serves the LA basin.

Established in 1973, the firm is now overseen by second generation siblings Shannon, Dane and Michael Frank. They head a dedicated staff of 32, many of whom have been with the company for years. Certified's collective experience means that the staff knows what is available and can therefore give clients options. Sources tell us that Certified is a great source of information about the various rebates available from LA's many municipalities for installing energy-efficient equipment.

"Responsible, reliable and always helpful." "I had them over for installation, but they gave me real piece of mind."

Comfort Control Corp.
14649 Titus Street, Van Nuys, CA 91402
(818) 781 - 7666   www.comfortz.com

4.5   4   4.5   4.5

HVAC installation and service

This company puts the client in the driver's seat when it comes to comfort. The firm provides installations and retrofits of large custom homes and service all across the city. Comfort Control's commercial projects include designing and building super-sensitive HVAC systems for recording studios and editing suites. Designers and contractors turn to Comfort Control for ozone-safe equipment, high-efficiency designs and computerized zoned-control systems. The architecturally sensitive firm supplies all manner of custom architectural grills to conceal its handiwork. Because of its stellar reputation, the firm is frequently called in to fix other technicians' less exacting work.

Owner Russ Cox established the company in 1973. He coordinates the service side of things while twenty-year Comfort Control vet George Pershin oversees the installation crews. The firm has 21 employees who reflect the two principals' attention to detail and commitment to customer satisfaction. Responding to demand for its quality service, the company recently expanded its maintenance program to include systems it did not originally install. Service calls include a reasonable diagnostic fee that is applied to charges for any work performed. The popular maintenance plan now boasts over a thousand customers.

"Every time I've moved, I've had them do my AC." "They've been around a long time." "These guys are professionals: reliable and efficient."

	Quality	Cost	Value	Recommend?
	✚	$	◆	★

Continental Refrigeration/Heating & Air Inc.

3   3   4   4

5900 Smiley Drive, Culver City, CA 90232
(310) 838 - 6666   www.continentalheating.com

HVAC installation and service

We hear the Continental drift is to provide comfort, quiet and quality. The company will repair any type of equipment, sending its radio-dispatched technicians to homeowners and businesses on the west side at any hour of the day or night. Continental is a Lennox dealer and also comes highly recommended by Unico, the manufacturer of high-pressure air-conditioning systems.

"It's refreshing to deal with a firm with their integrity and diligence after hearing so many horror stories about contractors and subcontractors."

Custom Heating & Air

3.5   3   4.5   4

Huntington Beach, CA 92646
(714) 596 - 9796

HVAC installation and service

When it comes to HVAC solutions, Custom isn't just blowing hot air. We hear this company is extremely creative in solving installation problems. Owner Dan Burr designs, installs and services high-end systems from the South Bay to Beverly Hills. Projects tend to be new construction, from condo build-outs to ground-up estates. The firm specializes in Unico high-pressure air-conditioning systems, and is known for its expertise in zoned and centrally ducted split systems.

Burr started his small company ten years ago and remains the point person. He is known to blend his mechanical designs seamlessly into architectural elements and is said to be "meticulous on installation."

"Very satisfied. They did a great job on my business." "A worry-free experience. They took care of everything."

E. L. Payne Co.

3   3   4   4

106 Cerrocrest Road, Beverly Hills, CA 90210
(800) 357 - 2963   www.elpayne.com

HVAC installation and service

Los Angeles builders, homeowners and commercial customers trust this large, long-standing HVAC contractor. A Lennox dealer, the firm offers installation and services and repairs just about any heating and AC system out there. With Payne's shop location across the basin and a fleet of 25 driver-technicians, clients can expect quick, dependable service—including emergency service.

"A company that has been around for years and does excellent work." "He is a gentleman of the old school."

	Quality	Cost	Value	Recommend?
	✚	$	◆	★

John K. Keefe Inc.

9221 West Olympic Boulevard, Beverly Hills, CA 90212
(310) 274 - 9888

Plumbing and HVAC service and repair

See John K. Keefe Inc.'s full report under the heading Plumbers

M.B.A. Mechanical   4   3.5   4.5   4.5

960 Enchanted Way, Simi Valley, CA 93065
(805) 520 - 0603

HVAC installation and service

References attest that this firm graduates among the best in its class. M.B.A. complements its commercial retail and industrial maintenance work with new installations of HVAC systems in high-end homes. Whether it's controlling the climate of an art dealer's collections or improving a family's indoor air quality, the company earns high marks. The firm takes on jobs in the San Fernando Valley, West LA, Woodland Hills and Agoura, working directly with homeowners. Larger projects are negotiated, while smaller jobs are priced per hour.

Old hands with some of the biggest HVAC companies in the area, principals David Jaffo and Kevin Ferguson bring a combined 38 years of industry experience to the table. They oversee a well-trained and serious-minded staff of eleven, who we hear deliver excellent, professional service.

"Consummate professionals. Reliable service." "They're a no-nonsense company."

Surfside Plumbing and Rooter

1917 Roscomare Road, Los Angeles, CA 90077
(866) 321 - 7473   www.surfsideplumbing.com

Plumbing installation and service, sewer cleaning and replacement, HVAC installation and service

See Surfside Plumbing and Rooter's full report under the heading Plumbers

Temperature Equipment Corporation   4   3.5   4.5   4.5

10667 Louis Avenue, Granada Hills, CA 91344
(818) 368 - 5749

HVAC installation and service with a personal touch

Past clients of this installation and remodeling firm tell us the temperature is just right. The company's territory stretches across LA and to parts of Orange and Ventura counties, and its jobs range from $100 register replacements to $400,000 multi-zoned systems. Temperature provides full design/build services to homeowners and works with engineering consultants. Bells and whistles include UV-sterile air filtration, quiet systems and high-efficiency designs. Temperature also offers preventive maintenance plans, doing one of the most comprehensive system check-ups in LA.

President James Kontos has been in the heating and air-conditioning field for 35 years and started Temperature Equipment in 1979. When you hire Kontos's firm, you get Kontos: he personally sizes up each job and gives the estimate. He fields twelve technicians schooled in the latest HVAC technology, taught to deliver excellent customer service. Outstanding quality at standard prices makes Temperature a hot commodity.

"Jim Kontos and his entire staff have always provided us with exceptional work." "We have used Temperature Equipment for over 25 years as our sole suppliers of new equipment and service. Very professional." "Pleasant and responsive."

	Quality	Cost	Value	Recommend?

Thermal-Cool

Quality 4 Cost 4 Value 4 Recommend? 4

1995 Down Street, Riverside, CA 92507
(909) 656 - 6333

The poet Robert Frost speculated that the world would end in fire or in ice. Obviously, he never experienced the sweet moderation of a Thermal-Cool system that balances these eternal opposites. "Everything we do is for the comfort of our clients," proclaims the Thermal-Cool motto, and their unimpeachable record with the Better Business Bureau, Refrigeration Service Engineers Society and Air Conditioning Contractors of America speaks to their commitment to fair-dealing with the client. In fact, we hear their service is "top notch."

Since 1985, Thermal-Cool has served the inland hills of LA with quality Bryant and Premier systems. Thermal-Cool installs and services AC, heating, humidifiers, air cleaners and thermostats. They also offer air quality tests and air balancing services to optimize the air flow in your home.

"We are so glad we went with Thermal-Cool. Our house is now comfortable and we want you to know how much we appreciate the integrity of everyone involved with putting in our new system."

Hiring an Architect

Creating a home will be one of the largest investments in your lifetime. An excellent architect can make your dreams come true and, just as importantly, help you avoid construction nightmares. He is the protector of your investment, and your ally in ensuring that the subcontractors deliver exactly what you have envisioned.

Famous architects have made history with their brilliant work as well as their eccentricities: Frank Lloyd Wright demanded control over every inch of a house's design, right down to the table settings; Stanford White brought as much drama to his life (and death) as he did to the stunning spaces he created. An architect's work lives on indefinitely, leaving an indelible mark on people's lives and on the community. But don't get your heart set on achieving fame through an architect who brings celebrity to your address. The best matches are usually made with talented, hard-working and experienced professionals who are able to commit themselves fully to your project.

The architect is your guide through the entire building process—from refining your vision and defining your needs to documenting them in plans and specifications; from suggesting contractors to counseling on budget; from monitoring the progress and quality of construction to certifying payment to the contractor and from answering questions to settling disputes. He or she is the point person working on behalf of your interests. The clarity and thoroughness of the architect's drawings and the extensiveness of his or her involvement in the design and building process are keystones to a successful project. If the architect forgets a beam, the whole job could come crashing down—or more likely, you'll have to pay a little extra to get that beam retrofitted.

Where Do I Start?

Choosing an architect isn't easy. Each professional has his or her own design philosophy, style and way of doing business. Talk to friends, realtors and contractors. Review the online portfolios on the Franklin Report (www.franklinreport.com) and look in magazines. You should interview three to five firms to get a sense of what you're looking for. Make sure to meet with the individual who will be designing the project, not just a principal selling you on the firm. If you and the architect don't click, move on. The most important thing to look for is stylistic understanding and good chemistry. You're going to be working closely for a long time, bouncing ideas and problems off each other with a lot at stake. You want somebody with whom you'll enjoy the ride. Not surprisingly, architects consider the same thing when choosing which clients to take on.

Get a sense of the quality of the architect's past designs. Ask to see not only his portfolio, but the blueprints of those past jobs. The architect's clarity and thoroughness will be evident in the detailing and the notes. Not all blueprints are created equal, and the same goes for the people who draft them. Another important step is to get feedback from past clients. You want to know if a prospect was accessible and collaborative, if he was expedient in turning drawings around, responsive to questions and revisions and if he visited the site and met with the contractor regularly.

If an architect makes his living doing leading-edge homes and you have an English Tudor house, it's clear that this collaboration isn't going to work. Go with somebody who is well-versed in the style you're looking for. Also keep in mind that the specific structure to be designed is as important as the style. An architect who has never designed a beachfront home in Santa Monica is bound to be ignorant of certain details and codes that will inevitably become major factors in the job. This may also be the case if you are renovating an old Craftsman bungalow in Highland Park and are subject to historic preservation restrictions. Your architect should relate to your personality, preferences, vision, logistical constraints and lifestyle.

SPECIFIC CONSIDERATIONS

It's very important to have a realistic sense of the constraints and possibilities regarding budget and building codes. It's the architect's job to define these things for you. Identify how familiar a candidate is with the local codes, and whether he is sensitive to cost. He needs to be able to help you navigate the permitting and inspection process and massage the budget by substituting materials and methods or modifying the design. Also, you should be vocal about any special stylistic interests and timing specifications you have from the outset. If using a particular contractor or building an environmentally considerate and efficient home is important to you, speak up. Remember, certain architects only dip their toes in certain ponds.

ON COST AND CONTRACTS

If you think you've found a partner, it's time to start thinking about the fee. When thinking about architectural-related costs there are two important factors to consider: 1) the cost per square foot that this particular architect will design (what is typical for them) and 2) the architect's fee as a percentage of construction costs.

Costs per square foot have significantly increased in the past few years. Whereas $250 a square foot was possible for the high quality architecture designed by those in the Franklin Report, now the typical higher budget cost is $300 to $350 for the "4 quality" architect, and is thus considered a 4 in cost in the ratings in the Franklin Report. The higher quality architects correspondingly and, not surprisingly, usually design higher-cost homes. So the 4.5 or 5 quality-rated architect is often doing $400 to $800+ per square foot, some as high as $1,500 to $2,000 on a regular basis. This is critical to discuss with the architect up front so he will not spend the time and energy to design plans incompatible with your budget.

In terms of the architect fee, the standard range as a percentage of construction is usually from 13 to 15 percent, which includes the design up to finished surfaces (no landscape, no non-attached furniture). Thus, a cost rating of "4" in the Franklin Report equates to a 13 to 15 percent fee. Larger projects generally have smaller fee percentages, down to about 11 percent. At some of the more established and high-profile firms, the percentage might be as high as 18 to 22 percent, based on the architect's status and reputation in the industry. The scope of the job, the level of quality and detail, the pace and length of schedule, and the client's personality all factor into how an architect calculates his fee.

This fee may be based either upon an hourly rate or a flat percentage of construction or a combination of the two. For example, some architects may charge hourly through the schematics stage, then charge a percentage of construction cost from there. Alternatively, there may be a fixed or maximum ("capped") fee based on accumulated hourly rates. Regardless of the method of calculation, standard fees for the Los Angeles area should be in the above ranges for the corresponding quality of work.

The fee, the responsibilities associated with it (revisions through permitting, frequency of on-site visits, payment certifications and punch list review), and the compensation procedure for any extra work should be spelled out in a contract. This can be an Architect's Letter of Agreement or a standard contract issued by the American Institute of Architects (AIA).

LICENSES AND PERMITS

To earn his title, an architect must have a state license. He does not have to be a member of the AIA, which is purely a professional membership association. (Frank Lloyd Wright never joined.) The typical qualifications for licensing are: 1) a degree from an accredited school of architecture, requiring three or more years of study, 2) three years of apprenticeship under the supervision of a licensed architect and 3) passing a five-day exam. Exact requirements vary from state to state. Cities require that drawings submitted for permit review be certified by a state-licensed professional.

It is also essential that your architect be very familiar with local building code requirements and regulations. Local codes vary widely, and a small misunderstanding can lead to a big inflation of budget and schedule after everyone's committed to a particular plan. In Los Angeles, as in most places, any alteration that does not fit the building code's definition of a minor repair requires an architect's application and certification of plans for approval and issuance of a building permit. The city building department also requires the architect to certify completion of the construction before anyone can occupy the space. If you live in a landmark building, you will also have to consider the approval of your plans by the cultural heritage commission. Your architect should be responsible for filing all the appropriate paperwork and addressing any code concerns during the permitting process.

THE ARCHITECTURAL DESIGN PROCESS

Whether you're courting your architect or have already made the plunge, communication is critical. You're choosing someone to translate an epic fantasy that only you have imagined into three-dimensional reality. For an architect to develop an idea, you need to be able to convey in detail what it is you are looking for. Bring sketches, pictures, notes, clippings, Rorschach tests—anything that will tune him in to the same frequency. And take your turn to listen. Your architect will invariably come up with design ideas, offering inventive solutions and innovative alternatives to your rough-hewn proposal. Also, you want an architect who can deliver options.

Once you've made your architect the designer of record, your first big discussion should involve fleshing out your nebulous dreams into cold hard details. The number of rooms, how and when you will use them and the flow of space are questions he will need answered in order to come up with a first round of schematic designs. Don't panic if these are incomplete. These rough sketches and drawings will be revised and refined as you review them until you are satisfied. The architect may produce a model to help you visualize the layout of your future residence.

How Long Will It Take to Draw Up a Plan?

The easy answer is as long as you keep changing your mind. But even when you are finally satisfied, you'd be astounded by the number of people who get to throw in their two cents before construction begins.

After you and your architect have agreed on the drawings, they may pass through the hands of various historical, design or landmark review boards; planning and zoning boards; structural, mechanical, electrical and plumbing engineers; fire life/safety and Americans with Disabilities Act (ADA) reviewers; and your kids. After the experience, you'll know how a writer feels when he tries to get his screenplay through the Hollywood system unscathed. Depending on the complexity of the job and profile of the location, expect the review process to take from two to six months.

Once the basic layout is approved, the architect can move forward and prepare more detailed drawings to define the scale and scope of the project. It's never more true than in construction that the devil is in the details. You must communicate absolutely everything your heart desires. Finishes, brands, models, installation methods, notations on code, fixture selection, materials to be used—all need to be documented in plans and specs by the architect. At this point, the estimate for cost gets a whole lot clearer.

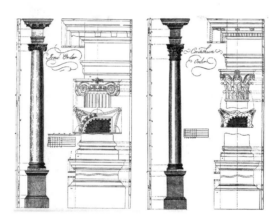

The Architect Through the Process

Most people approach contracting candidates with thorough and clear documents in hand. However, it is recommended that you include a contractor at the outset of the design process in order to get a realistic assessment of construction costs, otherwise you may be disappointed by budget-busting bids. Your architect should assist you in the process of hiring a contractor to coordinate construction. (See the Franklin Report contractor section for reliable and recommended choices.) It is typical for several contractors to bid on a job. Your architect can help you sift through the proposals to make sure that everything necessary is included and that you are comparing apples to apples. While the architect may have some existing relationships (which can be helpful), ultimately, the hiring decision is yours.

Throughout construction, the architect is responsible for making frequent appearances on site to monitor job progress, troubleshoot, answer questions and verify that all details and code requirements are being met per his plans and specs. It is becoming increasingly common for banks to require the architect of record to certify pay applications in order to release funding to the contractor.

Again, this requires the architect to visit the site to assess whether or not the work completed is commensurate with the request for payment. As construction draws to a close, the architect must lead the "punch list process" of those missing, incomplete, unpolished and mishandled loose ends.

Working with an architect who matches your personality, ideas and particular project will make this one of the most memorable adventures of your life. You may enjoy building your house so much that, like Thomas Jefferson, you'll immediately make a habit of it. "Architecture is my delight," wrote Jefferson, "and putting up and pulling down one of my favorite amusements."

DRAWING IS JUST THE BEGINNING. YOU HIRE AN ARCHITECT TO:

- ✧ Interpret code.
- ✧ Estimate budget and schedule.
- ✧ Offer options for materials and methods.
- ✧ Recommend contractors and review bids.
- ✧ Document contractual obligations.
- ✧ Sign and seal plans for permitting.
- ✧ Review and certify pay applications.
- ✧ Monitor progress and quality.
- ✧ Lead the punch list process.
- ✧ Be your advocate! Take on project management responsibilities (determine the extent up front).

Quality	Cost	Value	Recommend?
+	$	◆	★

ARCHITECTS

🧳 FIRMS WITH PORTFOLIOS 🧳

Appleton & Associates Inc.   5   5   5   5
1556 17th Street, Santa Monica, CA 90404
(310) 828 - 0430   www.appleton-architects.com

Historically-based, exquisitely-crafted, appropriate architecture

Clients and peers deem Marc Appleton a master of historical architectural languages, interlacing tradition with his own California lilt. There is no one signature look to Appleton's work, but rather there is a feeling that the buildings belong to the land and a certainty that they will fulfill the clients' dreams. His "bigger isn't necessarily better" approach keeps his designs warm and intimate; however, the "significant achievements" require a substantial investment. Landscape is seen as integral to the process, with the perimeter of the home dissolved with resonant plant materials. Intellectually dexterous, Appleton has been praised for "elegantly solving architectural problems that confound others."

The sole principal of this firm of twenty, Appleton is active in the design process, yet this "collaborator extraordinaire" can delegate to associates in his two offices. Paul Williger heads the sixteen-person Santa Monica office, while Ken Mineau helms the nine-person Santa Barbara office. Those who know Appleton are quick to point out that his love for architecture "began in building tree forts as a kid." He went on to earn an undergraduate degree in English literature from Harvard and a graduate architecture degree at Yale before working with the inimitable Frank Gehry for four years.

The firm will work anywhere in the US, but most of its clients can be found in Bel Air, Beverly Hills, Brentwood, Malibu, Santa Monica, Santa Barbara—and up and down the California coast. The firm splits its slate between remodels and ground-up single-family homes, occasionally taking on a boutique hotel or an institutional or civic project. The firm can work at lower ranges, but they generally accept ambitious $500+ per square foot projects of between 4,000 and 7,000 square feet, with standard architectural fees as a percentage of construction. AD 100, 2000, 2002, 2004.

"The homes do not look like an architect's creation, but like it is the right house in the right place." "Will do a perfect Georgian mansion, but with slightly softer California edges." "Marc has a unique ability to travel within a local vernacular with great depth and ease." "The most generous human on earth. Cares more about his clients than his own pocketbook. If he has made enough, he will stop charging." "Unbridled client service." "Absolutely makes the most of the property that is available, especially in a challenging situation." "Set in his ways in a good way." "Grounded and stays traditional—within that region's definition of traditional." "A straight shooter—tells it like it is." "We became great friends with Marc and his wife through the process." "Not the person to go to if you are on a tight budget." "You are undertaking a once-in-a-lifetime project with correspondingly high costs, but it is so worth it."

BAM Construction/Design

| | | | |
| 4 | 3 | 5 | 4.5 |

150 West Channel Road, Santa Monica, CA 90402
(310) 459 - 0955   www.bamcdi.com

Creative, innovative, green residential architecture

Artist first, architect second, but uniquely talented in both disciplines, Brian Murphy is open to new ways of doing everything, even after twenty years heading up his own firm. As practical as he is creative, Murphy works in all contexts and budgets. Delighted clients tell us he even does interiors, designing down to the salt and pepper shakers. Murphy learned the ropes of the construction/design business working for the family construction company, and he brings this unique perspective, occasionally filling the role of general contractor for the firm's twenty to thirty annual projects himself.

Clients find Murphy a kick to work with, calling him "a gestalt kind of guy." With an office overlooking the ocean, Murphy has been known to grab one of the five surfboards that adorn his office and catch a couple of waves while thinking about his latest project. Insiders say his evolutionary, inventive approach necessitates a "super-confident" contractor—if the job is not helmed by Murphy himself. Though he works primarily in an intellectually engaged, modern style, Murphy can and will design in vocabularies ranging from classical to wildly contemporary. We're also told that the environmentally sensitive Murphy is a proponent of "green" building practices and materials and drives a hybrid electric/gas car. Always pushing the envelope in terms of both form and function, BAM is capable of experimenting with offbeat materials for efficiency or shock value, but the backgrounds retain a quiet neutrality.

BAM works primarily in Los Angeles, although the firm has completed projects in Japan, Hawaii and New York. Most of Murphy's commissions are residential single-family homes. Of these, the work is divided evenly between new home construction and remodels and renovations. BAM will accept projects as small as one room. While the firm's fees are standard and generally billed out with respect to time and materials, we hear typical new houses come in at about 4,000 square feet, at a $200 to $300 per square foot cost which is described as quite reasonable. However Murphy is not afraid of any budget, having done a commercial job for fifteen dollars per square foot. Fees are also on the moderate side.

"Brian's a calm, engaging and fascinating individual. He really enjoys thinking about the meaning of architecture in life." "Brian's very pragmatic—not one of those guys who shoot the moon and worry about costs later." "Murphy found us a contractor who walks on water, because he's so knowledgeable about building." "I just love going around and looking at his work because he's always coming up with new and innovative things." "Such a good guy. His creativity is incredible." "My steam shower is so seductive, featuring an abstract mosaic of Greek gods." "Good understanding of space and really knowing what can be done." "Brian takes a lot of joy in figuring out the less expensive." "He can do it all from nice classic fresh changes to over-the-top abstract." "So positive, so upbeat."

Belzberg Architects

| | | | |
| 4.5 | 4 | 4.5 | 4.5 |

1507 20th Street, Santa Monica, CA 90404
(310) 453 - 9611   www.belzbergarchitects.com

Hip, creative modern architecture

This innovative and exciting architecture firm is noted for pushing the technological envelope with "sculpturally creative" homes. A masterful designer and creator of articulated surfaces, Hagy Belzberg uses proprietary compositional milling technologies to mold becoming wooden curtains onto the face of modern concrete structures. We're told Belzberg thoughtfully integrates outdoor spaces with indoor living, remaining environmentally consistent with an industrial twist.

Clients find Belzberg a "fabulous" creative champion and "incredible" working partner who "listens so well." A graduate of the Harvard School of Design, Belzberg heads up a firm of nine architects based in a spacious warehouse in Santa Monica. An LA native, Belzberg landed a job in Frank Gehry's office just three months before venturing off to found his own company in 1993. The firm's rapid ascent is reflected by the fact that it was chosen from a long list of hopefuls in a national competition to design the restaurants and retail store at the Walt Disney Concert Hall.

The firm splits its time between commercial and residential commissions, with homes generally ranging from 5,000 to 12,000 square feet. Belzberg's reasonable fees increase with interior buildouts, with price per square foot typically at $300 to $500. By the end of the experience, clients say, they think of Belzberg as "a friend"—albeit one with impeccable architectural marksmanship.

"A marriage made in heaven based on aesthetics. Hagy absolutely 'got' us." "He always is so calm and always has a solution." "Created these incredible sliding doors that treated the pool like an extension of the living room. Incredible." "Excellent at returning calls." "We had a budget issue with the contractor and Hagy stood with us all the way." "A lovely, warm, engaging guy." "As delightful at a dinner party as he is on the job."

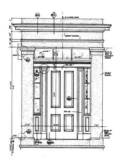

Benjamin Clavan, Architect, AIA 📷   3.5   3   4.5   4.5

755 North Laurel Avenue, Los Angeles, CA 90046
(323) 653 - 6320   benjamic@earthlink.net

Contemporary architecture with personalized client services

Clients consider Benjamin Clavan an invaluable guide through the creative and logistical labyrinth of design and construction. His fresh, livable take on mid-century modern features eclectic interiors that use color as an architectural quiver. We're told Clavan is equally adept working with small or awkward sites in dense neighborhoods or on large multi-acre estates. And as a past member of the Planning and Public Facilities commissions in West Hollywood, Clavan is an ace at navigating complicated permitting, zoning and entitlement issues on the Westside.

Clavan started his firm of three in 1982 and holds an undergraduate architecture degree from Virginia, as well as a Master's Degree and a PhD in architecture from UC Berkeley. We hear Clavan goes "way beyond the call of duty" in dealing with clients and managing contractors. He is also known to design the interiors for most of his projects.

Clavan works most often in Beverly Hills, Los Feliz, Hancock Park and other exclusive neighborhoods in LA and San Francisco. His residential work includes new home construction, large renovations and the restoration of architecturally significant homes with floor plans from 1,200 to 5,000-plus square feet. With costs per square foot occasionally dipping below $300, Clavan's firm offers options more modest than standard.

"If I wanted to do something he would elaborate options that inevitably offered better flow or access. He has very good spatial awareness." "We've not only enjoyed working with him, but have been very impressed with how quickly he was able to incorporate our specific needs and desires into a beautiful, interesting and practical design." "He really stretched our budget. Took every penny we put in and doubled our investment." "Benjamin was very skilled at managing his way through our intricate community design restrictions and requirements."

Callas Shortridge Architects 💼   4.5   4.5   4   4.5

3621 Hayden Avenue, Culver City, CA 90232
(310) 280 - 0404   www.callas-shortridge.com

Highly contemporary, delineated architecture with panache

Callas Shortridge wins accolades from clients and peers alike for creating modern structures using rich materials and site-specific cues to complement the landscape in a striking form. Often there are asymmetrical roots, splayed columns and canted walls, but mostly there is a tribute to the light and space they arrange. Principals Barbara Callas and Steven Shortridge have carried the torch passed to them from the inspired design legacy of their friend and partner, the late Frank Israel—but they also ignited their own bright light. We hear the partners' clean, abstract designs are also sensitive to the nuances of livability.

Clients find this small firm of eight "very dedicated" and say the principals personally see each project through. The company has been in business under its current name since 1996. Callas holds a graduate architecture degree from UCLA, while Shortridge's is from MIT. The firm deals primarily with residential commissions, but it does accept an occasional commercial or institutional project.

Callas Shortridge works mainly in the Pacific Palisades, Bel Air, Venice and Beverly Hills areas. However, they have completed projects in London, Las Vegas, Tel Aviv, Canada and Florida. Many of the firm's jobs are "transformative remodeling" projects of both significant and modest size, and these are always highly collaborative with the client. The firm's fees are said to be expensive, but worth an end result that is "the envy of everyone who comes into the house."

"We wanted to go for the best and we did." "They are both very meticulous and have incredibly good taste, to say the least." "You might have the idea that modern means cold, but what I got was wonderfully warm." "After two years in this house, I like it even better now—they had amazing foresight." "It has spectacular views that are framed in a magnificent way." "We have become good friends."

Chu + Gooding Architects 💼   4   4   4   4.5

2020 North Main Street, Suite 13, Los Angeles, CA 90031
(323) 222 - 6268   www.cg-arch.com

Modern, uplifting, artistic architecture

Annie Chu and her husband Rick Gooding are said to "elevate the architectural experience" with their intelligence, eloquence and willingness to listen to clients and collaborators. Chu and Gooding founded their firm on the conviction that an environment must be both beautiful and useful, exuding a "poetic materiality" that reflects both the emotional quality and the sensuality of the space. Bright and becoming, their work transcends stark modernism, arriving at a clean, post-modern aesthetic utility. Clients happily report that the principals are as warm as their luminescent designs and light-splashed interiors.

Chu and Gooding collaborated on their first project in 1987, and formally established the company in 1996. Both studied with architectural icons—Chu with

Frank Israel, Gooding with Richard Meier—and both hold architecture degrees from Columbia University. They garnered great laurels in 2002, when their firm was selected to design the interiors of two floors in Frank Gehry's LA Philharmonic Center.

With a staff of six architects, Chu + Gooding takes about ten projects annually, about half of which are residential homes averaging 3,000 square feet. The lion's share of the firm's work comes from Santa Monica, Venice, Brentwood and Beverly Hills, but Chu and Gooding have also done work in Kentucky, New York City, Ireland and the Netherlands. The cost of residential design with this highly respected firm comes in at $350 to $600 per square foot—an expense we're told is well worth it.

"Absolutely fabulous. They are easy to work with, and they have an uncanny understanding of space and how to mold it." "Annie is so great. She listens. Never talks at you. Really loves to hear your ideas but will guide you and educate you along the way." "I chose them because they were the only architects who I felt really listened and seemed to care about my dream project." "They elevate the whole team—makes everyone work in a collaborative manner." "Annie really displayed, both verbally and through drawings, an amazing grasp of form and function." "I am in the building business myself, and I was so impressed by their intellectual quality. But they were never intimidating." "Dramatic, happy, clean rooms with upsweeping lines."

Dean Nota Architect   4   3   5   4.5

2465 Myrtle Avenue, Hermosa Beach, CA 90254
(310) 374 - 5535   www.nota.net

Contemporary architecture; narrow beachfront and urban lot specialist

Rather than show them pictures or talk about his designs, Dean Nota takes clients through one of his existing houses "as quickly as possible" in order to inspire them—"and inspire, he does." As the principal of this small firm of three, Nota is said to take great pride in the personal attention he gives each project and its owner. After extensive interviews to identify site issues of the home-to-be and lifestyle issues of its owners, Nota creates "contemporary homes with a distinct mid-century modern feel." These spaces feature open plans, creative level changes and abundant natural light, and are constructed with various materials, including concrete block, metal and wood.

Clients call Nota "gifted in his ability to collaborate" and say he is notable for having "clients who really like him and clients whom he really likes." Insiders admire his skill at packaging spacious floor plans in narrow beachfront lots or dense urban neighborhoods. We're told he enhances each location with deft incorporation of city and ocean views as well as outdoor living areas.

Nota established his firm in 1982 after graduating from the first-ever class at SCI-Arc, where he was one of the founding students. He went on to teach at his alma mater until 1988. A major player in the South Bay, Nota has also completed projects in Montana and Oregon. He handles four to five major projects each year, mainly residential commissions consisting of ground-up new home construction of 2,500 to 4,000 square feet and the occasional apartment build-out. Noted for his "sensitivity to budgetary constraints," Nota's modest to standard fee is based on a percentage of overall construction costs, hourly rates or a fixed price.

"I am from a family of artists and he listened to my needs for a studio/ residence and responded with ideas that would serve me over my lifetime." "He creates intimate spaces that are livable and inviting, while staying true to the contemporary ideal." "Dean has a magnificent way with framing panoramic views." "Remains calm, even around stressed-out clients." "I was surprised by his diligence in solving design challenges and would do another project with him in a minute. The experience was truly one of the high points of my life."

	Quality	Cost	Value	Recommend?
	✚	$	◆	★

Dennis Gibbens Architect

| 4.5 | 4.5 | 4 | 4.5 |

1628 1/2 Ocean Park Boulevard, Santa Monica, CA 90405
(310) 452 - 8438   www.gibbensarchitect.com

Architecture rooted in scale and proportion

For many traditionalists looking to delve into the modern game, Dennis Gibbens is the architect of choice. While Gibbens is best known for his work in classical framework, more recently he has been creating clean, streamlined contemporary spaces with "the warmth and the woods of past eras." A New York transplant, Gibbens brought a classical sense of proportion with him when he came to Los Angeles fifteen years ago, and he has gained a reputation for incorporating fine details. Clients say Gibbens is "more like a magician than an architect" in his ability to translate abstract concepts into tangible design. This "highly responsive and professional" firm's workload includes both substantial remodels and ground-up designs of free-standing single-family homes. Gibbens also incorporates interiors and the surrounding landscape into his designs.

Clients appreciate how Gibbens "listens and interprets," tailoring his ideas into "what you envisioned, as long as he thinks it is a good idea." They tell us "he's got great taste" and proves "delightful to work with." Gibbons received his Master of Architecture from Columbia and worked as a designer in the offices of I.M. Pei and Partners before starting his private practice in 1986. He moved to Los Angeles in 1991 and is the sole principal of a firm of five.

While Gibbens has maintained a working presence in New York City, he's mostly found these days in celebrity-saturated neighborhoods like Beverly Hills, Hancock Park, Bel Air and Brentwood. Recent clients have included Kevin Costner, Debra Messing, Renée Zellweger and David Hyde Pierce. The firm concentrates on residential commissions that average 7,000 square feet and generally range from $300 to $400 per square foot, but can go much higher.

"The process can be incredibly disruptive in the client's life, but Dennis is an excellent coordinator, taking the load off my shoulders." "He will continue to modify his ideas until you both agree." "David is such a calm, warm presence, and is so discreet." "Because we were doing an addition to an old shingle-style home, he had to mesh the old with the new, and he did it seamlessly and in an appealing way." "Unlike a lot of LA architects, he understood that with three dogs I couldn't have a yellow couch made out of rice paper." "An incredibly talented and humble man."

Ferguson & Shamamian Architects, LLP

| 5 | 5 | 4 | 5 |

270 Lafayette Street, Suite 300, New York, NY 10012
(212) 941 - 8088   www.fergusonshamamian.com

Significant, traditional, regal architecture

Ferguson & Shamamian's stunning realizations of classically inspired traditional architecture have propelled the firm into the highest echelons of the profession. Sometimes described as the "Rolls-Royce" of residential architects, the firm's clients are equally select. Designs are exceptional in their detail and their knack for referencing historical traditions while staying true to the site—so that in California the firm's Georgian homes tend to be less lugubrious, boasting clean lines and attenuated details.

Founded in 1988 by three former employees of Parish-Hadley Associates, the firm has since grown to a staff of 65, many of whom have been with them ten plus years. Partners Mark Ferguson (who holds a Masters of Architecture from Princeton) and Oscar Shamamian (his Masters of Architecture came from Columbia) lead the firm today.

We hear one of the company's two principals is involved in every project, whether it takes place in Beverly Hills or the Hamptons. Based in New York, the

Quality	Cost	Value	Recommend?
✚	$	◆	★

firm collaborates with several local architects of record to execute its projects in Southern California and works seamlessly with the area's finest interior decorators. Ferguson & Shamamian is reputed to be extremely efficient in managing the design and construction process, offering "incredible" personal service. In addition to residential commissions, this company also offers master planning and design of resort communities.

About fifteen residential projects are taken each year across the country, with six to eight in Los Angeles. More than half the firm's current commissions consist of single-family new-home construction, the remainder being gut renovations or alterations and additions of apartments, townhouses and free-standing homes. Though the partnership gravitates to high profile, 10,000+ square-foot, big budget projects, it remains grounded and takes on some mid-level budget projects. Charging an hourly rate for its fee and designing homes that can average $600 per square foot, the firm is widely considered "one of the very best, if you can afford it."

"The definition of organized." "They take great care with every detail. You can trust them to pick all the doorknobs and do it right." "Unbelievable team of professionals." "The spirit of their work is of the craftsmanship of generations past." "Exceptionally expensive but exactly correct." "The best you can hire in that genre and they are also incredibly delightful."

Goldman-Firth Architects   4.5   3.5   5   4.5

24955 Pacific Coast Highway, Suite A202, Malibu, CA 90265
(310) 456 - 1831   www.gfarchitects.com

Modern, light-infused, harmonious architecture

Partners Ron Goldman and Robert Firth layer light and space as an expression of the exterior landscape and the client's inner needs. The firm's use of harmonious lines, historically derived courtyards and simple materials gives its work a soft, comfortable feel. Modern in style, Goldman-Firth designs possess an uplifting joy that brings a personality to each home. The firm does not draw a line between the inside and the outside of the house and will also take on independent landscaping projects. We're told the principals are "warm and direct" in their dealings with the client, maintaining flexibility and responsiveness.

Goldman is a fellow of the American Institute of Architects and studied architecture and planning at Princeton University and MIT. He has been in practice for more than 37 years and opened his own firm in 1976. Firth, who holds a Bachelor of Architecture degree from Arizona State University, joined the firm in 1983. On the institutional side, Goldman-Firth has carved a niche for itself as the designers of choice for religious institutions and private schools, working on such projects as the Hillel Center at UCLA and the Mirman School for Gifted Children in LA.

Located in Malibu, the office has nine employees. Today, about a third of the firm's fifteen active projects are residential and repeat business constitutes over half the docket. Ground-up homes average 6,000 square feet with lower than standard per square foot costs and lower fees either at a fixed cost or capped.

"They stay true to the design expression—will not mix motifs; but will always develop an appropriate answer for the client that maintains the integrity of the project." "They built on a bluff corner and really took advantage of views and positions of the lot." "Innovative expertise." "They get joy from their work." "Modern minded, but not somber or too serious." "Their strong exposure to institutional projects allows them to find lower-cost yet becoming alternatives, making them very attractive pricewise."

	Quality +	Cost $	Value ◆	Recommend? ★

Harry Newman 💼

4.5   4   4.5   4.5

634 Tree Top Lane, Thousand Oaks, CA 91360
(818) 889 - 0880

Highly detailed, intricate traditional architecture

Harry Newman built his name working as a highly sought-after architectural illustrator for the likes of Skidmore Owens & Merrill and Mies van der Rohe for more than twenty years. Now he works as the sole proprietor of his own firm, creating high-end designs for an esteemed clientele that includes Steven Spielberg (his LA residence) and Meryl Streep. Clients most often turn to Newman for fresh takes on Arts & Crafts and Mediterranean styles, though many say he has at least equal strengths in the modern genre.

Newman reportedly excels in large-scale renovations, where the structure is essentially stripped down to its bones. A University of Illinois graduate, he takes on about six major projects each year, carrying budgets up to and beyond $5 million. Newman is well known for his enthusiasm and charisma, and this "real character" will take on smaller projects on a whim if he "connects" with the client.

The majority of Newman's 35-year-old practice is residential, and he often designs the interiors of his projects, right down to the furniture and lamps. The firm works exclusively in Southern California in places like Malibu, Pacific Palisades, Bel Air and Hollywood Hills. He charges a standard percentage of overall construction costs.

"Before we began, we spent days together looking at different houses and seeing which elements I liked best." "He's extremely independent and definitely has an opinion about everything." "I think he's unique in that he really can figure out any architectural challenge." "Every square inch of space was maximized." "He named the house Symphony, and he's exactly right. The house is just like a symphony, with every note sitting right where it's supposed to be." "I didn't want typical modern. I wanted something new, and he was able to come up with a sketch in the blink of an eye."

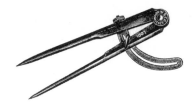

KAA Design Group Inc. 💼

5   4.5   4.5   5

4201 Redwood Avenue, Los Angeles, CA 90066
(310) 821 - 1400   www.kaadesigngroup.com

Evolved, traditional architecture and landscaping with a modern view

In its quest for an evolved "New Regionalism," KAA takes the great historic Mediterranean, Spanish Colonial, Romanesque and European traditions and instills them with a compelling, contemporary spirit. KAA's homes embrace all the details of the past, yet are marked by an indoor/outdoor flow awash in ambient light, offering extraordinary views with extensive glass walls and enormous pocket doors. There is also an excellent balance between a highly analytical approach to the craft ("a finely oiled machine") and a sincere respect for timeless domestic sentimentality, making the process pleasurable and the results heartwarming.

Founded in 1987 by Grant Kirpatrick, the firm recently changed names and has three additional partners: Steve Straughan, Erik Evens and Michael Eserts. Clients work with one of the four partners, all of whom are said to be "very responsive" and "incredibly sharp." The firm's staff, numbering 50, is praised just as highly, and the nontraditional office has a "fresh young openness of approach" with the architects riding razor scooters to get to the next department. Kirkpatrick and Eserts received their architecture degrees from USC, while Straughan earned his at Tulane and Evens from California Polytechnic State University, San Luis Obispo. In addition to residential renovations and ground-up construction, the firm also does independent landscaping and accepts occasional retail, museum or gallery projects.

Many of the firm's commissions are in Brentwood, Pacific Palisades, Beverly Hills and the South Bay, but it has also completed projects in Beirut, Cabo San Lucas, Miami, New York and Chicago. Projects range from 4,000-square-foot urban beach homes to 12,000+ square-foot suburban estates. Price per square foot starts at the standard $350 and goes up from there, with standard fees.

"They are confidently bridging the classical and contemporary forms." "They are so rational. When we wanted to talk about what our house should look like, they said we first needed to figure out how it would function." "Grant's ability to listen and translate our thoughts into images is uncanny." "We didn't want drama, we didn't want 'in your face' architecture, and their sensitivity to that was marvelous." "They never get rattled." "Beautiful—not stupid—modern." "On a path of discovery." "No two homes look alike. No signature style, it is all about the client." "Always looking for a unique approach that is respectful of history."

Kevin Oreck Architect, Inc. 📷   4   3   5   4.5

113 1/2 North La Brea Avenue, Suite 114, Los Angeles, CA 90036
(323) 692 - 0896   kevin_oreck@msn.com
Astute period renovations and additions specialist

Kevin Oreck is particularly credited for his astute restorations of period homes, bringing older spaces back to life and making them "wonderful centers of family occasion." "As classically fresh today as they might have been 40 years ago," Oreck's artful layouts successfully combine open space, historical integrity and modern practicality. Oreck is said to have a "heart of gold" and to bring a contagiously upbeat, yet calm attitude to collaboration with the client.

Established in 1990, Oreck's practice has only two on staff. Clients appreciate Oreck's full attention "from beginning to end" and tell us "he's caught a lot of mistakes before they happened." We hear he personally attends each meeting and keeps the contractors focused to the finish line. The vast majority of the ten to fifteen projects the firm does each year are residential.

Beyond Los Angeles, Oreck's designs can be found in San Francisco and Hawaii. Most projects seem to be 1920s renovations and additions, with new residences and retail and production spaces rounding out the slate. There are some new contemporary homes, including a recent Japanese-inspired loft-like remodel of a 1960s Bel Air home. The average new home runs about 3,000 square feet, and the firm is creative and nimble enough to design at $200 per square foot. In relation to other class act firms, Oreck charges lower than standard fees that are billed hourly with a cap.

"Everyone thinks it is completely original even though most of it was gutted." "Kevin has orchestrated a seamless renovation for us, following the detail throughout the house." "He was very compatible with us in his design sensibility as well as his personality. We had a great exchange of ideas." "I thought I wanted to scratch the breakfast nook in favor of enlarging the kitchen. He begged me off and was right. The nook is now my favorite part of the house." "I wanted a modern half-wall into the family room, but he implored me to use half-arches that were more consistent with the architecture, and he was completely on target." "If I could have anyone it would be him." "So humble for being the most amazing person." "It was such a plain-Jane house that he cleaned up and made amazing."

Kiyohara & Moffitt 👜 4 2.5 5 5

620 Moulton Avenue, Studio 106, Los Angeles, CA 90031
(323) 227 - 5647 www.km-arch.com

Detail-oriented architecture responsive to clients' needs and budgetary constraints

Kiyohara & Moffitt's designs are transitional blends of the best of the past and the best of the present, resulting in a "stunningly becoming work that speaks to both worlds." While traditional materials, such as clapboard or Craftsman millwork, may be employed, they are used in a clean, modern, fresh manner. California contemporary and Spanish Mediterranean are also successfully executed. The firm is further distinguished by its "incredibly accommodating" nature and its "excellent execution" of highly detailed designs—right down to the insides of the drawers. Moreover, the firm is committed to providing good value to the client.

Ko Kiyohara and Gina Moffitt are said to be masterful communicators who "get involved with the clients' emotions to create the perfect house." The principals started their practice, which currently has six employees, in 1987. Kiyohara received his BA in architecture from USC and Moffitt graduated Phi Beta Kappa from UC Berkeley.

The firm divides its focus between ground-up designs and extensive renovations mostly in the Beverly Hills, Malibu, Pasadena and Manhattan Beach areas. Homes average 3,000 to 6,000 square feet, but the firm recently completed a single-room remodel and a 13,000-square-foot ground up in Bel Air. Most projects are done at a budget-conscious cost of $175 to $250 per square foot, delivering "a lot of house for the money."

"They are the Yin and the Yang of the architect world. Ko brings to the party a sense of calm and a methodical creative process, while Gina infuses her own creativity and sensibility into the mix." "At the onset of our job, Gina promised that she was going to create a haven for us. She more than delivered." "They really care that the client is super happy." "Gina makes sure that the contractor does not make mistakes." "While standing firm on their principles, and gently guiding you in the right direction, they never forget who's paying the bill!" "A thoroughly enjoyable experience. We love them." "They kept us from becoming a divorce statistic."

Kovac Architects, Inc. 👜 4 4 4 4.5

2330 Pontius Avenue, Suite 202, Los Angeles, CA 90064
(310) 575 - 3621 www.kovacarchitects.com

Open-minded, modernist architecture

Michael Kovac is known for his ability to "catapult past the obvious modern idioms," offering dramatic Cubist paradigms that reflect the special interests of his clients. There are strong multilevel planes, cantilevered spaces that seem to defy gravity and maximize views. The works are warmed with naturalistic materials like wood and stone. Many are green projects that use photovoltaic power components, recycled wood insulations and/or radiant heat.

Clients enjoy collaborating with Kovac, who they say is "good tempered" with a "non-ego." They also speak of his clout with the city when navigating the permitting process, saying he gets particularly energized when tackling challenging hillside sites. Kovac received his Bachelor of Architecture at USC, trained with Rockefeller/Hricak and regional modernist Jerrold Lomax, and established his firm in 1988. There are twenty people in the office, including six architects, and about 80 percent of the work is residential.

The firm works mostly on the Westside, but has taken projects from San Diego to Utah. Though Kovac has been at the beck and call of some of LA's highest-profile residents with eight-figure budgets, he is happy to take on a few rooms for new clients and do work as small as a mailbox for past clients. His average home runs 6,000 square feet, at $300 to $350 per, putting him on par with other high-mark modernists.

"His strength is his ability to understand the client's wishes, synthesize and create something really unique. Out of the box thinking." "Can run out of time when it comes to the day-to-day execution." "He was able to grab a bit of extra land beside the house for the HVAC to maximize our space." "We were extremely impressed." "More than reasonable for what they charge." "He met my needs, respected the environment and California architecture, all while making my home architecturally significant." "You can feel the strength of the design on the napkin rendering."

Landry Design Group, Inc.   4.5   4.5   4   5

11333 Iowa Avenue, Los Angeles, CA 90025
(310) 444 - 1404   www.landrydesigngroup.com

Incredible, substantial, statement architecture

If you're looking for the ultimate fantasy home, Richard Landry is the go-to guy. Nothing fazes this architect, renowned for creating "phenomenal and extravagant" homes in LA's most exclusive neighborhoods for marquee names such as Eddie Murphy, Sylvester Stallone, Rod Stewart and Michael Bolton. Landry works both in derivative classical and "transitional" contemporary styles, borrowing from established architectural vocabularies and adding his own creative twist. Clients rely on Landry to work independently and efficiently, calling him "a talented professional who needs little if any direction." Landry and his staff are said to be detail-oriented, conducting tireless research on whatever style the client desires.

Despite being "very sought after and very successful," Landry remains extremely grounded and approachable. Clients tell us he personally sets the pace and spends time with each client, returning phone calls promptly and paving the way for a fun and easy process. Originally hailing from Montreal, Landry established this firm of 25 in 1987 after receiving degrees from the University of Montreal and the University of Copenhagen.

New homes tend to be in the 10,000 to 15,000 square foot range, with some as large as 40,000 square feet, with 5,000 to 7,000 considered small. Interestingly, Landry generally works in the $350 to $400 per square foot range, which is actually standard for normal-sized, high-quality homes in LA today. While some of Landry's commissions have countless types of marble imported from Italy and incredible carved limestone, most forgo the details to keep the budgets lower than one might imagine. AD 100, 2000, 2002.

"He takes your dream concept and develops the most extraordinary version possible. And then he and his team work diligently to make it happen." "Perfectly executed. If I were doing a house on the moon I'd use Richard." "It might sound crazy, but Richard can kind of read your mind. It might be something that you can't necessarily picture, but he'll come up with something that's right on target." "He takes care of everything. All I have to do is go out there and make enough money to pay for this enormous house." "He delegates, so if he's not around, things don't stop. There is a great support staff." "We met every week to make sure we were on the same page, and the house absolutely reflects how we live and entertain." "Richard loves what he is doing and does not take himself too seriously. It is an absolutely pleasure."

Lehrer Architects   4   4   4   4

2140 Hyperion Avenue, Silver Lake District, Los Angeles, CA 90027
(323) 664 - 4747   www.lehrerarchitects.com
Contextual, collaborative contemporary architecture

Michael Lehrer's homes have a strong sense of place, realized through a clear spatial order. Known for the consistency of related linear elements that assume a vastness of light, a Lehrer home is also grounded in the clients' "rituals of life." Preoccupied with space, views and the integration of the outdoor with the indoor, his aesthetic tends toward a refined modernism.

An AIA Fellow, Lehrer brings a "stable" and intellectually thorough presence to the proceedings. The sole principal of this eight-person firm, he has an undergraduate architectural degree from UC Berkeley and a graduate degree from Harvard. Prior to starting his own business in 1985, Lehrer served as senior project architect with renowned architect Frank Gehry. Whether working on the renovation of an older home or the conceptual design of a sleek single-family home, Lehrer earns kudos for his abstract problem-solving skills and preternatural ability to maximize space. Sources tell us Lehrer and his "responsible and talented" team incorporate state-of-the-art technology to create dynamic and highly detailed renderings and schematics.

Lehrer works mostly in LA, including enclaves such as Brentwood, Silver Lake, Pacific Palisades and parts of Orange County, and has also completed projects in Northern California, Florida and Pennsylvania. Residential commissions constitute about 30 percent of the firm's commissions. The outdoor work on many of his projects (including the recent Jamie Lee Curtis/Christopher Guest home) is done in conjunction with his wife, the renowned LA landscaper Mia Lehrer. New homes are typically 5,000 to 7,000 square feet at approximately $350 per square foot, with the architect charging an hourly based fee that works out to roughly a standard percentage of construction.

"Mike really believes in the preservation of the home as a sanctuary. To reach this elevated perspective, he puts more thought into the project than most other architects." "Very reliable and responsible." "Mike deeply cares about his clients and wants them to enjoy the process as much as the result." "He's very warm and friendly and we liked him immediately." "The project architects are also excellent." "If you have an idea, Mike will always try to make it work." "He goes after each corner until it makes complete sense and is beautiful." "The design he gave us was creative and unusual, and it fit the site like a glove." "Very sensitive to the environment, incorporating natural elements and the landscape into the design." "It is intimate and grand at the same time." "Mike is so thoughtful, and yet so practical."

Lewin Wertheimer Architect   4   4   4   4.5

115 Wavecrest Avenue, Venice, CA 90291
(310) 392 - 4252   lewin@wertheimer-architect.com
Custom, appropriate, livable architecture

Blessed with an excellent eye for detail, Lewin Wertheimer has found much favor designing homes that "look as if they have always been here and should be here." He is known for meticulously rendering and realizing designs in a wide array of vernaculars, from Mediterranean to Mission, Craftsman to Italian villa, and he can also expertly realize rustic contemporary. Clients appreciate Wertheimer's "high energy" and find him a "very balanced, discreet team player." We're told the firm's grip on each project element extends to its budgeting and accounting, which are described as "second to none."

Wertheimer enjoys collaborating with clients who are "involved in every phase" of designing and building their dream home. We hear he blends the tried-and-true

Quality	Cost	Value	Recommend?
✚	$	◆	★

with the new in his drawings, using both hand-sketched schematics and computer-aided design construction documents. The firm, established in 1993, has remained small to allow for personalized service and Wertheimer's "total commitment to each project." He holds an undergraduate degree from USC and also studied at the University of Madrid and in Florence, Italy.

The firm's work can be seen most often along the coast in places like Malibu, Santa Monica and Pacific Palisades, although Wertheimer has also worked on projects in Hawaii and Spain. His residential projects start at $300 per square foot and are split between large single-family ground-up designs averaging 6,000 square feet and renovations at 1,000 to 3,000 square feet. Projects can top out at 10,000 square feet and $500 per square foot. The firm's fee is charged hourly through schematics and negotiated subsequently.

"Extremely organized and meticulous." "Lewin's homes sit gracefully on their sites and beautifully capture the nuances of their respective traditions." "He is not pushing the envelope of modern architecture, but delivering warm, livable spaces that clients love." "He did my neighbor's amazing house, and I knew immediately I wanted to use him." "Fabulous accounting system. Tracked everything week by week so we were never surprised." "His process is so complete that he reduces the mistakes and cost overruns that bedevil many building projects." "May take him a little longer to turn around the detailed drawings up front, but it's so worth it." "He will point things out that are not worth the money." "He was always there and can see what needs to be done." "Lewin is so kind, so clear, so honest. He is never stressful."

Lise Claiborne Matthews and Associates 4   4   4   4.5

1510 Abbot Kinney Boulevard, Venice, CA 90291
(310) 399 - 7108   lisem@lcmstudio.com

Site- and client-specific architecture born of classical roots

Lise Claiborne Matthews designs her homes from the inside out, first considering the way in which the homeowners will live—their interests and lifestyle, and the visual perspective from the interior. Then the house is thoughtfully designed to match the site. Matthews contrasts this with certain random "deus ex machina" LA homes where it appears as if "the thing dropped out of sky." Some of LA's most renowned architects highly recommend Matthews for her skill with a wide range of styles, from Craftsman to contemporary. However, most of the designs reflect her New Orleans heritage, with traditional appointments even in contemporary contexts. Whatever the style, Matthews proves fluent in the language of space and flow that "manifest a sense of timelessness without being pretentious." Detailed to the point of "obsessive in a good way," Matthews' plans are said to be "heartfelt" and "nothing less than remarkable." She is also highly involved in the interiors of her projects, designing all cabinetry and collaborating on colors. Clients tell us she strives to achieve their vision while remaining faithful to her own sensibility and the spirit of the house. Her firm was established in 1983 and now includes seven. Matthews, its sole principal, holds degrees from Tulane and SCI-Arc.

Nearly all of Matthews' annual commissions are residential, and they tend to be significant remodels and additions of 1,000 to 2,000 square feet or 5,000 to 12,000 square foot ground-up homes. Fees are charged hourly or as a percentage of overall construction costs, with the firm keeping its fees and the cost per square foot to a reasonable level. Clients happily pay Matthews' bills, asserting their belief that "the uniqueness of her vision results in something truly amazing."

"Thanks to Lise, the city uses us as a poster child for the advantages of not going the McMansion route and preserving the integrity of an existing structure." "Her persistence so helped us discover the nuances of what we wanted." "Lise thinks of everything and then measures for it. She suggested we create a 'ker-plunking space' from the kitchen to the garage where we can place briefcases and

other daily items." "She takes her cue from her father who was an old-time family doctor and made house calls—Lise is always there for you." "People walk by our house all the time and tell us they wish they lived there. I think that says it all." "Lise is excellent at knowing the city codes and making things happen." "I defy anyone who comes here to figure out where the old house ends and the new one begins. I've never seen anything so seamless." "She's a visionary and has the team to make it happen."

Marmol Radziner + Associates   5   4.5   4.5   4.5

12210 Nebraska Avenue, Los Angeles, CA 90025
(310) 826 - 6222   www.marmol-radziner.com

Engaging, contemporary design/build services with seamless execution

Admired and highly recommended by clients and peers, Marmol Radziner builds elegant contemporary structures that resound with simplicity and utter youthful exuberance. For inspiration, the partners look to modernist architecture overseas, and to the local site's landscape dimensions. Designs are built upon organized proportions, the warmth of natural materials and the maximization of natural light. What sets this firm apart is its creativity in combination with its "down-to-earth attitude" and its eminently buildable designs—they make sure the blueprints work, as they build most of them. As one of the few design/build firms in the country led by architects, we're told Marmol Radziner creates a streamlined process from the first drawing to the last punch-list item, and furthermore, "you feel as if you are working with a design boutique." Principals of the firm are Leo Marmol, who holds an undergraduate architecture degree from Cal Poly/San Luis Obispo, and Ron Radziner, who holds a BA in science from San Luis Obispo and an M.Arch. from Colorado. Established in 1989, the firm is quite the behemoth, consisting of 135 staffers, about one half designers and the other half builders and craftsmen. Rising beyond the call of duty, much pro bono time and energy is devoted to improving upon LA's urban sprawl with local community organizations.

Most of Marmol Radziner + Associates residential projects take place in the greater Los Angeles area, in neighborhoods like Beverly Hills, Bel Air and Santa Monica, though the firm has built homes in London and Paris. The firm takes on historic restorations of modern homes (Neutra, Schindler), extensive renovations and large ground-up residences from 2,000 square foot case studies to 25,000 square foot mansions, with 3,000 to 5,000 more typical. Clients include the likes of fashion icon Tom Ford and photographer Steven Meisel. At $400 to $600 a square foot at standard fees, references say, "you're not going to get better, but remember—you're going to pay for it."

"Their work is perfect. With most people you have to nag them and point out what's wrong, but these guys are all over it before you have a chance." "More thorough than the clients themselves—they're obsessed." "Every time I write them a check I want to beat them with a bar stool, but I have no choice but to pay. They're that good." "As a traditional architect, I so admire the quality. They are the first choice for modern." "They never waste your time." "Designs less about the style and more about the authenticity of California expressionism—thick plaster, divided light, wooden frames." "I've seen it all as a top celebrity LA decorator—they are incredibly responsible and so personable."

Meyer Architecture   4   4   4   4

2300 Westwood Boulevard, Suite 200, Los Angeles, CA 90064
(310) 234 - 3300   www.meyer-architecture.com

Nuanced, detailed restorations of historic homes

Drawing on their expertise in historic restoration work, Walter and Pamela Meyer "find the original soul of the house" and update and expand it for modern living. The firm collaborates very closely with each owner to work through every detail.

Sources say the Meyers will be there "from the very beginning to the very end." Head architect Walter Meyer was born on Frank Lloyd Wright's birthday and is passionate about the discipline of architecture. He received a BA in Architecture from Arizona State and moved to LA in 1979, where he worked for several architecture firms. In 1993 he started Meyer Architecture with his wife Pamela, who studied psychology at UCLA and has passed the NCIDQ exam. She is a professional member of the ASID and on the board of directors of the LA chapter. Today, Pamela heads the interiors side of the firm. There are four others on staff, and about four residences are taken on at a time, mostly renovations of historically interesting properties. Ground-up projects have also been done with developers. The successful reconstruction of the Armand Hammer residence in 1998 was the firm's springboard into the high-end market.

The firm offers an extremely high level of service and detailed design specifications. Homes are usually in the 7,000-square-foot range, with the fees a bit higher than standard for the extra level of attention.

"They promise a seamless result, and we really did get that with the new addition." "The new flow was a tremendous improvement." "The level of detail in the planning is way beyond the call of duty. Full-scale models are made of marble floors, including every marble vein." "You do not feel that they are anxious to get to the next project." "We would clearly use them again on our next home."

Moore Ruble Yudell   5   5   4   5

933 Pico Boulevard, Santa Monica, CA 90405
(310) 450 - 1400   www.moorerubleyudell.com
Meticulously crafted architecture and landscape design

Moore Ruble Yudell is applauded for delivering "a richness of experience" in both the form of its "humanistic" designs and in its collaborative approach. The firm's architecture is joyfully contemporary—contextually connecting the home to its site, employing the latest technologies and also enhancing "the comforting qualities of a family home." Clients tell us the practice's designs include "marvelously framed scenes that manifest themselves the moment you walk in the door," reminding them "of the wonderful feeling" of collaborating with Moore Ruble Yudell.

The firm's staff is said to communicate with patience and execute with authority. Partners John Ruble and Buzz Yudell (both Fellows of the AIA) work with designer Tina Beebe to carry on the tradition of the late founder Charles Moore. We hear Moore "was quite a little Johnny Appleseed," planting numerous architectural firms across the country, with Moore Ruble Yudell his last and arguably most successful. Established in 1977, with Ruble and Yudell at the helm since 1985, the firm staffs 60. Ruble holds architecture degrees from Virginia and UCLA, while Yudell earned his from Yale. Beebe heads up an interiors group of five, which completes about half the firm's commissions.

Moore Ruble Yudell has created homes in some of the country's most affluent neighborhoods in LA, Boston and New York City, as well as in Germany, Sweden, Australia, Japan and Turkey. Most of Moore Ruble Yudell's commissions are institutional, university, civic or urban design projects (two in China right now), though the firm does a select number of ground-up residences each year. These fall between 5,000 and 8,000 square feet, with higher costs per square foot and standard fees (before administration). AD 100, 2000, 2002, 2004.

"Working with Buzz and his staff was an extraordinary experience, because all the players worked so well together." "The firm has a depth of integrity in design, process and intellectual honesty." "The house gets better as time goes on, and that's a compliment of the highest order." "While they only do a few homes at a time, they are the 'pet projects' lavished with attention." "Metaphorically and physically they sleep on the site to get a feel for the space." "They make you feel so comfortable. Not at all pretentious." "What they gave me is a design that is both enormously humble and completely overwhelming in its beauty."

Richardson Robertson III/ Robertson Partners

4.5   4.5   4   4

10940 Wilshire Boulevard, Suite 100, Los Angeles, CA 90024
(310) 208 - 4200   www.robertsonpartners.net

Historically derived "New Beaux Arts" architecture

Rick Robertson is hailed for his larger-than-life designs that realize the most ambitious fantasies—and for his indefatigable spirit. Robertson has a special fondness for historical replication and built his reputation with new Beverly Hills mansions that successfully blend with the neighboring 1920s and 1930s homes. The firm strongly believes in using timeless, iconic architectural styles conceived well before the advent of the modern to perpetuate and further establish a sense of heritage to each location in which it builds. We hear Robertson is fostering its own "New Beaux Arts" style that incorporates classic historical forms in its designs.

Born and raised in Dallas, fourth generation architect Robertson studied urban architecture at SMU and earned a Master of Architecture from the University of Texas. He established his firm in Dallas before moving to LA three years later. Today, Robertson and his staff of five take on residential projects ranking in the upper echelon—often in Bel Air, Beverly Hills and Malibu. They have also done master planning for towns near LA and New York, creating plans noted for their excellent consistency and vision. A New York office was opened in 1999, focusing on substantial residential projects in Greenwich and Westchester.

New homes generally run in the 15,000 to 20,000 square foot ballpark, with 45,000 not unheard of. Extensive renovations are also undertaken. Most clients are self-made entrepreneurs with a distinct point of view. Cost per square foot is typically $350 to $400 with architect fees at the standard percentage.

"He re-created the most incredible sunroom from my favorite hotel in Paris. Rick loves to fulfill your dreams." "He has great artistic insight into French and Tuscan motifs." "All the hardware details were custom designed, and people absolutely notice." "He turned a boring side room into a handsome library with imagination." "Very personable and fun."

Rios Clementi Hale Studios

4.5   4.5   4   5

6824 Melrose Avenue, Los Angeles, CA 90038
(323) 634 - 9220   www.rchstudio.com

Contextual contemporary architecture and landscape design

Peers and clients alike admire Mark Rios and his partners for their clean, uplifting modern architecture, their agility in truly harmonizing the inside and out, and for the enjoyable and professional process. "They can do it all" is the consensus, and indeed, that seems to be the case. Most of the interiors are done in-house and the firm recently introduced a highly successful home products company called NotNeutral to completely coordinate the look.

A fully integrated team approach is reflective of the principal's multidisciplinary talents. Rios, who holds degrees from Harvard, is also the director of landscape architecture at USC. Robert Hale, who has a Master of Architecture from UCLA, was VP of design at Universal Studios, while Frank Clementi, a graduate of Cal Poly-Pomona practiced for years in Italy. Julie Smith-Clementi began her career at Hodgetts + Fung Design. Rios launched the firm under his moniker in 1985. The current name was adopted in 2005, and 30 people are now employed. A player in Bel Air, Brentwood, Pacific Palisades and Malibu, the studio has worked nationally in New York City, San Francisco, Chicago and Atlanta.

The firm's commissions are about 40 percent architecture (half residential), 40 percent landscape and 20 percent interiors, graphics and designs. The landscapes are edited and geometric with unique water details, such as negative edge reflection pools and fountains that bow to sustainable ideals. The firm's interest rests more in the challenge of an architectural project than its size, resulting in a range of projects from 3,000 to 12,000 square feet. Finished per-square-foot cost can be from $300 to $600 with $400 more typical, along with standard architectural fees. Clients place Rios, Clementi and Hale in the superstar league of architects and adamantly believe the investment to be worth every penny.

"I hear nothing but good about this firm." "They do everything with energy and verve and it is consistently excellent." "There is a focused point of view and a clear professionalism that comes with a firm of this quality." "The projects speak for themselves." "Mark can see what's possible in any situation." "They are very patient and good listeners." "Mark is involved with every project, and a capable project leader handles the day-to-day." "A tremendous amount of time is taken to make sure every detail holistically fits into the strategic design." "Sustainable architecture, and particularly sod roofs, have become a big recent interest." "I don't think there's anyone more talented in design."

RoTo Architects ▇   4.5   3.5   5   4.5

600 Moulton Avenue, Suite 405, Los Angeles, CA 90031
(323) 226 - 1112   www.rotoark.com

Original, distilled, highly modern architecture

References describe RoTo's work as "masterpieces of intellectual thought"— refined, distilled, "visually exciting and sleek." With a diverse portfolio that includes the planning of rural communities and land use design for natural conservation, RoTo Architects takes on only a select few private residences, treating each one like a teaching case study. The firm's designs tend toward the modern, but always derive their form from the shape and texture of the land. The company enjoys a robust referral business, and we're told clients are impressed with the partners' detailed, collaborative approach and their careful execution of the designs.

Partners Michael Rotondi and Clark Stevens bring almost 40 years of combined experience to this firm of fifteen, founded in 1991. Rotondi is a faculty and board of directors member of SCI-Arc, which he helped found in 1972. He served as director of the institute for a decade, from 1987 to 1997. He is also the University of Kentucky's architectural chair. A founding partner of Morphosis in 1976, Rotondi established RoTo Architects in 1991 with Stevens, who holds a Bachelor Degree from the University of Michigan and a Master of Architecture from Harvard.

The firm's institutional work includes Sinte Gleska University in Kyle, South Dakota, the Liberty Wildlife Center in Scottsdale, Arizona, and the Kohala Center in Hawaii. It has also designed a number of private residences and has been

Quality	Cost	Value	Recommend?
✚	$	◆	★

chosen as one of 30 internationally known architects to participate in the architectural initiative "The Houses at Sagaponac," in which each selected firm will design a contemporary home in Sagaponac, New York. Homes range from 3,000 to 7,000 square feet and are built for a remarkably low $250 per square foot (but we hear, sell for $600 per square foot). The firm's educational and iterative process results in higher than standard fees.

"RoTo is a beautiful balance of talent and experience—a pleasure to work with." "Beautiful, interesting, aesthetic space." "They are particular about their work and big on connecting with the client." "Out there, but really good designers. Truly in a unique category." "Part of the cutting edge crowd." "Distilled to the greatest point of simplicity."

Serrurier Architects and Associates   4 4 4 4.5
8474 Santa Monica Boulevard, West Hollywood, CA 90069
(323) 848 - 7449 serrassocs@sbcglobal.net

Updated traditional architecture with authentic charm

David Serrurier is depended upon in the Pasadena and Beverly Hills communities to respect the integrity of older structures during renovation and to create new homes that look "authentic and dignified." Serrurier has also proven architecturally faithful in his more modern projects, including restorations of Neutra and Craftsman-style homes. His reputation among an impressive and varied clientele is built on long-term relationships, with many having commissioned him to design several homes. These clients tell us Serrurier is expert at updating houses with modern technologies and "refuses to settle for almost right—it has to be perfect."

Serrurier's understated elegance and professional demeanor also finds favor with interior designers and landscape architects. They tell us he "works smoothly" in collaboration and oversees an organized design process.

A native Californian, Serrurier holds a Bachelor of Architecture from USC and has stayed close to his community roots. Primarily a residential architect, Serrurier has also designed country clubs, art galleries and stores in the neighboring communities. Much of his work is centered on remodeling and restoring older residences, such as traditional cottages and Mediterranean villas in the 3,000 to 5,000 square foot bracket. With costs usually falling at $350 per square foot, the firm's costs are in step with its high-end quality.

"People can't believe it's a new house. He made it look like old Pasadena." "Absolutely dedicated to detail." "Master at integrating the old with the new." "David is sophisticated as well as easy and talented." "He uses extremely high-end materials and makes them look older—never looks shiny new." "Sticks to the budget and the schedule." "I've been working with him over 25 years." "Not a show off. Very personable." "Likes to collaborate—listens to your ideas and gives you what you want."

SF Jones Architects, Inc.   4   3.5   4.5   4.5

4218 Glencoe Avenue, Studio Two, Marina Del Rey, CA 90292
(310) 822 - 3822   www.sfjones.com

Contemporary architecture with Craftsman attitude

An accomplished star in the restaurant design constellation, Stephen Jones is now turning to the architecture of residences with the same individual spirit and love of fine craftsmanship. Jones is best known for the drama and intimacy of such legendary creations as Spago in Beverly Hills, Lucky Strike Lanes in Hollywood, the Hump at Santa Monica Airport and the renovation of the Century Plaza Hotel. His homes capture that same excitement, yet exude a tranquility of familiar warmth.

Jones grew up in Orlando, where his dad worked for Disney World (are we surprised?). After receiving a BA in Architecture from the University of Florida, he worked on a high rise project for a large commercial firm in Boston, and then headed to UCLA for postgraduate work. Before receiving his master's in architecture, Jones had an interlude in Barcelona, where he worked for the internationally acclaimed Ricardo Bofill and honed his sketchbook and watercolor skills. His practical side was further developed shortly thereafter while forming a design/build company after Hurricane Andrew, where he slept with his team in living rooms (no working hotels in sight) and did everything necessary to get the job done—including frequent runs to Home Depot. After school, Jones worked for two design firms and then joined Wolfgang Puck's in-house architecture team, staying for three years before forming his own hospitality design firm in 1996.

While this firm of seven is mostly focused on restaurant and other commercial enterprises, a few select homes are done at a time. New homes tend to be 3,000 to 5,000 square feet and run at a controlled $275 to $375 per square foot, with standard fees.

"Steve was very sensitive to our 75-year-old Spanish Colonial and also managed to make it work so well for our needs." "He was quite responsive and his office was great about filling in." "Engaging, creative, humorous—and yet focused." "Delightful and great fun. I never thought it would be fun, but it was." "Steve can design anything. He is so talented and so flexible." "He brought our house to life."

Shubin + Donaldson Architects   4.5   4   4.5   4.5

3834 Willat Avenue, Culver City, CA 90232
(310) 204 - 0688   www.shubinanddonaldson.com

Strikingly simplified, becoming modern architecture

The firm of Shubin + Donaldson is admired for its handsome, linear Cubist architecture that seeks to reflect the clients' interests, desires and intentions. The firm uses innovative materials to create dramatic and sleek structures to encase private and serene environments. We hear the firm's approach to the design process is "versatile and thorough," while its management skill, communication and systematic back office are considered among the best. Devoid of big egos, partners Russell Shubin and Robin Donaldson are finely attuned to their clients' priorities and "win quality points for their service orientation." Clients are drawn to the firm's "confident, easygoing manner" and its clear and dynamic ideas. Shubin began practicing architecture in 1985 after studying in France and completing architecture and business degrees. Donaldson began his career with LA's Morphosis Architects. Since opening its doors in 1990, the firm has received numerous industry accolades, including the prestigious Business Week/ Architectural Record Award.

With offices in Santa Barbara and Culver City, Shubin + Donaldson now handles a full range of residential, commercial and institutional clients with a staff of fifteen. The company's notable residential projects average 4,000 to 7,000 square feet, with $300 to $400 per square foot being typical, pacing the firm as a strong value given the excellent quality.

"Incredible architecture at a relatively reasonable budget and you do not get lost in the shuffle, as you do at other great LA firms." "Two nice guys from California who happen to be fabulous architects." "They exhibited great artistic communication skills, innovative designs with glass and stone, an easy flexibility, and had a greater respect for our budget than I did." "Russell and Robin work to complement each other. Their approach is aligned." "They are totally committed to being great architects." "They handle problems with reasonable solutions, not drama queen antics." "Among the rising stars in architecture." "There is spirituality about the work that is born of care."

Sinclair Associates Architects 💼   4.5   4.5   4   4.5

1007 Broxton Avenue, Studio 210, Westwood Village, Los Angeles, CA 90024
(310) 824 - 9420   www.sinclairaia.com

Historically enhanced, warmly detailed, open architecture

Robert Sinclair is distinguished by designs that incorporate the modern idioms with light and space while at once retaining an enchanting European sense of intimacy. The architect brings a discerning eye and fresh spin to traditional California styles like Spanish Colonial, Tuscan villa and Southern Mediterranean, unlocking the essence of a site, opening the space with light and "down to earth" historical context. Clients tell us Sinclair gets "incredibly keyed into the clients' needs and design dreams" and "factors in all the details well ahead of time." Also he proves "flexible" and "not ruffled" during the execution phase.

As a personality we hear Sinclair is humble and charming and rallies everyone to get along effectively as whole. A graduate of California Polytechnic College, Sinclair started his firm in 1982. The sole proprietor, he oversees a staff of four. Clients tend to be substantial government and industry leaders.

Mostly working in the Newport Beach area, Sinclair has been commissioned from San Francisco to San Diego. The firm strives to maintain a select roster of residential projects that are one-of-a kind architectural experiences. Sizes vary from a manageable 3,000 square feet to a substantial 15,000 square feet. While the architectural fees are quite low (given the low overhead), the cost per square foot ($450+) is substantial.

"Rob gets to know the clients' desires and makes it happen." "He created a very warm and welcoming room which encourages good times." "He asked for our wish list up front so there were no surprises later." "He works incredibly well with husbands and wives who have different ideas about what they want." "Does not fall into a formula—there is no architectural stamp." "He will always be a boutique firm because he loves involvement with the client."

Steven Ehrlich Architects 💼   5   4.5   4.5   4.5

10865 Washington Boulevard, Culver City, CA 90232
(310) 838 - 9700   www.s-ehrlich.com

Idealistic, progressive modern architecture emphasizing natural elements

A pioneer in modern progressive design, Steven Ehrlich continues to employ new technologies in glass and metal to visually eliminate the building's envelope, fusing the indoor spaces to the contiguous gardens, courtyards and landscapes. His palette of natural colors, materials and textures contributes to this contextual unification. A self-proclaimed "architectural anthropologist," Ehrlich's work reflects a joining of African and Asian influences with modern masters who have influenced his work—such as Louis Kahn, Frank Lloyd Wright and Richard Neutra, to name a few. Each project builds upon the last, with clear design objectives in mind.

Clients say Ehrlich is a "true force in the project's beginning" before giving his blessing to a project architect at his "terrific organization" to run with the day-to-day details. After graduating from the Rensselaer Polytechnic Institute in 1969, Ehrlich spent six years in Africa serving as the first architect with the Peace Corps in Marrakesh, Morocco. His practice, founded in 1979, has grown to a firm of twenty.

Before starting any design plan, clients are asked to complete a twelve-page questionnaire that covers lifestyle issues as well as personal needs and preferences. Although the planning process may be long (typically one year), clients say the firm's thoroughness makes for very few work order changes and no surprises. The firm balances its institutional and commercial efforts with residential projects that are primarily ground-up, 5,000 to 15,000 square foot structures. Per square foot in an Ehrlich home falls between $350 and $700, with clients insisting the outstanding result is "money well spent."

"Great creativity but always a rationale behind his thoughts." "Steve is clear, reasonable and very articulate. He has an exciting and specific point of view that is engaged in finding that next level of modernist ideal." "Only will use the finest materials, which can put a dent in the budget." "Excellent collaborator, making it work for the client's lifestyle." "So helpful when working out change orders. Usually the bane of every project, but so well handled here." "Steve is readily accessible, with a great eye for detail." "The result is spectacular. The neighbors come over all the time to admire it."

Tichenor & Thorp Architects 📷   5   4.5   4.5   5
8730 Wilshire Boulevard, Penthouse, Beverly Hills, CA 90211
(310) 358 - 8444
Superbly rendered traditional architecture and landscape design

Principals Brian Tichenor and Raun Thorpe bring a unique personal spirit to their stylish, historically rooted designs. While most architects in LA say they integrate the indoors with the out, this is one of the only firms that have principals formally trained in both architecture and landscape design. Any number of architectural canvases may be rendered, from Spanish Revival to neo-Portuguese, Provençal to American traditional, all with "incredible ambiance." Thorp's noted sensitivity to interiors makes them a particular favorite of some of the best interior designers in LA. In addition, Tichenor's historically accurate landscape designs—characterized by lush gardens, a palette rich in texture, and carefully orchestrated color in passageways—have found many devotees.

Clients rave that "the process was always fun" with this "extremely articulate" husband and wife team, who we hear bring a budget-conscious attitude to their designs. Both Tichenor and Thorp received master's degrees in architecture from UCLA and worked for Moore Ruble Yudell. They started their own firm in 1990, and now employ a staff of twelve. Both architects are members of the Society of Architectural Historians and each has served on a number of historic preservation or advisory boards in the area.

Though Tichenor + Thorp started with technically pure restoration and remodel efforts on historically and architecturally significant structures in Southern California, the firm now focuses exclusively on ground-up residential architectural design and will do independent landscape design for a home "if the architecture is in place." Residences are usually substantially sized at 6,000 to 18,000 square feet, with square-foot costs and fees tending toward the high end. Clients tell us every cent is worth the collaboration with this highly "creative team."

"The designs are warmly inventive. Exciting, yet classical." "I love how the house reduces on the outside—it's very unassuming despite the large volume on the inside." "Brian is a creative genius—he made me love and appreciate my garden." "Raun is so together. She should be on the cover of Vogue." "As a

designer, I think they are incredibly effective and efficient as well as being extremely talented." "Sharp, but thankfully not edgy. Incredible attention to detail." "So connected to California history and architecture."

Tighe Architecture 4 3.5 4.5 5

1632 Ocean Park Boulevard, Santa Monica, CA 90405
(310) 450 - 8823 www.tighearchitecture.com

Angular, innovative, modern architecture

Pushing the proverbial envelope, Patrick Tighe takes a hands-on approach, creating innovative, abstract, geometric architecture with a sustainable edge. While exteriors are starkly bold in form and in spirit, the designs are rich through the use of natural materials, particularly wood. Clients effuse about working with Tighe, who is roundly described as modest, extraordinarily nice and fun.

Tighe earned a BA in fine arts from U-Mass and an MA from UCLA. He was affiliated with Morphosis for seven years, an influence that clearly informed his work, and founded his own firm in 2000. In less than two years, the firm received AIA national and LA awards, and in the short life of the firm, there have already been six repeat clients—always a good sign.

Tighe has a passion for residential work, which constitutes about 75 percent of the commissions. There are five in the office taking on about six projects at a time. The firm is known for its interest and sensitivity with smaller homes, with an average ground-up footprint of 2,500 square feet. The cost per square foot is relatively modest for the quality of the work at $250 to $300. Fees come in at a standard percentage of construction.

"Patrick was always available and worked in a very organized way." "My only complaint is that the closets are too small." "An excellent listener, definitely not an egomaniac." "There is an incredible understanding of the client's interests." "The house is really quite spiritual in a very contemporary way." "Far exceeded my expectations." "In the realm of Frank Gehry, Patrick is a visionary." "An undiscovered gem."

Tim Nicol 4 4 4 4.5

604 Vista Lane, Laguna Beach, CA 92651
(949) 494 - 0026 nicolarchitecture@verizon.net

Updated traditional architecture

Tim Nicol built his excellent reputation working with neighbors in Laguna Beach to give their homes a "warm, cottage-like feel." Nowadays Nicol consistently infuses his work with that same familial warmth, on projects that range from a classic contemporary structure to an updated remodel of a traditional home. We're told that clients appreciated his "calm, relaxed nature" and his clear sense of direction.

Nicol grew up in the Bay Area and received an undergraduate degree in architecture from Berkeley. He moved to Southern California in 1991, working for a commercial architecture firm, yet his heart was always in residential. Through his contacts in Laguna, Nicol started doing work for the neighbors and today his firm of three still works primarily in that neighborhood. About 30 percent of the work is ground up, with the remaining being additions and remodels, mostly for young professionals with growing families.

New homes are generally in the 3,000 to 5,000 square foot range and are done at $350 to $450 a foot, depending upon the client's preferences. The firm works on an hourly basis or as a percentage of construction, which averages out to be lower than the standard architectural fee.

"We interviewed eight architects for the job. Tim won with his inherently better understanding of the site and of our interests." "Tim created such a calm and soothing environment, maximizing the views." "Extremely pleasant, but will tell you what is right." "He reshapes your ideas in a practical way." "He totally knows his way around Laguna, the town boards respect him." "Tim has a great sense of responsibility—I totally trusted his judgment."

Virgil W. McDowell Inc.    4   4   4   4.5

15304 Sunset Boulevard, Suite 202, Los Angeles, CA 90272
(310) 459 - 8838   www.virgilmcdowell.com

Meticulously detailed, period architecture

Impressed patrons tell us Virgil McDowell possesses an "almost innate and effortless" skill at recreating period architecture and classical design "without over-ornamentation." McDowell's creations include meticulous renovations of historic properties in styles such as English Georgian, Spanish Colonial, French country and Medieval Tudor. We hear McDowell's keen eye zeroes right down to the knobs and hinges, and he provides intricate design documents crafted entirely by hand.

McDowell's personalized attention and pride in the details make him a favorite among his well-heeled celebrity and entrepreneurial clients. On projects for which he manages the architecture, McDowell can also be enlisted to perform the decorating. It is important to note that while McDowell is not a licensed architect, legally (thus limiting him to projects of two stories plus basement in California) clients report that he is an experienced and talented draftsman who nonetheless manages the process with high marks. The firm most often works in Hancock Park, Bel Air, Holmby Hills and Hollywood Hills, but has completed homes in St. Louis and Chicago. McDowell generally accepts projects with budgets in the six figures, with architectural and interior design fees tallying up to a standard percentage.

McDowell grew up in the Watts neighborhood and is a true example of the American Dream. While attending Cal State at North Ridge on a football scholarship, he separated his shoulder and lost his scholarship. He went to work as a draftsman for a local architect and the rest is history. A self-educated devotee of the classical tradition, he has particular expertise in the American Renaissance (1880–1930) and was a draftsman for ten years before establishing this small firm of three in 1989. McDowell teaches classes to architects and interior designers at the Institute of Classical Architecture about classical installations.

"Virgil has the extraordinary ability to take our often poorly articulated concepts and transfer them into reality with a design, often on the first iteration." "You can't go to school to learn how to do his kind of work—you're either born with it or you're not." "Other architects can apply these classical techniques, but Virgil feels them. It's an emotional response that his architecture just feels right to him and to the client." "Virgil is so passionate about his craft." "I learned to trust his instincts and ignore my own, often misguided plans." "The result is astonishingly true to classical form."

	Quality	Cost	Value	Recommend?
	+	$	◆	★

William Hefner Architecture ▣   4   3.5   4.5   4.5

5820 Wilshire Boulevard, Suite 500, Los Angeles, CA 90036
(323) 931 - 1365   www.williamhefner.com

Restrained, elegant, comprehensive architecture and interior design

Clients adore William Hefner and his designs, which are described as "contextual and beguiling" and harmoniously incorporate outdoor living environments. The firm's restrained architecture brings a "timeless elegance" to its traditional-style residences and calming warmth to its more modern structures, a genre Hefner has done more of lately. Designs are punctuated with a use of natural materials and infused with natural light. We're told a building experience with the well-liked Hefner is as "life-enhancing" as the fine final product.

Sources say Hefner is a guiding force in all aspects of the design process and a stickler for details—from the design of doorknobs to bathroom fixtures. The firm usually provides a package of services, including landscaping and interior design with Hefner's wife, Kazuko Hoshino, serving as in-house designer. Hefner holds a graduate degree in architecture from UCLA and spent eight years with the prestigious architectural firm Skidmore, Owings & Merrill. He founded his own firm in 1989, which now is twenty people strong and does about five projects at a time.

Hefner's work can be seen in New York, Washington DC, Sun Valley and Seoul, South Korea. The majority of his endeavors are residential, including ground-up homes, remodeling jobs and additions in the Los Angeles area. These residential projects average $300 to $400 per square foot and are typically between 5,000 to 10,000 square feet, though they can be much larger. Hefner charges a standard fixed fee for phases up to construction and hourly after that, with interior design work charged hourly with a markup.

"As a decorator, I so admire William." "He did a Tuscan that is one of the most beautiful houses ever built. It could be in Capri." "He cares about every detail." "I trust him completely—our partnership was a great success!" "The outsides are like an extension of your interior living rooms." "The house looks like it has been there forever." "There is an amazing consistency in the look and continuity in the flow." "I didn't feel as if I was just another project." "Great team works with his wife on the interiors." "Low key personality and great listener."

FIRMS WITHOUT PORTFOLIOS

Barton Myers Associates   4   4   4   4

1025 Westwood Boulevard, Los Angeles, CA 90024
(310) 208 - 2227   www.bartonmyers.com

Innovative steel and glass architecture

"A legend in the field," principal Barton Myers has been creating "classic," "edgy" modern architecture since the late 1960s. Myers' firm takes on pioneering new projects and sensitive remodeling for public, private and institutional clients. Myers is known for his explorations in steel housing, incorporating steel-and-glass construction with off-the-shelf industrial components, and for creating environmentally intelligent design. There are often seamless integrations of the indoors and outdoors, with sliding walls on tracks and adjustable canvas awnings. References say the results are both interesting and elegant.

Myers received his Master of Architecture degree at the University of Pennsylvania before working with Louis I. Kahn. He began practicing architecture in Toronto and opened his Los Angeles office in 1984. Twenty professionals are currently on staff. Myers holds a continuing appointment as professor of architecture at UCLA and has been visiting professor at both Harvard and his alma mater

Penn. In 1994 he received a gold medal from the Royal Architectural Institute of Canada, and in 2002 a gold medal from the Los Angeles Chapter of the American Institute of Architects.

Barton Phelps & Associates   4.5   4.5   4   4
5514 Wilshire Boulevard, Los Angeles, CA 90036
(323) 934 - 8615   www.bpala.com
Contemporary, light-imbued, personalized architecture

Combining a reverence for highly unique contours and natural light with academic integrity, Barton Phelps produces work that "transcends style." Phelps' firm meticulously plans, designs and executes distinctly contemporary spaces rich in natural materials and colors. Phelps successfully blends the context of the site, lifestyle of the client and the character of the home into an "exciting and livable" end product. He is also known for designing "humanizing" interior office spaces.

Clients find the accessible Phelps to be "very bright and very talented," offering "options every step of the way." His focus is mentioned as frequently as his intimidating pedigree. He holds a BA in art from Williams College and a Master's in Architecture from Yale, and he trained with Frank Gehry and the late Charles Moore. After collaborating with numerous architects in the LA area, Phelps created his own firm in 1984 and was named a Fellow of the American Institute of Architects in 1993.

Phelps and his staff of ten take on about three to five big-ticket residential projects each year, both renovations/additions and ground-up homes of 6,000 to 10,000 square feet. About 40 percent of the firm's commissions are residential, with the balance comprised of large institutional projects, including public and private universities, libraries, aquariums and prep schools. Clients comment that the firm is "plugged into the dramatically changing market" of products and materials, which helps to keep the budgets in line. However, at $600+ per square foot these budgets are "in line" for those looking for a distinctive experience and a result that is the very "top of the line in every way."

"The house doesn't scream at you about how different it is, yet it's undeniably unique." "He adapts design in ways that are practical for the client, yet maintains his own architectural identity." "To Barton, an interesting setting makes an interesting house." "He uses conventional materials and forms, but creates something both ordinary and incredible." "Great historical perspective." "While I know we are small potatoes in his world, he was always there for us." "I told Barton that I thought he was crazy to try some of the things he did with my house. It turns out I was the crazy one, because I just love what he did."

Bill Bernstein AIA   3.5   3   4.5   4
11436 Victoria Avenue, Mar Vista, CA 90066
(310) 391 - 9976   bbaia@comcast.net
Internationally influenced, collaborative architecture

Clients tell us Bill Bernstein delivers "what we want way better than we could express it ourselves" while remaining faithful to his own design ideals. Bernstein excels in a range of architectural styles, from glass-clad contemporary to Spanish colonial. And for the past sixteen years, Bernstein has served as the executive architect in LA for Ricardo Legorreta, the esteemed Mexican architect. Clients applaud his ability to stay on an even keel and to stick to reasonable budgets.

Bernstein's enthusiastic commitment to every phase of the project rubs off on clients, who find he's an "ingenious and resourceful" solver of problems. Bernstein, who holds an undergraduate architecture degree from Ohio State University, started the company five years ago. Today, he leads a three-person firm that takes on five to ten projects annually.

	Quality	Cost	Value	Recommend?
	✛	$	◆	★

New single-family homes dominate his residential docket, with a number of renovations, additions and historical preservation jobs in the mix. Bernstein most often works in Pasadena, Santa Monica, Beverly Hills, Bel Air, Marina Del Rey and Hollywood. Homes average 5,000 square feet, and jobs run from an economic $200 per square foot to a more standard $300 per, with highly reasonable fees.

"We interviewed two other architects but they were only interested in furthering their own concepts. Bill was just the opposite. He said 'I need to understand you better and get to know you before I propose a plan.'" "Bill's greatest attribute is dealing with the fickle powers that be—he manages to get through the red tape unscathed." "He's very accommodating, but firm in terms of holding the line with contractors." "I'm very difficult to work with and he did phenomenal work."

"Bill did wonders with my 1950s track house. With lots of glass he brought the outdoors inside." "I had mushrooms growing over the walls before he got here, and it's just beautiful now." "The other bids from architects were two to three times more. And he came in under budget!"

Charles Bernstein Architects   4   3.5   4.5   4.5

904 Pacific Avenue, Venice, CA 90291
(310) 452 - 1560   www.mcharlesbernstein.com

Harmonious modern architecture awash in space and natural light

Charles Bernstein offers happy clients "a real architectural experience" shaped by his sincere dedication to the integrity of his craft. His timeless, harmonious and balanced designs are very clean, somewhat minimalistic and highlighted by the use of natural materials, making them both contemporary and accessible. Presently Bernstein's talents may be flying slightly under the radar—clients say they have pointed out designs in magazines of what they wanted, only to discover that the designs in question were actually his.

Clients find Bernstein to be genuine and laid back, yet "nothing is lost on him." He's even been known to live in a space for three days to fully understand the environment and the project. Bernstein established his five-person firm in 1980 after working for such esteemed architects as Frank Israel and Steven Erlich. He has been practicing for 30 years and remains the "hands-on" contact for his clients, taking only a select number of projects at any one time. Bernstein holds a Bachelor of Architecture degree from the University of Illinois and a Master of Architecture degree from UCLA. He has also completed a master's in counseling, a skill he uses to help discover the client's inner interests.

Typically in 2,000 to 8,000 square foot custom ground-up single-family homes, the firm has also accepted renovations and historic preservation projects. In addition, Bernstein takes on small institutional projects, such as libraries and interior architecture for private colleges. Los Angeles-focused, the firm has also done work in Aspen and New York City. The company's fees are reasonable and can be structured to suit the client, or even to suit Bernstein's passion. We hear he approached one client about doing some special metalwork for the ceiling, saying "I'll reduce my fee, but you have to do this." Who can say no?

"I did not think I was a modernist but he said 'Everything you show me is contemporary, so I'm going to do a contemporary house for you and you will love it.' He was right." "So likable, but not the expected." "For the amount of time he spent on my house, I'd be surprised if he made $.10 on the hour." "He's quite a deep person, with a real spiritual sense." "He's a very grand thinker and invested in his design but also understands it's a commercial enterprise. Once he's done trying to sell me on an idea, if I don't want to do it, he'll back down." "He is highly atypical LA—when he calls you for lunch he genuinely wants to know how you are doing."

	Quality +	Cost $	Value ◆	Recommend? ★

Daly Genik Architects

1558C 10th Street, Santa Monica, CA 90401
(310) 656 - 3180   www.dalygenik.com

Forward, inventive, modern architecture

4.5   4.5   4   4.5

Clients compliment Daly Genik for its "clean, handsome designs" that realize a stylized image of California modern. The firm's aesthetic is free of clutter and rich in materials, often incorporating common products in unexpected ways and also calling upon green and sustainable materials. We're told the firm shows exceptional skill in "handling the bureaucracy that goes along with building a new home," and is equally adept at navigating extreme site conditions, all while keeping an eye on the budget.

Patrons remark that the "dependable and pleasant" duo of Kevin Daly and Chris Genik lavish personal attention on each and every project. The two principals founded their firm in 1989 and now oversee a staff of nine. Daly holds architecture degrees from UC Berkeley and worked for Hodgetts + Fung and Frank Gehry before partnering with Genik, who holds degrees from Canada's Carleton University and Rice. The partners have lectured and taught at colleges and universities across the country.

The firm is known for its excellence in the adaptive reuse of large urban spaces, its outstanding neighborhood designs for low-income housing, its work on educational facilities—and a limited number of ground-up, single-family homes.

Daly Genik works mainly in the Hollywood Hills, Malibu and Santa Monica, but they have traveled to jobs in British Columbia, San Diego and across Northern California. Fees are based on an hourly charge through schematics and a fixed fee after that. Sources report that the firm keeps the number of its projects low to ensure the personal attention its principals believe is the core strength of the practice.

"Very inventive in process and materials." "We think they're terrific. They had an aesthetic ideal that we totally agreed with." "Kevin and Chris were both acutely aware of our lifestyle and folded that into the overall design scheme." "There were lots of limitations and constraints, such as height restrictions, permit and zoning issues, yet Kevin and Chris managed to come up with a house that looks great and functions even better."

David Hertz/Syndesis

2908 Colorado Avenue, Santa Monica, CA 90404
(310) 829 - 9932   www.syndesisinc.com

Site-specific contemporary architecture with Far East influences

4.5   4.5   4   4

Clients "marvel" at the "daring yet tasteful" settings created by architect David Hertz, whose designs feature contemporary, Japanese-inspired interiors softened with natural materials. Insiders say Hertz's emphasis on the use of glass, contiguous space and natural light maximizes views and seamlessly links indoor lounging with outdoor beauty. Sources appreciate Hertz's passion for bringing inventive technological advancements to his practice, implementing alternative heating and power sources for his environmentally responsible and sustainable homes. Hertz's firm also designs the interiors of many of its projects.

	Quality	Cost	Value	Recommend?
	✚	$	◆	★

Clients find it "comfortable communicating and collaborating" with Hertz, who they characterize as a "real straight shooter." Prior to starting the firm in 1983, Hertz earned his stripes at the establishments of Frank Gehry and John Lautner. He holds a Bachelor's Degree in Architecture from SCI-Arc, and his wife and co-principal Stacy Fong holds a degree from UC Berkeley. In addition to leading his architectural design firm, Hertz is also an educator, currently teaching at UCLA, as well as an active inventor of new building materials.

The practice generally designs ground-up single-family homes averaging 5,000 square feet. Hertz charges almost exclusively on an hourly rate, which can increase the total tally, but pleased clients counter that they "will forever be indebted to him for what he made happen."

"The detailed work, the commitment, the creativity, the ability to work with the contractor and individual craftsmen, and the willingness to stay engaged made our work with David a very special experience." "His design sense is rooted in classical philosophies combined with modern architecture practices." "People who visit reach out to touch the various textures in our home."

David Lawrence Gray Architects   4   4   4   4

1548 9th Street, Suite 200, Santa Monica, CA 90401
(310) 394 - 5707   www.davidgrayarchitects.com

Ardently modern reflective architecture

Clients tell us David Lawrence Gray perfectly balances the roles of architect, artist and friend, creating austere yet playful modern architecture. Many of Gray's projects feature facades clad in massive sheets of industrial glass, copious use of steel and concrete and vaulted loft-like living space. Gray is roundly applauded for his inventive use of standard materials and his attention to the client's lifestyle. More recently, we've been hearing good things about his successful use of green design.

Gray is described as "a lovely man" who is "extremely competent" at facilitating the process and executing the design. Founded in 1979, there are currently seven on staff. Gray holds degrees from the University of Washington and UC Berkeley. The firm's local work can be seen most frequently in Santa Monica, Beverly Hills, Bel Air, Malibu and West Hollywood. Seattle, Sun Valley and La Jolla are other cities in which these well-liked architects have completed projects. The firm takes on office and adaptive reuse projects, as well as residential commissions consisting of ground-up single-family homes with substantial budgets.

"He knows the subtle taste, metaphorically speaking, between dark chocolate and milk chocolate." "David really gets it. He understands his clients and spends a great deal of time with them to fully understand their objectives." "What amazes me is his vision. Sometimes I'll think I know what I want and he'll come up with something that I could never have imagined." "Just last month, someone drove by, came up and asked if they could buy the house." "I trust him implicitly." "We think he is a genius." "All the homes in my neighborhood are just boxes, but he built us the most innovative house with a dramatically inverted pitch roof."

David Martin Architect   4.5   4.5   4   4.5

10401 Wilshire Boulevard, Westwood, CA 90024
(310) 441 - 9533   dmkailva@aol.com

Large-scale, client-oriented architecture

David Martin has cultivated a faithful following with his roll-up-the-sleeves approach to architecture and his "impeccable" taste. We hear Martin designs homes in any style, offering architectural statements that are "neither too embellished nor under-embellished." As skilled at crafting Spanish Colonial and Tuscan-style homes as modern residences, Martin has a particular affection for contemporary projects.

Collaborators appreciate Martin's diligent nature, telling us "he doesn't give an off-the-cuff answer, but he will sit down and draw it up." Described as highly accessible and "one of the nicest human beings I've ever met," the personable Martin opened his own practice in 1995, after working for seventeen years at I.M. Pei and Partners.

Martin works almost exclusively in the LA area, from Beverly Hills and Bel Air down to Laguna Beach and parts of Orange County. In the past the firm has taken on projects in New York City, Monte Carlo and Hawaii. Martin accepts just a few new single-family homes a year averaging 5,000 to 7,500+ square feet, with costs in line with high-end quality.

"Not often can you get an architect with David's abilities and qualifications who actually does the work himself." "Doesn't spread himself too thin. Only takes the top of the top projects." "He has the best drawings I've ever seen." "He is excellent at thinking and drawing through complex problems."

Durfee/Regn   3.5   3   4.5   4.5
639 South Spring Street, Suite 4A, Los Angeles, CA 90014
(213) 244 - 9676   www.drsstudio.com
Modern, innovative architecture

Tim Durfee and Iris Regn are in demand for their expert art installations and for their hot residential commissions, often for the trendy art community. We hear that the "thesis or vision for the house" is created collaboratively so that everyone feels a sense of ownership before the blueprints are drawn. The outside-inside dialogue is taken very seriously—the membrane of the home may be extended into the garden. The firm is also involved with the evolution of advanced milling techniques with a sophisticated CAD-CAM system, creating undulating wooded walls that are surprisingly thin. The result of these developments is a contemporary-eclectic style with "large, open volumes coupled with strong, geometric designs."

Clients say husband and wife Durfee and Regn bring a "cool, innovative and helpful demeanor" to the process. Durfee received a Bachelor's Degree from the University of Rochester and a Master's in Architecture from Yale. Before forming his own firm in 1995, he taught at the Center of Creative Imaging, a school started by Apple Computer, and he currently heads up the visual studies program at SCI-Arc. Regn received her undergraduate degree from Smith College and a graduate degree from SCI-Arc. On some projects Regn may also act as interior designer, creating custom built-ins for clients, often in a modern 1950s or Scandinavian style.

The firm's museum installations are in collaboration with Louise Sandhaus and include projects in the UCLA Hammer Museum, Los Angeles County Museum of Art and Huntington Library in Pasadena. Residential projects are modest in size, at 1,800 to 3,000 square feet, reflecting the firm's approach to keeping costs reasonable.

"Smart, hip and so cool." "They were such a calming influence during the job." "The form of the house was derived from our use of the space. Not the other way around, like I felt with the last architect I used." "Pleasant, serene, yet professional." "They did the layout, sourced and designed the furniture. Just everything." "Incredible built-ins with hidden compartments. Amazing floating walnut headboard that pivots for enclosure." "Always available and very diligent." "They enjoy keeping costs low." "They finish the project on excellent terms with the client, which is highly commendable."

	Quality ✚	Cost $	Value ◆	Recommend? ★

Eric Owen Moss Architects

Quality	Cost	Value	Recommend?
4.5	4.5	4	4.5

8557 Higuera Street, Culver City, CA 90232
(310) 839 - 1199   www.ericowenmoss.com

High contemporary, sculptural architecture

The select group of clients who get the opportunity to work with iconoclast architect Eric Owen Moss know it's all about his signature style and singular vision. His widely published residential designs are an alchemy of jutting angles and Caligarian geometric shapes set in glass, steel and concrete, at once forward-thinking and highly sculptural.

Moss holds two Master of Architecture degrees—one from UC Berkeley and the other from Harvard. He founded the firm in 1973 and has been a professor at SCI-Arc for nearly as long. He is now serving as director of the esteemed institution—despite his long-held reputation as a counter-cultural enfant terrible.

Sources tell us the firm's staff of 25 works in a loft-like space and takes a communal approach to architecture, continuously exchanging and developing design ideas on projects budgeted from a few thousand to tens of millions of dollars. While not everything on paper is ultimately realized, we're told that Moss mounts his architectural challenges with creative site placement and an eye on budgetary constraints.

"Eric has a strong profile and only works for very special, exclusive clients." "It's his way or the highway. He has a specific style and is tireless in pursuit of the next great architectural idea." "You pay for a masterpiece and get a masterpiece."

Escher GuneWardena Architecture

Quality	Cost	Value	Recommend?
4	3	5	4.5

815 Silver Lake Boulevard, Los Angeles, CA 90026
(323) 665 - 9100   www.egarch.net

Internationally inspired, cutting-edge architecture

Frank Escher and Ravi GuneWardena carry on Los Angeles's storied modernist tradition through faithful renovations of important mid-20th-century structures and stunning realizations of their own cutting-edge ground-up designs. The firm's work features elegantly simplified expressions that succeed in creating clean lines, clutter-free interiors and open spaces swimming with light, often on daunting and dramatic hillside and canyon sites. Escher GuneWardena is also applauded for its commitment to affordable, sustainable design experiments with innovative materials, such as thermoplastic roof membranes and aerospace material paneling.

We're told the firm executes commissions with foresight, professionalism and a wealth of exploratory creativity. Escher hails from Switzerland, where he studied at the ETH in Zurich, while GuneWardena, originally from Sri Lanka, studied in Italy and holds an architecture degree from Cal Poly/Pomona. The firm recently won the Dwell II competition to design and build a completely green and sustainable residence in Topanga Canyon. Recently, its notable Jamie Residence was transformed into an international art event when bathed in light by Icelandic artist Olafur Eliasson.

Escher GuneWardena's work on both commercial spaces and private homes takes the firm from LA to New York and from Chicago to Seattle. The firm's residential work always involves an interesting or challenging scenario within a modern context, from a 500 square foot renovation of a Neutra house to a new 17,000 square foot estate. Its build costs come in at a very competitive $250 per square feet. The hard part, clients say, is to get Escher GuneWardena involved in the first place, since the principals will only oversee projects of intellectual interest.

"They're perfectionists—they pored over the plans relentlessly." "They're obsessed, in a good way, with getting it done right." "They really used the site to its maximum, while leaving the integrity of the site completely intact." "It took some convincing for us to go ahead with this radical design, but in the end it was a perfect concept for the site." "We wanted something unique, and they sure gave it to us!"

Frederick Fisher & Partners Architects   4   4   4   4

12248 Santa Monica Boulevard, West Los Angeles, CA 90025
(310) 820 - 6680   www.fisherpartners.net
Minimalist, thoughtful, contained architecture

Known as a member of the Santa Monica School, Frederick Fisher (along with Eric Owen Moss, Frank Gehry and Frank Israel) was part of that innovative generation of 1970s architects who believed in form following function. Most recently, Fisher has become known for designs that stress "fluidity of function," with open-space settings and a deft use of exposed natural and organic materials. With a strong contextual reference to site conditions, we hear the firm also develops excellent design flow between indoor and outdoor spaces.

A "solid and thoughtful" presence, Fisher has developed a reputation for delivering a high level of personalized service. The sizable practice, which also handles numerous institutional, commercial and retail projects, currently employs 23, including six licensed architects. Fisher holds a Master of Architecture from UCLA, while partners Joseph Coriaty and David Ross were educated at USC and SCI-Arc respectively.

"Interesting and caring, Fred develops clean, spacious, light-filled homes." "He created beautiful light-filled rooms from little dull compartments someone thought were rooms." "I practically had to put a gun to his head to get a hook to hang my bathrobe, but that is how true he is to the design." "Fred's a humanitarian—he really cares about people and he cares desperately about his work."

Giannetti Architecture + Interiors   4.5   4   4.5   4.5

11740 San Vicente Boulevard, Suite 204, Los Angeles, CA 90049
(310) 820 - 1329   www.giannettiarchitects.com
Historically derived, detailed architecture

Remaining true to his Old World, European ideals, Stephen Giannetti is said to bring a "joyful spirit" to the design process. Whether working with shingle style, Mediterranean or English Tudor, Giannetti balances the traditional proportions of older villa-like homes with a modern flow of space. "Open to test ideas," Giannetti always maintains integrity of the design concept, evident in one of his recent projects, a 10,000 square foot home painstakingly patterned after Thomas Jefferson's historic Monticello.

On projects, patrons tell us Giannetti stands firm to a "great vision" while participating "comfortably" with all players in the process. They call Giannetti an "expert listener" who "manages himself well and understands the job site." A graduate of the University of Maryland, Giannetti began his career on the East

Coast and moved to California in 1990. A relatively small firm of six, Giannetti Architecture's full-service staff also offers interior and landscaping design capabilities, which can sometimes get backlogged in the process.

The firm has a strong following in the affluent Newport Beach, Beverly Hills, Montecito and Pasadena communities. Giannetti routinely draws up five-figure floor plans, but he is said to be reasonable with budgets.

"He picked up on what we wanted." "Artistic by nature, he's incredibly attentive to the construction process." "A lovely, sweet gentleman." "Aesthetics are so important to Stephen—he's a perfectionist." "Moving one window around 42 times can be slow, but he never makes a mistake." "Perfect for the right kind of client." "Not only client-driven, but he throws himself into project."

Giovannini Associates   4   3.5   4.5   4

2209 North Broadway, Los Angeles, CA 90031
(323) 221 - 7297   www.giovanniniarchitecture.com

Enigmatic, spare, abstract architecture

Joseph Giovannini's playful, abstract architecture appeals to patrons who appreciate innovative, experimental design and are interested in how architecture can be both be an art form and an inscrutable habitat. In his trademark style widely known to be "intensely modern," intellectual and spare, planes intersect randomly and frequently, creating self-conflicting corners. Equally angular free-standing furniture adds to the fun and the illusion of non-gravitational pull.

Giovannini established the firm in 1988 after receiving an English literature degree from Yale, a French literature degree from the Sorbonne and a master's in architecture from Harvard. The multi-talented Giovannini is also the architecture critic for *New York Magazine*, an editor-at-large for *Architecture Magazine* and a frequent contributor to *Architectural Digest.* He has taught at UCLA, USC, Harvard and Columbia.

With practices in Los Angeles and New York, Giovannini has a Manhattanite's "respect for inches," maximizing any available space by creating loft-like areas. He takes on about five new projects annually, with at least half in LA. Much of the firm's work is residential, appearing on tricky hillsides or adaptive-use industrial sites in Santa Monica, Venice, Pasadena, Italy, Washington DC and New York. Gut renovations are tackled with gusto and some ground-up single-family homes are created, all on quite palatable budgets. The firm charges standard fees based upon a percentage of overall construction.

"These are not mere architecture projects but intellectual journeys." "Well-liked by peers and clients." "He needs clients who are interested in how architecture can expand their lives."

Gray Matter Architecture   4   3.5   4.5   4

639 East Channel Road, Santa Monica, CA 90402
(310) 454 - 7960   www.graymatterarchitecture.com

Experimental architecture employing offbeat materials

Melinda Gray brings her iconoclastic nature to modern architecture that is definitely not your standard black and white. Gray's work is admired by her clients for its "sculptural feel" that is enhanced by experimentation with exposed materials, such as logs and steel I-beams. Sources say that Gray will contribute her creative matter to every aspect of every project—right down to the hardware, light fixtures, cabinetry and furniture.

Quality	Cost	Value	Recommend?
+	**$**	**◆**	**★**

Gray's "strength of perspective" and "tremendous patience" are seen as real assets in "getting the job done." She is the sole principal of this firm of five, which she founded in 1984 after getting a graduate degree in architecture from UCLA and working at the revered firms of Eric Owen Moss and Frank Israel.

This firm's five to six projects a year are predominantly residential and can be seen in seaside Santa Monica or on the tricky hillside and landslide-prone sites of Malibu. We're told Gray takes on single-room renovations to new 4,000 square foot homes. Working in the $200 to $300+ per square foot range is not uncommon for Gray, making her work a very good value for clients who share her viewpoint.

"Melinda's greatest strength is her dedication. She will work and rework until she is satisfied." "She developed a really interesting staircase that solved the structural challenges." "Melinda really covered all the issues and made it a collaborative process." "I did not want a RoboCop house. She made it both warm and edgy modern, which is hard to do both well." "She has a very strong point of view, which works really well if you agree!" "All the contractors really enjoyed working with her. There are tremendous details in her plans, and she works in boots and a pair of jeans." "She thought of things that would never have crossed my mind."

Gwathmey Siegel & Associates Architects   4.5   5   5   5
475 Tenth Avenue, 3rd Floor, New York, NY 10018
(212) 947 - 1240   www.gwathmeysiegel.com

Modern, dramatic, geometric architecture

Geometric, precise and with great clarity of design, this firm's projects have won principals Charles Gwathmey and Robert Siegel a devoted following and more than 100 awards. Clients hail the company for its intricate, original designs and passion for creating spaces of the highest quality and stylistic integrity. They say the firm leaves its indelible signature on every project and it is very sympathetic to clients' needs. The architects in this firm of 80 put forth a distinct, unquestionable modernism, and they are commended for displaying a sculptor's sensitivity to form and light. We're told these architects believe that complete architectural solutions include the details of interior design.

Gwathmey, a Fulbright scholar, graduated from Yale in 1962 with a Master's Degree in Architecture and became a Fellow of the AIA in 1981. Siegel, a graduate of Pratt and Harvard, is president of Pratt's board of trustees and became a Fellow of the AIA in 1991. Both architects have taught at some of the country's most prestigious universities. Their high-powered partnership was founded in 1967, and today the venerable firm only accepts residential projects with exceptional budgets—usually exceeding $5 million. The projects are generally large-scale single-family homes and apartment renovations in Los Angeles and New York.

Recent projects include the construction of a 20,000 square foot dynamic home in Bel Air, significant homes in Malibu and Pacific Palisades, and commissions for numerous celebrities, including Jerry Seinfeld and Steven Spielberg in New York. Notable institutional commissions include the 1992 addition to the Solomon R. Guggenheim Museum and buildings for Harvard, Princeton and Cornell. The firm expectedly charges a significantly higher percentage of total construction costs. AD 100, 2000, 2002. ID Hall of Fame.

"We were able to get an architectural masterpiece without sacrificing practical living comfort." "The most amazing part was watching Charles's ideas come to

fruition. I would happily do it all again." "The execution, right down to the last detail, was absolutely flawless." "We were a relatively small client, and it took forever to get their attention." "It was a perfect collaboration between our ideas and their illumination of them." "They were imaginative and creative—and it came out magnificently."

Hablinski + Manion Architecture   5   5   4   4

2150 Summitridge Drive, Beverly Hills, CA 90210
(310) 858 - 8525   www.hablinski-manion.com

Traditional, European-influenced grand architecture

Best known for realizing 20,000 square foot historical mansions that rival the finest chateaus in France and the grandest villas in Italy, Hablinski + Manion caters to the wealthy and fabulous. Notable clients include Warren Beatty and Annette Bening, Arnold Schwarzenegger and Maria Shriver, Jennifer Lopez and Ben Affleck, Jim Carrey and Vanna White. Partners William Hablinski and Richard Manion draw on their extensive study and frequent travels throughout the US and Europe to create opulent interpretations of Italian, Spanish Colonial, 18th-century French and Georgian style architecture. While each residence is crafted with pinpoint period accuracy, the modern interior living space is geared toward today's family living. Supporters applaud the results as "elegant," "graceful" and "timeless."

We're told the firm takes a highly collaborative and personalized approach to the process. Hablinski has a bachelor of arts in architecture from the University of Texas and began his own firm in 1978. In 1995, Hablinski and Manion joined forces, creating a full-service firm with 27 employees and offices in Beverly Hills and Austin, Texas. Manion, who received an architecture degree from Columbia, where he studied American and European architectural history, worked for the venerable Robert A.M. Stern and Robert Venturi before coming to Los Angeles in 1987.

The firm's award-winning mega-residences dot the mountainous Mulholland Drive corridor and exclusive streets in Beverly Hills, Bel Air and Pacific Palisades. In 2005, the firm received an unprecedented 5.9 million dollar settlement from a group including a former employee who used the firm's blueprints to create a "copycat" 14 million dollar house down the road. Some projects are as huge as 40,000 square feet (with lower than standard fees) and all are ultra-luxurious, placing this firm beyond the reach of all but the most established of clients.

"If you know what they deliver, they are the place to go." "Restrained work through all the correct details, given the magnitude." "Sensitive to their heavy European influences." "Hablinski is a real gentleman and a true perfectionist." "Even the contemporary works seem to incorporate medieval turrets." "They have the system down, totally in control." "The Stanford White of LA—classically unbelievable." "While outrageously large, they get all the details correct. The result is dignified." "They actively monitor the construction process and are on top of the workmen."

Hodgetts + Fung Design Associates   4   4   4   4

5837 Adams Boulevard, Culver City, CA 90232
(323) 937 - 2150   www.hplusf.com

Spare, clean, warm modernist architecture

With a distinct 21st-century style described by insiders as "somewhere between minimalist and California funk," this husband-and-wife team has been making waves in LA since 1984. Hodgetts + Fung creates spare and clean designs that feature natural materials, particularly glass, cement and steel. Clients praise this dynamic duo for "thinking outside the box" and listening to a wide range of solutions, "even if an idea is not their own."

Principals Craig Hodgetts, who holds a Master's of Architecture from Yale and Hsin-Ming Fung, who holds a Master's of Architecture from UCLA, lead this firm of sixteen. About 50 percent of Hodgetts + Fung's body of work is residential, with the remainder being exhibition spaces and institutional installations. The firm is also involved in the preservation of the Case Study Houses of the 1950s and 1960s.

Taking on about ten projects per year across the western US, Argentina, Germany, China and Switzerland, the practice works with "moderate" budgets of $1 million and up, but they will work with budgets of less than half of that. Hodgetts + Fung works most often in the city's exclusive neighborhoods, including West Hollywood, Brentwood and Sylmar. The firm's fees are based on a slightly higher-than-standard percentage of overall construction costs.

"Craig and Ming are constantly looking for a challenge and experimenting, looking to advance their craft. They strongly prefer clients of that mentality." "They play off each other very well as they can have quite different viewpoints, but it comes together beautifully." "Other architects are highly impressed." "Not at all dogmatic (unlike other architects I have known) and very good about budgetary restraints." "They have the ability to design very creatively with inexpensive materials." "Craig and Ming have a knack for designing a functional home with amazing aesthetics. You get the best of both worlds." "Their style is based on the needs of the project and the client, and not on leaving their signature concept."

James R. Harlan Architect   4   4   4   4

844 Milwood Avenue, Venice, CA 90291
(310) 306 - 4936   www.jamesharlan.com
Minimalist architecture with updated mid-century modern flair

When homeowners employ James Harlan as an architect, they usually end up finding a friend for life as well as a designer. Immensely satisfied clients say Harlan is a creator "not of homes, but of living works of art." Concentrating entirely on single-family residences, we are told Harlan does not limit himself to just the shells of the homes he designs, but he will often also design the complete interiors—and in some cases, he'll design interiors on projects for which he was not the architect. Described as "urban and sophisticated" in his design sensibility, Harlan has earned a reputation for taming difficult hillside sites and maximizing views. Sources add that Harlan has a pleasant, low-key personality and listens intently to clients' input.

Harlan, whose designs are distinctly modern, is the sole practitioner of the firm he created twelve years ago after earning an undergraduate degree in architecture from USC and working for the late Frank Israel. The firm is a true LA establishment, with 90 percent of its work taking place in and around Los Angeles. Harlan does not shy away from smaller projects, but the bulk of his commissions come with sizeable budgets of up to $3 million.

Recent noteworthy jobs include the renovation of a home originally designed by John Lautner, an ultramodern 4,500 square foot Krause residence in Malibu.

Harlan's six yearly projects are split evenly between ground-up single-family homes, renovations and additions. The firm's architecture fees are based on a standard percentage of overall construction costs. Interior design fees are based on a standard design fee and markup.

"He's like a dream." "I'm almost ready to build another house just so I can work with him again." "When I saw a remodel he had done, I felt like I had discovered someone who knew my soul in a way that nobody else did." "The home he created for us is a piece of art, brilliantly created—and the ingenuity that went into it was spectacular." "Immediately after meeting him at a party, I went home and told my husband that we just had to find something for him to build for us."

	Quality +	Cost $	Value ◆	Recommend? ★

Kanner Architects

5　4.5　4.5　4.5

10924 Le Conte Avenue, Los Angeles, CA 90024
(310) 208 - 0028　www.kannerarch.com

Highly intellectual, forward-thinking, innovative modern architecture

Clients say Steve Kanner remains grounded and approachable despite his award-winning status in the industry. The third-generation to head up this respected 55-year-old firm, Kanner has developed a loyal following by "treating clients as intelligent individuals" and "accepting their ideas and making them feel comfortable with the design process." Kanner originated the style that was dubbed "Pop Architecture" in the 1990s, and is now creating highly contemporary designs in residential and commercial markets. Sources describe Kanner's current style as "minimal," "linear," "simple" and "exuberant." We're told he takes a highly intellectual approach to problem-solving while incorporating light, weather and views into the overall scheme.

This widely published firm of twenty can have as many as thirty projects in various stages at any given time, about a third of which are residential. The remaining commissions are retail, institutional and commercial endeavors, including the largest "dark ride" ever built—Universal's Men In Black attraction. In terms of his residential work, we're told Kanner deals primarily with ground-up construction, though he does some additions and renovations. The majority of the new homes range from 3,500 to 6,000 square feet and command budgets in the $1 million to $2 million range. On occasion, the firm will take on smaller projects.

Kanner holds undergraduate and graduate architecture degrees from UC Berkeley. Prior to taking over the family firm, he worked for Cambridge 7 and Associates in Boston as well as Skidmore, Owings and Merrill. Kanner and his firm work mostly in Malibu, Benedict Canyon, Bel Air and Hollywood Hills. In addition to Southern California, the firm has completed projects in New York, Tokyo, Paris, Rome, Milan, Frankfurt and Amsterdam.

"Steve knows proportions so well that he spotted some lines that were less than an inch off from 30 feet away—when we put a level on it, he was right on. I couldn't believe it." "I get a very warm feeling from him. I almost feel as if he is part of my family." "He's truly a perfectionist, which I fully appreciate." "He came up with a design that was simply inspiring. I just think so highly of him." "I feel that he has treated this project like a favorite pet. He put so much into making it special." "His mother does lots of the interiors." "No ego issues." "Well respected by peers and industry leaders." "Fabulous, fun architect and a lovely man."

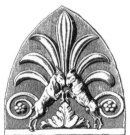

Koning Eizenberg Architecture

4　3　5　4.5

1454 25th Street, Santa Monica, CA 90404
(310) 828 - 6131　www.kearch.com

Organic, site-specific architecture

Distinguishing themselves by their commitment to thoughtful, socially responsible architecture that is markedly affordable, principals Julie Eizenberg and Hendrik Koning have earned the respect of clients and peers. On the residential side, they are best known for their remodels of relatively modest Spanish style cottages in a manner that blurs the line between traditional and modern styles. A glamorous glass and steel bedroom may sit atop a thick, sloping stucco base. Outside spaces are integrated into the blueprints, generating a harmonious overall impression. Generally the belief is that a little modern embellishment goes a long way, greatly relieving the budget. The aim is to intelligently create unadorned, appealing designs appropriate for relatively simple, everyday family life.

We're told this husband-and-wife team works well with clients and that together they are excellent "solvers of difficult problems." Each holds an architecture degree from both the University of Melbourne in Australia and UCLA. They established the practice in 1981 and work mostly within a 25-mile radius of their Santa Monica studio. The firm's mix of residential commissions includes both new construction and renovations, from evocatively modern remodels to sprawling, new single-level homes that "meld into the surrounding landscape." Their housing and community-based projects have won many awards, especially their expansion of the Pittsburgh Children's Museum.

The firm enjoys budgetary challenges, and has created home additions as exceptionally low as $120 per square foot a few years ago. New homes tend to be in the 3,000 square foot range, but can also be 7,000+ square feet.

"They do not just take on exclusive projects, but are completely involved in improving the world around them." "They are interested in creating excellent work without pretension." "Extremely collaborative." "Not interested in being cutting-edge visionaries in a dramatic way, but in an understated, community way." "Easy and so nice to work with." "You really feel as if you are part of the team, creating something interesting and wonderful."

Lewis Schoeplein Architects   4   4   4   4
10590 1/2 West Pico Boulevard, Los Angeles, CA 90064
(310) 842 - 8620   www.lewisschoeplein.com
Warm, modern architecture and interiors

Clients tell us this firm's "tactile, humanist and livable" modern designs "cater to the senses." Lewis Schoeplein creates interior spaces that are quite spare in detail, yet rich in color and natural materials—and bathed in natural light. For the majority of its projects, the firm also designs everything, from cabinetry and flooring to interior colors and lighting.

We hear principals Toni Lewis and Marc Schoeplein work shoulder to shoulder with clients from concept design to moving day. The husband-and-wife team opened the firm in 1998 and together they currently oversee a staff of six. Lewis holds architecture degrees from UC Berkeley and UCLA while Schoeplein collected his from UCLA and UConn, respectively. Schoeplein previously worked for the firm of Moore Ruble Yudell, while Lewis worked for Frank Gehry.

Regularly at work in Malibu, Pacific Palisades, Westwood, Brentwood and Manhattan Beach, the firm takes on retail, corporate and civic projects—including a number of fire stations throughout LA—as well as residential jobs. Lewis Schoeplein most often handles renovations and additions, but it is also active in ground-up construction, with mid-sized budgets.

Lorcan O'Herlihy Architects   4.5   4   4.5   4.5
5709 Mesmer Avenue, Culver City, CA 90230
(310) 398 - 0394   www.loharchitects.com
Experimental yet sensible, warm modern architecture

Angelenos with trend-setting tastes flock to this "much in demand," eager-to-innovate practice like Bright Young Things to the Viper Room. Part of LA's progressive architecture movement, Lorcan O'Herlihy brings warmth to the modern aesthetic. Clients cite his penchant for open floor plans, rich woods and an emphasis on natural light and maximized views via substantial glassworks. While the firm is constantly rethinking and experimenting with materials and fabrications to accommodate both the physical and financial, every choice is grounded in a solid design sensibility.

Clients tell us O'Herlihy is "very meticulous" in supervising the process, making sure "every line is straight and clean." The sole principal of this firm of eight, O'Herlihy holds an architecture degree from Cal Poly/San Luis Obispo. Prior to going out on his own in 1990, O'Herlihy was employed by the respected firm of I.M. Pei and Associates, where he worked on the acclaimed Louvre Museum project in Paris.

Most of O'Herlihy's projects are built in the greater Los Angeles area, including Pacific Palisades, Palos Verdes Marina Del Rey, Hollywood Hills and Malibu. However, the firm also works in locations such as Chicago, San Francisco, San Diego, Tokyo and China. Single-family ground-up residences of moderate size and high expectations make up the firm's residential slate. Fees are said to be lower than standard and can be based on a percentage of construction, an hourly or flat fee.

"He is among the hottest architects in LA and does not mind telling you that." "I love what he did for me. It's like a floating space drenched in light. There is so much glass you hardly notice the superstructure." "His use of wood really gives it warmth." "He's very easy to talk to and truly understands what you want, but he also knows when to take control, especially when monitoring the construction process." "The scheduling can be problematic." "Timeless and architectonic."

Lubowicki & Lanier Architects   4   4   4   4

141 Sierra Street, El Segundo, CA 90245
(310) 322 - 0211   www.lubowickilanier.com

Pared-down, elemental modern architecture

We hear Lubowicki & Lanier's work is imbued with a "material-ness" that reflects an honesty about how architecture is realized in form. By editing their designs to the essence, the complexity of construction reveals an unusually "lovely and really interesting" modern space. Much is left in its raw natural form, allowing the light to soften the edges. The firm has designed several award-winning and widely published residential and commercial projects, for which it has fabricated furniture pieces. Insiders applaud Lubowicki & Lanier for its thrilling integration of art and architecture, client and environment.

Clients tell us principals Paul Lubowicki and Susan Lanier are "unusually helpful." Before founding the firm in 1988, Lanier received a Masters in Architecture from SCI-Arc and worked for Morphosis Architects, while Lubowicki graduated from Cooper Union School of Architecture and worked with Frank Gehry. They are clearly a bright and intellectual pair—Lanier brings a psychology and literature background to her work, while Lubowicki currently teaches at SCI-Arc. The duo lectures on architecture frequently, from the UCLA School of Architecture to The Architectural League of New York.

"They are so much fun to work with." "You'd be remiss not to consider them." "A protégé of Frank Gehry. Frank has incredible regard for Paul." "Not for everybody, their work can be quite intellectually driven." "There is an openness of spirit, physical lines that are so unique and so inviting." "What modern would be like if visualized by a pioneer of the Great Plains."

M2A Architects   4   4   4   4

6253 Hollywood Boulevard, Suite 210, Hollywood, CA 90028
(323) 464 - 0600   www.m2a-architects.com

Thoughtful, sensitively updated historic renovations

We're told M2A masterfully carves modern living space out of historical renovations without disturbing the integrity of original architecture. Working in styles as varied as Spanish Colonial, Art Deco and Craftsman, these "are the only guys who can bring old buildings back to life," say many happy clients. The firm actively and personably engages its clients throughout the process, from concept to turnkey. M2A's principals, Barry Milofsky and Tom Michali, are said to be "talented and knowledgeable," and their staff "professional, courteous and punctual."

References report Michali is an expert at sensitive rehabilitation of historic architecture, having served as the chair of the Preservation Committee for the Los Angeles Conservancy. He received his undergraduate architecture degree from SCI-Arc. Milofsky has an architecture degree from Cincinnati and extensive experience in creating large-scale urban design projects; he's also an active member of the Hollywood Design Review Board. The duo founded the firm together in 1988. Clients "would recommend them in a heartbeat," and further recommend them because "your heart won't skip a beat when the final the bill comes in."

"Tom includes us in every aspect of the process, and no matter what problems arise, he gives us a creative and practical solution that we are nothing less than satisfied with." "Deals very confidently with obstacles." "It's special to have an architect who will take my calls several times a day if necessary." "Nothing but a pleasant experience in every respect."

Michael C.F. Chan & Associates Inc.   4   4   4   4

3550 West 6th Street, Los Angeles, CA 90020
(213) 383 - 2162   mcfca@earthlink.net

Elegant, versatile, refined large-scale architecture

Sources tell us Michael C.F. Chan demonstrates "an artist's touch in perfect balance with an architect's eye." From impeccably detailed neoclassical Louis XV to picture-perfect stark modernism, Chan has an excellent feel for fine subtleties and puts a tremendous amount of research into whatever style or period his client desires. We're told his firm is one of LA's best-kept secrets, accepting large high-end custom estates and sprawling single-family homes. It also designs the interiors for limited projects.

The sole principal of his firm, Chan gets good reviews for his refined personality and elegant taste. He holds architecture degrees from USC and Harvard. The practice was established more than 25 years ago and currently oversees ten employees, working most often in Beverly Hills, Malibu, Thousand Oaks, Pasadena and other affluent neighborhoods. He also takes on a significant number of assignments in New York City and London, and he has been commissioned globally in Indonesia, Saudi Arabia and Asia.

Approximately 80 percent of Chan's practice is the design of residential projects, with the remainder of his efforts on projects such as corporate headquarters for large companies. For large budgets, the firm's costs are standard.

"He's not afraid to be different. You can find a lot of 'cut and paste' architects out there, but Michael is his own man, no doubt." "The mood created by the lighting and its placement is an absolute perfect combination of artificial and ambient light." "He's very innovative, but it's not forced—it comes naturally to him."

Michael Maltzan Architecture Inc   4.5   4   4.5   4

2801 Hyperion Avenue, Studio 107, Los Angeles, CA 90027
(323) 913 - 3098   www.mmaltzan.com

Abstract, modernist architecture with art world inflections

This sociable architect has become the darling of art world aficionados and Hollywood heavyweights by creating some of the most noted public spaces in the country, including MoMA QNS in Long Island City, New York and UCLA's Hammer Museum. Michael Maltzan twists sleek, white surfaces into abstract modernist spaces that look "reconfigured by the forces of time." The firm brings the same public consciousness to its residential work as its institutional commissions, remaining as sensitive to how the architecture relates to the community as to how it works for the client. Maltzan's depth of experience with lighting and curatorial issues attracts patrons with significant art collections.

Maltzan received his undergraduate degree from the Rhode Island School of Design and later attended Harvard Graduate School of Design. After a seven-year stint working for Frank Gehry, where he helped prepare the winning submission for the Disney Concert Hall competition, Maltzan started his own studio in Silver Lake. Today, Michael Maltzan prides himself on having a full-service architectural firm reaching the arts, performing arts, institutional, educational, commercial and residential facilities. The practice has won numerous accolades, including awards from the American Institute of Architects and Progressive Architecture.

"Michael really thought about the art—he left plenty of wall space without sacrificing great views." "He created a complex yet serene environment for the family." "The house feels like a piece of artistic sculpture." "Brilliantly partners the structure and lighting with the outside environment." "We really enjoyed working with him. Michael has a very thoughtful personality."

Mickey Muennig   4.5   4   4.5   5

Village Shops, Highway One, Big Sur, CA 93920
(831) 667 - 2471   www.mickeymuennig.com

Unorthodox, creative architecture with an emphasis on organic materials

Mickey Muennig's unusual, organic structures have become the stuff of legend, stirring excitement among peers, clients and architectural historians. One of the more innovative of architects, Muennig's work evinces a deliberate, modern design sense, while mixing in elements of Tuscan and Greek styles. With a distinct taste for working in free form, Muennig is particularly fond of natural materials, reaching beyond staples like concrete and glass to dirt and grass. Muennig has been called to work in off-the-map locations where his only source of power is the sun, so the architect has become an expert in solar power, including radiant floor heating with sun-warmed water.

We're told the humble Muennig maintains a sense of humor and takes an unconventional approach to architecture that can be seen in his own house. The residence took twenty years to construct, is built in the shape of a clover leaf— and is completely underground. It has a sod roof, with a cutout for a skylight for his underground garden, replete with banana trees and a host of other fruit-bearing tropical flora. The Post Ranch Inn in Big Sur, where guests stay in tiny tree house "rooms," is probably his best-known work.

Muennig graduated from the University of Oklahoma in 1959 and trained with the equally individualistic Bruce Goff, who created isolated single-family homes tucked among tree groves of the Great Plains. Today, Muennig keeps a small firm of three, which takes on about five projects a year almost exclusively in the Big Sur area. Muennig has also worked in Denver and parts of Missouri as well as China and Germany, where he designed several resort communities. The majority of the firm's projects are new home designs or the occasional renovation. AD 100, 2000, 2002.

"Mickey's design magically blends the interior with the exterior using floor to ceiling glass and wood panels." "He was always very respectful of the environment." "Mickey likes to keep it organic, by using local and natural materials." "His living spaces allow you to live in peace with nature." "He worked really hard to maximize the ocean views with a cantilevered terrace."

Minarc   3.5   2.5   5   4.5
2324 Michigan Avenue, Santa Monica, CA 90404
(310) 998 - 8899   www.minarc.com
Forward thinking, modern architecture of international (and acquired) taste

Formerly Pizzinini Luxemburg Thorsteinsson, now rechristened Minarc, this international firm brings a playful, avant-garde approach to its Bauhaus-flavored modern designs. The firm is known both for its distinct skills in converting centuries-old spaces and is designing ground-up homes that lean toward a brave new world. We're told Minarc pushes the envelope of form and function, using bold primary colors and low-maintenance concrete panels in exteriors. The firm's interiors go for a relaxed livability, simple not spare, with lots of wood finishing.

In business since 1989, this firm has offices in LA, Luxembourg and Vienna. There are five people in the LA office, which takes on about ten projects annually. Principals Regina Pizzinini and Leon Luxemburg both worked with the esteemed firm of Moore Ruble Yudell and both studied in Austria and UCLA. Fellow principal Tryggvi Thorsteinsson holds a degree from SCI-Arc.

The firm takes on historic rehabilitation, new single-family home construction and remodeling in Europe (three projects in Ireland at press time) and LA. On the side, the firm is independently developing some very attractive modular homes at $100 per square foot. Minarc's Los Angeles homes average 3,000 to 4,000 square feet, with the firm taking on something as small as a kitchen and bath redo or as large as a renovation of a 14,000 square foot castle in Malibu. With cost per square foot going from $200 to $350+, the firm can cater to quite different audiences, and does offer lower budget alternatives.

"We just hit it off—they're young with a lot of positive energy." "They're definitely ethereal and conceptual." "He was so good about solving the issues we were having with the city." "They never limited the scope of what we wanted. It was fun for them to design and fun for us to live in."

Morphosis   5   5   4   4
2041 Colorado Avenue, Santa Monica, CA 90404
(310) 453 - 2247   www.morphosis.net
Radical, abstract, mostly institutional architecture

Known for its authentic innovative architecture, Morphosis surpasses the bounds of traditional form and materials and pushes the envelope of modern and postmodern design. Sloped structures, canted walls, electronic windowpanes that appear opaque with the push of a button and unusual geometric shapes are their

	Quality	Cost	Value	Recommend?
	+	$	◆	★

quintessential trademark. Principal Thom Mayne's "radical and original" work fuses art and technology and has won this pathfinder many awards, most recently the 2005 Pritzker Architecture Prize.

Aficionados and clients are intrigued with the firms "risk-taking" style. Born in Connecticut, Mayne's family moved west when he was quite young and settled in Southern California. After graduating from USC he taught at Pomona and teamed up with other notables to form the unorthodox school of architecture, SCI-Arc. Apart from serving on many faculties here and aboard, he holds a faculty position at the UCLA School of Arts and Architecture and serves on the board of directors at SCI-Arc. Together, Mayne and Jim Stafford formed Morphosis in 1972 and were joined by the lauded architect Michael Rotondi. During the latter part of the 1970s, Mayne received a master's degree from Harvard. Currently, the firm employs approximately twenty architects directed by Mayne, John Enright and Kim Groves. The establishment's accolades include the renowned Diamond Ranch High School in Pomona. Recently they were commissioned to build the new Alaska State Capitol building in Juneau.

Morphosis's star continues to rise, creating rootless architecture that flourishes on the West Coast and all over the world. The majority of its commissions are drawn from commercial and institutional sectors with some residential projects.

"Thom's best work comes from taking a risk." "He is a contributor to the impressive Los Angeles architecture." "Thom is determined to get his design ideas realized." "A confident trailblazer who is not afraid to take chances." "His ideas are so revolutionary, definitely not for everyone." "He is a remarkable talent."

Pugh + Scarpa   4   3   5   4

2525 Michigan Avenue, Building F1, Santa Monica, CA 90404
(310) 828 - 0226   www.pugh-scarpa.com

Unconventional, postmodern architecture

Pugh + Scarpa's popularity rests on a modernist yet practical approach to architecture that is reflected in its "richly layered" and "progressive" use of relatively simple materials. Clients characterize Gwynne Pugh and Larry Scarpa as both innovative in spirit and "reliable and dependable" in their oversight. The firm takes on a wide range of residential and commercial projects, many crafted with special attention to providing unique solutions to site and space constraints. The partners' groundbreaking environmental and sustainable designs have earned the respect of a devoted following.

Clients tell us principals Pugh and Scarpa "make a good marriage" of creative zest and technical expertise. A full-service firm established in 1984, Pugh + Scarpa is involved in all aspects of planning and design, including architecture, engineering, interior design and furniture design. Pugh holds an engineering degree from Leeds University in England and a graduate degree in architecture from UCLA, while Scarpa joined the firm in 1987 after receiving his degree from the University of Florida.

The firm fields offices in Santa Monica, San Francisco and Charlotte, North Carolina, and caters to a wide range of residential, institutional and commercial projects. Ground-up residences average 3,000 square feet, at $300 to $350 per. We're told the firm is sensitive to budget needs and inventive in material selection to keep costs down. Widely published, the firm received National AIA awards in 2001 and 2002.

"They are extremely hot right now and have lots of varied work." "They were very flexible with our budget and space limitations." "The partners have a deep personal and creative commitment to the end product." "Everyone in the LA design community is interested in what they are going to come up with next." "They think a lot about 'responsible living' in the 21st century." "They consider

the client's attitude as much as the site when deciding to take on a new project."
"Their work is a running commentary on the developments of LA's urban sprawl."

Richard Meier & Partners   5   5   4   4.5

1001 Gayley Avenue, 3rd Floor, Los Angeles, CA 90024
(310) 208 - 6464   www.richardmeier.com

Significant, masterful, legendary modernist architecture

A legend among 20th-century modernists, Richard Meier is recognized world-wide for his emphasis on light, geometric precision and extensive use of glass. His renowned work shows the influence of Le Corbusier in the balance, mathematical rhythm and cubic forms it employs, yet Meier focuses on creating volumes of livable space within a building. A predominantly white palette highlights vertical and horizontal elements, with porcelain panels often lending luminosity to otherwise monochromatic surfaces.

A winner of the prestigious Pritzker Award in 1984, Meier's arguably most acclaimed work is the Getty Center in Los Angeles. His firm's many other impressive structures of large scale include the Barcelona Museum of Contemporary Art and the Hague City Hall and Central Library. As the recipient of the commission for the Jubilee Church, Meier has the distinct honor of being the only American to design a church in Rome.

While museums, commercial buildings and major civic commissions constitute much of Meier's work, he still finds time to complete several residential projects a year. It's no secret that the Cornell-educated Meier limits his residential practice to significant projects with serious budgets. AD 100, 2000, 2002, 2004. ID Hall of Fame.

"I was an active participant in the process, and so enjoyed the intellectual exercise and time with Richard and Michael." "The house was statically modern before, but now it reverberates with the light and the seasons."

Ronchetti Design   4.5   4.5   4   4.5

531 North Highway 101, Solana Beach, CA 92075
(858) 523 - 9555   www.ronchettidesign.com

Site-specific, sensual, natural modern architecture

Be it a bluffside lot curving along the ocean or a triangle nestled between two canyons, Ken Ronchetti sculpts his creations from the land. The result is architecture that has "a soft strength in its simplicity." We're told Ronchetti's homes evince Frank Lloyd Wright in their cantilevered structures and unique site placements. His technical prowess draws as much admiration from clients and contemporaries as his sensual aesthetic, which employs stone, glass and other natural materials.

Acutely aware of his clients' needs, Ronchetti works collaboratively in the design process. We're told his background in art, engineering and architecture is blended into bursts of splendid invention. He also has an interest in the blurring of the indoor/outdoor line, incorporating unique sliding wall systems and outdoor fireplaces into his designs. Located in Rancho Sante Fe for over 32 years, Ronchetti's firm staffs ten and has excellent ongoing working relationships with outside design professionals.

Open to commercial clients as well, most of the firm's residential projects are in Southern California and typically run 5,000 to 10,000 square feet. Ronchetti's one-of-a-kind style, eager to please hands-on approach and reasonable costs woo many customers back for a second experience.

"An innovator who continually is looking to improve his design passion." "He is just as happy designing a fabulous station wagon as he is a Ferrari." "The designs

are more than client specific, they are deeply personal." "He has a strong sense of himself and a sensitivity to the client." "He is a genius with light." "There is a spiritualistic sense—a Mayan influence."

Scott Joyce Design   4.5   4   4.5   4.5

1024 Palm Avenue, West Hollywood, CA 90069
(310) 289 - 4999   www.scottjoycedesign.com

Highly customized high-end architecture infused with technology

We hear this hip, young architect strives for a synthesis of old and new, coupling cutting-edge design with classic comfort. The firm works expertly in an array of styles and can create anything from a modern Hollywood celebrity bachelor pad with "all the bells and whistles" to a traditional Mediterranean-style estate, often incorporating historical elements into contemporary frameworks. Clients tell us principal Scott Joyce revels in the hi-tech, coming up with such elements as a 30-foot retractable skylight or a glass-backed fireplace. The firm also designs custom-built furniture for architectural clients and offers landscaping services.

Joyce is said to rise to the challenge of developing ideas "outside the box" and to manage each project with a keen strategic style. Clients also appreciate his relaxed, upbeat demeanor. A graduate of SCI-Arc with a Master's in Architecture, he started his firm in 1996 while still a thesis student. He continues to teach at the institution.

Though most work is along the California coast, the firm has been commissioned to design homes in New York, Pennsylvania and Connecticut. Sources tell us this small firm takes on no more than ten residential clients per year to focus attention on each project. These are mostly ground-up homes that average 10,000 to 15,000 square feet, as well as the occasional remodel. Price per square foot is reasonable for the high-end work at about $300.

"Scott loves a good challenge—and always comes up with a good solution." "He makes a very stressful process manageable." "Great business sense." "Scott has a wide breadth of knowledge that he brings to each project."

Shigetomi Pratt Architects   4   3   4.5   4

113 1/2 North La Brea Avenue, Suite 114, Los Angeles, CA 90036
(323) 692 - 0897   www.sparchitectsla.com

Versatile boutique architecture sensitive to difficult sites

Clients appreciate principal Dean Pratt's low-key, all-encompassing approach. Shigetomi-Pratt's discerning eye may be seen in its sensitive renovation of classic California genres such as Mediterranean, Craftsman and Italianate, and its original Cottage Craftsman, ground-up designs. The firm has also found success realizing modern structures. Clients mention the establishment's ability to blend the old with the new with its additions that "look like they have been there forever." Given Pratt's down-to-earth attitude and unpretentious style, supporters would be surprised to know that the young architect has an impressive roster of clients.

We hear Pratt is "likable, serious and focused" and has "great subcontractor resources." A graduate of the University of Colorado at Boulder in environmental design and the University of California with an Master's in Architecture, Pratt spent three years working as the internal project architect liaison for the contractor on projects for Frank Gehry and Steven Ehrlich, giving him unusual hands-on experience before starting his one-man architecture firm in 1990. We hear his broad knowledge of construction and site issues inform his thoughtful, well-documented designs.

A small boutique shop of two, Shigetomi Pratt is a full-service architectural firm with a primarily residential practice. Though most of the firm's work is in Southern California, it has been known to travel as far as Taipei, Taiwan for a project. Homes typically are built at $225 a square foot, ranging in size from 3,000 to 5,000 square feet, delivering plenty of bang for the buck. The firm takes lower than standard fees and will do remodels of a few rooms.

"He goes beyond aesthetic aspects to look at long-term solutions." "Dean puts your concerns to rest in a knowledgeable form." "Compulsive in his thoroughness." "Doesn't flaunt celebrities because that's not his attitude. Everyone is important to him." "Really listens and comes up with good design solutions." "He's amazing. Addresses all issues." "Hillside projects are a strength."

Space International Inc.   4   4   4   4.5

5727 Venice Boulevard, Los Angeles, CA 90019
(323) 954 - 9084 www.space-intl.com

Contextual, functional modern architecture

Best known for its "hyper-functional modernism," Space International pursues "the beauty of simplicity" with its extremely restrained minimalism. Catering to a younger crowd in the film, music and fashion communities, the firm is careful to consider the social and environmental context of its spaces. The designs "do not use a lot of aesthetic gymnastics" but instead employ a limited palette and humble yet intriguing materials to stretch budgets and imaginations. Principals Mike Ferguson and John Hirsch, who also design custom furniture, have entered into a collective called Hedge with other home design companies, including Dry Design Landscape, to pool resources and knowledge.

Clients call Hirsch "cool as a cucumber" with a "great personality." He and Ferguson are said to be personally invested in realizing each and every project to its fullest. Ferguson, who previously worked with Frank Gehry, holds degrees from Clemson and SCI-Arc. Hirsch has degrees from UC Santa Barbara and SCI-Arc. This small firm of four has been in business since 1997, and generally takes about eight projects at a time.

Working most often in Hollywood Hills, Malibu and Beverly Hills, the firm's services have been enlisted in places as far away as Dallas, Orlando, Ohio and Japan. Space International takes a few select residential projects between office and retail commissions. These involve significant renovations, additions and new homes going from 1,500 to 6,000 square feet, available to like-minded adventuresome clients. Per-square-foot costs start at $200 and average $350. Larger projects come with a flat fee while the firm charges an hourly rate for smaller projects.

"They delivered a dream home for us." "John was able to add a lot of subtle touches and details that truly enhanced the design." "He had a wall done in poured concrete pressed with a pine imprint that perfectly matched the 1960s look." "They really know how to bring out the character and style of the home through their keen design sensibility." "We gave John and Mike what we had to work with, which was a very difficult downsloping site, and they simply worked magic with it." "They did not do much work to the house, but really made it special and substantially increased the resale value." "They respect and honor the home." "We have used many from the gang at Hedge, and they all worked well for us."

Stamps & Stamps

318 Fairview Avenue, South Pasadena, CA 91030
(626) 441 - 5600 www.stampsandstamps.com

Delightful, thoughtful, tradition-based interior design

See Stamps & Stamps's full report under the heading Interior Designers & Decorators

	Quality	Cost	Value	Recommend?
	✚	$	◆	★

Studio 0.10 Architects   4   4   4   4

1500 South Los Angeles Street, Suite 4B, Los Angeles, CA 90015
(213) 745 - 4900   www.studio010.com

Intellectual, modern, integrated architecture

This ideas-based firm creates "powerful architecture" in an international modern aesthetic. Clients praise principals Andrew Liang and Li Wen for an intellectually minimalist design that maximizes budget. Studio 0.10 also exhibits an admirable consciousness of "green" issues, incorporating radiant floor heating, natural ventilation systems and alternative power sources whenever possible. The firm's built-in millwork accents its structures with details of exceptional quality. Further, clients say Liang and Wen provide "excellent representation for the client" to contractors and persevere to get things done properly.

The two partners trained with quite a list of firms, including SOM, Peter Eisenman, Norman Foster and Richard Keating. The small practice of five has been in business since 1997 and about half the commissions are residential.

Studio 0.10 works mainly in the Malibu and Hollywood Hills areas, as well as elsewhere along the coastline, completing ground-up single-family homes and occasional remodel projects. These need not be large, but they are ambitious in scope. One of the recently completed projects is a 4,500 square foot modern home on a hilltop site in Agoura Hills complete with a temperature-controlled, thirteen-car, 3,500 square foot garage. Satisfied clients say this firm can forge a spectacular design from a very tight budget.

"An excellent representative for the client, with all the trades." "What can I say? They have given me one of the most beautiful spaces I've ever seen." "They really know how to orchestrate the design and spread around resources without compromising." "They understand the economic restraints of building as much as they know the concept, design and mechanics of creating a home."

The Warner Group Architects, Inc.   4.5   4.5   4   4.5

1250 Coast Village Road, Suite J, Santa Barbara, CA 93108
(805) 969 - 5074   www.wgarch.com

Dignified, bold high-end architecture and interior design

This widely published and honored Santa Barbara-based practice exudes professionalism. Principal Jack Warner's distinguished and restrained aesthetic defines both the firm's classic and contemporary architectural efforts, and his expertise extends to interior design. The modern facades are often boldly simplistic and the traditional structures boldly grand—both often surrounded by reflecting pools, fountains and a multitude of flowering plants. The firm builds new homes and remodels beyond Santa Barbara County, working as far down the coast as Manhattan Beach and Laguna Beach. These projects are often considerable in size and ambition.

Sources tell us Warner turns over impeccably detailed renderings that result in historically accurate creations. He founded the firm in 1966 as Warner Morris Wilson Architects, and led it through its 35-year evolution, including a name change to The Warner Group Architects in 2000. In five decades of architectural practice, Warner has designed hundreds of houses in Santa Barbara. Country clubs are a specialty, and the firm has completed renovations to the Montecito Country Club, the Annandale Golf Club, The Birnam Wood Golf Club, the Los Angeles Country Club, the Monterey Peninsula Country Club, the Bel Air Country Club and the Hunter Ranch—all in appropriately distinguished styles. A full-service architectural firm, there are eleven on staff. AD 100, 2002, 2004.

"Every angle from the interior perspective is thoughtfully crafted so an incredible view awaits you." "Jack now has a really professional team of associate architects

	Quality	Cost	Value	Recommend?
	✚	$	◆	★

that manage the projects." "Even the contemporary projects are grandiose in their striking calm."

Thomas Proctor, Architect   4.5   3.5   5   5

8650 Holloway Plaza Drive, Los Angeles, CA 90069
(310) 659 - 2125   tom@thomasproctorarchitect.com

Highly customized, elegant, detailed traditional architecture

Thomas Proctor is praised for his precise and diligent approach to design and his affinity for "doing it all himself—including all drawings and all site meetings—to make sure it gets done right." Proctor excels in crafting "beautifully detailed" traditional homes in the Mediterranean-revival and American-classical styles, as well as more modern designs. Proctor, a sole proprietor for eighteen years who is "not big on middle people," delights in his direct and personal working relationship with the client and contractors.

Clients love being exposed to Proctor's deep reservoir of knowledge about historic architecture, calling the experience an "education." Proctor holds architecture degrees from UC Berkeley and UCLA and also trained in Florence, Italy. He shares office space with architect Tim Morrison, with whom he occasionally teams on projects.

Proctor's forte is designing large ground-up single-family homes. Once the neighbors see what he has done, they sign up for a project themselves as soon as he is available. Proctor practices mainly in Brentwood, Holmby Hills, Beverly Hills and Bel Air, and his clientele tends to be executives from the finance/banking community. Current projects range from 7,500 to 12,000 square feet, although he's happy working on something as small as a pool house "as long as it's an intellectual challenge." Proctor's fees skew slightly on the lower end, with costs per square foot at standard levels for the excellent result.

"Tom is by far the most talented architect I have ever met." "He's so well educated and really shows an understanding of historic precedent and the principles of proportion." "Superb taste. Hovers over construction with an eagle's eye." "I got an education from the man in Italian architecture." "Is so attuned to detail that sometimes things take longer than you might hope, but I'm not complaining." "He has so much work he does not list the firm in the phone book." "He can consider 36 ways a window might hang in the wall." "Incredibly traditional one-man show, an old school gentleman." "He understands the architecture beautifully but also knows how to make it beautifully livable."

Tim Barber Architect   3.5   3.5   4   4

8455 Beverly Boulevard, Suite 409, Los Angeles, CA 90048
(323) 782 - 1000   www.timbarber.net

Traditionally crafted architecture

Principal Tim Barber wins kudos for his "fresh and functional" interpretations of classic California regional traditions. The firm's commissions include both focused renovations and ground-up residences, from the transformation of a 1960s track house into a stately California Craftsman to the creation of Catalan Spanish and Brentwood Cape Cod homes. We hear Barber's historically respectful designs feel like they have evolved over time, bringing with them a modern livability. The firm also performs interior design services on a number of its projects.

Educated at the University of Ohio at Cincinnati, Barber is licensed and oversees eleven associates and staffers. In 1993, he established the firm that today works across Southern California, from San Diego to Santa Barbara. While the firm welcomes kitchen-remodeling assignments, its projects typically are 4,000 to 7,000 square foot homes, averaging a reasonable $250 to $350 per square foot with standard fees.

Hiring an Audio/Visual or Telecommunication Service Provider

These days, one doesn't have to crave global domination to enjoy a room that can, at the push of a button, transform itself into a ground-control headquarters that rivals any James Bond movie scene. Home theaters, multi-zone entertainment systems, home-automation and lighting controls, online capability—if you can dream it, they can hook it up. Just make sure you ask for the remote, or you may never be able to use what you paid for.

Audio/Visual (A/V) home service providers can seamlessly integrate almost anything—media walls, touch-screen panels, speakers, structured cabling—into your existing components or the architectural integrity of any room. And if they can't, they will build new cabinets to accommodate the equipment. Custom installation is the name of the game.

What to Expect From an A/V Specialist

A/V providers can be contracted through general contractors, designers or directly by you. Whomever they bill, communication between the installer and the homeowner is essential. When courting your A/V guru, remember that they may specialize in only a few of the following areas: audio, video, telephone, Internet, security, lighting and climate control. The vast majority of A/V designers and installers in LA are also experts in telephone network installations, so keep this in mind when you are planning the various communication and A/V systems for your home.

You should also keep in mind the following regarding A/V and telecommunication systems:

✧ Local telephone companies now offer a wide array of services: voice mail, call forwarding, three-way calling and caller ID (with or without ID block). A good telecom service provider will be able to customize a system that integrates multiple phone lines, intercoms and door buzzers to a networked and net-savvy home office.

✧ If you're putting in a home office, know how many lines you will need, where the fax and printers are going to be located, which computers will be networked and online and where you're going to sit.

✧ Most telephone system service providers have licensing agreements with certain system manufacturers and will deal only with them. If you're keen on a particular system, it's a good idea to contact the manufacturer for preferred service providers in your area. On the whole, all systems perform the same functions (automated directories, voice mail boxes, multiple lines/extensions, on-hold music, interoffice paging, caller ID) and offer the same accessories (headsets, holsters). It's the brand, sophistication, complexity of integration and convenience of use that affect the cost. Systems can be purchased outright, leased or financed.

✧ Don't forget that a service provider who excels in home theater installation and telecommunication systems may not be as well versed in, or even deal with, security. You should also know whether the service provider can perform all the functions of integration. Determine your needs, get references, ask questions. Do you want a 35mm screening room with reclining leather seats or maybe just a simple surround sound system? Will the A/V specialist both design and engineer your project, or will he or she be coordinating with other professionals in trades?

✧ Even when working through a designer, a good A/V contractor will want to meet with you one-on-one to assess your needs. Make the time. You don't want your system to outreach your ability or desire to operate it. Don't get swept up in your tech-happy A/V provider's enthusiasm for all the bells and whistles available to you. Stand firm. Are you really looking for a movie palace complete with stadium seating, and does it really need to be tied into the landscape lighting and the air conditioner in the kitchen? Remember, the latest may not be the greatest if it hasn't been around long enough to be tested. Some A/V contractors prefer a lag time of six months after the introduction of a product so they can follow its performance before recommending it to their customers. If you're the first one in on a new gizmo, know that you may be the first one to discover its flaws.

✧ The means of customization and the materials used differ widely from shop to shop. Some contractors only work in certain brands. Others will install anything you want. Request an itemized bid proposal and a sketch if you want the finished product to match your dreams.

WHO WILL INSTALL MY NEW SYSTEM?

Although you'll talk first with either a principal or a representative of the A/V firm, traditionally a crew of field technicians will be dispatched to perform the installation and service. Don't fret—this crew is likely to be as well-informed and passionate about its business as any front man, so you should feel you're in good hands. But it's invaluable to be able to speak to the same person from the beginning to the end of the project.

Miscommunication commonly surrounds the role of the electrician in an A/V installation. Some A/V providers want your electrician to pull the low-voltage cable if he's already on site and holds a permit, eliminating a coordination headache. Many prefer to do it themselves, knowing that some electricians treat delicate cables with the care of baggage handlers at LAX. Check that someone's on top of it before the walls close up. Also, know that A/V contractors usually won't install or relocate the electrical outlets needed to power your system.

Pricing and Service Warranties

The cost of your A/V project will be a reflection of the design work involved, the degree of customization, the type and number of devices and pieces of equipment to be installed, the length of cable to be pulled and the anticipated man hours, plus overhead and profit. Many jobs require a deposit of up to 50 percent, with progress payments to be made when materials and equipment arrive on site, and a final payment upon job completion. Consider your own level of knowledge when interviewing A/V companies. Will you need 24-hour emergency tech support? Some of the highest end A/V designers can automate your world but aren't much help when your appliances rise in noisy revolt at three a.m. The warranty should appear on the bid proposal. A year of free service is standard.

License Considerations

Because this is a relatively new field, there is currently no licensing requirement for A/V services in Los Angeles. Fortunately, this also means that no permit is required. Check your municipality, however, because some areas require that these service providers be licensed and insured. If you're still confused, the Custom Electronic Design and Installation Association (CEDIA, at www.cedia.org) is an excellent resource.

The Hottest New Trends

When it comes to home theater, Digital Video Disc (DVD) players have become ubiquitous in good A/V systems, offering much higher sound and visual quality than videos or laser discs. A movie on a DVD comes through with 500 lines of resolution, double the clarity of a 250-line videocassette. DVD players also offer lush Dolby Digital Surround Sound (DDSS). The quality of television output has advanced, too, with the advent of High Definition Television (HDTV) and Plasma TVs (those sleek, thin TVs, only four inches in depth, that can be hung on the wall). Multi-zone entertainment systems allow you to play CDs jukebox-style or listen to the radio or TV in any room of the house. For example, programming the system to air your favorite classical radio station through the bathroom speakers while you relax in the jacuzzi can be simply a matter of pressing a touch screen.

Numerous A/V companies also provide a full line of home automation services, including wireless lighting controls that you can operate from your phone (to turn the lights on if you'll be working late) or from a pad clipped onto your car's sun visor. Home automation also applies to climate control, with wireless systems that let you turn on the heat, air conditioning or lawn sprinklers from any room in the house—or from virtually anywhere, via telephone. Thanks to the latest user-friendly A/V programming systems, the days of not being able to program your VCR are over.

How to Get the Most Out of Your System

- ✧ Sit down with the installer to discuss your wants and needs in detail.
- ✧ Don't rush to install the newest technology.
- ✧ Only install gear you'll actually use.
- ✧ Don't fall asleep during the technician's instructions on how to program each device.

	Quality	Cost	Value	Recommend?
	✚	$	◆	★

AUDIO/VISUAL & TELECOMMUNICATION

📁 FIRMS WITH PORTFOLIOS 📁

DSI Entertainment Systems   4   4   4   4
13317 Ventura Boulevard, Suite H, Sherman Oaks, CA 91423
(818) 906 - 9940   www.dsientertainment.com
Custom A/V installation, home theaters, home automation

No-hassle, custom A/V firm, DSI Entertainment has been cloaking great systems in Southern California residences since 1994. We hear that this firm specializes in creative solutions to integrate and disguise their systems, so your home doesn't end up looking like a "stereo store." DSI installs integrated house-wide audio systems, full home automation, and they specialize in squeezing home theaters into extant and awkward spaces. A word-of-mouth firm, DSI has grown from 35 to over 4,000 clients in eleven years. Reports state that flexible customer service comes first, and that is reflected in the enthusiastic loyalty of their clientele.

DSI is always willing to come in for a system tune-up, and many clients have retained them for several jobs. Their prices are described as reasonable for the high quality of work.

"They stood behind all of their work, even when some problems (not of their making) caused a substantial increase in labor. No additional cost was assessed to us." "They provide quality work and are reliable. I am always happy with the prospects and service that are recommended and received." "Flawless execution from start to finish. Polite and professional customer service."

FIRMS WITHOUT PORTFOLIOS

Atlantic Stereo   4   3.5   4.5   3.5
445 East 17th Street, Suite A, Costa Mesa, CA 92627
(949) 646 - 8895   www.atlanticstereo.com
A/V systems, home automation, telephone networking

Situated about 2,500 miles east of its namesake and two minutes away from the Pacific Coast Highway, Atlantic Stereo has proudly pioneered high-end A/V in Orange County. Since 1961, this firm has designed and installed custom audio and video systems in residences up and down the West Coast—plus automated systems and telephone networks.

Atlantic was founded on the principle that integration of technology is about "a better way of living." Not only can this firm make all your gadgets and gizmos work, but they can also make them work together to simplify your life. Clients tell us this philosophy applies especially during installation when Atlantic installers take that extra hour to make sure everything works perfectly and the client understands his or her new system.

Quality	Cost	Value	Recommend?
✚	$	◆	★

Audio Command Systems

5	4	5	4.5

1527 Pontius Avenue, Los Angeles, CA 90025
(310) 444 - 3882   www.audiocommand.com

Custom A/V systems

This expert firm consistently delivers cutting-edge technology—and is frequently called upon to give a command performance in a celebrity's home. Industry professionals, clients and *CE Pro* magazine agree that Audio Command Systems is one of the premier designers and installers in the country. With offices in Los Angeles, New York and Southern Florida, Audio Command Systems has 28 years of experience in high-end markets.

Audio Command is in demand. According to *CE Pro*, the company has been one of the top five revenue-producing A/V firms in the country for five years in a row. Audio Command handles about 25 large-scale projects annually, with budgets starting at $100,000. But the firm is anything but cookie-cutter. The company maintains no inventory and orders components and materials on a project-by-project basis. Clients say the lack of pressure to move stock contributes to its emphasis on customer service.

The LA office's thirteen employees, seven of whom are installers, work with the city's best architects to design highly customized, state-of-the-art systems. Examples include building glass "media walls" to display video, designing custom cabinetry to conceal speakers, and creating integrated wireless networks that answer to a single remote control. Each ACS A/V system is unique, built to customer specifications after a free consultation. All work comes with a one-year parts and labor warranty, and service calls are typically answered within 24 hours. Clients who want the gold standard—and are willing to pay for it—are happy to command this firm's extraordinary services.

"The installation crew was like a team of engineers. They had 3-D computer-generated architectural schematics of my house prepared upon consultation. Throughout the process they kept me fully informed with consistent and detailed reports." "If you want a truly unique A/V system, these are the guys."

Audiovisions Inc.

5	4	5	4.5

25741 Atlantic Ocean Drive, Lake Forest, CA 92630
(949) 206 - 0606 www.avisions.com

A/V systems, home automation, lighting, climate control, telephone networks

These visionaries bill themselves as the "complete solution" for clients' home electronics systems, and their demanding customers agree. Since 1990 principals Mark Hoffenberg and Bob Walpert have developed Audiovisions into an industry standard, now boasting a staff of 55, including 30 installers. They regularly send employees to CEDIA training sessions to keep them current with the latest technologies.

	Quality	Cost	Value	Recommend?
	✚	$	◆	★

Audiovisions designs custom home theaters, lighting, climate control and telephone systems. The firm will also perform electronic integration to control all of a home's low-voltage systems. Most of its residential work is centered in LA, Orange and Marin counties. About half of the company's roughly 130 annual projects come from contractors and designers. This high-powered firm also handles the A/V systems in Virgin Megastores around the country. Audiovisions annually ranks in the top ten of *CE Pro's* top-50 list and has also been named dealer of the year by the CEDIA trade organization.

The average project carries a budget of $80,000 to $100,000, but we're told the firm has installed much pricier systems. All work is covered by a one-year parts and labor warranty. Clients insist you can't do better than Audiovisions if you're looking for up-to-the-minute A/V and other home electronic systems.

"These guys do it right the first time!" "Everything works now, and what's better—it works together." "It's a bit pricey but worth it."

Brad Scherick   4   4.5   3.5   4
1680 North Beverly Drive, Beverly Hills, CA 90210
(310) 777 - 5200

A/V systems, computer systems

Brad Scherick brings an artisan's ethos to his highly technical craft, devoting himself to one project at a time. For his highly personalized approach, Scherick has become a Westside favorite for the installation of high-end A/V systems, home theaters and computer networks for private residences and small businesses. Described by one client as a "digital guru," Scherick's talent may seem to belong to another astral plane, but his feet are firmly planted in Beverly Hills. Integrating the latest technology into your household can be a hassle, but clients say Scherick "makes it all simple and unobtrusive."

Scherick started his own company seven years ago and has a group of consultants that he works with for larger projects, which can get well into six-figure budgets. While Scherick's fees are near the top of the range, he's considered a good value by clients who appreciate his individualized service, one-year craftsmanship warranty and support of manufacturers' warranties.

"Supremely tech savvy!" "He's expensive, but he'll take the time to find out exactly what you want and how best to make it happen." "Brad put so much effort into the design, he could have been designing his own system."

Chapman A/V Systems   4   4   4   4
7411 Laurel Canyon Boulevard, Suite 7, North Hollywood, CA 91605
(818) 764 - 3722

A/V systems, home automation, lighting, telephone networks

Owner Chip Corbin draws 80 percent of his business from word-of-mouth referrals. In report after report, we keep hearing just what a "nice guy" Corbin is, so he must be doing something right. With 30 years' experience and a staff of five, Corbin handles large-scale A/V systems and home theaters in addition to installing home automation, lighting control and telephone systems. Corbin's unusually long two-year warranties for all workmanship and his genuine enthusiasm for each project are also a draw for his loyal clientele.

Corbin stays up on the hot technology that is requested by his demanding clientele, like touch-screen media and the newest remote controls. The 21-year-old company covers all of Southern California and has done work across the United States and Europe. Widely published, Chapman has designed systems for an impressive list of clients, including Disneyland and the Academy Awards. Fees are said to be a fair deal considering the level of craftsmanship and service.

"I don't know how Chip did what he did. But I don't have to! It just works!"
"Chapman is my secret weapon, I brought them in and his work really put a cherry on top of the whole project." "He's got a great staff and a good personality in addition to being very knowledgeable at what he does."

Current Electric Contracting and Design Inc. (CECAD)

	Quality	Cost	Value	Recommend?
	4.5	4	4.5	4.5

18425 Napa Street, Northridge, CA 91325
(818) 885 - 5567   www.currentelectric.com

A/V, home automation, electrical service, CCTV, security surveillance

Staying ahead of the current in Hollywood digital technology isn't easy, but this firm works hard to make last year's movie magic this year's off-screen reality. With more than seventeen years of experience, the licensed electricians at CECAD can deliver the thrills: home integration systems, multi-room audio, telephone pre-wire, computer network cabling and interior/landscape lighting design and control, as well as straight electrical work. The result is a seamless home network whose nifty little gadgets actually work.

Changing CDs poolside is cool, but even more eye-catching is Current's custom surveillance technology, which allows clients to monitor their homes and adjust settings via the Internet from anywhere in the world. The company's alarm and monitoring systems apply a modified version of the technology used by the military to keep an eye on nuclear facilities. Clients in the service area (the west side of LA and the San Fernando Valley) tell us that Current does it all—design, installation, and repair from small remodeling jobs to new estates.

"I don't know how I got along before my house was automated." "They've got gadgets for everything!" "I could not function without their help. Many hours of great, reliable, dependable service."

Eagle Alarms Company

14358 Magnolia Boulevard, Sherman Oaks, CA 91423
(800) 946 - 5200

Custom design and installation of residential security, A/V, computer and telephone systems

See Eagle Alarms Company's full report under the heading Security Systems

Favarger Consulting

50 Wavecrest Avenue, Venice, CA 90291
(310) 664 - 1320

Computer installation and support; integration of mixed-vendor systems

See Favarger Consulting's full report under the heading Computer Installation & Maintenance

Genesis Audio & Video

	Quality	Cost	Value	Recommend?
	4	3.5	4.5	4

16163 Lake Forest Drive, Suite L, Irvine, CA 92618
(714) 727 - 3700   www.genesis-audio.com

A/V systems, home automation, lighting, telephone networks

Genesis Audio & Video is among the most popular of residential A/V installation, serving most locations west of the Rockies with its team of 25 employees (eleven installers). Owner Bill Anderson sits on the board of directors at CEDIA and has made a name for his company by creating systems that are both powerful and unobtrusive since 1976. Genesis also offers home theater design, home automation, climate control, lighting and installation of telephone networks. Fans say they know "just how to simplify the process."

Genesis handles up to 250 projects per year. Prices start at $12,000 but can run into the hundreds of thousands. The firm stands by its work, offering a one-year warranty on parts and labor and honoring manufacturers' warranties that extend beyond a year. We're told that their fees are substantial but very reasonable in light of the quality of the work.

"Wizards! Technology wizards!" "Genesis A/V is simply the best. Their whole crew was prompt and very courteous." "I've already recommended them to friends."

Home Automator Inc.   3.5   3.5   4   4
1060 Aviation Boulevard, Hermosa Beach, CA 90254
(310) 379 - 2222

A/V, home automation, security systems

Home Automator is the automatic choice for its dedicated following in the South Bay. With fourteen years of experience in the area, Doug Kleven and his staff of eight know the local decorators, architects and contractors well and are able to integrate their systems into houses with a minimum of disturbance. Home Automator offers custom installation of low-voltage systems, ranging from A/V, home theater and security to climate control and telephone networks. The firm handles about 30 A/V projects annually, with budgets ranging from $15,000 at the low end up to $350,000.

Though the firm has a showroom, it only sells retail as part of an installation package. We're told the company favors Marantz, Mitsubishi, Stuart and JBL components. Home Automator works with a distinguished clientele that includes numerous actors and professional athletes. All work is supported by a one-year warranty that covers all parts and labor.

"Doug is the only guy to go to in the South Bay if you want it done right."

Home Cinema Entertainment   4.5   4   4.5   4.5
561 Valley Gate Road, Simi Valley, CA 93065
(805) 583 - 4231

A/V systems, home theater specialists, home automation, lighting control, telephone networks

A lifetime warranty is nothing to scoff at in the ephemeral world of A/V technology, and that is exactly what Home Cinema Entertainment offers its clients. The extraordinary warranty is just one clue to the fact that this thirteen-year-old company is one of the industry's best quality firms. A darling of celebrities and athletes, HCE sells high-end systems with a floor of $100,000. But reports say that the elite service is worth the price of admission, citing the excellent results and seven-member staff's "professionalism and enthusiasm" for the job.

About half of the company's 35 yearly projects come from architects and contractors, with the remainder coming directly from client referrals. Some of Hollywood's best-known directors and producers have turned to HCE to design and install their customized home screening rooms. In addition to A/V, Home Cinema also installs home automation, lighting control and telephone networks.

The company works across LA and has a handful of clients outside of California. Home Cinema's prices are on the high end, but sources attach great value to the company's lifetime warranty and no-questions-asked service. *"You pay top dollar, but they definitely don't nickel and dime you." "They're a very quiet company with an elite customer base."*

Home Tech Inc. 4 4 4 4
7661 Densmore Avenue, Suite 1, Van Nuys, CA 91406
(818) 781 - 0976 www.htssystems.com
A/V systems, computer systems, security systems and telephone networks

Past customers tell us that Home Tech Inc. continually asks the question, "Is this making things easier or harder?"—then implements the most user-friendly options. Since 1992, this customer-centered firm has made a name for itself designing high-end A/V systems, security systems with CCTV surveillance, and computer and telephone networks for some of LA and Orange Counties' most upscale homes.

Clients say they find it easy to manage their Home Tech systems, but if a problem arises they can always turn to the company's 24-hour on-call technicians. Home Tech's eighteen staff members (fourteen installers) take their cues from owner Moshe Bar, who is reported to be an excellent listener. Home Tech also has a reputation within the industry for collaborating well with interior designers to overcome any design issues that arise. The firm's fees are said to be reasonable and all work is backed up with a one-year parts and labor warranty. Technicians are typically on-site within 24 hours of a service request. Potential customers are invited to accompany Home Tech to the homes of past clients for a working demo of the company's services.

"Excellent service, prompt response, thorough follow-up." "Superb." "Moshe's crew was spectacular, all polite and quick."

Interior Systems Design 4.5 4.5 4 4
9860 Glenoaks Boulevard, Sun Valley, CA 91352
(818) 767 - 3162 www.interiorsystems.net
A/V systems, home automation, security systems and telephone systems

Clients tell us they like Interior Systems Design's low-key approach. Because the company holds no inventory and orders every component on a case-by-case basis, its salespeople and technicians aren't pressured to move merchandise. Customers praise Interior for sitting down with each client to find the best brand and style for a given budget and aesthetic. Fans say the company manages to be both easy-going and cutting-edge, describing owners Yves Richarz and Toby Kaufman as "veteran techies with a human touch."

This 22-year-old firm does it all, from home theaters to security to climate control. A typical Interior Systems project carries a budget of $100,000, but we understand the company is able to handle much larger or smaller projects depending on a client's needs. Interior Systems does most of its work in Beverly Hills, Malibu, Brentwood and Pacific Palisades, but has worked around the world, including jobs in Australia and Europe. The company does not have a showroom, but Richarz will take potential customers to the homes of existing clients. A one-year warranty on parts and labor is standard and we're told prices match the high-end quality.

"I got a quote within 24 hours of contacting them." "If it's electronic, they're on top of it. The installation crew was efficient and professional."

	Quality	Cost	Value	Recommend?
	✛	$	◆	★

Lee Entertainment Systems   4   4   4   4

1190 South La Brea Avenue, Los Angeles, CA 90019
(323) 935 - 7520

A/V systems, home theater specialists, home automation

"Master of Sound" Joseph Lee satisfies even the most demanding movie directors and producers with his exceptional screening rooms and home theaters. Lee learned to be exacting during the years he spent designing and installing professional recording equipment before founding Lee Entertainment in 1979. His techie background is complemented by his frequently praised aesthetic judgment.

Today, Lee and his small band of three installers specialize in installing home theaters and 35mm screening rooms for the residential market, but they also supply the full spectrum of home automation and control systems. We're told the company favors the use of Crestron touch-panel systems, Tannoy speakers and other superior product lines. Reasonable fees for the high-end service are no surprise, since everything is top-notch. Instead of offering a showroom, Lee takes potential customers into the homes of past clients to show them what his systems can do. The firm backs up all work with a one-year parts and labor warranty.

"My system is custom designed to fit me. I don't even think about it now. It's that easy." "Like he says, he's the sound master." "He grasped immediately what I wanted and made it cooler than I imagined."

Micro Connection   4   3   5   4

13125 Lakeland Road, Santa Fe Springs, CA 90670
(562) 903 - 9330   www.m-c.com

A/V systems, home automation, computer systems, telephone networks

If you're looking for one-stop shopping for A/V systems, Micro Connection has the hook-up, and it's "so convenient." We hear that dealing with Micro Connection is a breeze because they design and install almost every low-voltage system there is: home theaters, home automation, telephones, lighting, climate control, security, CCTV. Clients appreciate not having to waste time hiring and managing a different company for each task: "They come in and do it all." Adding to the convenience factor, the firm covers all of LA and Orange Counties.

Since 1985, principal John Pounder has grown Micro Connection into a big player on the LA scene, building the company largely via trade referrals from designers, architects and contractors. Pounder currently has six installers on staff who work closely with some of LA's best-known contractors to ensure that every job runs smoothly. Micro Connection's A/V systems are generally large scale, averaging more than $100,000, although the firm has projects that range from $35,000 to $500,000. The company offers a one-year warranty on parts and labor and charges competitive fees.

"If you've got a big job to do, I couldn't recommend them more."

R Squared Custom Audio & Video Systems   4   3.5   4.5   4

1618 Stanford Street, Suite D, Santa Monica, CA 90404
(310) 829 - 3115

A/V systems

With its philosophy that the A/V industry is "a service business and not a materials business," R Squared takes good care of its clients. Even if it takes three trips to a home to show a client how to use a new system, Rick Jurasky and his staff of six will be there with smiles. Members of its loyal following call R Squared "easy to deal with" and "relaxed," adding that they are eager to refer friends to the firm.

	Quality	Cost	Value	Recommend?
	+	$	◆	★

Serving a mostly residential clientele that stretches from Santa Barbara to San Diego, R Squared is said to charge reasonable fees for its work, which consists primarily of audio system and home theater installation. Three installers on staff enable the company to handle projects that range from those with modest budgets to those in the hundreds of thousands of dollars. The company, founded in 1979, offers a one-year parts and labor warranty on all of its systems and 24-hour response times to service inquiries.

"They're fantastic. The installation was so much easier than I thought."

Roberts Home Audio and Video   5   4.5   4.5   4
1611 South La Cienega Boulevard, Los Angeles, CA 90035
(310) 276 - 3955   www.robertshomeav.com
A/V systems, home theater specialists, telephone networks

Insiders say "the sky's the limit" when it comes to the lavish home theaters and screening rooms Roberts Home Audio and Video builds around the world. Since the 1987 appearance of Dolby Pro Logic surround sound, Robert Eitel has been tailoring home theaters to an all-star list of actors and jet-setters with extremely specific demands. Roberts Home A/V now boasts a staff of ten field technicians who install systems from Beverly Hills to Saudi Arabia. With three tricked-out demo rooms at their spacious showroom, you don't have to take reports like "mind-blowing" on faith: you can see for yourself.

In addition to A/V systems, Roberts will also install telephone networks and do hardwiring for any low-voltage system in the home. However, the company generally subcontracts out the actual installations of systems outside of A/V and telecom. Roberts has recently generated some buzz in LA for creating some very elaborate private theaters with budgets of several hundred thousand dollars. But we hear the company will also design systems well under $100,000.

"You'd have to see my new home theater to believe it." "If you want to truly experience your media, these guys are the best!"

Sheehan & Associates   4   3   5   5
312B South Catalina, Redondo Beach, CA 90277
(310) 374 - 8980
A/V systems, home theater specialists, home automation

When Sheehan & Associates gets a customer, it's literally for life. We're told the firm has lost only one client—and then only because he passed away. Customer loyalty like that can only be based on a deep appreciation of services rendered, and we hear that this company does it all well: A/V systems, home theaters, screening rooms, climate control, lighting and telephone systems.

Based in Redondo Beach, Sheehan serves all of Southern California, the East Coast, Canada and Hawaii. The vast majority of the company's jobs come directly from client referrals. The remainder arrive through architects and contractors, one of whom recently called principal Frederick Sheehan "the only A/V guy you need."

Sheehan has six employees, all of whom are installers. A typical A/V system runs $50,000 to $100,000, and screening rooms can reach six figures. A one-year warranty on parts and labor comes with each system, which we're told features manufacturers like Lutron, Crestron and Draper. Standard prices keep loyal customers coming back for more.

"After my friends saw my new system, I ended up giving out his name to several of them. Everybody loved Frederick." "He's at the very top of my list."

SuperVision   4   4   4   4

8687 Melrose Avenue, Suite B-120, Los Angeles, CA 90069
(310) 652 - 9510   www.supervisionav.com
A/V systems, home theater specialists

Clients tell us this firm needs no supervision. Describing the company's consummate professionalism, one client explained, "Whatever it is—whatever brand, style or technology—they've done it before."

With a service-call response time of less than 24 hours and free system tune-ups for the first year, SuperVision delivers superior customer service and a quality product to match. Most of SuperVision's work is in residential A/V systems, home theaters and dedicated screening rooms near its home base in LA. But the company also has a presence in the world of haute couture, performing all A/V installations for Louis Vuitton and Christian Dior boutiques, working in locations across the country.

SuperVision was established in 1977 and currently has six employees, three of whom are installers, and a showroom located in the heart of the Pacific Design Center. About half of the company's projects are substantial systems costing more than $50,000, although SuperVision has done much larger (and smaller) commissions. Rates are at the upper end of the range. The company backs its work up with a one-year parts and labor warranty. In addition to being affiliated with CEDIA, the firm is also an industry partner of the American Society of Interior Designers.

"Their technical experience and breadth of knowledge is staggering."

TechTricians Consulting Services

12719 Foothill Boulevard, Sylmar, CA 91342
(866) 793 - 0500   www.tz-cs.com
Home network installation, specializing in new construction sites

See TechTricians Consulting Services' full report under the heading Computer Installation & Maintenance

Theatre Design Concepts   4.5   4.5   4   4.5

1660 Corinth Avenue, Los Angeles, CA 90025
(310) 479 - 3568   www.tdc4av.com
A/V systems, specialists in home theaters, home automation, security systems

Across the Southwest, Theatre Design Concepts is considered an authority in elite home automation systems, home theaters, screening rooms, matrix switching networks, CCTVs and HVACs. Owner Joe Cali prides himself on using only the best lines of equipment (e.g., Crestron touch screen panels) for his demanding clientele. Cali even custom-calibrates his own in-house line of sub-woofers, pre-amps, digital equalizers and surround processors to guarantee the best sound around.

Theatre Design Concepts primarily handles major projects that can cost more than $150,000 for home theaters and more than $350,000 for 35mm screening rooms. The company's staff of sixteen features ten installers who work very

	Quality	Cost	Value	Recommend?
	✚	$	◆	★

closely with decorators, designers and architects to ensure that installations run smoothly. The company also offers card-access security systems with CCTV surveillance. For a monthly fee, TDC will even help you construct and manage a collection or playlist of media to enjoy on your new system.

In the service department, TDC gets high marks for its one-year, no-questions-asked parts and labor warranty and 24-hour-or-less service call response time. Prices are reported to be at the expensive end, but sources explain that "their depth of involvement creates a quality product—and that's what you're paying for."

"The installation crew spent so long testing and calibrating every speaker, just so everything would be perfect. And it was." "With all the technology in their showroom you could create the 'bat cave' if you wanted to."

Wilson Home Theater Systems   4.5   4   4.5   4
14450 Ventura Boulevard, Sherman Oaks, CA 91423
(818) 783 - 7625   www.wilsonhometheater.com
A/V systems, home theater specialists, telephone systems

"Genuinely nice guy" Randy Wilson is said to be "impeccably efficient" and "a real class act," and you'd expect nothing less from a man who was instrumental in formulating his industry's ethical standards and practices. His talents at designing and installing elaborate A/V, home theater and screening room systems have earned the respect of some of the biggest action directors in the business, and we all know how they feel about special effects. Prospective clients can check out the pyrotechnics at the firm's 4,000 square foot showroom.

Wilson, who founded his firm in 1986, has an impressive list of commercial clients, including Caesar's Palace in Las Vegas, but the lion's share of his work is in residential Southern California. In addition to A/V and home theaters, Wilson and his staff of thirteen (including eight certified installers) will also put in telephone systems and the hardwiring for computer networks. Systems are regularly in the ballpark of the hundreds of thousands of dollars, and usually feature elite brand names. Wilson Home Theater guarantees its wiring for life and supports all manufacturers' warranties.

"Everything from consultation to final touches was handled with the utmost professionalism and efficiency." "Over-the-top and very, very luxurious. If you love going to the movies, this is the way."

HIRING A COMPUTER INSTALLATION & MAINTENANCE SERVICE PROVIDER

Maybe you'd like to connect the computer in your home office to the one in your teenager's room to share Internet access. You're worried, however, that if you do it yourself, your "network" will turn on the ceiling fans and trip the security system. Fortunately, there are plenty of computer service providers who install networks and software, set up new computer systems and perform other tasks that may require more technical expertise than you possess. Today's world requires a new approach to home computer needs, and computer technicians have up-to-the-minute knowledge. Home networks are fast becoming essential in a high-speed world of connectivity. Your computer setup needs to be as custom fit as a tailored suit for you to get the full benefit. While common sense dictates that you should leave the nitty-gritty details to a skilled technician, knowing what to expect will streamline the process.

DO I NEED A COMPUTER NETWORK?

What is a network, exactly? A cable modem? DSL? A wireless network? A firewall? And, most importantly, are any of these relevant to your needs or current system?

The most basic network is two computers connected to each other so they can share files, Internet access and printers. If you have to save something to a disk, then put that disk into another computer to open a file on the second machine, you are not on a network. Network size is almost limitless, and the largest corporations and government offices have a mind-boggling number of computers exchanging information. A common home network consists of three computers: the home office machine, the kids' computer and maybe a laptop. In a network, computers are linked to an Ethernet hub, which is then linked to a printer and a modem. This usually requires running wire throughout the house and coordinating phone/cable jacks.

Why should you consider a home network? Quite simply, convenience. With a home network files can be transferred easily, printers and Internet access shared and phone lines freed up for that important incoming call from your mother-in-law. While this may seem like a sophisticated setup for a home, times are changing. Many kids now do their homework on the computer, more people work from home and everyone wants to be on the Internet—all at the same time. Home networks can save money because they avoid the added expense of multiple printers and Internet hookups. You'll need to buy a hub, the connection point for all elements of a network, which starts at about $50. Though most new computers (and all Macintoshes) already have network adapters installed, older computers may require purchase of a network card, which costs from $15 to $50. And the addition of wireless capabilities to most computers will require an additional adapter purchase.

HIGH-SPEED INTERNET CONNECTIONS

Internet access through a conventional phone line severely limits your online speed and efficiency. Both a Digital Subscriber Line (DSL) and a cable modem are as much as 100 times faster than a standard analog (telephone) hook-up. A DSL line uses the same cabling as regular telephone lines, but it operates on a higher, idle frequency, allowing the user to be on the Internet and the telephone at the same time. Also, DSL service is always connected, so the user never has to dial up and wait for a connection. Cable is a broadband connection, which means that lots of information can travel simultaneously. (That's how all those cable channels can be available at the same time.) A cable modem is also always "on," but it runs on TV cable lines. The speed is comparable to DSL, with one difference: cable modems use a shared bandwidth. This means that speed depends on how many subscribers in the neighborhood are using that cable service: the more users, the more traffic, and the slower the connection. Because DSL runs on single telephone lines, this isn't an issue. In both cases, find out whether the telephone lines and cable connections in your area are equipped with this service. There are various providers, and promotions offering free installation are common. Computer technician companies will install the DSL connection, but generally are not themselves providers of Internet connectivity. Monthly service for your connection will cost between $35 and $90. The monthly charge for broadband connection (usually for businesses) can be as high as $300.

Most broadband service packages and home network packages come with a firewall installed. This indispensable part of any Internet-ready computer protects the system from hackers and includes options, such as a parental control feature that allows parents to block inappropriate sites.

The Wireless Alternative

Wireless networking is now commonly available and can be a practical choice for home networks. Wireless saves having to drill holes through walls or floors and makes the layout of a home office or computer network more flexible. If the network needs to be expanded, wireless networking makes the change easy and inexpensive. A wireless network consists of an Ethernet hub and PC cards inserted into the computers. These cards extend slightly from the machine and each has a small antenna which sends and receives information. Wireless networks can operate as quickly as a standard network. A home quality wireless access point or router can cost anywhere from $50 to $300. Have a computer technician advise you on whether or not a wireless system is best for you. He'll likely do so based on actual tests, the results of which will vary depending upon distance, home construction type, and the location of steel beams and ductwork.

Buying a New Computer: Where Do I Start?

If your experience lies specifically with PCs (IBM compatible) or Macintoshes, you may want to stick with the type of computer already familiar to you. (Some technicians focus on one type or the other, which can narrow your search for a good techie, too.) If there are children in the house, consider what machines their schools use. One computer technician suggests starting with an issue of *PC Magazine* or *Macworld* to see what's available and use it as a reference when you speak to someone about models, memory sizes and accessories. This way you can get a clear idea of what appeals to you and have a more productive conversation with your computer consultant. It's not a wise idea to buy the cheapest model available. There is, after all, a reason they are cheap.

On Cost

Computer technicians generally charge an hourly service fee, which can range from $35 to almost $150 per hour. In *The Franklin Report,* standard costs fall in the range of $75 to $90 per hour. However, please remember there are other factors that may affect the final cost. Before you hire a technician, ask whether the fee is calculated only in hourly increments. If you go fifteen minutes into the next hour, are you charged for a full additional hour? Will there be a charge for travel? You will be charged extra for whatever hardware or software you purchase. Discuss exactly what will be installed to avoid hidden costs.

The key to any home service is the quality of the time spent, not the quantity. A good service provider will not squander the hours for which they are billing you, but will arrive prepared to solve your problem as quickly as possible. Ask whether the technician charges for support on the phone after he's made a house call. Often he won't if you just need clarification on the service he recently provided. Once you're a customer, some technicians will even respond to a new question if it doesn't take too long, but others will want the clock to start running again. Find out your techie's policy and how flexible he is. Some consultants offer a package containing a given number of help hours, which can be a combination of an initial house call, follow-up visits at home and time on the phone. This might be a good option for someone just starting out.

INSURANCE AND CONTRACTS

Most computer maintenance technicians carry some sort of business insurance that protects them from the repercussions of damaging your computer or network. This insurance is for everyone's benefit, and any service that handles office networks will carry it. If you choose a smaller operation, find out if and how they are covered. Computer service providers may have contracts with business accounts, but this is rare with home service. Ask your technician about the firm's policy.

WHAT TO EXPECT FROM A TECHIE

Depending on the scope of the service, the principal of the company may perform the work personally or send out technicians. The key is finding someone who responds quickly and who is well-versed in the equipment to be serviced. Also, since the computer industry moves at such a fast pace, it's infinitely helpful to work with someone who has a sense of the future of the industry, both in terms of hardware and software.

Steer clear of computer service professionals who act as if everyone should have been born with a computer gene. In truth, a lot of people just nod when they are told they need an updated USB port to handle the increased amount of EDI coming in over the DSL lines. You want someone who will listen to you, set up exactly what you need and ensure that you fully understand it. Quickly try to get a sense of whether the techie helping you only speaks in techno-babble. Believe it or not, there are technicians out there who can make computers understandable, and you shouldn't have to put up with someone who does not patiently explain things in plain English.

INTERNET JARGON
(AT LEAST YOU CAN SOUND LIKE YOU KNOW WHAT YOU'RE TALKING ABOUT.)

✧ **bandwidth:** Measured in bits per second (bps), bandwidth is the amount of data that can be both sent and received through a connection.

✧ **bozo filter:** An e-mail feature that allows the user to block messages from specific individuals. Can help reduce spam by creating a list of unwanted addresses affectionately named a "bozo list."

✧ **cookie:** A message a Web server sends to your browser when certain Web pages are visited. The cookie is stored and a message is sent back every time the user requests that page. This allows the page to be customized. For example, after you purchase something on Amazon.com, your user name will appear to welcome you every time you log on from the same computer.

✧ **cyberspace:** The interconnected, non-physical space created by the Internet and the World Wide Web, where information is transferred and people communicate electronically through computer networks.

✧ **DSL (Digital Subscriber Line):** A method for sending data over regular phone lines. A DSL circuit is much faster than a regular phone connection. It uses the same wires already in place for regular phone service, but since it uses an unused frequency you can talk on the phone while connected to the Internet.

✧ **ISP (Internet Service Provider):** A company that provides access to the Internet, usually for a monthly fee. Most homes use an ISP, such as AOL or Compuserve, to connect to the Internet.

✧ **LAN (Local Area Network):** A computer network limited to the immediate area, for example, a private residence. Ethernet is the most common type of connection used for LANs.

✧ **modem:** A communication device that allows a computer to talk to other computers. Modems vary in speed from slower telephone modems to significantly faster DSL and cable modems.

✧ **netiquette:** The accepted rules of conduct that define polite behavior in cyberspace. If you breach the rules of netiquette, you can be sure your fellow users will let you know.

✧ **network:** Any two or more computers connected together to share resources, such as files, a printer or Internet access.

✧ **newbie:** Term for someone who is new to computers or the Internet. It is not an insult, just a description. If you are reading this, you could be a newbie.

✧ **snail mail:** Regular paper mail delivered by the US Postal Service. Why use the Postal Service when you can shoot a letter over in seconds via e-mail?

✧ **spam:** Junk mail over your e-mail, which wastes your time and the network's bandwidth. Ways of combating spam include filters or private service providers, such as AOL.

✧ **T-1:** A wide bandwidth Internet connection that can carry data at 1.544 megabits per second.

✧ **URL (Uniform Resource Locator):** Represents the address used to locate a certain file, directory or page on the World Wide Web.

✧ **Web browser:** Software, such as Netscape Navigator or Internet Explorer, that allows the user to access the World Wide Web by translating the language used to build Web pages. Short term: "browser."

Computer Installation & Maintenance Service Providers

Brad Scherick
1680 North Beverly Drive, Beverly Hills, CA 90210
(310) 777 - 5200
A/V systems, computer systems
   See Brad Scherick's full report under the heading Audio/Video Design & Installation

ClearCut Solutions Inc.   **4.5   3   4.5   4.5**
2200 Pacific Coast Highway, Suite 202, Hermosa Beach, CA 90254
(877) 230 - 0631   www.clearcutsolutions.net
User-friendly computer installation and support
   Like learning a musical instrument, getting the most out of your computer takes consistent dedication. We hear that ClearCut Solutions understands that and schedules tutorial follow-ups on how to best utilize your system. This firm specializes in Mac, PC and network installation, education, repair and support. Partners Patrick Short and Kevin McManus have learned in more than twenty years in the IT business that education is the only solution to the blistering pace of technology.
   We're told that ClearCut excels in the smooth installation of wireless networks. Size of jobs ranges from networks serving a whole gated neighborhood to a PC and internet connection for a single nuclear family. Most of their work is drawn from Los Angeles and Orange Counties, although the firm will travel anywhere in a 30-mile radius from their Hermosa Beach office. Clients praise their preventative measures to combat spyware, malware and viruses. ClearCut Solutions offers "self-healing" software, for which you can download the latest updates to keep you safe from the latest internet malaise. We hear ClearCut's fees are very reasonable but increase after hours.
   "They'll even help grandma figure out how to send e-mail." "What they're selling is their excellent service."

Favarger Consulting   **4.5   3   5   4**
50 Wavecrest Avenue, Venice, CA 90291
(310) 664 - 1320
Computer installation and support; integration of mixed-vendor systems
   Communication is key to any relationship—but what if your speakers and your hard drive aren't on speaking terms? Steve Favarger specializes in integrating the computer into the home and making these devices work together. Favarger Consulting offers comprehensive installation and support for computer networks, mixed-vendor systems and home automation systems. Clients laud Favarger's seamless networks, linking home and office and offering remote control over both.
   Favarger also ranges into home entertainment, security and digital "building support" systems. While he prefers to create installations "from scratch," picking and choosing his own ingredients with care, Favarger can also step into an

existing network installation and quickly develop a thorough understanding of the network and its requirements. The fees are described as very reasonable for the quality of service.

"Steve brings a New York work ethic to Los Angeles: he's always prompt, doesn't miss appointments and is totally reliable."

Goodman Consulting 4.5 4.5 4 4.5
10730 Wellworth Avenue, Los Angeles, CA 90024
(310) 470 - 2998   www.goodmanconsulting.com
Personalized Macintosh computer consulting services

Phil Goodman wrote the book on computers, literally. While a mathematics professor at UCLA he penned the introductory textbook read by thousands of incoming students. That experience comes in handy when it comes to "speaking English" to clients about their networks. Goodman Consulting deals only with Macs, performing installations, repairs, residential and office networks, consulting and on-site training. However, it's best to call early since this Apple guru is generally booked two weeks in advance.

Flanked by an experienced staff of four, Goodman carries a brace of accolades from Macintosh, including Apple Certified Technical Coordinator and Apple Help Desk Specialist. The firm says its combined expertise in Apple and FileMaker provides an economical solution to many home and small business computing issues.

In business since 1987, Goodman is not only a consultant—he's also an educator. This plain-speaking expert leads seminars and workshops across the country for both the public and those in the trade. If you want the teacher all to yourself, Goodman offers phone support that is billed out incrementally based on his pricey hourly rate. Though his rates are higher, we hear they are relative to his overall expertise and stature in the field.

"Phil saved us a lot of money by recommending a FileMaker database solution. Development was quick and much less costly than if we'd used a more complex approach." "We relied heavily on them for our transition from the OS9 to the OSX platform. It could have been painful, but thanks to Phil everything went smoothly." "We really appreciated his educational approach to retraining the staff."

Gretzinger Consulting 3.5 3 4 4
PO Box 7035, Northridge, CA 91327
(818) 831 - 9512
Computer maintenance, installation, repair and sales

Mr. Fixit John Gretzinger has been impressing clients since 1979 with his knack for "fixing things that other people break." His consulting firm offers support, installation, repair and networking services for PCs and to a lesser degree Macs. After managing computer networks for the military, NASA and Sprint, Gretzinger took his experience to the residential realm and never looked back.

Gretzinger covers most of Los Angeles but doesn't charge a travel fee. He works with a number of nonprofit organizations as well as with residential clients in some of LA's most exclusive neighborhoods. The company currently employs two full-time technicians, but it has a network of consultants available anytime. Existing clients get free phone support, and sources tell us Gretzinger's prices are very reasonable.

MacRescue LLC   4.5   2   5   5
3419 Colville Place, Encino, CA 91436
(818) 784 - 7039   www.macrescue.com

High-end, large-scale residential Macintosh system installation, repair and maintenance

Mac users are notoriously loyal to their brand and attached to their computers, and when their beloved machines crash, they want an expert pronto. For many in Los Angeles that expert is MacRescue, a ten-year-old firm that runs "like a well-oiled machine." Given the proximity to Tinseltown, it's not surprising to learn that MacRescue's practice emphasizes graphic design system support, including pre-press support, Quicktime support and audio-visual system support. As a certified member of the Apple Consultants Network, MacRescue has access to the Apple Developers resources and support database.

Owner Steve Leebove earns high marks for giving personalized attention to each and every project, from picking out the right computer to synching an iPod to a computer's address book. MacRescue services both OS9 and OSX systems, including industrial-level support for X-Serve installations. The company tends to take on larger, more complex residential and commercial projects and works with many LA celebs.

As the name suggests, MacRescue deals exclusively with Macintosh computers and offers 24-hour service. All fees are spelled out up front. But before you request the services of Leebove and his small staff at 3 a.m. while trying to get your e-mail, don't forget his rates double after 10 PM. MacRescue also has a travel charge that kicks in after the first ten miles.

Micro Connection
13125 Lakeland Road, Santa Fe Springs, CA 90670
(562) 903 - 9330   www.m-c.com

A/V systems, home automation, computer systems, telephone networks

See Micro Connection's full report under the heading Audio/Video Design & Installation

Nicholas Curran Computer Consulting   4.5   2.5   4.5   4.5
1223 Wilshire Boulevard, Suite 213, Santa Monica, CA 90403
(310) 213 - 1000   www.nicholascurran.com

One-stop consulting for installation, web development and tech support

Always current with the latest trends in computing, Nicholas Curran Computer Consulting stays up on the creative as well as the technical side of the digital divide. In addition to network consultation, Curran offers web development and hosting, technical support, training, graphic design and video conferencing services.

For busy people with a wide range of computing, Curran is a natural choice. His impressive list of clients includes some of the Los Angeles area's more prominent firms and individuals. Though he has corporate clients, Curran offers his services to home-based businesses as well. Jobs range from website production to setting up networking and communications between the home and corporate offices. While managing to be a lot of things to a lot of people, Nicholas Curran Computer Consulting is said to keep its prices moderate and its quality high.

"Mr. Curran was willing to undertake our home-office integration project on a consultation basis, with an initial assessment of our needs and then an hourly fee." "Extremely effective. We recommend him highly."

	Quality	Cost	Value	Recommend?
	✚	$	◆	★

Sky Computer Services LLC   4   4   4   4

1223 Wilshire Boulevard, Suite 316, Santa Monica, CA 90403
(310) 587 - 2525   www.skycomputerservices.com

Customers say the sky's the limit when dealing with this computer management firm. Sky Computer Services LLC was founded by Skye Southwick in 1998 and has made a name for itself through word-of-mouth referrals. We hear Southwick's expertise and personal, friendly service have grown the firm to servicing the networks, PCs and Macs of hundreds of small and medium-sized businesses. The tech team at Sky provides full-service system integration, professional laser printer support, laptop repair, business solutions, outsourcing and data cabling services.

Customers rely on Sky's 100 percent confidence in all their work, a confidence that is borne out by the number of referrals and repeat customers. We hear customers appreciate the reasonable to very reasonable fees and the courteous customer service.

"[An] excellent business. Thank you." "Great techs. Knowledgeable . . . no hype, fast [problem] solvers and fair. I told my neighbor about you." "We love that you [guys] deal with all aspects of computers—from networking to specific database [development] to website design. Everyone has been great."

Solutions Consulting   4.5   4   4   4.5

2723 Canfield Avenue, Los Angeles, CA 90034
(310) 838 - 5224   www.rockinbeat.com

Macintosh system design, installation and support

Troubleshooter Ben Levy doesn't just fix problems, he creates solutions. His firm, Solutions Consulting, designs high-end business networks and rock-solid home systems. Renowned for his presentations at national Macintosh conventions, sources say Levy is the real deal.

With a staff of three, Levy started his business in 1990, after a career animating short films in Hollywood, a background that endears him to Mac users who work extensively with graphics and video. We're told Levy is a technical guru who will plan systems to fit a single home computer or several hundred for a large business.

The company covers all of LA County and charges for travel time. Levy's prices are definitely on the high end and he does not typically offer 24-hour service, but phone service is free for existing clients. We're told Levy coordinates very well with architects and contractors, and his fees are described as reasonable.

"The thing about Levy is that he understood exactly what we needed and designed it right away." "He is extremely skilled, both technically and at explaining things thoroughly."

Sunderland Technology Consulting   4   2.5   4.5   4.5

331 South Reeves Drive, Beverly Hills, CA 90212
(310) 277 - 0857   www.matthewsunderland.com

Computer training and troubleshooting; small business specialists

Tech wiz Matthew Sunderland outfits small businesses and some individual customers with full-service networks. Said to be skilled at translating tech-speak and educating his clients, we hear Sunderland is patient and doesn't pressure clients, explaining fully the choices between software and hardware options. The firm serves all of Los Angeles County but focuses primarily on northern and western LA.

Sunderland, who holds a degree in IT from American International College, is the sole practitioner of this three-year-old company, but he has two consultants who come in on a regular basis. Fees are quite modest, and for existing clients, Sunderland doesn't charge for travel time or phone support.

	Quality	Cost	Value	Recommend?
	+	$	◆	★

"Doesn't give people stuff they don't need." "Prompt and calm if there is a crisis. It's very reassuring to be able to call Matthew."

TechTricians Consulting Services   3.5   3   4   4
12719 Foothill Boulevard, Sylmar, CA 91342
(866) 793 - 0500   www.tz-cs.com

Home network installation, specializing in new construction sites

TechTricians Consulting specializes in planning and integrating residential computer wiring and networks on new construction sites. Aided by a staff of five, principal Robert Mitchell has installed everything from a full wired office to a wireless network in homes and small businesses across California. With offices in LA and San Francisco, TechTricians is regularly brought in by respected GCs up and down the coast.

The firm generally charges by the job, and pricing is said to be competitive. Free estimates are available, as well as free on-site consultations for home theater reviews or integration of a computer-controlled operations center in your home. Since opening its doors in 2002, TechTricians has earned its solid reputation for customer service, offering free phone support and—for the real techies out there—a sponsored discussion forum on Yahoo to answer questions in cyberspace.

"TechTricians worked effectively with my architect and builder to integrate my computers and my home entertainment system." "Courteous and thorough."

The Geek Squad   4.5   4   4.5   4.5
1213 Washington Avenue North, Minneapolis, MN 55401
(800) 433 - 5778   www.geeksquad.com

Comprehensive home and business computer services and support

The Geek Squad drives around in black-and-white faux police cruisers; and yes, they come to your door in full uniform, brandishing computer badges. Clients say the company lives up to its nerdy name, offering soup-to-nuts computer service—they will install anything from a wireless home network to a 150-machine corporate system.

The LA precinct of the Minneapolis-based Geek Squad features two technicians, both of whom are well-versed in PC and Mac. Clients praise the company's free phone support for existing customers. The Geek Squad is now officially associated with Best Buy, maintaining service centers in many of the chain's stores, so the firm sells Best Buy and Geek Squad hardware products.

LA's Geek Squad patrols most of the Westside and up to Pasadena and Burbank. "Special Agent 101" (a.k.a. principal Jonathan Jedeikin) and his sidekick are available 24 hours a day and charge prices that are on the higher end of the spectrum. However, the good citizens they serve appreciate their expertise and advice, even if "the novelty act can get a little tired."

Hiring a Contractor, Builder or Construction Manager

Major repairs or renovations can be intimidating, especially the thought of selecting the top person in charge, the commander-in-chief—the contractor. That's why an excellent contractor is vital to any major household work. This professional, like a general, takes in the big picture as well as the details, is seasoned by experience, knows his troops and the system, gets the job done well and on time and wins your admiration in the process. Here's a field guide to enlisting a five-star contractor:

Job Description

A traditional general contractor (GC) bids and builds from an architect's or designer's plans and specifications (the contract documents). The GC's duties are to interpret the drawings, execute the contracts, secure the permits, supervise the trades, manage the budget, make the schedule, deliver the quality and call it a day. There are design/build contracting firms that will draw up the contract documents, eliminating the need for an architect. Be aware, however, many firms that call themselves design/build really only offer conceptual assistance. They do not have practicing architects in-house, and must farm out design services to certified professionals.

Some say that this "one-stop shopping" approach more often than not results in uninspired design and cookie-cutter "McMansions," while others believe that nobody is more qualified to see a set of plans realized than its designer. It really depends on the builder—a number in LA hold architecture degrees from esteemed schools like SCI-Arc. While the design/build route often appears less costly than hiring an outside architect, the architect serves as a critical check balance to the GC. Construction management offers an alternative to hiring the traditional GC. Clients themselves contract with individual trades and the construction manager handles all payments and project administration for a fee based on total job cost. Some clients laud this "open book" approach, while others say it lacks an incentive to save and adds another layer of costs.

We've often found the best GCs want to be involved early in the project and work closely with the architect or designer, even at the conceptual stage. It is at this point that they can lend their experience to head off potential problems with the execution of certain designs, and help formulate a more precise picture of the project budget. Often homeowners will have the architect design the house of their dreams, and then keel over when the bids come in 30 percent over budget. Using a GC in pre-construction gives homeowners the ability to tailor their dreams to their budget without losing sleep.

What to Look for in a Contractor

Picking the right general contractor is all about communication. A homeowner needs to know as much about the GC's capabilities as the GC needs to know about a homeowner's expectations. With stakes this high—mortgages, reputations, living another day at your in-laws—it's crucial for everyone to feel completely secure in the leadership on the job and the direction of the project. You should feel comfortable stating your wishes to the contractor and have confidence in his ability to listen, explain, cooperate and delegate. Is this someone you can work with?

If you take the traditional bid-and-build route, make sure your contract documents are clear and thorough before you approach any GC. If you choose to go design/build, look for a firm sympathetic and attuned to your sense of style, and make sure the company does indeed produce quality detailed drawings. Signing up for pre-construction services gives you an opportunity to vet your GC without committing to the whole job. Your candidate should be experienced in jobs of a similar type: restoration, renovation or new construction. Do you want a versatile GC or one that specializes? The GC should be well-versed in the architectural features, building applications, specialty installations, customization and level of quality you expect. Consider the scale of the GC's past jobs, including cost and total square footage. You don't want to be the job stuck below the radar screen of a commercial-minded contractor, or hook your wagon to a little guy who can't muster the horsepower.

You want the GC to be fluent in the code requirements and logistical considerations of your locale. Negotiating the elevators and neighbors of Wilshire Corridor condos is very different from negotiating site restrictions promised by hanging homes off Hollywood Hills or building on the beaches of Malibu. The city and state permitting and inspection processes, gated community boards and building management companies are notorious instruments of delay. Also, nail down your GC's availability. If he can't commit to a target start date, you cannot depend on his ability to stick to a completion date, and chances are you'll be living in a construction battle zone for an indefinite time.

Finally, you wouldn't let a stranger in your door, so before you invite a platoon of workers brandishing power tools and sack lunches, get references. The GCs listed in this section are certainly among the most reputable we've found, but talk to clients and inspect jobs in progress yourself to get a feel for a GC's abilities and current slate of jobs. Also talk to those clients with jobs completed to get a reading on how a GC maintains his word and work. More than 30 states now require licensing or registration for GCs. In Los Angeles a GC shouldn't be able to get a permit without a C-2 California Contractor's License.

ON COST

Typically, three bids should suffice for a clear and fair comparison of estimates of project cost. But in a hot market it still may mean approaching twice that number just to get a telephone call returned. The more established GCs may bid only for architects with whom they have a relationship, or referrals, or on particularly plum projects. The most sought-after work on a negotiated fee, and are hired not for the bottom line, but for the fact a client feels 110 percent secure with his or her choice.

Cost is a reflection of material and labor (as provided directly or through subcontractors), bonding and insurance, the general conditions (overhead to keep the job running) and the fee. General conditions and the fee are calculated as percentages of the total hard-construction costs, approximately 12 to 30 percent in Los Angeles these days (twenty percent is the norm), though the percentage will vary depending on the cost, size, complexity and location of the job. Bonding offers insurance against a GC's failure to perform or pay subcontractors. It's a protection against negligence and liens—claims of debt that can be attached to the title of your property and prevent it from being sold until all liens are settled. Insurance covers full liability and workman's compensation. Any and all associated permit fees (calculated by the city as a percentage of total job cost), deposits or taxes also figure into the cost.

For the most part, bids should fall within several thousand dollars, and the degree to which prices vary depends on the quality and cost of their subcontractors, internal resources and overhead, their ability to interpret plans accurately and honestly, their ability to meet the schedule, how conservative they wish to estimate and, of course, you. At the end of the day your choice of materials and methods of construction, as well as change orders, determine where the chips are likely to fall.

In *The Franklin Report* a "3" cost rating reflects a contractor typically charging twenty percent profit and overhead on $50,000 to $500,000 projects that involve standard high-end technical or decorative work.

NEGOTIATING THE BIDS

Jumping on the low bid may be tempting, but don't take the bait. If a bid is enticingly low, it almost assuredly signals that the GC doesn't fully grasp the scope or has value-engineered without your consent. If a major cost discrepancy in the bidding process does arise, chances are someone either caught an unnoticed problem and accounted for it (in which case hire them), did not thoroughly read the plans (in which case don't hire them), or the architectural documents themselves are too vague (in which case get on your architect).

A good GC doesn't lowball, he negotiates. Don't be shy about requesting a thorough cost breakdown. If the GC's numbers come from subcontractors, you may ask for the subs' bid sheets. Remember, the more subcontractors employed, the more overhead and fee markups will inflate the bottom line. In-house carpenters, for example, are a plus, giving the GC direct control over a trade that many consider to be the engine that drives the job. Any top GC draws from a small, consistent stable of subcontractors. These prices tend to be higher due to lack of competition and constant demand for the subs' service. While loyalty speaks for standards of quality, it's always your prerogative to ask the GC for an alternative sub. Just don't be surprised if he refuses.

COMMISSIONING YOUR GENERAL

Cost is always a factor, but at the end of the day personality is at least as important. Again, can you work together? Don't settle for anything less than a principal of a contracting firm that expresses interest in the status of your job both at the outset and throughout. The tone is set from the top. You should feel like you can not only trust your GC with the keys to your house, but also enjoy having him around. Goodness knows he'll be spending enough time there.

Once the job begins, he should dispatch an on-site supervisor and assign a project manager. In some cases a working foreman will super on-site, in others it may be the company owner. In any case, these on-site managers will be the ones coordinating with your architect or designer. Weekly site meetings are a must. As with picking the right GC, running a smooth and successful job is all about communication.

GET IT IN WRITING

About the only thing that doesn't need to be detailed in your contract documents are the middle names of the contractor's children. Otherwise every detail should be recorded on paper. The plans and specs furnished by your designer provide the fundamental outline of the job. This means noting every raw material and product—including brand, model number, color and installation method. Be meticulous. If it's not on the drawings, it's not going to show up in your home, unless of course you're willing to sign the change order.

The change order, you ask? If you make a request that deviates from the project's scope as defined by the contract documents, expect to pay. Some changes may be inevitable, if you are unfortunate enough not to have x-ray vision or if you fall prey to your own whimsical inclinations halfway through the job. But be sure that any charges passed under your nose weren't already in the original contract. Ask your architect or construction manager to investigate each submission to make sure everything's on the level. Otherwise, it's up to you. Spell out in the contract how change orders will be handled. It's a smart idea to fix the unit costs for labor and material that were established with the original contract, so there are no surprises about the price of extras.

Be forewarned, a GC's obligation to meet code does not shield you from a city's permitting and inspection schizophrenia. Your contract documents must refer to the applicable codes. Because many are open to interpretation, a city official on a bad day can be a major source of change orders. The rub: if it's not on the drawings, the GC will not claim responsibility. Remember, however, that the GC should be absolutely responsible for obtaining the necessary permits for the job. This includes filing your plans and specs with the city for review and approval.

DECIDE UPON A PAYMENT SCHEDULE

If your partnership with a GC is a waltz, and contract documents the choreography, then payment provides the music. Your contract should specify the schedule of payment. Nothing will undermine a job more than misunderstandings about money. If payment is expected on a certain date, don't expect workers to show up if you miss it. Commit to what you can do. The most desirable arrangement is progressive payment on a phase-completion basis. Use benchmarks, such as pouring the foundation or rocking up the walls, to close the end of a phase. Agree on the amount of each payment beforehand. It's a great incentive to push the GC through each phase.

Monthly payments are an alternative, but this setup commands more attention to accounting and is less of an incentive. A request for biweekly payments does not bode well—it may indicate that the GC doesn't have the capital to run the job properly. In any case, if you don't want to be dropped, keep the music going. Be sure to hold on to retention—ten percent of the money owed on the job—until all punch list items have been completed and all warranties, manuals, etc. have been handed over.

With many mortgage agreements mandating higher interest charges during construction, penalties charged for not making move-in deadlines and the cost of renting space elsewhere, you might find a bust schedule more painful than a bust budget. Use incentives to motivate the GC to keep costs low and to make schedule. Bonuses go over much better than "damages clauses" that threaten penalties for blowing a deadline. Most GCs won't go for them, and anyway, they're almost impossible to enforce.

TIE UP LOOSE ENDS

Punch-list items are loose ends, such as missing fixtures, polishing finishes and fine-tuning systems. Left hanging, the punch list and warranties are things that will keep your GC in your life much longer than either of you care for. Spell out the procedure and schedule for generating, attacking and revisiting punch-list issues. A good GC doesn't need to be hand-held through the process, but it should be clear from the outset who's doing what. And give him a break if everything is not perfect at first. Be patient.

Most of the warranties passed on by the GC are from the subs and manufacturers. Many GCs will offer an umbrella warranty. Ideally you want to have one contact person if things go wrong. Some firms have a computerized database for tracking customer warranties. Warranties can range from one year on parts and labor for equipment to ten years on workmanship items. Any decent GC will be attentive to past clients long into the future. No warranty should kick in until the day the certificate of occupation or completion is issued by the city or municipality.

COVER YOUR BACK

Remember, success is as much about being thorough in your research and preparation as it is about personal chemistry and communication. All this can be wrapped up in a tidy little standard AIA (American Institute of Architects) contract with the usual qualifications attached: plans and specs, the GC's bid proposal, terms and conditions, gated community regulations and anything else you want to include.

TIPS FOR A PAINLESS JOB

✧ Make contract documents as detailed, clear and complete as possible.
✧ Establish good chemistry and communication between yourself, the GC and the architect.
✧ Have the GC hold weekly site meetings with subcontractors.
✧ Make payments on schedule.
✧ Trust the contractor and maintain your sense of humor.

Quality	Cost	Value	Recommend?
	$	◆	★

Contractors, Builders & Construction Managers

FIRMS WITH PORTFOLIOS

All Coast Construction   5   4   5   5

5364 North Sterling Center Drive, Westlake Village, CA 91361
(818) 865 - 8371   www.allcoastconstruction.com

Significant renovations and high-end new construction

All Coast principals Michael Grosswendt and Gerald Sette give clients the kind of confidence that only comes from a lifetime devotion to craftsmanship. With 50 years of combined building experience, "All Coast does it right the first time." A pet contractor of many finicky designers, the word is, "If a client doesn't use them, we have no other recommendations."

References tell us this firm is "not closed-minded" to aggressive design and pays "very close attention to detail" in its execution. Once a job is completed, clients can turn to All Coast's new Estate Maintenance division to provide full "soup-to-nuts" handyman service on high-end residential renovations, additions and ground-up new construction.

Sources report that principal Michael Grosswendt is a consistent force in the field. Clients find him personable, easy to communicate with and prompt on follow-through. Though All Coast's staff has grown to 35 to take on five major residential projects at a time, we're told Grosswendt runs a very tight ship. Punch lists are KO'd and sites are kept neat. Recently, All Coast has done extensive work in home automation and mechanization, where the importance of trustworthy lifetime maintenance is incalculable.

"I am really picky, and he does a great job." "The crew was superb and very respectful of my space." "This firm is first tier in my opinion."

Bulldog Construction Inc.   4   3.5   4.5   4.5

1513 6th Street, Suite 202, Santa Monica, CA 90401
(310) 260 - 3280   www.bulldogconstruction.com

High-end custom homes and remodels

We hear that Bulldog Construction has a firm grip on full-service, residential construction and remodeling. Clients tell us this "generous" and "customer-focused" firm aims to please "beyond the scope of the job." Working from Hidden Hills to Santa Monica, the firm takes on high-end residential and commercial ground-up construction and remodeling work from $500,000 and up.

In his more than twenty years in the business, President Steve Barnes has learned the value of being meticulous and hands on. Bulldog gets very much into the design process at early stages, even if it isn't the contractor of record. The firm provides an inspection, which we hear makes its bids not always the lowest, but often the most reliable. Sources report that the firm is a real bulldog about keeping its subcontractors well-marshaled and on task, so there are fewer slowdowns and conflicts. References report this reasonable, attentive firm can wind up being a man's best friend.

	Quality	Cost	Value	Recommend?
	✚	$	◆	★

"In less than five months, Bulldog completed my home remodel/addition and exceeded my expectations with its excellent customer service, speed and efficiency in overcoming any obstacles that occurred during the job." "The office staff could not have been more friendly and efficient." "The quality of workmanship as well as the attention to detail that Steve and his company put into our home is evident in every room." "In less than four months we were back in the house. Wow!" "There were no excuses about how something couldn't be done, only reassurances that we would be completely happy, and Bulldog always delivered as promised." "They are always reachable. Any questions or concerns I had were answered immediately, which gave me peace of mind throughout the construction process."

Custom Design & Construction 📷   4   3   5   **4.5**

2143 South Sepulveda Boulevard, Suite 201, Los Angeles, CA 90025
(310) 815 - 4815 www.remodelwithus.com

Remodels and additions

This design/build firm specializes in custom remodeling and takes a "fully integrated" approach to the construction process. Blessed with the resources and experience of a large firm, Custom Design & Construction is also said to take a "genuine interest" in its clients, just like a small firm would. (The company even offers an in-house financing program to work with limited budgets.) Sources say Custom delivers a well-built product on a reasonable budget, time and again.

CD&C focuses on remodels and additions, from bathrooms to whole-house guts. The firm's work stretches from Huntington Beach to West LA and up into Ventura County, covering both established communities and smaller niche markets. Led by Bill Simone (who has two degrees in architecture) and Randy Ricciotti, this design-oriented firm is praised for being "courteous, friendly and extremely competent." The firm has a standard operating procedure for every aspect of the business, keeping "everything executed and delivered in a professional manner," clients say. CD&C was selected by *Professional Remodeler Magazine* as 2003 Benchmark Market Leader.

Design comes for a flat fee, with construction contracts fixed price. The firm provides financing through Custom Funding Inc. We hear the company works well within the constraints of a budget, especially for remodels.

"My kitchen is gorgeous! It's a dream! This company did what they promised to do when they promised to do it." "The friendliness, honesty and artistry of everyone involved was exemplary and greatly appreciated." "No less than outstanding!" "Randy Ricciotti must be recognized for his coordinating skill, effort and patience with our innumerable questions, from the initial consultation to the completed product."

Louis Bourassa & Company Inc. 🛍   4.5   3.5   5   5

120 1/2 South La Brea Avenue, Los Angeles, CA 90036
(323) 857 - 1660

High-end gut renovations

Louis Bourassa puts "a little bit of himself" into each job, and that attribute is said to account for the Boston-bred contractor's meteoric rise in the Los Angeles residential market. Details that might escape another contractor—like lead tracking or consistent accurate budgeting—are tightly controlled under Bourassa's watchful eye. Reportedly, his on-site presence is key to his style of management. Clients say he sees "the big picture, not just the quality of the sub-floor," showing as much integrity in his product as in his relations with the client. Bourassa's small firm focuses on full-on renovations of the entire house from over $150,000 to into the multimillions. Bourassa's New England heritage informs his expert traditional work, though recently the firm has successfully taken on clean, modern designs.

Bourassa hails from a family of builders. After getting a degree in English and economics, he passed over the professional route, taking an opportunity to work as a union carpenter. Soon after, he started his own general contracting company and cut his high-end teeth renovating the Boston Four Seasons into a five-star hotel. He moved to LA in 1995 and has built his stellar reputation on enthusiasm and effort. We hear Bourassa "enjoys what he does" as much as clients enjoy him. In particular, women who have experience with other contractors find Bourassa "approachable" and "not patronizing." For movie people used to fast-track schedules, we hear LB&C keeps things moving at a breakneck pace.

Bourassa nails down costs in the early planning phases, so contracts are fixed. Pre-construction services bill out hourly (at $150) for analysis of design and budget. At prices that are slightly above standard, satisfied clients say, "Look no further."

"I liked him right away. You could tell he was the same with everybody." *"He returns my phone calls. He doesn't stress too hard. He's the whole package."* *"I like that he's a little younger. Older contractors were inflexible, but Louis was open-minded. I'd recommend him to anybody."* *"Above and beyond expectations."* *"I could ask for something and the next day it was turned around."* *"You've got to enjoy the people you're working with. These jobs take so long. And we were absolutely thrilled with Louis."*

Richard Holz Inc. 💼   5   4   5   5
11740 San Vicente Boulevard, Suite 207, Los Angeles, CA 90049
(310) 442 - 8158
New construction and selected renovation

Clients paint Richard Holz as an absolutely extraordinary contractor with a "soft touch." His small, enormously respected firm has 27 years of quality work behind it and some of the best word-of-mouth in LA. Today, the company focuses on new construction of high-end residences over the $1 million mark and selected renovation projects. Holz, a licensed architect, is said to tap his roots in design to work closely with architects, taking the extra time to execute the nuances of their work, from Cape Cod to contemporary. Architects admire Holz as much for his conceptual solutions as his technical ones, and clients admire him for entertaining a variety of choices. The firm may be enlisted for design/build.

We're told Holz is a "nuts-and-bolts guy" who displays a "depth of involvement" with homeowners that corporate contractors just can't match. Clients marvel that "there's no job he's not on every day." He manages five supers and views himself as a broker of subs, buying flexibility and enlisting the appropriate craftsman for the appropriate task. Clients describe him as honest and organized, while tradespeople say "he is one of the nicest contractors to work for," with a calm and respectful approach that designers tell us "makes people work all the harder for him." The overall atmosphere Holz fosters improves both the experience and the finished product.

Clients rave that Holz offers one of the best blends of speed, quality and pricing in LA. The firm works on a cost-plus basis with standard overhead and profit, and can be hired for preconstruction services for a flat price per month.

"Rick has time for the small things. He sweats the small stuff." "As good as anyone in LA." "Treats people around him with equal respect." "Wears the striped shirt and balances between all the players." "Not many owners of big GCs are as involved." "He's got honesty and integrity, and no one can beat him on scheduling." "Brings a strong design side to the equation." "Excellent man. Built several homes for me over the years." "Fantastic execution with the conscience of a Boy Scout. Very well respected."

The I. Grace Company, West Coast, Inc. 💼 5 4.5 4.5 5
1516 South Bundy Drive, Suite 300, Los Angeles, CA 90025
(310) 442 - 8121 www.theigracecompany.com
High-end residential construction, service and maintenance

This large, nationally renowned, residential construction company possesses both finesse and firepower. I. Grace offers end-to-end building and renovation services and is equally at home creating anything from Mission to Modern, beach homes to condominium interiors. In addition to the large-scale museum quality projects for which the company is best known, I. Grace maintains ongoing support to their clients from Santa Barbara to Malibu, from the Wilshire Corridor to Bel Air, completing small jobs through its service arm. An impressive roster of patrons includes high-profile executives, celebrities and other power players.

Founded in 1987 by David Cohen, I. Grace extends across the continent with six divisions, including its flagship headquarters in New York City. The same business philosophy of quality and integrity extends to the West Coast, New England and Long Island markets, as well as to divisions dedicated to Special Projects and Service/Maintenance. We hear the firm's hundred-plus team "consistently demonstrates a responsiveness to the needs, concerns and ambitions of the customer." From the CEO to the project manager, the company exemplifies "old-school" values by building lasting relationships. For those who can afford it, I. Grace promises white-glove treatment with white-collar acumen.

"I. Grace has brought the finest quality of East Coast building to the West." "Very hands on . . . available via cell 24/7." "I wouldn't think of doing another home without them." "In an industry that sometimes lacks professionalism and integrity, they are a breath of fresh air." "I can't imagine another large construction firm that would have an executive pick up and deliver a barbecue to verify it would fit correctly." "Their reputation in New York is stellar and certainly carries forward in Los Angeles." "A welcome addition to the West Coast marketplace."

FIRMS WITHOUT PORTFOLIOS

ACS Design/Build Group 3.5 3.5 4 4
787 West Woodbury Road, Suite 11, Altadena, CA 91001
(626) 535 - 9335

Residential design/build

ACS Design/Build Group, a single company run by partners Marco and Rafael Quezada, brings homes from "concept to completion." We're told the Quezadas are creative, inventive problem solvers who can often see solutions to difficult design issues that others cannot. This company not only builds its own designs, but has also worked with some of the most reputable architects in the area. Over half of this work is high-end residential, with the rest being commercial.

A family-run business with more than 27 years of experience, the company's small size means clients get personal attention from the owners. Ongoing relationships with clients are important to ACS, and the staff promptly attends to customers when even the smallest issue arises—even if the work was completed a decade ago. Clients say they trust the company and recommend it to family and friends. Quezada and his crew are said to see every detail through to the end. The company is noted for not having a specific style—they design in a variety of genres, basing their work on the project's setting and the client's interest and tastes. We hear that the firm's specialty is millwork and cabinetry.

Albino Construction   5   4.5   4.5   5
860 Via De La Paz, Suite B-5, Pacific Palisades, CA 90272
(310) 454 - 9908
Fast-track, high-end construction and gut renovation

There is something unique about Albino Construction. Always in high demand, the firm does things the "Albino way," which means doing extensive planning, then pushing the envelope with double crews and six-day weeks. Reflecting the personality of its principal, Albino Martinez, the firm is "bright, honest and hardworking," sources tell us.

Top-shelf architects and designers seek out Martinez, whose ironclad timetables and dependable crews simplify even the most daunting projects. Residential projects center in the Malibu/Beverly Hills/Pacific Palisades area and consist of both ground-up construction and renovation. Projects range from 8,000 to 17,000 square feet. Flanked by their own cabinet shop and finish carpenters, the firm specializes in traditional residential (rather than contemporary style) construction.

While insiders say meeting aggressive timetables is what makes Albino great, others find the atmosphere a little brusque. Martinez makes his presence known daily at every project site, exerting control through masterful orchestration of highly responsible trades on site, who largely supervise each other. Clients tell us "every workman was fantastic" and at the end of the project they "actually missed them terribly." Albino bills on a weekly time-and-materials basis. While the books are always transparent, the numbers are big. Of course, for Albino's clients, the numbers on the calendar are the ones that count.

"It could not have been a more positive experience. They are dedicated, honest, stand by their word and every promise is always kept." "Albino himself will strap on a belt and work it out." "I never saw anyone who will not go back to him." "Such a pleasure. Clients and designers love him." "In this land of litigation he's not into paperwork, just getting the job done." "Will make the house happen even if the design is incompetent." "The actual cost of Albino will always feel like it was a bargain, regardless of how much they charge." "Everything in our house works beautifully."

Alisal Builders Inc.   4.5   4   4.5   4
734 Washington Boulevard, Marina del Rey, CA 90292
(310) 574 - 9507   www.alisalbuilders.com
Restoration, renovation and new construction

Alisal Builders Inc. strives to offer every client a unique home that "calls to mind the days of manor houses, with their distinct touch of personality." Martin Leon's commitment to individuality in home construction means that his firm started small and has stayed small. Nevertheless, this firm has managed to build a big reputation, thanks to its sterling service from bidding to billing.

Leon's homes are scattered along the Southern California coast. An almost palatial opulence pervades the design of Alisal's coastal manors, but the style remains open and leisurely. We hear Alisal is highly sensitive to clients' needs,

	Quality	Cost	Value	Recommend?
	✚	$	◆	★

and has handled several celebrity projects with aplomb. Although the tab is expensive, clients still consider the firm an excellent value, praising its reliable high-end quality.

Balcorp Construction 4.5 4.5 4 5
2852 Colorado Avenue, Santa Monica, CA 90404
(310) 451 - 5838

New construction and renovation with in-house craftsmen

Clients who want a "younger," "edgier" approach to custom residential construction often request the "deft touch" of Brian Lushing and Balcorp Construction. This firm typically takes on projects very large and very custom, aided by a reservoir of in-house craftsmen. What really sets Balcorp apart is its ability to perform carpentry, finishes, concrete, tile and even exterior stonework with its own men, who clients call "polite and highly competent." This allows for better control over the quality and pace of each and every job. Bids also prove more accurate and change orders less painful.

Established as a development company, the firm eased into building custom homes twenty years ago, and has focused exclusively on GC work since the mid-1990s. References find owner Brian Lushing, who comes from several generations of builders, "down to earth" and very involved. From preconstruction to site meetings, Lushing acts as the liaison between the client, the architects and the issues. Layers of in-house supervisors and consultants lend support. While Balcorp's craftsmen are versed in a variety of styles, most of their work falls under traditional ground-up construction or addition within the framework of original architecture. The firm zeroes in on the zone between Beverly Hills and Malibu.

Clients say they'd "recommend many times over" the "phenomenal experience" of working with Balcorp. Lushing is especially praised for his friendly manner: "It's like having your friend build your house," one source says. "He treats it like he'll be back to sit across the dinner table." The firm takes on seven to eight projects at a time, ranging from a $1 million, 3,000 square foot office and guesthouse addition to a $9 million expansion of an 18,000 square foot residence. While generally more expensive than most, Balcorp's in-house talent gives it a pricing edge on larger jobs versus LA's contracting moguls.

"Coherent and realistic cost estimates." "I've walked into other homes that cost twice as much where the quality is not half as good." "Brian knows what's needed in certain renovations and how to get the vintage feel of things." "Big in his own right." "Brian was the reason it went so smoothly. With his guidance we put together the team." "Brian was there for us when the architect and decorator fought over turf." "Genuinely cares on a personal level." "We leave Brian's number with the person who house-sits." "Information was clear, easy to understand. He was always on target or close to it. No huge surprises." "Very friendly and open to suggestion. There's no ego to work past. He makes it comfortable."

Bonura Building 4 3.5 4.5 5
3235 San Fernando Road, Building 5, Los Angeles, CA 90065
(323) 478 - 0101   www.bonurabuilding.com

Progressive residential custom construction, design/build

Bonura Building fuses elite architecture with a progressive aesthetic, a combination that has been winning fans for over a decade, especially in Santa Monica and the Hollywood Hills. About 70 percent of the firm's work is in residential remodels, with the other 30 percent in ground-up custom homes, where Bonura specializes in contemporary and mid-century modern architecture.

Principal C.J. Bonura is a licensed architect (SCIA) with the trench-hewn experience of a contractor. Clients describe him as a "very straightforward" and "trustworthy" man who is obsessed with detail. Customers say they have come to value Bonura's aesthetic opinion as much as his technical know-how. He is said to be able to simplify design without stifling quality, and to offer better options for each dollar spent. Clients appreciate the fact that Bonura anticipates concerns and asks the right questions ahead of time.

Bonura is supported by a stable of architecture-oriented superintendents and a framing/finish carpentry crew. The firm also offers a consultant service to review plans in a cost-plus/open-book arrangement for contracting a job. Jobs start at $200,000 and average around $400,000 to $500,000.

"He establishes a personal relationship from the get-go." "Understands the modern aesthetic very well." "The lines of communication are wide open here!" "Exceptionally cautious in what he tells you." "Exceptional attention to detail. Anal-retentive, even." "Would hire again in a heartbeat." "Most important thing— we trusted him."

Brown Osvaldsson Builders Inc.   4   4.5   3.5   4
1333 Pine Street, Santa Monica, CA 90405
(310) 392 - 8899   www.bob-inc.com
Significant renovations and high-end new construction

Brown Osvaldsson is often called in to execute the designs of the city's most discriminating architects. From Craftsman to contemporary, the Malibu beachfront to the Hollywood Hills, this firm takes on ground-up residential projects and larger remodels. While some jobs top $700,000, the firm also enjoys doing challenging smaller pet projects with favorite architects. Despite the significant volume of business, Brown Osvaldsson still forms a special bond with the homeowner. Clients often come back to the principals directly, even ten years later.

Bruce Brown and Arnie Osvaldsson formed the firm in 1990, and one of the two owners is always at the job to keep control and ensure quality. Brown and Osvaldsson bring more than 35 years of building experience to the company, as finish carpenters, framers and construction managers. Not surprisingly, they have a lot of input into design elements, producing mock-ups when necessary. We hear they know what the architect likes to see and are expert in determining finishes. Reports describe them as anything but pushy. Clients are encouraged to entertain ideas and weigh options through the course of the project. A balance between a consistent, focused schedule and a little room for whimsy and innovation typifies Brown Osvaldsson's approach.

The firm's preconstruction services are offered on an hourly basis or per square foot. Contracts are split between time and material and fixed.

"You get a special outcome. Denmark-craftsman quality." "I've hired them for many of my interior design projects. When I do my house, they will be my contractor."

| | Quality | Cost | Value | Recommend? |

Bruder Construction 4 4 4 4
23679 Calabasas Road, Suite 536, Calabasas, CA 91302
(818) 992 - 3315 www.bruderconstruction.com

Historic renovation specialists; remodeling and custom homes

Jay Bruder brings a variety of talents to the table. As a native Angeleno, Bruder has a profound interest in architecture, and we hear that translates into a very sensitive approach to renovation and good working relationships with project architects. Bruder is said to carry "a heartfelt appreciation for the intrinsic beauty of classic architecture" into every job, including renovations of homes by the likes of Paul Williams and Summer Spaulding. Clients remark on the firm's ability to reproduce levels of craftsmanship and attention to detail of older homes.

While this eighteen-year-old firm does ground-up custom homes, the majority of its work consists of additions and renovations. Bruder helms two to three big projects a year, ranging from $500,000 to $2 million. The firm specializes in photographic restoration of old homes to their former glory. However, on a more progressive note, Bruder has more than once added a low-voltage sliding roof for star gazing. The firm's work can be seen from Pasadena to Malibu to Rancho Santa Fe, and has been featured several times in *This Old House* magazine.

Clients cite Bruder's "aesthetic sensibility and grace in handling clients" as a major strength. He attends all project meetings and manages the time-line schedule, assisted by his office, the field project managers and finish carpenters. We hear that the amount of paperwork can be overwhelming, but ultimately clients agree that the firm makes working together "a sheer joy." Bruder will even work around a client's lifestyle, starting work later in the day so as not to disturb their sleep.

"Over a six month period, I worked with Jay Bruder on a daily basis and found it to be the most satisfying relationship I've ever had with a builder." "His work is outstanding and his subcontractors are excellent in every area."

Built Inc. 3.5 3 4.5 4.5
7527 Beverly Boulevard, Los Angeles, CA 90036
(323) 857 - 0409 www.builtinc.com

Modernist-inspired furniture design, residential design/build

In the shadow of the "Hollywood" sign, nestled in the hip haven of Silver Lake, the designers' collective at Built Inc. takes funky inspiration from the modernist gems scattered among the hills. A New York transplant, "candid" founder John Sofio helms a boutique design/build shop—as well as an art and design gallery retail space. In both his custom renovations and new ground-up construction projects, Sofio is said to create unique, environmentally cool bits of contemporary craftsmanship from historical bones. Whether playing upon the indoor/outdoor vibe, exploring color, or trying out different materials, Sofio is said to enjoy the experimental. The less adventurous should look elsewhere.

Which is not to say that Sofio is a renegade on the job. On the contrary, all projects are developed in close consultation with clients and then taken from concept to completion together. Sofio's construction division implements the design, and is so sensitive to every nuance that Sofio is sometimes approached by other architects to execute their visions. In all cases, he controls volume to maintain high standards.

While Sofio no doubt comes to projects with a designer's eye, he never loses his GC heart. As the builder of his own designs, he is very flexible in delivering an array of possibilities that can be executed and still conform to the budget. Two draftsmen and two project managers work with Sofio to keep budgets and subs well in check. We hear Built Inc. is also developing fixer-uppers in Silver Lake with

Sofio's colorful, industrial aesthetic. It may not be for everyone, but Sofio has plenty of admirers. One satisfied client said of her home, "They'll have to carry me out in a box."

"The golden part of working with John is you're creating a project as you go." "He's committed to getting through it as friends." "The reality is amazing." "The process is one of flexibility with John. He definitely brings a style but the design is always negotiable." "Cost conscious and creative." "John is good at listening. He took what we wanted with functionality and flow and applied his unique aesthetic."

Bunge Construction Inc.   4.5   4.5   4   5
2323 California Avenue, Santa Monica, CA 90403
(310) 581 - 0839

Detailed historic renovation, new construction

It was while restoring several 1920s and 1930s Hancock Park homes to their former glory that Jose Bunge established his reputation for masterful handling of tedious, highly detailed restoration work. Clients who must live at home during these jobs especially admire his sensitivity to their situations, and applaud his effort to tiptoe (as much as one can while bearing power tools) around their lives. He also constructs new custom homes, and has proven to be a player on hillside properties. Commercial work includes editing bays and studios that require special sound barrier walls and floors. Finally, this jack-of-all-trades also develops residential property on his own, working mostly on the west side of LA.

A native of Argentina, Bunge's knowledge of his craft goes back over twenty years. Clients share a good rapport with Bunge, whom they describe as friendly and highly capable of overseeing his firm of fifteen. Each job site gets a foreman and full office set-up to expedite documentation, a necessity given the unexpected twists inherent in remodels. Bunge's own finishers and painters perform decorative and faux finish specialty work. His in-house craftsmen can match stone, brick, cast moldings or wood floors.

Bunge's thoughtful work keeps him under the wing of top-tier LA designers. He limits his slate to no more than three projects at a time, often working for the same clients over and over again. Contracts are fixed price, and costs are upper echelon, starting at $300,000. While Bunge's designer and homeowner clients are among the fussiest out there, we hear there isn't one among them who wouldn't call him again.

Chai Contractors Inc.   4.5   4   4.5   5
838 Elyria Drive, Los Angeles, CA 90065
(323) 225 - 1658

Gut renovations and interior remodels

The bold team at Chai Contractors "can execute novel, inventive design" with "complete honesty" and "incredible forethought." The firm focuses on gut renovations and interior remodels, from tenant improvement to the resuscitation of 14,000 square foot homes. With more than a dozen years in contracting and a background in carpentry, Chai guy Dana Lance is said to seek out architecturally ambitious projects over $250,000. We hear he revels in reproducing the integrity of Craftsman or Spanish deco—yet appreciates the modern aesthetic, too.

Lance takes only a limited number of projects and personally drives each job. Clients consider this a major asset. They tell us that Lance is a "joy to work with" and is available day or night, whether during the job or years later. He works closely with designers who compliment his "intense passion for detail," and he surrounds himself with "reliable" and "delightful" craftsmen, according to references. Lance has his pick of projects and works on a cost-plus basis, giving

	Quality	Cost	Value	Recommend?
	✚	$	◆	★

clients a choice of subs or allowing them to bring their own to the team. We hear Lance makes life as comfortable for the client as possible throughout a project, and by the end of the job he often "feels like one of the family."

"There are people who just do their job and there are people who do it so well that it impacts your life in an amazing way. That's Dana." "If he's not sure, he tells you, then researches the solution and returns with options." "Totally gets it about modern architecture." "A complete pleasure." "About as good as it gets, and we've worked with a lot of contractors." "We wanted Dana and his guys to stay for dinner every night." "I give Dana my keys when I go on vacation. Once, when there was a disaster, he saved the day."

Davis Development Group   4.5   4   4.5   5

4247 Bluebell Avenue, Studio City, CA 91604
(818) 985 - 9884

Large-scale renovations and new custom homes

An avant-garde contractor who has worked with the likes of Frank Gehry and Brian Murphy for the past three decades, Jim Davis has built on beaches and hillsides, constructing projects with reclaimed lumber from North Carolina and handmade hardware from Mexico. He's done ad agencies, loft office spaces, and tenant improvement projects, but his bread and butter is large-scale renovations and new custom homes in the multiple-million-dollar range (with some smaller jobs for existing clients). A popular force in Los Angeles contracting, Davis is known to refer clients to architects as much as architects refer their clients to him.

Davis got his start fashioning hip furniture and interiors for decorators. Nowadays we hear that Davis makes an interesting contractor: he thinks like an architect, walks like a builder and talks straight to clients. Sources say this firm really helps them to assess their needs, grasp detail and design concepts, and keep them comfortable around budget issues. As a result, the firm is often hired early in the process on a consultancy basis, with the fee to be ultimately credited toward the construction contract if Davis gets it—which he always does.

The modest-sized firm takes on only a small number of projects at any one time and dispatches a full-time super to each job site. Davis himself is present at job meetings once a week and is deeply involved with bidding and the shaping of budgets. At his tier, Davis has a slight edge over the competition in terms of costs, since their outsourced trades prove less practical in their pricing structure than his. Clients say Davis puts the money into the project and doesn't cut corners. He takes pride in fomenting long relationships with his clients, for several of whom he has been entrusted to build two to three homes over the course of his career.

"Excellent cost estimating and preconstruction services. Delivers quality while maintaining schedule and budget." "Timely, reliable, honest—and they always use good judgment. I give them the highest recommendation."

Duran + Associates   4   3.5   4.5   4

29301 Hillrise Drive, Agoura Hills, CA 91301
(818) 865 - 9658

Residential new construction, renovation of mid-century modern aesthetic

A keen aesthetic sense of classic 1940s and 1950s architecture and attention to detail characterize Ken Duran's firm, which has made a name for itself by resuscitating modern buildings in the style of Los Angeles icon R.M. Schindler. His firm does both extensive renovations and ground-up residences that reflect the straight lines and warmer elements of mid-century modern architecture. We hear that Duran likes to apply his conceptual understanding of building and design, whether or not he is the designer of a project. References report that Duran's designs show off redwood and mahogany, finished concrete surfaces, glass, steel, free-standing columns, imperial plaster, carrara marble—and lots of mosaic tile.

Duran attended SCI-Arc and began building to pay his way through school. As a result, he offers a wealth of design input on every project, and is well prepared to both complement an architect's vision and realize it. Indeed, clients sometimes go directly to Duran for design/build services. The company is a small operation and the passionately involved Duran likes to take no more than two projects at a time. He runs everything himself and utilizes the skill of a loyal and long-standing group of subs. Billing and invoicing are tight—however, Duran is not the least expensive contractor out there, and clients can expect to pay standard prices for the work.

"Ken does incredibly detailed work." "His abilities go beyond just general construction—he also has a good eye." "He becomes a very happy creature when it's time to come up with a solution." "He is competent and knows how to coordinate the job with a minimum number of change orders." "He was on the job. The communication was great. The project was delivered on time and within budget." "Worked with my designer to make structural changes to reduce budget."

Escrofani Construction　　　　　　　4　　4　　4　　4.5
248 Calle Larios, Camarillo, CA　93010
(805) 987 - 4568

Residential renovations and additions

Escrofani Construction can offer a truly global perspective on all kinds of construction styles and technical challenges. After receiving an engineering degree in his native Argentina, principal Hector Escrofani globe trotted through Europe, Hawaii and the Midwest while working contracting jobs. This experience schooled him in a variety of building techniques, materials and styles, all of which inform his work today. Escrofani founded the company almost twenty years ago to take on additions, restorations, remodeling and new construction of all types. Today, the firm specializes in complex hillside engineering or structural foundation work—and we hear his tremendous breadth of experience really pays off on these tough jobs.

Escrofani Construction works one job at a time, usually lasting six months. We're told that Escrofani has kept his firm small to focus on quality and spend time with his three boys. Clients describe him as "very conscientious" and "extremely responsive." He gets along with clients quite well, notably celebs, with whom the "down to earth" Escrofani does not become star-struck. The pride he takes in his work is unquestionable—he will work shoulder to shoulder with his subs to get it done right. A supervisor supports him in the field and his wife, Barbara, keeps the books and the office.

Work is done by fixed contract or on a time-and-materials basis. While Escrofani is "not the cheapest guy—not by a long shot," he stacks up favorably against the bigger firms who are also executing at his heightened level. Escrofani looks to massage the budget and minimize extras at the conceptual phase and "knows how to work with clients who can't quite afford the very best of everything."

"Given my druthers, I'd go to him first." "Hector's a craftsmen, a good businessman, ethical, reliable and has staying power." "He anticipates problems,

supervises well and delivers what he promises." "You want to work with someone who cares about his reputation, not the bottom line. That's Hector." "Fine quality work." "For a business that is known for stress and disagreements, there is very little of it with Hector."

Finton Associates Inc.   4.5   4.5   4   4.5
401 Roylyn Place, Arcadia, CA 91007
(626) 445 - 1044   www.fintonassociates.com
High-end custom homes and remodeling

This "very well respected" team has built its muscle in high-end custom homes and remodeling while growing to an industry standard over the last seventeen years. John Finton and Mike Reeves met at California Polytechnic at Pomona and forged a lasting partnership. Today, Finton Associates undertakes a large slate of projects, all upper-end and strictly residential $1 million-plus tear-downs or gut renovations from Laguna Beach to Santa Barbara. A Newport Beach office handles smaller projects starting at $300,000 in and around South Bay. Newest partner Dan Tontini helms the freshly-minted Santa Barbara operation. Having built over 125 custom homes across Southern California, Finton Associates clearly holds a venerated place in the trade.

Clients tell us the firm displays an "extraordinary strength in three areas: field supervision, management support and executive leadership." Laptop-ready and business savvy, a field supervisor steers each job. The firm boasts an army of 30 such individuals. However, Finton, Reeves and Tontini all participate at a micro level, from the conception of the design to weekly meetings. We hear Finton and his associates are "cool under pressure and honest to a fault." The firm has been recognized as a top-ten remodeling contractor by *Remodeling* magazine from 1994 to 1998, and was nominated as Custom Homebuilder of the Year by *Custom Home* magazine in 1995.

All work is cost plus the fee determined by the budget and complexity of the project. While Finton charges a pretty penny, supervisors are praised for "watching every penny as if it were their own."

"They are available from 4:30 AM to 10 PM any day." "John helped me to research materials and suppliers, which I feel have ultimately enhanced our home significantly." "We have never worked with a nicer group of people on any project." "Able to problem-solve without pointing fingers." "The results exceeded our expectations—the home has the integrity of a centuries-old villa."

Fort Hill Construction   5   5   4   5
8118 Hollywood Boulevard, Los Angeles, CA 90069
(323) 656 - 7425   www.forthill.com
Large-scale, high-end renovation and new construction

A high-powered family firm from back East, Fort Hill is the contractor of choice for many of LA's elite. The firm helms tent-pole projects from studio lots to ocean-view villas, from custom new homes to historic restoration, from minimalist to mammoth. Fort Hill takes on a select number of projects each year, pairing with creative clientele and acclaimed design professionals who provide challenging, inspired opportunities. Even the A-list is awed by the museum-quality work and ceaseless attention to detail delivered by this 35-year-old construction management and general contracting firm.

Founded in 1971, Fort Hill is still a family-run business, dedicated to its roots in quality crafsmanship and renovation even after moving its base to Los Angeles. (Fort Hill also remains firmly entrenched in Boston and New York.) George Peper, Jim Kweskin and the other original partners have cultivated a family business into a "factory of perfectionism." The Fort Hill family extends to ranks of craftsmen, supervisors and managers that run generations deep. A number of the city's high-end general contractors cut their teeth on the proving grounds of Fort Hill projects. Fort Hill also maintains a drafting/minor design division to accommodate smaller projects and a service unit to care for existing customers. We hear the firm's famously unflappable staff does very well to get even the biggest egos through the front door.

Undoubtedly the place to go for superior service, Fort Hill's cache comes with "take it or leave it bids." However, clients who sign on to the program confess they love every minute of it.

"Can't beat Fort Hill's experience. The team at the table was amazing." "First line, all celebs." "Very attentive. Hard to find better." "They are a wonderful group—organized, detail-oriented. We had a great project manager on site." "Everyone falls over dead when they see the numbers." "There's Fort Hill, and then there's everyone else." "A+++."

Gordon Gibson Construction   4   4   4   4
3000 31st Street, Suite G, Santa Monica, CA 90405
(310) 396 - 9310 www.gordongibsonconst.com
Custom residential construction

Insiders claim Gordon Gibson Construction is leading LA construction into the digital age. With mobile on-site offices with fax, e-mail and phones, this is one wired firm. With a kind of futuristic precision, these mobile offices issue detailed, bi-weekly reports to the client. Today the firm's mobile offices can be found at some of LA's largest and most custom residential project sites.

The firm was founded in 1966 on a tripartite principle of "ethics, integrity and stability." Principal Gordon Gibson learned every aspect of the home building business, working first as a framing contractor before moving on to small residential building. From the first bid to the punch list, Gibson himself collaborates closely with the architect and homeowner. A staff of full-time field supervisors work with Gibson to meet the needs of a discriminating clientele. These patrons are comforted by the thought that Gibson, his staff and savvy included, will be there years down the road as needed.

"Delightful to work with." "Gordon Gibson is very involved day-to-day." "Long after the money is spent, the quality remains."

Horizon General Contractors Inc.   4.5   4   4.5   5
1512 Eleventh Street, Suite 202, Santa Monica, CA 90401
(310) 393 - 3329
Custom residential construction

Contemplating this Horizon gives clients a warm, fuzzy feeling. Sources can't stop talking about the "remarkable experience" of working with principal Dan Andrews and his crew. With a quarter century in the business, the firm's skills lie in high-end custom residential, often second homes, where clients can devote what money they want to the project. Properties tend to fall between 3,500 and 14,000 square feet, but the firm will also build out Wilshire corridor condo interiors. $250,000 is a minimum for new jobs. Until recently limited to Malibu, Horizon now works in West LA and Beverly Hills.

Andrews is the lead contact, fostering a "warm relationship" with the client while keeping a handle on the financial end of affairs. References tell us he is "forthright, honest and extremely reliable." Andrews is said to be flexible about client-generated changes during construction, and we've heard some clients trust him so much they'll build a second house with him without plans. Horizon offers preconstruction services in design development to nail down the budget. Six full-time superintendents, counting four licensed contractors with more than twenty years experience among them, keep job sites running like clockwork. All come equipped with laptop computers on site.

Horizon charges hourly for its preconstruction consultancy and will refund 50 percent of this fee as an incentive for being awarded the construction contract. References report that by putting up accurate, price-competitive numbers, the firm hasn't lost a bid yet. Contracts can be cost plus or fixed price, with each job issued a separate checking account. Blissed-out clients are moved to declare: "Mortgage your house if you have to, just make sure you use him."

"The proof in the pudding is that we are best friends." "Outstanding communication with architects. Costs were clearly delineated." "Never rejected responsibility." "Don't know anyone who has been disappointed." "Excellent workmen: personable and conscientious." "Dan is a great person to deal with. Someone you can trust. I wouldn't work with anyone else." "We were burned by another experience and were leery, but Dan made it fun." "Dan really researched the job."

Houck Construction Inc.   4   3.5   4.5   4.5
1531 Pontius Avenue, Los Angeles, CA 90025
(310) 235 - 2800   www.houckinc.com

Custom homes and remodels; estate management

The "something extra" that Houck Construction brings to the job is a combination of a sharply honed aesthetic sensibility and an "every nail perfect" delivery. For over a decade, this firm has handled mostly remodels and restorations of revered architects' work, earning high marks for being "completely invested" in its work. More recently, the company has branched out into high-end retail build out and design/build residential services. Houck also provides a full-service estate management service that will deal with everything from toppled mailboxes to loose shingles.

Clients tell us owner David Houck brings his personal authority to the craftsmanship of each job. Reports say Houck, a confessed gearhead and frustrated architect, has a fine technical understanding of all aspects of construction. Clients and architects recognize the value of his input in the "amazing" finished product. He oversees upwards of 50 employees, including management gurus, trade vets, design pros and administrative staff. Weekly job meetings keep the captain on the bridge, heads above water and the voyage on target. The firm subs out when possible, and will always get three bids to show.

"A real perfectionist." "Said three months and was done in three months." "Young and energetic." "The meticulous nature of his staff can make the project proceed slowly and the firm's work is pricey. As such, probably better suited to high-end clients (with the luxury of time and money)." "David has a good aesthetic sense for what's right for the house." "Introduced us to many high-quality craftspeople." "David gave prompt feedback, was reachable and was always courteous." "He made sure everything got completed properly, even if it had to be redone. He was helpful in fixing up things he didn't even do."

	Quality +	Cost $	Value ◆	Recommend? ★

J. Stuart Hilliard Inc.   5   4.5   4.5   5

520 South Sepulveda Boulevard, Los Angeles, CA 90049
(310) 471 - 7595

Design/build; residential remodels and new construction

Like Star Wars fans lining up in front of a theater on opening night, homeowners and architects are willing to queue up for J.S. Hilliard's Bob Glaus. Clients have almost a mystical respect for Glaus's "total honesty" and "creative ideas" that keeps them coming back to this master of the Force.

More often than not, the firm's "beyond excellent work" is design/build. $200,000 sets the floor for smaller projects such as master bath and bedroom additions, with celebrity estates reaching into the multimillions. JSH will attend to past clients for anything from maintenance to larger projects in New York or France. Most of the firm's work, however, is centered within twenty minutes of its offices in Brentwood and Bel Air. The firm has worked in a variety of styles, from an ultra-contemporary home featured on the Venice Artwalk to the restoration of the Waterman Mansion, an 1893 sandstone building that was one of the first grand Montecito estates. Currently, Glaus has his feet firmly planted in the sand, working on three beach estates. Clients unsettled on questions of style can show Glaus pictures, from which he will extract a common thread.

J. Stuart Hilliard founded his namesake company in 1953, coincidentally, the year Glaus was born. At the age of twenty, Glaus began freelancing for Hilliard, and eventually became a partner. The firm's reputation has remained so stellar over the years that clients and homeowners have come back five or six times. Glaus guides projects from design through completion, splitting days between the studio and job sites, where supers assist him. All of the supers have architecture backgrounds and all have clients who are fans. We hear team members "don't have an ego, never lose their tempers and are great diplomats with decorators." Actually, Glaus has a degree in psychology, which may explain the firm's phenomenal record of making clients feel comfortable.

JSH shies away from business manager relationships or projects intended to be self-monuments, preferring to work on a personal level with its clients. A flat fee for design gets Glaus drawing until the client is happy, at which point working drawings are produced and a fixed contract is established. The process is pricey, but clients remark, "The only fight I had with him was when I wanted to pay him more than he would charge me." According to sources, this firm is well worth the wait.

"We loved the project that Bob did for us so much that we asked him to build our house in Virginia." "It was imperative that our new home fit into the old neighborhood . . . and the house looks like it has always been on the block." "I consider them friends and regret I am out of projects to collaborate with them." "A true professional and a joy to work with over and over again." "Bob is smart, talented and holds himself to the highest standards. All his clients consider him a good friend when the job is done." "Very humble with clients and designers." "My husband is very exacting and we made many changes. JSH never was frustrated by this and always tried to do whatever we asked." "The most special things about Bob Glaus and JSH are the honesty, integrity and care they bring to every client relationship." "They have redone work a year later for no charge when it wasn't done up to their standards originally."

	Quality	Cost	Value	Recommend?
	✚	$	◆	★

JD Group, Inc   4.5   4.5   4   5

2048 Cotner Avenue, Los Angeles, CA 90025
(310) 575 - 5551 www.jdgroupinc.com

High-end custom construction, design/build and renovation

JD Group receives virtually unanimous acclaim. From homeowners and subcontractors to high-profile designers and even competitors, it seems everybody has something nice to say about this sophisticated, full-service firm. JD Group's sterling reputation was forged building large estate compounds, a tradition it continues today. Commissions for ground-up residences and whole-house renovations run from $1 million to $40 million for 4,000 to 50,000 square foot homes. JD Group navigates the full gamut of high-end architecture, from big name architects to ambitious up-and-comers. Provincial French houses of limestone are on the firm's resumé next to contemporary structures. The JD Group is especially praised for historical projects, exemplified by a ground-up Greek villa home featured in *Architectural Digest*.

Principal Dan McGhee leads the charge for JD Group, formed over a dozen years ago. Clients describe McGhee as "a man of unquestionable integrity, vast experience and practical advice." McGhee's fingerprints are visible on every project, which he entrusts to a talented pool of field players. Projects are staffed with professional managers, creative site supervisors and, if a project requires it, clerical support. With 60 employees, all quality-oriented and owner advocates, the firm has great depth. JD Group takes only eight to twelve projects at any one time, working typically in the West LA area. It will consider the right projects, however, from Orange County to Santa Barbara, even up to Monterey.

Clients often turn to JD Group first for their consulting prowess. Budgets are tamed in preconstruction, for which the firm bills hourly or as not to exceed a certain lump sum above the estimate. Contracts are negotiated and cost plus. We hear everything about this firm is high-end, including its costs.

"If we ever build a house again, the first person we would go to see is Dan McGhee, not an architect." *"Other construction people think really well of him."* *"Dan has impeccable taste and that reflects in his workers and subcontractors."* *"Dan stands behind his word."* *"Very honest and dependable. Able to follow through and handle unforeseen situations."*

Jeff Schatz Construction   3.5   3   4.5   4

21071 Wave View Drive, Topanga, CA 90290
(310) 455 - 2874

Renovations, design/build and additions

Loyal patrons purr that Jeff Schatz Construction is "just a dream." This inventive, "enthusiastic" firm is often entrusted by architects and designers to execute ambitious, tricky or totally new designs. It engages in full makeovers and additions to high-end residences, and also constructs pools. Schatz signs on to either a single large project up to $800,000 or divides its efforts among smaller remodels running in the neighborhood of $180,000. The firm works on Los Angeles' west side, from Hollywood to Malibu.

A graduate of local design/build firms, principal Jeff Schatz opened his own practice in 1987. His firm has remained small and focused, clients tell us, so that Schatz always "has enough time for you." Customers "adore" him for his "even" demeanor and transparent integrity. He has untangled clients' accounting mistakes on a number of jobs—to the clients' benefit. Known as a "great listener," Schatz has no problem accommodating the whims of the client when it comes to design modifications, even in the middle of construction. A "courteous" crew of site supervision and carpenters rounds out the Schatz experience.

Sources say Schatz's collaboration during the design process can be especially cost effective. An hourly fee is charged for preconstruction based on the scope of the project, and construction contracts are fixed.

"Jeff takes it all in stride." "Nervous about the floors going in, I called Jeff, who was in the airport with his daughter about to go on vacation. His plane was cancelled and he offered to come by and check things out. I said, 'If you're willing to come here, then I'm willing to pick you up.' So I did. I met his lovely daughter, he calmed things down, and they made the later flight!" "Really proud of his work." "My designer came up with something our cabinetmaker thought could never work and refused to make. Jeff convinced him that it could be done, and it was beautiful." "There's no downside to Jeff. He does right by you."

Kerze Construction Corporation   3   3   4   4
7312 Jamieson Avenue, Reseda, CA 91335
(818) 344 - 2936
Full-service general contractor

Tight schedules are no problem for Kerze Construction. This general contractor caters to clients who demand work done right in record time. Kerze constructs hillside Hollywood homes from scratch for celebs, performs serious renovations for just about anybody, will even do jobs as small as a door for a good old client. Loyal customers have turned to Kerze to complete projects as far away as Montana and Florida.

Owner Frank Kerze has been at it for over twenty years, and he personally oversees each project through to completion, utilizing the skills of a strong stable of subs. For Kerze, getting it right the first time starts with working closely with the architect and client to produce the most comprehensive plans and specs possible. The result is an up-front bid.

"Frank is like clockwork—everything was neat and clean." "It's a tight ship over there, no doubt about it. Kerze does it right."

Knickerbocker & Associates   4   3.5   4.5   4.5
827 Deep Valley Drive, Rolling Hills, CA 90274
(310) 212 - 3200   www.riverlandresorts.com/html%20pages/knickerbocker.html
Project and estate management, owner representation

From Colorado to the coast, Knickerbocker & Associates has consulted, built and managed hundreds of estates. Clients can't say enough about their "strength, intellect and diplomacy." The firm vets and oversees both the architect and general contractor to ensure a successful project. Upon completion, the firm's estate management and small projects division is available to maintain its good work.

Knickerbocker's management expertise runs the gamut from residential to commercial real estate, and includes forensic consulting on project turnaround and defect issues. Principal Craig Knickerbocker delights customers with his even-handed, personal approach. He formed the company in the early 1980s, and is now supported by fifteen employees. Judging by the recommendations that flow freely from celebrities and business leaders—and from the very design and construction professionals his watchful eye oversees—Knickerbocker's hard work and management expertise are truly exceptional. Rates fall in the standard range.

"Craig Knickerbocker was always a gentleman" "Excellent work—and he saved me a great deal of money." "Craig was pivotal to the successful completion of two homes."

Kuipers Design Inc.　　　　4.5　　4　　5　　5
23852 Pacific Coast Highway, Suite 459, Malibu, CA 90265
(310) 292 - 2772
High-end home building and renovation; design/build

Reports say the German-born contractor Charles Kuipers has a "down-to-earth" attitude that makes a fine foundation for a new home. Kuipers's small outfit designs, builds and renovates high-end custom homes around Malibu. The lion's share of the firm's work is in residential remodels, and clients rave that his crew is "thorough, fun and hardworking." Kuipers Design is especially noted for its architectural acumen with remodels—and for taking the initiative in ironing out details with the architects. We hear their design aesthetic slides toward the modern, where Kuipers does his best work.

At sixteen, Kuipers began working as an apprentice for a furniture and cabinet-maker in Germany. He came to the States more than twenty years ago and turned his talent for solving building puzzles into a well-regarded general contracting business. Clients find Kuipers "upbeat" and "tremendously honest," to the point that "I had to make sure he charged me for the extra things he did." Two field superintendents assist Kuipers, who remains center stage and "handles the subs beautifully and gets the best out of them." Budgets for remodels have a floor of $100,000, and design/build can run into seven figures. While the firm's costs are on par with other contractors to the jet set, clients tell us "you see every dollar" in the finished product.

"Exceeded expectations." "I wanted my daughter in San Francisco to use him. I begged her to let me fly him up." "Came in with a price and that's what it cost. We had one change order—our fault, of course." "His interest is in building. He worries more about the craftsmanship than the business." "Design is a meaning-ful word in the title of his company. He has a real feel for it." "We're close friends now. It isn't 'I'm finished, goodbye.' He's still there three years later." "He was on top of the subs and they all seemed to respect him."

Kulhanek Construction　　　　4.5　　4　　5　　4.5
2009 Calgary Lane, Los Angeles, CA 90077
(310) 474 - 6722　www.kulhanek.com
Highly personalized new construction, additions and renovations

After 40 years in the industry, John Kulhanek's name commands a measure of authority in the Los Angeles full-service contractor market. From West LA to the hills, Kulhanek Construction has built a tremendous variety of adobe, colonial, Mediterranean, Tuscan, Spanish and Country French homes. And although Kulhanek's crews have been tapped by discriminating LA personae for impressive projects, it's the individual's vision and passion that attract Kulhanek. Huge imper-sonal projects smack of banality to this firm. Kulhanek is fond of saying, "If the people themselves don't care, why should I?" In order to get a grounding in the client's aesthetic, Kulhanek encourages all his customers to put together a kit of their favorite designs for him to peruse. He also urges them to go on field trips to further explore their tastes. Young couples with a genuine interest in creating a personal aesthetic are considered at Kulhanek Construction alongside established business and entertainment clients. Once Kulhanek takes a client on board, his "serious commitment" to the project is evident in his "great dependability."

Flanked by a loyal crew of longtime professionals, Kulhanek takes care to work within the means of his company. Personal involvement means this firm takes on only the amount of work Kulhanek can personally visit in a day. Unique for a firm of this caliber, the "fair" prices are calculated with the client in mind: budgets can go from $150 to $500 a square foot. Many clients retain Kulhanek Construction outright for design and build services.

"Everybody knows John is really busy, but he's the kind of contractor who makes time for the project that interests him." "Very committed." "Kulhanek was dependable, not spectacular or flashy—just straight worth the money I paid."

Lattanzi Construction   5   4.5   4.5   5
550 Barrington Avenue, Los Angeles, CA 90049
(310) 699 - 3705

High-end residential construction

Clients sing the praises of this mini-major, a sole proprietorship that produces "amazing" work for vanguard architects like Tom Proctor. Chris Lattanzi limits his slate to keep a close eye on the product that bears his name. He takes on just two projects a year, each one an 8,000 to 12,000 square foot home budgeted in the $2 to $3 million ballpark, working with owners who have a strong connection to their architects. We're told the design-sensitive Lattanzi shows a reverence for scale and proportion that inspires flawless execution of historically correct homes. He also builds in contemporary design. The overwhelming majority of his work falls within the borders of Brentwood and Santa Monica.

Lattanzi hails from Portland, Oregon, where he was a carpenter by trade. After seeing his star rise as a supervisor for another builder in LA, he went solo. Clients confirm Lattanzi is a man of "great integrity, a good communicator" and someone they can "absolutely trust." They are most impressed with the great amount of pride Lattanzi takes in pitch-perfect construction. He himself says he can feel every beam in the floor when he's walking on it and can tell if a single one is out of whack. Not only does Lattanzi get along famously with his clients, they say he is "good at matching the personality of the homeowner" with everyone else he brings on the job. Ask anyone on a Lattanzi crew to do something, clients attest, and "they drop what they are doing and respond."

In the end, clients muse, "With Chris, it's not about contracting, it's about people." Whether negotiated, cost plus or fixed, contracts are set according to the method desired by the client. While Lattanzi's service comes at a premium, it "isn't as outrageous as some in his class."

"Chris is very earnest. His crew is wonderful. Everyone works hard. There are no shenanigans." "So honest about costs and timing. It's unheard of." "When my grandmother had a stroke, Chris walked the house with the physical therapist and outfitted the whole place to accommodate her condition before she returned from the hospital. It wasn't worth his time in dollars and cents, but he did it." "Chris is for people who are willing to pay a little extra for the best level of integrity, service, communication and relationship with subs." "Never had the subs argue about responsibility." "Introduced to a number of friends." "If there's ever a problem, he's there. We had a leak in a rainstorm and he was right there with a roofer and laborer."

	Quality	Cost	Value	Recommend?
	+	$	◆	★

LaVigne Construction
4 3.5 4.5 4.5

7570 East Calle Granada, Anaheim Hills, CA 92808
(818) 981 - 7330

Residential new construction, renovations

Principal Don LaVigne takes a "no-nonsense," "matter-of-fact" attitude in his presentation and "impressive" execution, clients tell us. LaVigne Construction primarily builds ground-up, high-end custom homes averaging three million dollars. Past design styles from this chameleon firm have ranged from Mediterranean to contemporary. The remainder of the firm's work is in smaller additions and renovations on homes of 5,000 square feet and above. We hear the firm allies nicely with architects in shaping a more aggressive budget during preconstruction.

LaVigne, the Harley-riding head of the company, is known as a builder's builder. He worked both for his father's contracting business and as a union carpenter, and clients say he knows every last trade inside and out. LaVigne promises to be the point person for the client and architect, tours each site daily, and is fully engaged in its progress. He is assisted by several layers of oversight on each project. Clients say he displays "good judgment" and "puts his heart and soul into solving problems" when, or before, they arise. Neither is he afraid of experimenting with new applications and products. The firm works on an open-book basis, and clients get full approval on the subs they hire. LaVigne is said to offer a realistic bid with alternative options in pricing.

"Don knows how to build a good, well-built house. Not excessive." "He gets multiple bids and is willing to work with the client on budget." "Don is a lovable teddy bear of a man." "He worked really, really well with the architect."

LG Development
3.5 3.5 4 4

18820 Pacific Coast Highway, Malibu, CA 90265
(310) 456 - 7776 www.lgdevelopment.com

Residential general contracting

The "well-integrated and intelligent team" at LG Development has garnered some very high praise. In 2002, the firm took home a Gold Medal from the Home Book Design Excellence Award for Custom Home Building in the "over 5,000 square feet" category.

Established in 1988, the firm specializes in construction of custom, ground-up residences between 7,000 and 20,000 square feet, as well as the odd remodel and even some hotel work. LG takes on about ten projects at any given time and regularly takes on work from Newport to Monterey. We hear this firm leaves no technological slack to pick up, outfitting all job sites with PDAs, digital cameras and laptops to send out progress reports to clients as far away as Indonesia. Acting as a communication nexus between the client and the architect is key to LG's strategy for creating a "harmonious environment" in which to live. Clients note the solidness of an LG home—the result of a firm dedicated to sorting out every minute detail.

President Ron Levy presides over a team of site supervisors at LG. While Levy shares the playbook with the client, the firm's vice president quarterbacks the field. While giving 110 percent might be cliche on the gridiron, Levy's effort to satisfy a client's desire for an elevator—despite the architect's insistence that it was an impossibility—illustrates the firm's 110 percent approach. But such conflicts are rare, since clients say LG allies well with design professionals.

Contracts are usually cost plus or a variety thereof, whatever makes the client comfortable. For large projects, we're told LG can often beat the "usual suspect" contractors in price, while for smaller jobs costs are par for the course. Clients say LG gets value out of every dollar spent and is unwavering in its standards.

"Encourages communication." "They're very, very hands on. To get the most out of it you really have to be willing to engage in the process." "It's not a fight to get this firm to use the best materials throughout." "Ron comes to a project with not so much design ideas as design opportunities. He's dedicated to building a better box." "All operations are well-heeled."

M&A Builders   4   3.5   4.5   5

2510 West 171st Street, Torrance, CA 90504
(310) 324 - 2739
Custom construction, tear-downs, remodeling

This low-key firm leaves jobs on a high note, say the satisfied customers who sing its praises. Trained as a carpenter, sole proprietor Bill Morris specializes in tear-down renovations, typically going down to the home's footprint. Clients say the firm "does wonderful work" in the traditional scheme. Morris limits his projects to a couple at a time in the environs of Brentwood, Pacific Palisades and Santa Monica, typically ranging from 4,000 to 6,000 square feet. Morris does a small amount of remodeling and, due to strong word-of-mouth, must turn down as many jobs as he takes.

Morris oversees projects personally, lending a consistency of quality and level of investment clients find comforting. They describe him as an "honest, no-nonsense" person who is "difficult to ruffle" in the face of the inevitable surprises of renovation. We hear he stays on top of things and will smooth out any issue right away. Morris brings his own finish crew and is known to hire "good subs." Offering a can-do attitude at prices that clients can do, we're told M&A's work is a terrific value.

"After a big earthquake he was at our door at 8 AM to see if everything was all right months after the job was done! Our chimney was the only one left standing on the block. The only thing he built that fell was a soap dish." "He watched everything, was never overtaxed and here when he needed to be." "I knew he could walk the walk, not just talk the talk, because he was a tradesperson." "Doesn't pass the buck. It definitely stops with him." "It was the most fun process. The subs were so welcoming and the kids loved hanging around them." "Bill takes responsibility. Always says 'yes, we can do this.'" "After seeing him every day for ten months, we missed him."

Marmol Radziner + Associates

2902 Nebraska Avenue, Santa Monica, CA 90404
(310) 264 - 1814   www.marmol-radziner.com
Engaging, contemporary design/build services with seamless execution

See Marmol Radziner + Associates's full report under the heading Architects

McKiernan Contracting Corp.   4   4   4   4

8423 Fountain Avenue, Los Angeles, CA 90069
(323) 656 - 9919
Custom design/build, remodel

McKiernan Contracting Corporation crossed the continent to bring its New York City high-rise experience and engineering expertise to high-end residential projects in the City of Angels. Sources tell us the firm has adapted marvelously to local conditions, constructing and remodeling gravity-defying hillside residences with tennis courts on terraced lots in Hollywood Hills, not to mention ground-up projects from the beach communities to the Platinum Triangle of West LA. The firm looks to work with established architects and designers on significant projects. McKiernan is also willing to do smaller budgeted jobs down to $70,000 in certain cases. While the firm has proved itself on contemporary projects, McKiernan also looks for more classical commissions where his substantial training in Italy can be used. The company also has a commercial division for tenant improvements.

We hear the firm controls the volume of jobs so "hands-on" headliner Kieran McKiernan can be on site every day to fill in the gaps. McKiernan is praised for his highly effective habits: he'll "put things on paper," "keep people disciplined," and get in and out as quickly as possible. He is known as a straightforward bearer of bad news, believing the more you educate clients and the "more they are involved in the process, the more comfortable they are to take risks, and they won't feel slighted about what they wanted in the end." The firm's preconstruction consulting creates real, solid budgets, revealing to the client any bottom line-busting numbers.

"The planning stage seemed to take forever. But once they started I was impressed by the pace of the work." "It seemed like Kieran was always there. I wouldn't have believed it, but it's true."

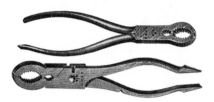

Mercados Construction   4   3   5   5
5812 Lubao Avenue, Woodland Hills, CA 91367
(818) 346 - 2658
Residential new construction and renovation

Owner Jesse Mercados has been called the "hardest working owner in the business." His family-owned-and-operated firm prides itself on "one on one" customer service and a "quick reply" policy for any issue that may arise. The firm's dedication is such that it is often the first stop for clients on a project—acting as the construction manager from the design phase until the move-in date, and taking on maintenance chores for years after. Be it a 20,000 square foot ground-up residence or a $27,000 studio build-out, we hear Mercados is indefatigable in its search for client satisfaction.

Insiders tell us Mercados's experience in working almost every trade means he knows personally how to build a house. His corporate education and high-end contracting know-how were developed during a stint as a project superintendent at Fort Hill. Mercados enjoys working in any style, from Tuscan to Georgian. Mercados and his wife, who manages the office, are bilingual, an advantage clients say does not go unnoticed in the firm's awe-inspiring ability to coordinate workers.

The firm is said to be quite budget-conscious. On top of hard construction costs, it takes a set fee for principal Mercados's time based on the estimated duration of the project. We hear savings on markups throughout the project, especially with changes, can be substantial, as long as they don't significantly delay the project.

"Fantastic organization. Worked great with the lady of the house." "Was quick to reply to any issues during and after the project." "I have had the opportunity to work with many of the finest contractors in the LA area. I prefer to work with Mercados Construction because they strive to provide excellent craftsmanship and focus on the needs of a few chosen clients at a time." "My project came in ahead of schedule."

	Quality	Cost	Value	Recommend?
	✚	$	◆	★

Michael Russo Corporation

4	4	4	4

1624 West Anaheim Street, Harbor City, CA 90710
(310) 539 - 9473

Residential remodeling; condo remodeling specialists

Well known in established Los Angeles circles, the company has built a reputation for a superior work ethic and highly successful tear-downs and remodels of homes and condos. The firm often takes jobs from demolition to post-construction maintenance, and we hear Russo even goes so far as to return to a client's home after twenty years to repair a light fixture.

Remodels average from $750,000 to $1 million and are often located in a small swath encompassing the Wilshire corridor. Insiders report that few in the trade are as attuned to special challenges of condo remodeling as this firm. Russo can provide design capabilities in-house and is open-minded on style and the client's choice of designer. The firm was even commissioned to relocate two Vermont barns as showpieces for a new estate, perfectly intact, from the East to the West Coast.

Clients tell us the firm follows up and follows through, and that owner Michael Russo himself shows up at each job site daily. Russo's office staff, supers, finishers and in-house plumbers contribute to the "get it right the first time" attitude. Happy customers are quick to recommend Russo—in fact, the firm has often visited the same condo complex multiple times, as the good word has passed from owner to owner. Russo's fees are described as reasonable for the high quality of his work.

"I've worked with plenty of builders, but condos are a different story. You have to have the know-how to maneuver around an entire extra set of restrictions. I would recommend Russo Corp highly for condo remodels."

Mike Galper General Building & Engineering

3.5	3.5	4	4

2214 South Beverly Drive, Los Angeles, CA 90034
(310) 837 - 3356

Mike Galper strives to make each home he works on a unique and lasting creation—a leakproof piece of art. The firm takes on only a couple projects at a time, located mostly in Beverly Hills and Bel Air. Versed in a variety of aesthetics, the firm shines in the Italianate style. Designers and clients bring in this small, dedicated firm for extensive renovations and ground-up residences often in excess of $2 million. And yes, Galper is fanatical about waterproofing.

The son of a landscape architect/contractor, Galper grew up in the business. He has been a licensed general contractor for 25 years and has focused on high-end residential work since 1989. Galper is the key figure on each project, aided by project managers. The firm's reputation for interfacing well with consultants is not lost on clients, who sign Galper up early in the process. Preconstruction minimums run $10,000, billed on a time-and-material basis. References report Galper is available 24 hours a day, with his cell and pager always on.

"Mike's not in it for the money." "He's really intent on making the process work with the client's lifestyle."

Minardos Construction & Associates

4	4	4	4.5

2800 28th Street, Suite 170, Santa Monica, CA 90405
(310) 450 - 6900   www.minardos.com

Residential and commercial construction and renovation

Don't let the hip, progressive aesthetic of Minardos Construction fool you—this experienced GC brings the efficiency of its commercial operations to custom residences as well. An evolution of Binder-Minardos Builders, a firm established fifteen years ago, Minardos Construction tackles assignments that range from tenant improvements to galleries to high-end custom homes. While the firm's resume includes notable architects and designers, it prides itself on working well with young, fresh talents—as long as communication is clear. Minardos also cites "joy and humor" as two on a long list of governing values, which should be a clue to the joie de vivre infusing this firm's blend of art and architecture.

A graduate of the Wharton Business School, principal George Minardos pursued a degree in architecture before his passion for building eclipsed his interest in pure design. References tell us this foundation enables Minardos to work well with architects. We hear the firm prefers to jump into projects early, during the strategic stage, providing insightful budgetary advice and details on the reality of executing challenging design elements. All projects have full-time field supervisors and project managers with GC experience. The firm is technically oriented, with DSL links, computers and schedule software on-site, allowing for immediate electronic communication and processing of paperwork. In-house carpenters and laborers round out the team. Minardos Construction's preconstruction services run from conceptual to schematic. The firm also provides risk analysis, with experience in hillside building.

Minardos Construction's familiarity with contemporary materials, such as steel and concrete, can be seen in its gallery and museum work, including the Santa Monica Museum of Art and Huntington Library. In 2002, Minardos captured the Golden Nugget Award for best Custom Home, in the 3,500 to 6,000 square foot category. All residential work is done at a negotiated fee.

"It's rare to be able to laugh on a job, especially a job with tight deadlines. But the mood just seemed lighter with them around." "Artists with calendars, it's amazing!" "If you look at mod, hillside homes from the last five years—they either did it or they studied it."

New West Construction Company   4   3.5   4.5   4.5

2326 Tuna Canyon Road, Topanga, CA 90290
(310) 455 - 3997

Tear-downs, additions, remodels

Integrity is a key concern of New West Construction, which keeps electrical, plumbing, carpentry and foundation work in-house. Fifteen years ago, Ken Hoff and Fernando Calisto created this partnership to take on ground-up construction, tear-downs, remodels and additions. Keeping essential trades on staff, instead of subbing them out, lends New West the hands-on agility to meet deadlines like clockwork. The firm will facilitate design services if and when necessary. Average budgets fall between $500,000 and $600,000, with a minimum near $50,000 for new clients. New West stays on the west side—concentrating on Pacific Palisades, Brentwood, Santa Monica and especially the Hollywood Hills areas. We're told the firm tirelessly explores possibilities, tweaking and enhancing—either in cost efficiency or aesthetic—every aspect of a project. Designers and clients looking for a flexible working relationship find New West fun to involve in the process.

One of the two principals always has the reins on any given job. Hoff often spends time on schematic layouts while Calisto, with a background in design, often focuses on the finish work. Between the two, they communicate well with both architect and owner, catching things other less-involved contractors tend to miss. In the heat of construction, they can whip up detailed drawings for everyone's approval. The comfort zone clients say they feel with New West's executives extends to the firm's in-house personnel and selection of subs. These tradesmen are tidy, professional and, most notably, honest—a relief for anyone living through a renovation.

Insiders say the firm's abundant in-house talent allows it to better control costs, as well as time and quality elements. In addition, its willingness to exercise options means New West works wonders for the budget, without disrespecting design.

"I have worked with other GCs, but Fernando is a perfectionist." "They are your best friends." "Not condescending." "I can just do sketches for them and they know what to do with the finishes." "I think they do a great job, but sometimes they can be hard to get ahold of."

Oliver Garrett Construction   4.5   4   4.5   5

881 Warren Avenue, Venice, CA 90291
(310) 581 - 5454   www.olivergarrettconstruction.com
New custom construction and historic renovation

Oliver Garrett believes in "the three p's"—practicality, professionalism and personability. From a 1910 cottage renovation with a modern twist to high-concept new constructions, Garrett offers full-service contracting and interior remodeling to top design professionals. "As thorough as they come," Garrett often links up with architects who are equally obsessed with the little details. Yet ego doesn't drive these projects—clients do.

Oliver Garrett graduated from UCLA in 1977 with an arts degree. He worked for his brother's contracting company while establishing relationships with young design talents coming out of SCI-Arc in the early 1980s that would later form the nucleus of his professional circle. He has been on his own for nearly fifteen years, overseeing a small crew with the help of right-hand man Hills Sutton, another former "art school brat." The firm takes on only two jobs at a time, so either Garrett or Sutton directs each gig full-time.

We're told quality control starts early on with this firm. Garrett likes to swing into a project's saddle as the first gun to wrangle in budget. We hear for every task the firm shows its clients options, and works hard to fine-tune the product throughout. Project budgets run from $250,000 to $3.5 million. Work takes place mainly in Hollywood Hills, West LA, Venice and Malibu for clients who don't flinch at high-end prices.

"I was impressed by his instinct in last-minute choices with architects. He has really good taste and ran his crew efficiently." "Always informed us what cost ramifications were." "Can't tell where work began, feels like part of the rest of the house." "He's not chauvinistic when working with women, whether they're owners or architects." "The firm comes organized and prepared throughout the process." "My neighbor really liked him. He kept them happy so I never had to talk to them." "The crew kept the site clean and organized." "Most people admire the quality of his work."

Pacific Design Estates Construction, Inc.   4   3.5   4.5   4.5

3198 Airport Loop Drive, Suite D2, Costa Mesa, CA 92626
(714) 428 - 1100   www.pacificdesignestates.com
Construction management and residential general contracting

Orange County golden boy David Close creates settings of "beauty and elegance" primarily along the coastal hillsides. Pacific Design Estates

Construction evolved five years ago out of the Newport Beach spec-home firm Pacific Design Estates, known for its premier homes utilizing the best locations, architects and materials. The company's general contracting and growing construction management operation primarily focuses on new construction in the Newport/Huntington Beach areas. It also tackles major remodels and is establishing a presence in Pasadena. Homes range from 5,000 to 17,000 square feet, and budgets start at $1.2 million.

Clients tell us Close sees the big picture from style to budget. They say his knowledge, reputation and relationship with Orange County development puts him in a position to not only educate them on requirements and procedures, but also to expedite the process.

While the firm does bid, it prefers assembling a team out of the gates, where budget can catch up with concept. Pacific Design is said to expose itself to different ideas, products and subcontractors to come up with the best bang for the buck. Clients say it gives up-front, realistic prices and doesn't bill for its preconstruction services until plans are filed for permit.

"David is the best. No one is more knowledgeable about how to get a dream home built in Orange County, without all the nonsense."

Paster Construction   4.5   4   4.5   5
30941 West Agoura Road, Suite 232, Westlake Village, CA 91361
(818) 889 - 3291
Residential construction and remodeling

Stars of the Los Angeles architecture scene turn to this grounded general contractor to keep their jobs well marshaled and their budgets under control. For over fifty years the Paster family has shepherded high-end custom remodels and additions, and a smaller amount of new construction. Jobs start at a minimum of $500,000—however, the firm limits its volume to no more than five at a time. Projects tend to cluster around LA's west side, so principal Gary Paster stays within quick driving distance of every job site.

In the LA area since 1966, Paster is a student of architectural history and travels across the country soaking in design elements. Clients tell us they benefit from this appreciation of the fine details. The firm's experience encompasses many architectural styles, from the challenge of contemporary to the refinement of traditional. Paster insists most successful projects must work from the beginning, and preaches his involvement early on. References say the firm brings a practical side to projects to determine real-world costs, and will coordinate with other consultants to make drawings as tight as possible before construction. The modest-sized firm of 30 includes some excellent foremen, one of whom is dedicated solely to servicing past clients. This level of expertise and service generates considerable expense, but a healthy roster of design pros don't mind paying for the peace of mind afforded by hiring this superb veteran firm.

"I have worked with Paster Construction as a client for over twenty years. The work has always been of the highest, most reliable quality." "A solid all-around firm." "The best and most honest contractor around. They find solutions to thorny problems." "Dedicated and loyal."

Paul White General Contractor   4.5   3.5   5   5
4127 Marcasel Avenue, Los Angeles, CA 90066
(310) 397 - 1593   www.paulwhitegc.com
Custom home construction, remodeling, condo renovations

Trustworthy is a word that just keeps popping up in references for this firm. Paul White General Contractor is praised for never forgetting the custom service aspect of custom home building. Started as a small company in 1985, this GC firm's projects run the gamut from new custom home construction to renovations/additions, including kitchen/bath remodels and condo build-outs. The firm takes on ten to fifteen jobs at a time within the zones of the west side, the San Fernando Valley and Malibu. New commissions are generally $200,000 and up, but clients are often repeat customers.

White himself keeps an ear to the ground throughout, offering "creative and thoughtful suggestions and advice" from concept to completion. His agreeable, earnest persona keeps owners, vendors, trades and designers in touch and on the same page. Job sites are skippered by his well-regarded "job captains." Patrons tell us White's crew go above and beyond—these "courteous and clean" workers will also look after the dog and bring out the trash can.

Contracts may be negotiated or bid, with preconstruction analysis credited back. Prices are considered a terrific value, leaving fans to wonder, "What more can you ask for?"

"Paul sat down with me and went over everything." "PWGC consistently meets every expectation for quality, schedule, service and trustworthiness." "Very professional and on time. Extremely happy with all aspects of service received." "I would not consider hiring another contractor for upcoming projects unless Mr. White was busy. Even then I would ask for recommendations from his firm." "For a renovation, there was minimal disruption in the rest of our household." "Paul can offer useful suggestions for improvement in design."

Peter McCoy Construction   5   4.5   4.5   4.5
136 El Camino Drive, Beverly Hills, CA 90212
(310) 278 - 3503
Estate construction and renovation

For big-budget performance with soul, this is the real McCoy. The choice of *Forbes*-profiled executives and A-list entertainers, Peter McCoy Construction executes massive projects, often new construction of 10,000 to 50,000 square foot residences or extensive gut renovations. Projects are typically on LA's west side and architecturally ambitious. Often brought in shortly after the architect, McCoy enjoys jumping into projects in which individual personalities are vividly expressed.

It's not surprising then, that this "society contracting firm" would be toplined by a man who was the one-time chief of Sotheby's West Coast operations and married to heiress Kacey Doheny. The non-adversarial Peter McCoy runs his firm with an eye on every project and every client. He limits his jobs so as to maximize his collaboration with clients and designers. We hear he tends to ask questions that aren't asked and head off problems before they creep up. Each job has its own project manager and superintendent, in addition to McCoy's supervision. The firm performs some of its own carpentry and concrete work and subs out the rest. While McCoy's projects represent a slice of the highest of the high end, he's known to be very considerate of budget discussions.

"Top-shelf crackerjack. As good as anyone out there." "Their entire team takes on a wonderful 'can do' attitude." "McCoy's paper documentation is outstanding. And there's no finger pointing." "Delightful guy." "Extremely high end." "As good as other big kahuna contractors but for ten percent less. His company's not a factory." "Big job. Easygoing foreman."

Peter Vracko   4.5   4.5   4   5
2005 North Sycamore Avenue, Los Angeles, CA 90068
(323) 883 - 0022 vracko@pacbell.net
Challenging residential commissions

We hear Peter Vracko knows "how to build a house with his bare hands." With his skilled crew of fourteen, Vracko performs spectacular gut renovations and restorations of some of the oldest properties in Los Angeles, as well as ground-up residential and commercial work. Projects that promise challenges and intriguing possibilities are greater considerations than size or budget for this firm. Principal Peter Vracko is known to have his finger on the pulse of LA design, and as word spreads, this firm finds itself doing more design/build than ever before. Aesthetically, Vracko is a purist who will not fight the character of the existing structure. We hear some of his signature work is in Japanese/Asian, Spanish and Mediterranean styles. The firm works mainly in Beverly Hills, Hollywood and Malibu.

Vracko grew up on a Washington State ranch and ended up building high-end homes. At the age of twenty he started his own company, and upon landing in LA quickly bumped into interior designer Craig Wright, for whom he has been building houses ever since—including Wright's own home. Limiting projects to two to three at a time, Vracko himself interacts on every level to keep the machine well oiled. Clients credit this "problem solver" as much for giving options as for his organization. "Fantastic" site managers keep expedited schedules on target. We hear that most of Vracko's crew has been with him for ten years, performing high-end plaster, masonry, cement and concrete work, and bringing a special expertise to hillside/structural issues. The firm also claims a landscape designer within its ranks, making it truly full service.

We're told Vracko "lives and sleeps his projects," a fact that has clients sleeping easier, even if it's in a construction site. The firm is reputed to be especially conscientious of these live-in clients. Job sites are clean and projects completed on a timely basis. Cost plus contracts reflect estimates backed by bids, and aren't for the faint of heart.

"Peter didn't just want quality construction, he also wanted the aesthetic to be right." "The city inspector said it was the best job he'd ever seen." "Peter had the foresight to know what I wanted and the design ideas to implement it." "Time frame was right. Run-over was minimal." "Peter kept his appointments, was always available and if he didn't have the answer, he would come back with a fistful of catalogues to get one." "At the end of the day I didn't come home to a disaster."

Plaskoff Construction   4   3   5   5

19301 Ventura Boulevard, Tarzana, CA 91356
(818) 654 - 2737   www.plaskoff.com

Design/build and general contracting

Matt Plaskoff's star soared when he was tapped to become lead Construction Consultant on ABC's *Extreme Makeover Home Edition* (2004). The appointment stirred up a flurry of media attention, including a cover story on his company, Plaskoff Construction, in *Remodel Magazine* this year. It turns out Plaskoff's reality TV fame has a basis in reality: his consummate professionalism and indefatigable energy. His firm specializes in residential renovations and remodels of around $250,000, but a couple of smaller $50,000 remodels and $4 million ground-up estates are undertaken each year. The majority of Plaskoff's work occurs on the west side of LA, from the San Fernando Valley to Pacific Palisades.

Plaskoff put himself through college doing finish carpentry and electrical work and, after working for another GC, realized the need for a company to provide executive-level service. Today, Plaskoff says of his company, "We have turned the complicated ritual of building and remodeling into a team quest for excellence." Perfectionist clients find the energetic Plaskoff to be a man after their own heart. Project managers armed with the latest digital technology provide the thrust for each job while Plaskoff and his office provide the anchor. The firm subs out all trades to hand-picked workers. Clients find the work to be professionally and efficiently executed and praise the good follow-up and maintenance. A phase I design fee is based on estimated budget and phase II construction contracts are fixed price. While Plaskoff isn't inexpensive, the firm charges standard rates for the upscale market, and will design to budget.

"Not only is the finished product spectacular, but the company was a pleasure to deal with each step of the way." "Every day we notice something new about the fine quality of the workmanship." "We found the entire crew to be very enthusiastic, hard working and detail oriented." "Tremendous success awaits you!"

Rac Design Build   4.5   3.5   5   5

3006 North Coolidge Avenue, Los Angeles, CA 90039
(323) 663 - 9898   www.racdb.com

Ambitious design/build

Rac Design/Build has long been a favorite of LA's premier architects, but clients can now turn directly to the firm for ambitious design/build projects. Customers rave about the team of "extremely professional and creative artisans" spearheaded by principals Rick and Tracy Cortez. While the company shines in new construction, it shows particular bravura in remodels. We hear the firm's design/build agility allows it to better roll with the punches often associated with tearing apart and putting together an existing home—and to fast-track the result.

Upon graduating SCI-Arc in 1990, Rick couldn't pass up the hands-on satisfaction of building, so he started a small firm. Tracy, also schooled in architecture at SCI-Arc, joined him in 1995. We hear they compliment each other greatly. While Rick works in the field and Tracy in the office, they often volley design ideas back and forth, their tastes often occupying the same aesthetic ground. The Cortezes bring a nice sense of proportion and a fresh understated look that aligns itself with the integrity of the site and vision of the client. We hear Rick always keeps an eye open for ways to improve and transform a project as it progresses. Rac is known to fawn over even the smallest details. A shop crew assists in fabricating cabinets, making furniture and installing just about anything.

Design and construction are contracted on a cost-plus basis. Budgets ballpark at $500,000 to $750,000, with a quarter of a million minimum. The firm takes a limited number of projects at a time, the better to oversee them. Rates are expensive, and sources warn that clients unwilling to pay for perfect execution "should look elsewhere."

"Every client should be as lucky as I was to have had an architect/designer like Rac Design." "I always trusted Rick's design choices and knew I was in good hands in every respect." "Rick and Tracy were always there. They are very ethical and productive." "I love to work with them. They are inspiring to be around." "I recommend them highly, but the client has to want quality and attention to detail." "Very creative—artists in their own right."

	Quality	Cost	Value	Recommend?
	✚	$	◆	★

RJ Design & Construction Inc.   3   3   4   3.5

9903 Santa Monica Boulevard, Suite 115, Beverly Hills, CA 90212
(310) 274 - 7200

Design/build, interior design

Originally established in Los Angeles in 1973 as an interior design company, this firm now specializes in sleek, livable design/build of high-end residential new construction, additions and remodels. It does commercial work too, with all projects ranging from $50,000 to $800,000. Five to six projects are on RJ's slate at any one time. Many are in LA, although the firm takes jobs across Southern California, from San Diego to Santa Barbara.

We're told the strength of the company is the design foundation of principal Ron Jacobs, who ushers clients from concept to completion. He oversees a smallish firm of eight, including supervisors at every job site. RJ Design is known to get creative with the customer, and it also offers interior design services. Its trademark style tends toward the traditional, but the firm has also worked on some modern projects. Jobs are cost plus and rates are standard.

RLD Heltzer Construction   4   4   4   4.5

9428 Dayton Way, Second Floor, Beverly Hills, CA 90210
(310) 278 - 6699

Property development, construction management, high-end general contracting

When a time crunch is a major factor, many high-powered Angelenos turn to RLD Heltzer. We hear this firm helps select property, match a client with the right design professionals and consultants, and contracts the general construction. For those looking for a fully formed home, RLD Heltzer also develops high-end spec homes. The firm takes on four to five major projects a year in the $3 to $6 million range, with a small-job division to care for existing clients and five to six $150,000 to $200,000 remodels a year.

Partners Rob Heltzer and Bobby Dean come to RLD with owner's rep backgrounds, and we hear they complement each other's talents well. Heltzer administers communication between clients, engineers and supers with a nonreactionary approach, while Dean works with the subcontractors to resolve the technical challenges of the building process. The two are known to excel at expediting the process and be highly responsive to their patrons. Whether brought on board in the preconstruction or bidding phase, RLD produces very detailed bids and can contribute cost-saving measures. A retainer secures the firm's real estate/preconstruction services.

"For a remodel that was not just cosmetic but to repair earthquake damage, they were the right people to do all the consulting and contracting." "Could carry through on everything. Came up with good suggestions. Worked well with other consultants." "Rob came up with slight modifications that were better without intruding on the design." "No friction between consultants." "Came in on budget. Quality compared very favorably to other contractors I've used."

Robin Thom Construction   4   3   5   4.5

23852 Pacific Coast Highway, Suite 915, Malibu, CA 90265
(310) 457 - 2407   www.robinthom.com

High-end custom homes, renovations and consultations

Robin Thom is passionate about evolving a new ethic for contractors. With over 30 years of work experience, a master's degree, eight years as an architect, and two years training in the 3D CAD design program, Thom has the depth of intellect to back up his ambition. This innovator advocates putting as much information in the client's hands as possible, providing spreadsheets down to every nut and bolt. Toward that end, Robin Thom Construction has spawned two ancillary companies—a consulting firm for customers, and a free consumer services website to help educate clients on how not to get "fleeced." Not surprisingly, reports describe Thom as a "client's contractor."

References find Thom "smart and inventive" and relish the personal attention he pays to their projects. His work has a cutting-edge "left coast" aesthetic, but Thom is only too happy to be a chameleon to his clients' desires. His "hands on" site philosophy allows him to take on only about five projects at a time, but it's quality and satisfaction that matter to this perfectionist. Years ago he cut back from a much higher volume to choose only jobs on which he could really make a difference. Three office and two field personnel support him in day-to-day operations. From the sunny southern beach towns to the Palisades to Ventura county, Thom has made a name for himself as a problem solver, so much so that he's in high demand as a "pinch hitter" for failed and corrupt contractors.

This company prides itself on making realistic initial cost analysis and then delivering a high-end aesthetic on budget. Thom will credit his pre-construction analysis fee to the construction contract if hired. For the building phase he works on a fixed management oversight fee that is based on the project's estimated duration. "A telephone call is not a change," declares Thom, and upgrades on materials and other changes that keep the schedule don't impact his fees. Given this philosophy, the firm is very competitive at its level for delivering a high-end aesthetic on a fair budget.

"Robin has extraordinary artistic and design sense." "Timely, trustworthy workmen." "He can do something imaginative." "Robin's a perfectionist. Great about details." "Very happy with the experience. He had brilliant ideas."

S&N Construction   3.5   3   4.5   4.5
170 East Fillmore Street, Pasadena, CA 91105
(626) 792 - 2020

Historic restoration

Top designers trust this niche contractor for restoration work and renovation of old, historic homes. We're told S&N resuscitates residences strangled by successive insensitive remodels and recaptures the old character, rekindling the property's past glory. In addition to being expert at matching moldings and replicating master craftsmanship, we hear principal Nate Pugh, whose background is in mechanical engineering, can also execute a designer's wild ideas with great verve.

Sierra Coastal Builders Inc.   4   4   4   4
2222 Careful Avenue, Agoura Hills, CA 91301
(818) 991 - 7655

Gut renovations

Sierra Coastal principal John Kayton cut his contracting teeth on the east coast, resuscitating Pennsylvania colonial homes and outfitting Manhattan penthouses. Kayton's Southern California incarnation involves commercial as well as high-end residential work, from art galleries to estates, Spanish-style to mid-century modern. He and his small firm are geared toward gut renovations of $300,000 and up. In addition to executing the plans of notable area designers, the firm offers design/build services. We hear the firm does its homework, working closely with clients and thoughtfully tailoring the new architecture with the old character of the house. It takes on only three projects at a time, working mostly in the neighborhoods of Brentwood and Beverly Hills.

Kayton takes the reins of each project, with a site foreman and carpenters working under his umbrella. The firm performs its own foundation, framing, siding and finish carpentry work, controlling the pace of the job and building the bones of house. We hear that, to a man, Kayton's crew really takes pride in its work and keeps the site ship-shape. Clients especially appreciate the firm's commitment to getting families back into their homes on schedule, even if it means running extra crews. We're told the company T-shirts sum up both the nature of Sierra Coastal Builders and the quality of its work, proclaiming "Built to Live." Detailed contracts frame the firm's not insubstantial numbers.

"He is a god." "I'm a producer, so time is a factor in everything I do. But John gave me the timetables I needed to make this house painless." "Little guy without a big office, but more effective than the big guys." "John is there every day."

Stephen Bloom Construction   4   4   4   4
3934 Coral Place, Calabasas, CA 91302
(818) 225 - 1880

High end custom homes and renovations

Clients credit this general contractor with "problem-free" projects built "beyond our expectations" in record time. Stephen Bloom Construction commissions include master bed/bath remodels of $100,000 and new custom residences into the millions. Homeowners may approach Bloom with blueprints in hand or with a strong conceptual game plan, in which case he will coach them through the process, recommending one of the A-list area architects with whom he works. While its portfolio includes contemporary projects, the firm's outlook has traditional underpinnings. The company works mostly in Malibu, West LA, Bel Air and Pacific Palisades.

We hear principal Stephen Bloom can make clients blush like a rose, indulging them as if they were the firm's only priority. Clients add there's a strong family feeling to Bloom Construction. Bloom's uncle was an architect and his father a building inspector and builder. Today, his wife keeps the "well-coordinated" office in order and is known for "superb" follow-up. Bloom himself is described as "good natured" and "constantly attentive to the smallest detail," serving as an approachable, understanding presence throughout the process.

We hear Bloom surrounds himself with a team of field personnel and stable of subcontractors who have been with him since Bloom Construction's beginnings nearly fifteen years ago. Clients say this group "to a man, was professional, friendly, neat and fast." Moreover, sources tell us they not only invite Stephen into their homes, but they would happily have prospective clients in to sell them on the company.

"They worked at a pace I had previously associated only with film crews." "Stephen submitted a list of very detailed questions regarding our plans, and was the only contractor to do so." "If there was a question about grout, a grout expert materialized the next day with a bulletproof solution." "I can't imagine anyone else willing to speak with me at six in the morning or late at night and not hesitate to come out on a Saturday to 'check things out.'" "Always met each challenge and provided solutions, not excuses."

Synergy Builders Inc.   5   4.5   4.5   5
7666 Woodrow Drive, Los Angeles, CA 90046
(323) 876 - 8897

High-end large-scale renovation

Synergy is more than a name, clients rave—it's an approach to building. What distinguishes this firm, we're told, is the esprit de corps that partners Tom Klinck and Peter Kratz engender throughout the entire building team. Homeowner, design professional and craftsman all have a strong sense of being appreciated—and the synergy really flows from there. A hands-on, meticulous firm, Synergy takes on one main project at a time, usually lasting a year. Its expertise is mainly in serious renovations up to $9 million. Older clients can call on the firm for smaller, highly creative projects.

The two principals go back 32 years. Klinck, described by clients as "verbal and cerebral," received his Ph.D. in business administration from UCLA in behavioral sciences and interpersonal relationships, where he met Kratz. Kratz's "intuitive and instinctive" building skills caught the eye of high-end designers and architects early on—Mark Rios for one, who conscripted him to work on his projects. While business boomed after that, the company has stayed small, with an assistant in the office and another in the field. Clients tell us the duo shows patience and good judgment. The two candidly communicate every step (or pitfall) of the process and present a range of options in decision-making.

References say Klinck and Kratz see their work as an artistic process as much as a mechanical one. They don't get frustrated with changes but look for solutions, and are willing to work with a client who likes to refine and rethink a project as they go. The firm has a wide-ranging resume of projects and it enjoys executing a diversity of styles. Synergy contracts are cost plus with an overall ceiling price. The firm keeps a stable of several subs in each trade to keep everyone honest and price-competitive. While certainly not cavalier about costs, we're told this firm's talents demand a commensurate level of financial commitment.

"I adore Tom and Peter. They have totally undone my previously negative impression of contractors." "Twelve years in our house and we continue to see Tom and Peter professionally as well as personally." "Tom had the generosity to teach me throughout the process. We would drive for hours to pick out marble so I wouldn't make a mistake." "Old-World values combined with contemporary know-how." "I have security issues, and they screen everyone properly." "It's the trickle-down theory. Everyone surrounding them is just as good and nice. They make you want to make lemonade for them."

The J. Alexander Company Inc.   3.5   3.5   4   4
23727 Hawthorne Boulevard, Torrance, CA 90505
(310) 375 - 9731

Tear-down/ground-up custom homes

We hear the J. Alexander Company can design on the fly and put your home on the fast-track to completion. However, ambitious scheduling and meticulous management does not mean a compromise in quality. J. Alexander specializes in tear-down/ground-up custom homes and also takes a minority of its work from renovation and the occasional condo build-out. Projects range from $60,000 additions to $4.5 million homes. The firm looks for clients who are interested in executing inspired design, which does not necessarily mean high-concept contemporary looks. While past clients have summoned J. Alexander from as far away as Israel in a management capacity, most of the firm's work is clustered around the South Bay, Palos Verdes, Rolling Hills and West LA.

Principal John Schoenfeld has an architecture degree and twenty-plus years of experience in high-end residential building. In addition to being on the same wavelength with other design professionals, his experience as a developer has him thinking like a homeowner. Superintendents run day-to-day operations on the job site, and all trades are subbed. Clients say the firm runs a tight, harmonious ship. Contracts are mostly negotiated and cost plus.

"Watching my house go up, it was like fast-forward. The whole thing just flew by." "He's talented, easy to work with and very, very helpful." "He made our house wonderful." "We had an architect, but you can let John loose on ideas. He knows all the materials." "There was no one else."

	Quality	Cost	Value	Recommend?
	✚	$	◆	★

Triumph Construction

| | 4 | 3.5 | 4.5 | 5 |

1309 Pico Boulevard, Santa Monica, CA 90404
(310) 396 - 9796

New custom construction, gut renovation

Custom residences by Triumph radiate across Southern California, beloved by clients who praise the firm for being "tuned into what each house wants to be." Pooling knowledge and resources gained from running their respective contracting companies, Bill Rosenberg and Steve Ferguson formed Triumph a decade ago. The firm concentrates on high-end custom new homes or extensive, detail-rich renovations and additions that range between $200,000 and $2 million. Many of the company's twenty-strong staff are veterans of previous Rosenberg and Ferguson projects stretching back fifteen years.

Rosenberg handles the bidding, customer relations and contract work with the trades. We hear he prepares a diligent, detailed and precise estimate, reflecting his close dialogue with the architect. Ferguson heads the field operations, commanding ranks of supers, foremen, in-house craftsmen and outside subcontractors, all of whom clients say perform "no shortage of hard work." Clients especially appreciate the firm's policy of going beyond line-item breakdowns, including a verbal description that spells out in clear terms not only where the money will be spent, but how each goal will be achieved. Triumph's stomping grounds include Malibu, Los Felix, Santa Monica, West LA and up to Pasadena.

Triumph is said to provide attentive, expert problem-solving, and friendly and professional service. Clients don't need to have plans to approach the firm, which likes to participate during the design phase to better inform the budget. Contracts are set up at a fixed cost, which often makes them less expensive than their high-end competitors. Triumph also owns a millworking business, Triumph Fine Cabinetry and Millwork, with a new shop in the San Fernando Valley.

"Triumph will not just restore the structure, but bring back the old-fashioned feeling." "They made a huge contribution to the fine points of detail—all the little things that make the whole feel of the house complete." "I can't imagine getting bids from anyone else." "It's not important that a cabinet door was warped. What's important is Bill and Steve stuck with it until it was fixed." "They both have the same calm energy. I'm always happy to see them. I could swear they were the same person if I hadn't only recently seen them in the same room together." "Bottom line is they are committed to giving you what you paid for."

Turpin-Levin Construction

| | 4 | 4 | 4 | 4.5 |

15445 Ventura Boulevard, Suite 153, Sherman Oaks, CA 91403
(818) 789 - 3000   www.turpin-levin.com

Construction management and general contracting

Turpin-Levin Construction recently came full circle: with 50 years of family-firm construction, they are now sometimes called in to renovate custom homes they built for the current owner's parents. This firm specializes in custom residential construction "of enduring quality." Beyond Turpin-Levin's noteworthy high-end residential work, the firm's far-reaching skills have been mined for hotels, restaurants, recording studios, country clubs and corporate offices, among other structures. Projects usually require six months of preconstruction. Average projects are budgeted above $750,000 and are located in West LA and the San Fernando Valley. The firm remains selective about its projects, signing on to only about five per year. The reason, we hear, is so that top-liners Mark Turpin and Moshe Levin stay actively involved with every job. One or the other acts as the point person, splitting his efforts between owner and architect. From their staff of twenty, a full-time super and general laborer are dispatched to each site. Turpin-Levin expects clients to approach the firm with an architect on board and a strong set of plans in hand.

"Ultra-personalized. I use them repeatedly. As good as others, but not as large." "Really good subs. Excellent foreman. The job went quite smoothly. It was the only job I can remember where the contractor was mutually respected." "For traditional styles, they're your GC." "Always on time." "Not cheap but very professional."

Wilson Custom Construction   3.5   3   4.5   4
6914 Canby Avenue, Reseda, CA 91335
(818) 996 - 7036   deanwcc@aol.com
Residential renovation, pools and landscaping

Insiders describe this general contracting company's work as "meticulous." WCC specializes in remodels of upper- and high-end homes. $100,000 is a typical starting point for kitchen and bath work, with projects going to full renovations of 4,000+ square foot homes. The firm's resume also includes landscaping and pools. WCC takes three to four projects at one time, all located within a twenty-five-mile radius of the San Fernando Valley. While most of WCC's efforts are coordinated in the West LA area, it also works in Sherman Oaks, Calabasas and Pasadena. Clients are delighted by the way the firm "gets on their side" on day one, treating the project as a partnership.

A former CPA and businessman, principal Dean Wilson was eventually bitten by the family bug—both of his brothers are contractors. In 1989 he got up from his desk to let loose his mechanical inclinations, and clients tell us they are happy he did. They say Wilson is unafraid of giving input and good at prompting decisions. He is said to work well with architects, running on-site meetings to keep everyone on the same page. A small staff of project managers and carpenter-foremen have been with him for five to eight years and are known to be good at driving subs. Clients applaud the firm's penchant for organization, open communication and dedication to keeping timetables. Contracts are fixed cost and bids are quite competitive.

"One of the most meticulous contractors." "Really easy to get along with."

Winters-Schram Associates   5   4.5   4.5   5
1631 21st Street, Santa Monica, CA 90404
(310) 396 - 0555

Executive-level general contracting and construction management services

Insiders tell us "no stone goes unturned" with this "class act" firm, fabled for its obsession with detail. From a historic hacienda dressed to the nines in redwood to an ultra-modern home stripped down to the purest of structural elements, the firm is highly regarded by the best in the design community for its ability to execute extreme challenges. Winters-Schram focuses on building new homes and performing significant gut renovations over seven figures, as well as doing commercial work—from LA to San Francisco. This "honest" and "adaptable" firm also acts as a construction manager or owner's rep, offering preconstruction plan analysis, value engineering and feasibility studies.

References tell us the principals are truly hands-on. Licensed builders with 25 years' experience, Peter Winters and Jim Schram know how to do the work themselves. One of the two always acts in the capacity of an executive project manager, directing job supervision and in-house crews. The firm's in-house concrete team, electricians and plumbers make it ideally set up for doing small maintenance jobs for past clients.

The two principals are legendary for getting down in the details, planning projects meticulously and wasting no time in their execution. Brought in at the drawing board stage, they will maximize a project's design efficiency and cost effectiveness. Insiders say the company's deserved reputation for being expensive only reflects its bull's-eye accurate budget forecasts. In the final analysis, Winters-Schram Associates realizes the architect's intent and delivers stunning service.

"The most professional and thorough contractors I have ever worked with. They dot every 'i' and cross every 't'." "So organized. Clients love them. Their paperwork is amazing." "Winters-Schram's ability to solve problems from an engineering standpoint is superb." "They inspect and watch the work like hawks." "They're just on their own level. They have a list of clients that boggles the mind." "They have a T-shirt hanging in the trailer that says it all: 'Is ANAL RETENTIVE spelled with a hyphen?'" "Peter's knowledge of materials and architectural detailing made his presence during the planning stage a very wise move." "I would not build anything—not even a pool house—with another company."

Hiring an Electrician or Lighting Designer

Birds of a different feather, these two professions still flock together, both peddling a little Thomas Edison magic. An electrician's main concerns are practicing safety and delivering convenience. A lighting designer's interest is in conjuring atmospheres that at once massage a client's mood, amplify architectural elements and provide late-night safety. While the true measure of a successful lighting design job is its inspiration to the eye, a good electrician's work is invisible.

How to Choose an Excellent Electrician

Dealing with electricity and wiring is intimidating, and for good reason—you are placing your family and home at risk if it is not handled properly. This is not the area for cutting costs by doing it yourself, or by choosing the lowest-priced service provider. Think of Chevy Chase putting his Christmas light cords into one giant, sagging cluster of adapters in *National Lampoon's Christmas Vacation*. Hilarious, but maybe a little close to home.

The first thing you should consider about an electrical contractor is the firm's commitment to safety. Companies that will not take the time to meticulously lay out projects, firms that perform hit-and-run installations or pass off cheap product should be avoided. Talk to contractor and homeowner references to get the inside scoop on what firms do inside the walls.

You'll also need to identify the right electrician for your scope of work. Some do only large installations while others concentrate on service and repairs. A company that specializes exclusively in "designer" electrical work, such as the lighting of artwork and retrofitting museum-quality finishes, may not be geared for a large gut renovation. In addition to providing the high-voltage infrastructure that supports the myriad outlets, switches, fixtures and appliances in your home, many electricians also install the low-voltage cabling that supports audio/visual, telecommunication, computer and lighting systems. For these low-voltage systems, they will typically not install the hardware or do the programming, but should coordinate with the specialists who do.

How to Choose an Excellent Lighting Designer

With the exception of its role in nighttime security, lighting design is an aesthetic enterprise. Whether bathing interiors in a soothing glow, dramatically highlighting the architectural features of your home's facade, illuminating artwork or bringing a magical feel to landscapes, a lighting designer tries to capture a mood. These professionals work as consultants, sitting down with the client and walking through the space to come up with a lighting scheme that best reflects one's lifestyle. As such, expect them to ask a lot of questions to pinpoint what presses your buttons. And speaking of buttons, don't be pressured into buying lighting schemes, fixtures or systems just because they're deemed the best technology out there. What's best for you is what counts.

A lighting design professional works with industrial and custom-created fixtures interfaced with high-tech lighting control systems such as Lutron HomeWorks, Vantage and Lighttouch, to achieve their vision. In some instances, especially when only low-voltage wiring is involved, they can install their own work without the help of an outside electrician. For the most part, these designers will produce lighting layouts and the electrician will perform the installation and interface with the control systems. Whoever is responsible for programming these systems should walk the homeowner through the control operations.

IMPORTANT PRE- AND POST-PROJECT CONSIDERATIONS

Electrical and lighting work often requires cutting into a wall to gain access to wires. There are two issues to think about here—cleanup and repair. Sheetrock debris and plaster dust are very difficult to clean up, so the electrician should either inform you of this at the time or put up protective plastic sheeting to keep dust from infiltrating your entire house. Some will repair the wall with plaster, but it is unlikely that they will sand and repaint it. Be sure to discuss this beforehand, clearly identifying the extent of the electrician's responsibility—and get it in writing.

When doing renovation or installation work, your electrician may suggest adding additional wiring for future use. This may sound like he's just trying to charge you more, but it's actually a very good idea. It is easier to add wiring and setups in the beginning for that dreamed-of central air-conditioning system, six-line phone system or computer network you envision in your future. This avoids the headache of having to tear up walls and floors several years down the road, and saves a great deal of money, too.

Also, before your electrician or lighting consultant leaves, make sure you know which switch controls do what and that all circuit breakers are labeled properly. Do not let him disappear without doing this, because he is the only one who knows. Wandering around in the dark in search of a phantom blown fuse, or being tormented nightly by landscape lights that snap on at 3am can be quite annoying.

ON COST

For smaller jobs and service calls, which include repair and maintenance, most companies charge an hourly rate. Hourlies for electricians in LA these days range anywhere from $50 to $110. Some companies charge a set fee for a visit, or a higher rate the first hour, then have flat-rate charges for each task performed, such as per outlet relocated or fixture installed. Others insist on doing a consultation to provide you with an estimate before any work is started.

On new, large-scale electrical installations and renovations, the electrical contractor will submit a total bid for the work. The price should be broken down by each task performed so you can compare apples to apples with other bids. A company's standards in relation to product and safety, the depth of its resources and the demand it's in can all affect cost. Fees for contract renovation work are typically higher per hour and per square foot than those for new construction.

A lighting designer may also charge an hourly rate—anywhere from $100 to $150 an hour—for design and oversight of installation. For larger projects they may charge a fee based upon the total budget or square footage of the project.

With a little preparation, you will be able to save money by saving the service provider's time. Many times an electrician will need to cut into walls to gain access to wires or to replace fixtures. This is something you should think about before the workmen arrive. You may want to move or cover up that priceless antique sideboard near where the sconces are being installed rather than leaving it to the electrical crew. By taking care of little things in advance, you allow your electrical professional to get right to work, you will not have to worry about the safety of various objects and your billable time will be shorter.

In the end, consider the company with the best reputation for quality and service, not just the low bidder.

LICENSING, INSURANCE AND PERMITS

You should only consider a full-time licensed professional for your electrical needs. A license from the Department of Labor is required for any electrical work, and all work must be filed with the city. This includes any installation related to light, heat and power. Lighting designers require no licensing, however, those that program lighting control systems should be certified by the manufacturers to do so. As always, ask for the contractor's license number and proof of workman's compensation and liability insurance. Your electrical contractor should always be responsible for obtaining all permits necessary for your job.

GUARANTEES AND SERVICE AGREEMENTS

Your service provider should always stand behind all of his or her work. Be sure to ask about service agreements. Many electrical professionals provide regular "check-ups" and inspections. It may seem like wasted money at first, but over time these measures can prevent an emergency. Lighting designers may offer focusing sessions to re-adjust and fine-tune your lighting scheme according to season.

ELECTRICIANS & LIGHTING DESIGNERS

Bonded Electric Construction   5   3.5   5   5
4284 Sawtelle Boulevard, Los Angeles, CA 90066
(310) 636 - 1060   www.bondedelectric.com
Electrical installation and service

The best general contractors in Los Angeles have an unbreakable bond with this can-do company. Founded in the early 1950s, Bonded Electric has remained true to its old-fashioned work ethic. The firm focuses on significant high-end residential installations, often in the five-figure square foot range. It also does commercial, retail and restaurant work. For past clients only, Bonded will take on service calls and small jobs. In fact, the company has three electricians who are solely dedicated to servicing Bonded's existing clientele and will do absolutely everything, right down to removing Christmas tree lights.

Ronald Jay helms Bonded today, but his 84-year-old dad Raymond (one of the firm's "founding brothers") still shows up for work. Bonded fields a team of more than 40 men and women. Many are long-standing employees, and all are connected to e-mail. The company's online help desk can walk clients through common questions and answers. Sources say Bonded's personnel are service-oriented and trustworthy. They work as a true team and are quick to help each other out in a crunch.

The firm also provides schematic, home automation and lighting design services, and installs video surveillance and motion detectors. It does no security programming. A 24-hour answering service is available for existing clients. While Bonded projects boast big budgets, its hourly service rates are as competitive as anyone's.

"Spectacular." "Ronald and his boys will always be my first choice, because I've known the company since his father was running it." "Just knowing they'll be on the job gives me confidence. I know I don't have to worry about them."

Brentwood Electrical Contractors   4.5   4   4.5   4.5
2129 Pontius Avenue, Los Angeles, CA 90025
(310) 477 - 2944
Electrical installation and service

When they need a firm to wire ground-up construction, many of the city's architects turn to Brentwood. Founded in 1953, Brentwood is a large electrical and lighting design company specializing in residential low-voltage installation. Owner Bruce Sobel and his team of 50 electricians ply their trade up and down the coastline of Los Angeles County. Their service/remodel work consists of small retrofit jobs and landscape lighting and is available to anyone. More often than not, jobs come from a referral from a satisfied client or a returning, quality-minded general contractor.

In addition to his electricians, Sobel employs a lighting design staff and his own in-house engineer. Fluent in Lutron and Vantage technology, the firm installs many low-voltage switching systems. We hear that Brentwood's prices might be steeper than some competitors, but clients say it's only because they are near the very peak of their craft.

		Quality	Cost	Value	Recommend?
		✚	$	◆	★

Bruce Liebert   4.5   4.5   4   5

1510 North Las Palmas Avenue, Suite 4, Hollywood, CA 90028
(323) 461 - 1007

Lighting design

Bruce Liebert's corporate work includes lighting designs for Geico and Verizon, but sources say Liebert's genius lies in creating environments without that commercial feeling. His museum-caliber lighting blends high-tech industrial and decorative fixtures to create friendly, warm interiors for residential and commercial spaces. He may illuminate artwork, or design ingenious, task-specific lighting.

Liebert got his start in San Francisco, where he imported lighting and furniture. In 1992, he turned his focus to lighting design. Today, Liebert works for both homeowners and design professionals, who report there are few who operate at his level. He is equally at home designing a lighting scheme for a single room or a new 15,000 square foot mansion.

Though he doesn't do installations, he will oversee contractors to make sure everything is done right. At the end of the job Liebert always comes in for editing and focusing—adjusting filters, grills and lenses for maximum effect. While we hear Liebert pushes the limits of technology, he is careful to make sure his clients are comfortable at the controls of their dimming systems and home entertainment networks. Liebert's fees are based on construction budget or square footage, and he charges $125 an hour for consulting. While the cost is at the high end of the scale, so is the client satisfaction.

"My interior designer brought him in on a remodeling job for one room. We ended up having him light our entire garden exterior." "An artist with light."

Cover-All Electric   3.5   3   4.5   5

8526 Washington Boulevard, Culver City, CA 90232
(310) 837 - 7219

Electrical installation, remodeling and service

Cover-All is more than just a name—it's a mantra. The company does it all, from fielding service calls to installing systems for residential, commercial and industrial clientele. Clients offer warm praise for this small, service-oriented, veteran electrical contractor. Partners Mike Derderian and Josh Weirsma have built a solid following over the course of 21 years, thriving on the quality work of their loyal, tight-knit crew and frequent word-of-mouth referrals.

Clients are grateful to discover that Cover-All won't try to sell them a high-tech rewiring of their house when all they need is a lightbulb replacement. But for those who want it, the firm will create lighting and full-tilt electrical design schemes, and will even run cable and consult on home computer networking.

Working within a radius of 40 miles from their office in Culver City, Cover-All works in West LA, Brentwood, Beverly Hills, Pacific Palisades and the San Fernando Valley. Cover-All accepts all clients, adopting the line that a successful service call brings in future business. We hear the firm has a huge database to prove that point. With a low hourly rate and one-way travel time fees, the firm is praised for completing most simple jobs within the hour.

"Mike personifies the dedicated, detailed, thorough craftsman." "He is always on time, gets the job done within the specified time frame and always comes in at or below prices quoted." "Hardworking, on time and extremely cost effective. I use him for both my business and home." "They're just the nicest people!" "Reachable and approachable."

	Quality	Cost	Value	Recommend?
	+	$	◆	★

Current Electric Contracting and Design Inc. (CECAD)

18425 Napa Street, Northridge, CA 91325
(818) 885 - 5567   www.currentelectric.com

A/V, home automation, electrical service, CCTV, security surveillance

See Current Electric Contracting and Design Inc. (CECAD)'s full report under the heading Audio/Video Design & Installation

F.I.R.E./L.T.D.   4.5   5   3.5   4

639 North Fairfax Avenue, Los Angeles, CA 90036
(310) 652 - 9110

Lighting design

The lights of F.I.R.E/L.T.D. are burning brightly up and down the California coast. From international airports to synagogues, garage renovations to spectacular new homes, this firm's lights can be glimpsed through windows everywhere.

F.I.R.E. is generating a lot of heat these days with its much-praised lighting consultant/materials lab that often manufactures the fixtures the firm specifies. Though F.I.R.E. is always developing new technologies, it is praised for never pressuring clients—even those with big budgets—to purchase unnecessary systems. We hear that 25 years' experience allows F.I.R.E. to deliver the best value by tailoring applications to the client's lifestyle. The firm will even create temporary light and work around furniture.

Principal David Steinitz is known always to meet the requirements of the customer. Steinitz and his team know everything there is to know about lighting automation, and are experts in working with Vantage, LightTouch and HomeWorks systems. In fact, F.I.R.E. often works as a consultant on behalf of these companies to make sure that other, less-knowledgeable electricians have installed their systems correctly. When standard options don't fit a client's needs, F.I.R.E. has been known to come up with hybrid designs. We hear there's "no fingerpointing" at F.I.R.E., only "focusing" until everything is tweaked just right. The firm's $200 per hour consultation rate can price it out of smaller projects.

Gannon Electric Light   4   4   4   4

3033 South Kerckhoff Avenue, San Pedro, CA 90731
(800) 443 - 2466

Architectural landscape lighting

Landscape lighting guru John Gannon offers sanctuaries for clients who want to relax, spectacles for those who want to entertain and peace of mind for showbiz professionals concerned with safety and security. Gannon is definitely an artist, but his background as an electrical contractor helps him realize his visions. His firm provides design, installation and maintenance of lighting systems. We hear that some of the hottest landscape architects and interior decorators hire Gannon for his unique sensibility—playful, new age and calm.

Gannon acts as chief designer and oversees three crews in the field. Clients tell us he comes up with a vision, walks them through the design and takes incredible pains to conceal fixtures. Gannon has been known to illuminate trees, water features, stairways, fountains, pathways and architectural elements.

The minimum cost of a Gannon job is $5,000. While some might find this excessive for lighting, satisfied clients point to his work's enormous intangible value in brightening their mood and creating a positive atmosphere.

"I sincerely believe there's nothing that John can't do." "He lit up my entire house without subcontracting any of the electrical work. The driveway, the garden, our pool, trees and practically everything in between. He's the best." "Couldn't be happier." "Thinks like a landscape designer, works like an electrician." "A pleasure to work with."

Kaplan Gehring and McCarroll Architectural Lighting   5   4   5   4.5

10351 Santa Monica Boulevard, Suite 410, Los Angeles, CA 90025
(310) 552 - 2191   www.kpal.net

Architectural lighting design

Experienced at putting the spotlight on the likes of Jimi Hendrix and Santana, Kaplan, Gehring and McCarroll Architectural Lighting knows how to create drama and atmosphere. With fifteen employees, KGM's lighting design team is larger than most, but the boss is never far away. Clients appreciate that one of the firm's three partners—Joe Kaplan, Michael Gehring or David McCarroll—manages each project.

KGM takes on about 80 projects per year, 50 percent of which are residential. Its high-profile, mostly Southern California clientele includes Leonardo di Caprio, Sony Pictures and the Universal Citywalk. But this deluxe firm has done jobs all over the world, ranging from renovations of less than 5,000 square feet to a 54,000 square foot log cabin in British Columbia to posh Las Vegas hotels and commercial projects in Asia.

Sources say the firm works closely and successfully with interior designers and architects. We hear the team at KGM is as sensitive to a client's needs as they are to a system's energy efficiency. The firm is noted for providing watertight plans and fixture specifications, which are particularly important since mountings are integral. While the firm knows product inside and out, KGM does not procure it, but acts as an owner's watchdog in the process. Fees are on a sliding scale based on price per square foot. Prices reflect this in-demand firm's illustrious reputation.

"Everybody knows these guys are the wizards of light." "Las Vegas, Tokyo, Seattle. They go everywhere, and everybody knows them." "The architect made my new home beautiful, but KGM made it luxurious."

Mark Jacksen Lighting Design   4.5   4   4.5   5

6 North 1st Avenue, Studio 102, Arcadia, CA 91006
(626) 821 - 2050

Architectural and landscape lighting design

Insiders say that Mark Jacksen's creations inspire "magic" and "warmth" indoors and outdoors. An unheard-of third-generation lighting designer, Jacksen logged fourteen years with his father before striking out on his own. Working with homeowners and other designers, he imagines custom schemes of accent lighting using form, shadow and color that dazzle at night. Focal points can include water features, furnishings, art, architectural detail and gardens.

Jacksen has been known to retrofit old light fixtures with optimal results. He will often use projectors to get the precise effect he wants. Clients and pros alike mention Jacksen's relentless pursuit of perfection. They tell us he strives to build his light sources into the architecture, tailoring his installations to new or existing plaster, millwork, glass and even sheet metal.

Jacksen offers design services, lighting adjustment and servicing recommendations, but he does not install. We hear he is sensitive to practical as well as aesthetic considerations, working to simplify lighting controls for a homeowner's ease of use. Jackson works for a fixed fee based on a house's square footage or on a time and material basis, charging $125 per hour for his own time, $85 per hour for an associate and $65 for a draftsman. Unique, lovely results lead clients to say they'd absolutely recommend him to friends.

"One of the best. Very intricate work." "As an installer, he makes life harder for me, but I have to admit the end result is awesome."

Oscar Plumbing & Electric
PO Box 6015, North Hollywood, CA 91602
(818) 506 - 4915

Plumbing installation and service; electrical service

See Oscar Plumbing & Electric's full report under the heading Plumbers

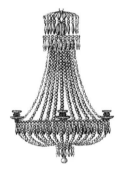

Pacific Lighting & Electric   4   4   4   4
13333 Saticoy Street, North Hollywood, CA 91605
(818) 504 - 6961

Lighting, electrical design and installation

Pacific Lighting & Electric navigates the complexities of the electrical world, so its clients don't have to. The firm takes a thorough, painstaking look at a project in its totality, then engineers its work around the client's lifestyle, while considering the home's structural elements.

Builders and designers turn to Pacific to install on small remodels and ground-up 5,000 to 10,000 square foot homes. The firm designs its own electrical and lighting systems, and is familiar with Lutron HomeWorks, LightTouch and Vantage systems. It also integrates its product with A/V, security and telephone systems in collaboration with those professionals. For those who have a bright idea just screaming to be a wall sconce, Pacific can custom-craft, fabricate or reproduce any light fixture.

After gaining valuable experience as a foreman for other electrical contractors, Warren Breveleri opened his own small shop in 1990. With three employees, his firm limits its job count to stay on top of the details, but Breveleri will accommodate larger jobs with more bodies as needed. Breveleri himself travels between his bucolic home in Washington state, where he keeps an office, and his LA projects. Costs are upper end, but Pacific delivers quality without headaches. Service work is limited to existing clients, who happily recommend the firm. Pacific is said to be very proactive in coming up with added touches to make a home feel unique, making it a good option for homeowners and an excellent collaborator with pros.

	Quality	Cost	Value	Recommend?
	✚	$	◆	★

Powerfull Electric Construction   3.5   3.5   4   4

3526 Overland Avenue, Los Angeles, CA 90034
(310) 837 - 9333

Design and installation of electrical and lighting systems

We hear Powerfull is a force to be reckoned with. Founded in 1989, the firm designs and installs top-tier electrical and lighting systems, bringing positive energy to every installation. The firm works mainly in high-end custom residences that range from 7,000 to 45,000 square feet. Service work is limited to existing customers.

Contractors say they rely on Powerfull to come through in a pinch. Powerfull's principal supervises each project while his twenty experienced electricians execute the details. The firm comes highly recommended by Lutron, makers of state-of-the-art electrical wiring control systems.

S&F Electric Inc.   4.5   4.5   4   4.5

1239 South Spaulding Avenue, Los Angeles, CA 90019
(323) 937 - 9357   www.sf-electric-inc.com

Custom electrical installation

Trade professionals turn to this "outstanding" electrical firm for large-scale custom installations in new construction and occasional gut remodels. Working within a five mile radius of Beverly Hills, Calabasas and Pacific Palisades, S&F books high-end projects with electrical budgets that range between $50,000 and $2 million, starting at a size of 5,000 square feet. It's no surprise that S&F owners Yacov Sasson and Shmuel Fligelman are known as big job specialists.

Sasson and Fligelman founded their small shop more than fifteen years ago, and now manage fifteen employees who are paired in rough, finish and service crews. Sasson and Fligelman shepherd jobs through the design phase and perform the punch-list programming themselves. Clients tell us S&F delivers expert design and installation of lighting automation systems such as Lutron, Vantage and LightTouch, and can integrate home theaters, audio and security into the mix.

References report S&F provides "very reliable" customer service, which the owners attribute to doing the job right the first time, so that the installations seldom require maintenance. The firm does not offer service on another company's work. The firm's work has been featured in *Electric House* magazine, *Architectural Digest* and *House & Garden*, further establishing Sasson and Fligelman as go-to guys for large-scale installations.

"Very pleased. Never had any problems." "They are the best."

W&W Son Electric   3.5   3   4.5   4

1152 Alamos Drive, Thousand Oaks, CA 91362
(805) 370 - 1395

Electrical installation and remodeling

A west side wonder, W&W Son Electric has emerged as the electrical contractor of choice for high-end general contractors. W&W also comes highly recommended by Lutron, whose HomeWorks home automation system the firm designs, installs and programs. Lutron even entrusts W&W to tune up systems installed by less-competent electricians. The firm also offers lighting design consultation along with expert installation.

W&W acquires work solely on referral. It will take jobs of any size, providing the client is quality-minded and the firm is available. This firm vows not to take more than it can handle, causing loyal clientele to line up work months in advance.

We hear that W&W is well staffed and that the principal gets along with everyone. The firm's superior service is limited to existing clients. However, anyone can take advantage of its yearly maintenance programs, if W&W deems your home's electrical innards worthy, that is. Clients say the firm is quick to respond to any problem and especially appreciate its follow-up calls.

"These guys are real superheroes." "I brought them in to fix another contractor's work, and it's been great ever since." "Your electrician isn't a guy you want to see every month. W&W did it right the first time."

Westco Electrical	**4**	**4**	**4**	**4.5**

28441 High Ridge Road, Rolling Hills Estates, CA 90274
(800) 293 - 7826   www.westcoelectrical.com
Design and installation of electrical and lighting systems

We hear the first thing Westco does on a job is to ask the right questions. Then the firm lays out the electrical and lighting options that offer the consumer the maximum in control—options such as home automation, dimming and lighting layouts.

Established in 1984, Westco does complicated electrical and lighting installation and design on residences between 5,000 and 35,000 square feet. Principal Jack Goldberg brings a degree in electrical engineering and 30 years of experience in high-end residential service to his company. Clients call Goldberg an "incredibly conscientious individual." He and his team are said to be "sticklers for perfection" who jump when clients need them. A good number of Goldberg's employees have been with him from the beginning.

Goldberg is well versed in the newest technologies, but he makes sure to always spend time listening to what the client wants. Westco's prices are in the expensive range, but clients say the caliber of service makes the fees more than fair.

"We had to do an eighteen-month project in seven. We took two bids from two electricians. Westco was twice as much, but I knew they could finish the project on time, and they did." "Really goes out of his way to put the client ahead." "My first choice, when product allows." "He constantly directs his attention to what's in the best interests of the project."

Hiring a Flooring
Service Provider

LA's outdoor-is-indoor culture and architectural diversity—from Mediterranean to mid-century modern, ultra-contemporary to 1920s Craftsman—make it a flooring free-for-all. Be it vinyl, wood, tile, stone, cork, rubber or concrete, flooring sets the ambience of a room, and must be as durable as it is attractive.

What Are My Choices?

There are many options in flooring, each falling into five basic categories: wood, laminate, vinyl, carpet and hard tile (see section introduction to Tile, Marble and Stone). To get ideas, look through home furnishing magazines and pay a visit to a flooring showroom or two. Internet sites that will help you learn more about flooring options and the best way to care for them include Floorfacts, a consumer site filled with links and information (www.floorfacts.com), the Carpet & Rug Institute (www.carpet-rug.com) and the National Wood Flooring Association's site (www.woodfloors.org). After considering the following descriptions of basic floor types, you should be able to choose flooring that best meets your specific demands for beauty and maintenance.

Wood

A real wood floor never goes out of style and probably has the best resale value. It complements every decor, from minimalist to Louis XIV, and generally ages gracefully. The most popular woods used in flooring are oak and maple, which can be stained or color-washed to your exact specifications. Wood flooring can be designed in numerous patterns, limited only by your imagination (and budget). Some of the most popular are parquet, plank, strip and herringbone. When choosing a stain color, have your contractor apply a few samples and look at them in different kinds of light. Think of the ambience you are trying to create in the room—traditional or modern, casual or formal, spacious or cozy. Wood floors can be bleached—for a light and airy look—or painted. Hardwood floors can be customized to satisfy every taste and personality and installed in any room, regardless of what type of flooring—concrete, existing boards or particleboard subflooring—is already there.

Aesthetically, a wood floor is stunning. But consider a few issues before you make this your final choice. What kind and how much traffic does the room get every day? Hardwood floors can be dented and scratched, especially from high-heeled shoes, and may not be the best choice for beachfront properties where sand and salt water are traipsed around. Although a variety of urethane finishes provide excellent protection (and shine), they do not completely prevent dents and scratches. These same finishes, however, make wood floors much easier to clean and maintain than those of previous generations. Humidity is another factor to consider. If the humidity in your area varies from season to season, a wood floor will expand and contract with the rise and fall of moisture in the air. Storing the wood on site for a period of time before installing will allow it to acclimatize to the specific humidity level in the home. The service provider should consider whether the floor is being installed in a particularly humid or dry time of the year, and make his measurements accordingly.

LAMINATES

If you love the look of real wood but have an active household, laminate flooring may be the perfect choice for you. Laminates are plastic- or wood-based products that look like hardwood. They come in various textures and are durable and easy to maintain. Laminates can also imitate the look of stone, marble or tile, offering a wide variety of creative styles you may not have imagined. A wood-patterned laminate floor has some significant advantages over the real thing—for example, it will not be discolored by sunlight and is very scratch-resistant. Laminate floors wear well and usually come with a guarantee of ten years or more. However, they cannot be refinished like wood.

Cleanups are also a breeze with laminate flooring. Laminates repel liquid and do not allow stains to set in. This point alone saves your floor, your time and your psychological well-being. Design snobs will, however, look down their noses at laminate as an imitation.

Both hardwood floors and laminates, while possessing the great qualities of longevity and beauty, are expensive. If you're looking to invest less money, you may want to explore vinyl or carpet floor coverings.

VINYL

The retro chic of vinyl or linoleum is often the least expensive choice and offers more options than any other type of flooring, with an eye-popping palette of colors, marbling, prints and patterns. Although it resists moisture, vinyl can stain, so spills need to be handled quickly and carefully according to the manufacturer's directions. The material is vulnerable to scuffing and can also tear—from furniture that may be moved across it or sharp objects that fall to the floor.

CARPETING

A cozy, lush floor covering, carpeting adds warmth, soundproofing, texture, color and insulation to a room. When considering carpeting, think about whether you'll need a light-, medium- or heavy-duty type. Industry experts suggest light-duty for occasionally trafficked areas, medium-duty for the bedroom or office and heavy-duty for hallways, stairs and other high-traffic areas. Carpeting requires extra maintenance, as stains are more difficult to remove and general cleaning is more work. Wool is a whole lot easier to deep steam-clean than nylon, but is more expensive. A protective sealant may be applied to carpeting to fend off future spills and stains. Lastly, if you or someone in your home is allergy-prone, carpeting is not a good option, because it retains dirt, dust and other particles.

HARD TILE

Ceramic, quarry (stone, including marble) and terra cotta make up this premium category of floor covering. The look and feel of a hard-tiled floor is unlike any other, with grooves and textures that can be felt underfoot. Often used in kitchens and baths, and ideal for indoor/outdoor rooms, tile flooring can give a distinct look and originality to any room in your home. In light colors, these materials do take on stains, so keep this in mind when choosing hard tile for particular rooms. Tile may be one of the most expensive kinds of flooring, but its remarkable beauty and longevity make it a good investment.

SPECIALTY OPTIONS

Cork floors, made from the ground-up bark of an oak tree, are a hot option these days. A natural material, each tile shows variations in shades and tones, and is finished like a hardwood floor. While comparable to wood in price, cork has a more buoyant feel under the feet. Cork's ability to weather spills receives mixed reviews.

A contemporary, cool option is polished or stamped concrete. Installation can be quite involved and comes at a higher price.

ON COST

Some floor installers charge by the square foot and others by the job. Most providers charge by the hour for cleaning and repairing. If your service provider charges by the hour, confirm whether this fee is per person/per hour or for the whole team. Will they charge for moving furniture around? Make sure your order includes extra quantities of flooring in your dye lot to replace broken, worn or stained sections in the future. This is especially crucial with hard tile, which can crack if something heavy is dropped on it, and any other material that stains easily.

KNOW YOUR FLOOR

Insist upon receiving written information about the care and maintenance of your new flooring. What cleaning products should you use and what should you definitely avoid? Is there a standard timetable for cleaning your hardwood floor or carpeting? Does your carpet warranty come with a consumer hotline for stain emergencies? Who can you call for advice about stains and/or damage?

SERVICE AND WARRANTIES

Before you sign a work agreement, find out exactly who will be installing your floor: will your contact from the firm be doing the job himself, or bringing in a different crew? Make sure that the firm will supply nails, glue and other installation accessories. Does the company have its own workshop or warehouse? If so, it will have more control over the product than one that purchases its materials from another supplier. Ask the company if it does repairs as well as installation. It's always a good idea to have the installer supply the material, so he can't point fingers at the product manufacturer if there is a problem. Both the flooring company and the flooring material manufacturers should have warranties for your new floor coverings. Remember, whatever material you choose, it's only as good as the installation.

FLOORING COMPARISON CHART

RATINGS: Very Poor *   Poor **   Average ***   Good ****   Excellent *****

BASIC FLOOR TYPES:	VINYL	WOOD	LAMINATE	HARD TILE	CARPET
Ease of Maintenance	****	***	****	****	***
Damage Resistance	**	***	****	*****	***
Moisture Resistance	****	*	***	*****	*
Stain Resistance	***	**	*****	*****	**
Fade Resistance	***	**	*****	*****	***
Scratch Resistance	**	***	****	****	N/A
Ease of Repair	*	***	**	**	*
Softness Under Foot	**	*	*	*	*****
Design/Color Selection	*****	**	**	***	****
◊Price Range (sq. ft.)	$ .50 - $ 4.50	$2.50 - $6.00	$2.50 - $5.00	$2.50 - $8.00	$ .50 - $ 5.00

◊The price range is for material only and is to be used as a general guideline.
Prices will vary from supplier to supplier.

	Quality	Cost	Value	Recommend?
	✚	$	◆	★

FLOORING

🛍 FIRMS WITH PORTFOLIOS 🛍

Contempo Floor Coverings Inc.   **4.5 3 5 4.5**
902 South Barrington Avenue, Los Angeles, CA 90049
(310) 826 - 8063 www.contempofloorcoverings.com

All types of flooring—retail and installation, plus upholstery and window treatments

Contempo Floor is the anti-boutique: the place to go for high-end one-stop shopping. Founded in 1976 by Mark Haloossim, the firm sells, installs, repairs and custom-designs wood, vinyl, linoleum, laminate, cork, rubber, tile, marble and granite floors, along with wall-to-wall carpeting. Contempo also deals in upholstery, drapery and window treatments. The firm is a member of the NWFA, the Western Floor Covering Association and the International Design Guild.

Contempo's impressive showroom is open to the public. With a sales force of 14 and 25 service technicians Contempo is able to serve many residential and commercial clients, most of them on LA's west side but with some out-of-state customers. Licensed, bonded and insured, Haloossim and his team work with architects, designers and contractors or directly with homeowners. Pricing is usually per square foot and estimates are free.

Clients tell us Haloossim and his men are easy to work with, responsible and competent. References also appreciate their wide inventory of floors and reasonable prices.

"Mark is a model contractor." "Reliable." "Accommodating with problems. More patient than most contractors." "Contempo will go the extra mile to please."

Dutko Hardwood Floors Inc. 🛍 3.5 2.5 4.5 4.5
4616 Manhattan Beach Boulevard, Lawndale, CA 90260
(310) 214 - 1813

Hardwood installation, restoration and service

Helmed by "down-to-earth" founder Mike Dutko, this firm installs, repairs, restores and cleans hardwood floors. The company also treats water and fire-damaged floors. This NWFA-member firm is licensed, bonded and insured, and currently has twenty full-time installers and service people.

Founded in 1992, Dutko Hardwood serves a primarily residential clientele from West LA to Newport Beach, but has also done jobs in San Francisco, Palm Springs, San Diego, Las Vegas, Colorado and Hawaii. Pricing is figured per square foot and average projects are in the 600 to 1,000 square foot range. Dutko works with architects, contractors and directly with homeowners. The showroom is open to the public, but be sure to call ahead to make an appointment.

Clients appreciate Dutko's efficiency and attention to detail, especially on complicated inlaid and patterned floors. Insiders report that Dutko is honest, fair, straightforward and reliable—and that his moderate prices are a good value.

"Knows about his work." "Customer-service oriented." "No-nonsense, straight-forward, cuts to the chase. He gets the job done." "One of the busiest contrac-tors around. Scheduling may be a bit difficult." "Can't say enough good things about him."

Henderson Wood Floors   5   4.5   4.5   5

3820 North Ventura Avenue, Ventura, CA 93001
(805) 648 - 7311   www.patinafloors.com
Hardwood manufacturing, design, installation and service

"Don't tell anyone," pleads one designer, "they're my best-kept secret." Indeed, insiders consider Henderson Wood Floors to be a rare find in the high-end wood flooring business. Not only does Henderson design and install superb antique-looking hardwood floors, but it also manufactures its own line of gorgeous hardwood under the name Patina Old-World Flooring. The firm's excellent crafts-men receive nothing but compliments.

Managed by husband-and-wife team Jim and Jane Henderson, the company was established in 1992 and serves mostly residential clients. Past projects include fancy floors in areas such as Montecito, Orange County, San Diego, San Francisco, even New York City and Aspen. The firm does mostly newly constructed homes and some remodels. Pricing is per square foot and clients describe fees as very expensive. Henderson's showroom is open to the public.

High-end designers, architects, contractors and homeowners alike cannot say enough good things about Henderson: "competent," "knowledgeable," "extremely professional." An impressive list of celebrities plant their feet on Henderson floors, including Cher, Rob Lowe, Olivia Newton-John, Gary Oldman and Jodie Foster. These spectacular Old-World floors have also been featured in *Town & Country, California Homes,* and *Architectural Digest.*

"Henderson's colors and fabrications are simply unparalleled." "No-nonsense. They get the job done on time—and beautifully, too." "Expensive, but worth every penny." "I hesitate to let you know about them."

Rode Bros. Inc.   4   3   5   5

8406 Osage Avenue, Los Angeles, CA 90045
(310) 670 - 0891   www.rodebros.com
Hardwood design, installation and service

A familiar and trusted name in the flooring industry, Rode Bros. has been in business since 1930, specializing in hardwood design (including inlays), installation and restoration. President Joe Audino is a natural choice to lead the firm into the 21st century—both he and his father worked for the Rode brothers before Joe bought the company in 1974.

With a mostly residential clientele, the company's range covers Los Angeles, Orange County, Palm Springs, San Francisco and Hawaii. But the firm can also claim some pretty impressive commercial jobs, including floors in the White House's Oval Office, the J. Paul Getty Museum in Malibu and the Reagan and Nixon presidential libraries. The firm is also a top choice of hoteliers in Las Vegas, where it has laid floors in the Paris, Caesar's Palace, Wynn and Bellagio Hotels. Pricing is generally by the square foot. Rode Bros. has offices and showrooms in Los Angeles, San Francisco and Las Vegas.

"Service oriented. Joe is one of the friendliest guys around." "Great installation and inlay work." "One of the more reliable flooring contractors." "Gets the job done with minimum fuss in a timely manner."

Scott4floors   4   2.5   5   5
17305 Gilmore Street, Lake Balboa, CA 91406
(877) 652 - 2343
Design, installation and service for all types of flooring

Scott4floors has consistently wowed its discriminating clients, delivering an outstanding product at quite moderate prices. The firm installs wood, vinyl, bamboo, linoleum, laminate, cork, rubber and carpet for a good mix of residential and commercial clients.

Owner Scott Hegyesi and his team of sixteen will work with architects, contractors, designers and homeowners. Most of the firm's clients are located in Pacific Palisades, Beverly Hills, Hancock Park, Bel Air, Malibu and Palos Verdes. The company does most of its work on site. It houses stock and special-order flooring at its Lake Balboa location. Scott4floors recently opened a Santa Fe location.

Clients say Hegyesi and his workers are very pleasant to work with and that Hegyesi himself is on top of things. Crews will move furniture for an extra charge. Scott4floors is said to be willing to go above and beyond: if necessary, the crew will "travel to any of the 50 states."

"Great personality." "Scott always calls the next day to check up on his work." "Floors are holding up beautifully." "Willing to work within a budget."

Wallpaper City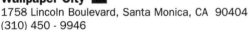
1758 Lincoln Boulevard, Santa Monica, CA 90404
(310) 450 - 9946

Wallpaper installation, straight and decorative painting, flooring, kitchen/bath design, installation and upholstery

See Wallpaper City's full report under the heading Painters & Wallpaperers

FIRMS WITHOUT PORTFOLIOS

AAA 1 Carpet & Upholstery Care
13127 Hartland Street, North Hollywood, CA 91605
(310) 451 - 3411   www.aaa1carpetcare.com

Area rug, carpet and upholstery cleaning and repair, hardwood floor maintenance and refinishing

See AAA 1 Carpet & Upholstery Care's full report under the heading Rugs: Cleaning, Installation & Repair

	Quality +	Cost $	Value ◆	Recommend? ★

Acorn Hardwood Flooring Inc.   3.5   2.5   4.5   5
12432-B Foothill Boulevard, Sylmar, CA 91342
(661) 255 - 9663   www.acornfloor.com

Hardwood design, installation, restoration and service

The husband-and-wife team of Greg and Donna Glasnow is the solid kernel at the heart of Acorn Hardwood Flooring. Over the years they've proved to be one of the most dynamic partnerships in the business, keeping in step with the latest trends in hardwood. Established in 1979, Acorn cleans, repairs, restores, installs, sands and finishes hardwood floors. The firm's specialty is "soft distressing," the process of making wood floors look old.

Acorn serves mostly high-end residential clients but has a small commercial following. The firm works all over LA, as well as in Santa Barbara, Santa Clarita and parts of Orange County—and occasionally as far away as Dallas and Denver. Pricing is usually per job, with a 500 square foot minimum in Los Angeles. Its showroom is open to the public, by appointment only. Licensed, bonded and insured, the firm is also an upstanding member of the NWFA. In October 2004, Acorn was featured in *Sunset Magazine* when it was selected to install the floors for the prestigious Sunset House project, confirming its status as an industry leader.

"One of the most reliable professionals." "Creative problem solvers." "Willing to go the extra mile to satisfy their clients."

Alpine Hardwood Floors Inc.   4   3   5   5
22516 Gilmore Street, West Hills, CA 91307
(818) 340 - 9806

Recycled hardwood design and installation

A sincere commitment to protecting the environment puts Alpine in rarefied air. Established by principal Bill Peiffer ten years ago, the firm has carved out a niche in hardwood flooring made from recycled lumber. Preferred by many eco-conscious clients, Alpine's recycled floors are distinguished by their deeper tones and darker colors, which can give them a rustic quality.

With nine full-time workmen, Alpine serves only residential clients around Beverly Hills, Malibu, Bel Air, Pacific Palisades, Brentwood and West Hollywood, though they have laid floors as far away as Aspen, Colorado. Pricing is per square foot and Alpine will work directly with designers, architects or contractors.

We hear Alpine is courteous and efficient, meets deadlines, and sticks to the budget. Reasonable prices and excellent quality put Alpine near the top of the heap in terms of value.

"Bill is definitely a problem solver. He's always on top of things." "He's very accessible—he even works on weekends." "Alpine submits its bids on time, and does what they say they will." "Top of the line."

Country Floors
8735 Melrose Avenue, West Hollywood, CA 90069
(310) 657 - 0510   www.countryfloors.com

Handmade and imported tile sales

See Country Floors' full report under the heading Tile, Marble & Stone

	Quality ✚	Cost $	Value ◆	Recommend? ★

Crogan Custom Inlay Floors   4.5   3.5   5   5

856 North Genesee Avenue, Los Angeles, CA 90046
(310) 474 - 1821   www.inlayfloors.com

Artistic inlaid flooring design and installation

Laurie Crogan's hip, unusual designs and materials reflect her beginnings as an artist. After designing clothing, jewelry and movie sets, she turned her exacting eye to flooring, founding Crogan Inlay Floors in 1981. It comes as no surprise that Crogan thinks outside the box, designing her custom inlaid floors in linoleum, cork, rubber and vinyl composition tile.

Described by clients as engaging, creative and efficient, Crogan designs, cuts and installs herself. In her capable hands, materials like linoleum and vinyl lose their supermarket associations and become sophisticated floors for high-end restaurants, clubs and homes. Licensed and insured, the firm works with architects, designers and homeowners in Beverly Hills, Bel Air, the Hollywood Hills, Malibu and Silver Lake. Other notable projects include a 3,000 square foot inlaid floor at the V2 Records headquarters in London and a restoration job at the Edison Building. Her work was recently featured in the glossy design book *Linoleum*.

Clients tell us the firm is efficient, precise and meets its deadlines. Customers don't mind paying a little more for a company they say is their first and only choice.

"Conscientious." "Incredible craftsmanship." "Creative and innovative."

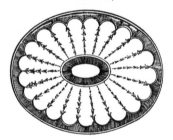

Eddie Egan & Associates   4.5   3   5   4.5

6136-38 West Washington Boulevard, Culver City, CA 90232
(310) 559 - 4341

Retail and installation for all types of flooring

A boutique legend in the business, Eddie Egan & Associates delivers stunning floors that are praised by decorators—along with architects, contractors and homeowners. This seasoned company works with all types of wood, vinyl, tile, cork and rubber, as well as wall-to-wall carpeting. The firm is good about maintaining its own work.

Founded in 1949, the company is now managed by Eddie Egan's sons, Dan and Armand, who supervise a team of twelve full-time, highly skilled workmen. Licensed, bonded and insured, the company primarily serves residential clients in Beverly Hills, Bel Air, Pacific Palisades and Malibu—but the firm has been spotted in Wyoming and as far away as Australia. The company's showroom is open to the public.

Egan prices by the job, offering free estimates, and there is typically no minimum per-project cost. We hear that Egan's workmen are professional, prompt and efficient—and that they will move small pieces of furniture. Clients appreciate the solid craftsmanship, the beautiful results, the very reasonable pricing and the "exuberant, extroverted, customer-oriented" management team.

"Outstanding. Well-established." "The boys grew up in the biz and know it inside and out." "On time. The workmen could do the job blindfolded." "Keeps up with technological advancements." "Service, reliability, longevity."

	Quality +	Cost $	Value ◆	Recommend? ★

Esh Hardwood Flooring Inc.

| | 3 | 3 | 4 | 4.5 |

23329 Hatteras Street, Woodland Hills, CA 91367
(818) 883 - 3326

Hardwood design, installation, restoration and service

Since 1995, Lee Esh's company has been building a reputation for color work and intricate detailing, one floor at a time. The company designs, installs, repairs, refinishes and distresses all types of regular and exotic hardwood floors. Licensed, bonded and insured, Esh serves mostly residential clients in Beverly Hills, Bel Air, West Hollywood, Pasadena, Malibu, Santa Monica and Santa Barbara. Some out-of-state projects have taken the firm to Washington, Colorado, Arizona and Nevada.

With twelve full-time installers, Esh Hardwood works with contractors, architects, designers and homeowners. The Fireman's Fund often calls on Esh to inspect and write up flood damage for insurance claimants. While Esh does not repair patterned floors, references agree that he is the man to call if you need someone to salvage another firm's dismal work. With reasonable prices, exquisite craftsmanship and quality service, this outfit is a favorite among Los Angeles' well-heeled residents.

"I've been giving him repeat business for years." "Scheduling is tight, but they're worth the wait." "After a flood, I thought my floors were beyond saving. Lee came to the rescue."

Holiday Carpet & Floor Covering Company

| | 3 | 2.5 | 4.5 | 4.5 |

505 North La Cienega Boulevard, Los Angeles, CA 90048
(310) 657 - 1301

All types of flooring—retail, design and installation

With its massive, well-stocked showroom filled with hardwood, vinyl, cork, rubber, tile, marble, granite and carpet, a visit to Holiday feels a little like a field trip. With so much to see and learn in one place, many Southern California residents find Holiday to be a one-stop resource for all their flooring needs. The company installs, sells and custom designs every conceivable type of flooring. It is also one of the few retailers in the city certified to lay Richard Marshall Olde Boards, a specialty hardwood line with a 31-step installation process. Established in 1957, Holiday is now owned and managed by Mark Cane, Mel Sapiro and Arnold Cane. Holiday's team of 40 full-time workers reflects the high demand for its moderately priced services. Rates vary per job and estimates are free. The impressive showroom is open to the public.

Hur Hardwood Flooring

| | 4 | 3 | 4.5 | 5 |

9614 Cozycroft Avenue, Unit C, Chatsworth, CA 91311
(818) 700 - 4985

Hardwood design, installation and service

Once upon a time, Michael Hur worked primarily in marble—but after discovering the beauty and pliancy of wood, he was hooked. Ever since he established Hur Hardwood Flooring in 1990, Hur has been a favorite among designers and homeowners in need of beautiful floor work. His firm's versatility extends to custom inlay work and restoring water-damaged floors.

Hur's nine-person firm has a strong following in the LA areas of Beverly Hills, Malibu, Pacific Palisades, Brentwood, Bel Air and the San Fernando Valley. With an equal number of residential and commercial clients, the firm works on new construction as well as remodels and renovations. Pricing is per square foot. For an additional charge, the crew will move furniture out and back.

References describe Hur and his team as hardworking, efficient, knowledgeable and open to direction. Hur is lauded as an honest and fair craftsman. Though prices are upper end, the large number of repeat customers reflects the value of Hur's work.

"A craftsman who makes sure the job is done right." *"Always met my expectations."* *"Will be there when he says. Reliable."* *"Great with follow-ups."* *"Hardworking, honest and fair."*

Melrose Carpet
7951 Melrose Avenue, Los Angeles, CA 90046
(323) 653 - 4653   www.melrosecarpet.com
Area rug and carpet retail, installation, repair and design; window treatments

See Melrose Carpet's full report under the heading Rugs: Cleaning, Installation & Repair

Michael D'Angelo Inc.   5   4   5   5
129 Oregon Street, El Segundo, CA 90245
(310) 647 - 6226   www.michaeldangeloinc.com
Hardwood design, installation and service

Insiders know the charming and well-spoken Michael D'Angelo as an institution in the hardwood flooring industry. Even in a crowd of amazing companies, D'Angelo's firm is a standout. Since establishing his business in 1987, D'Angelo has become a favorite of celebrity and other high-end residential clients from Newport to Santa Barbara, and as far away as New York, Denver, Washington and London.

The firm manufactures exquisite designs and inlays in its own factory. A loyal nine-member crew will also repair, restore and perform some upkeep, but only on D'Angelo floors. Workmen are said to be prompt and efficient. Head over to its showroom—by appointment only—and you may notice a plaque on the wall from the National Wood Flooring Association awarding the licensed, bonded and insured company Floor of the Year for 1997. Pricing is per square foot, with a 1,500 square foot minimum.

Clients praise this personable craftsman and rave about his unique floors. D'Angelo's floors are custom-designed to fit their spaces and have a furniture-quality finish. Some clients describe them as "artwork." As with a fine work of art, prices are high, but sources say the superb floors are worth it.

"The best floor man ever!" *"He's very expensive, but quality is there."* *"Works with the most unusual pieces of wood. Beautiful designs."* *"A real Old-World craftsman."*

Pacific Concrete & Design Inc.   5   3.5   5   4.5
PO Box 1288, La Quinta, CA 92253
(760) 773 - 9401
Concrete polymer specialty design and installation

When most people think of concrete, words like "plain," "gray" and "boring" come to mind. But after a visit to the innovative Pacific Concrete & Design, many clients are spellbound by the aesthetic possibilities of concrete flooring. Pacific's special process adds polymer to the concrete and trowels the mix to create floors that are "smooth as glass." Depending on a client's tastes, the firm will apply unique chemical pigments to stain, color and texturize the concrete, giving surfaces an ancient look. Or it will also stamp patterns onto the surface or stud it with rocks, bricks, tiles and other artifacts. The company recently introduced this application to furniture, developing tables and chairs made of concrete, but without the weight.

Founder and president Timothy Durnford was introduced to the concrete industry in Europe. He started his licensed, bonded and insured company in 1992. Durnford and twenty full-time craftsmen work with architects, designers, contractors and homeowners. The firm designs and installs concrete floors, walls, ceilings and columns. Examples of Pacific's handiwork can be found inside and outside homes and businesses in Beverly Hills, Palm Springs, Palos Verdes, Malibu, Bel Air, San Francisco and Seattle. Pricing is generally per job. The showroom is open to the public by appointment.

Customers and clients say Durnford and his company are creative, innovative and responsible. References tell us that although prices are at the high end of the scale, they are willing to pay for the firm's originality, longevity and quality service.

"Fabulous product. Extremely creative." "Durnford takes a personal interest in projects. Doesn't treat a job as just a job." "He's respectful and demands the highest quality from his staff." "I am constantly in search of craftsmen who can be innovative—Tim Durnford steps up to the challenge." "One in a million."

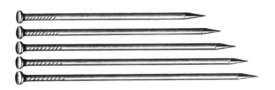

Renaissance Floor Inlays   5   4   5   5
1330 Egbert Avenue, San Francisco, CA 94124
(415) 822 - 3379 www.hardwoodfloorandinlays.com

Inlaid hardwood manufacturing, design, installation and service

Renaissance man Eugene Klotz's exquisite inlaid designs grow out of the marquetry techniques of Renaissance and Baroque craftsmen. Klotz, who learned fine woodworking at the School of Arts and Crafts in Cieplice, Poland, has been among the most respected names in hardwood inlays since establishing Renaissance in 1989.

The firm's largely residential clientele is concentrated in Los Angeles, San Francisco and San Diego, but Renaissance has also done projects abroad, such as the Queen of Thailand's summer residence in Bangkok. Licensed, bonded and insured, Renaissance has received seven Floor of the Year awards from the NWFA. The firm's work has been featured in *Architectural Digest* and on Home & Garden Television.

The company works with more than 30 species of both local and exotic wood and will soon publish a catalog of its original designs. In the past, Klotz has embedded stones, granite, marble and even semi-precious gems in his hardwood floors. Insiders tell us that Klotz and his crew are dedicated to their craft, and insist that Renaissance's beautiful original designs, unique inlays and superior service justify its competitive prices.

"Beautiful Old-World floors." "Unparalleled quality." "Great fabrication." "Competent and reliable." "Their inlay work is unbelievable." "Incredibly creative." "Responsive." "Can fuse Old-World and cutting-edge seamlessly."

153

Renteria Flooring Specialist

3.5 2 5 4.5

10228 1/2 San Gabriel Avenue, Southgate, CA 90280
(213) 422 - 2060

All types of flooring—retail, design and installation

An all-around resource for middle to high-end market flooring, Renteria Flooring works with wood, laminate, tile, vinyl, cork, rubber and linoleum, as well as wall-to-wall carpeting. Founded in 1985 by Jesus Renteria, who has been in the business since 1974, the firm is licensed, bonded and insured, and serves mostly residential clients in areas such as Hollywood, Beverly Hills, Palos Verdes, Malibu, Pasadena, San Marino and Brentwood.

Renteria prices by the job and clients describe its fees as moderate. Estimates are free. Our sources say this family business is professional and prompt. Renteria stands firmly behind the business that bears his name, offering a five-year warranty on labor.

"Personable demeanor and professional work attitude." *"Good quality for moderate prices."*

Richard-Marshall Fine Flooring Inc.

4.5 3.5 5 5

12520 Wilkie Avenue, Hawthorne, CA 90250
(800) 689 - 5981   www.oldeboards.com

Hardwood manufacturing, retail, design and installation

Clients report that Richard-Marshall Fine Flooring's impeccable floors look as if they could have been "taken from old English country houses." But the firm's Old-World craftsmanship is supported by cutting-edge techniques. The company is justifiably proud of its patented Olde Boards line of hardwood, for which it developed a unique 31-step installation technique called Craftech. Handcrafted in Richard-Marshall's LA workshop, Olde Boards planks come with an adhesive that has a high moisture barrier. The wood itself has a furniture-style finish that customers love. The firm is also known for creating specialty planks with marble, tile or even semi-precious stones embedded in them. Richard-Marshall's by-appointment-only showroom contains over 500 original designs created with a computerized drawing system.

This 110-person firm was established in 1995. Licensed, bonded and insured, Richard-Marshall is a member of the NWFA and an associate member of ASID. While it has a mostly high-end residential clientele, the firm is frequently called upon by top architects, contractors, builders and designers to work on jobs in Beverly Hills, Santa Barbara, the San Fernando Valley and San Diego. Out-of-California visits include Colorado, Arizona, Atlantic City, New York City and Las Vegas. Pricing is generally per job with no minimum.

Clients appreciate the minimal mess made during the installation process and the firm's incredible attention to detail, describing its workers as "hands-on craftsmen who will get down on their hands and knees to make sure every inch is perfect." Satisfied customers can't say enough about Richard-Marshall's courteous, responsive service. The floors' expensive look and exceptional durability make clients feel they get their money's worth. *"The floors look better as they grow older." "Each job is special. Not based on volume." "Passionate about their product." "They offer some features not available anywhere else." "Collaborative—worked with a pattern I liked and altered specs."*

S&J Biren Inc.   3.5   3   4.5   4.5

9563 West Pico Boulevard, Los Angeles, CA 90035
(310) 553 - 0971

All types of flooring—retail and installation

"Top notch" is how references describe S&J Biren Inc. Established back in 1948 by brothers Sam and John Biren, the firm has built a reputation for doing it all—selling and installing wall-to-wall carpets, area rugs and wood, vinyl, linoleum, laminate, rubber and cork floors. At 82, co-founder John Biren still manages the family business with his son Eric and nephew Evan, making sure that his eleven full-time installers and service people uphold the Biren standard of quality.

The licensed, bonded and insured firm caters to a primarily residential clientele in West LA, Santa Barbara, Palm Springs and San Diego. The company has also installed floors at LACMA and the Getty Museum. Prices for floors are determined by square footage, and by the square yard for carpets. There is a flat minimum for small jobs and area-rug delivery is free. S&J's eye-popping 3,500 square foot showroom is open to the public. Clients appreciate S&J's wide selection, excellent service and prompt follow-ups.

"Meets your needs." "Responds quickly." "Great inventory and top-notch installers."

Hiring a Furniture Repair &
Refinishing Service Provider

Does your prized baroque chair need restoration? Do you refuse to get rid of your comfortable thrift store couch but admit it needs sprucing up? Will your bedroom finally be complete with the addition of a twin reproduction of your favorite antique nightstand? Or perhaps you have a piece that has survived fire or flood damage, a teething puppy, climate changes or just general wear and tear. Before surrendering your furniture to the hands of a professional, you should know a few things about it and the artisan who will repair, restore or conserve it.

Where Do I Start?

Before hiring a professional to repair your piece, take the time to verify that your thrift shop bargain isn't a priceless antique in disguise and that your heirloom isn't actually an ordinary reproduction. Inappropriate restoration of an antique can greatly compromise its value. Sometimes a seemingly simple repair can actually cause further, irreparable damage. So be sure to have your piece's history and condition closely examined—preferably by several people—before allowing any work to be done.

Most professionals will visit your home to provide a price estimate and a detailed explanation of how your piece should be treated. Some charge fees for on-site verbal and written estimates, others don't. Estimates should include the cost of labor, materials and transportation. You should also discuss how your piece will be insured and whether or not a warranty will be provided for the work and under what conditions.

Knowing the value of your piece is important not only in determining the type of work that it needs and how well it should be insured, but also how much to invest in the work. If your thrift store table simply needs its broken leg replaced, you may not want to pay top dollar for labor fees. However, if you're concerned about transporting your original Louis XIV dining room table, you may opt to keep it at home and pay for a specialized restorer to work on site.

On Cost

Many professionals base their fees on an hourly or daily rate that is subject to increase, depending on the condition of your piece, the work it needs and where the work takes place. As a general guideline, hourly rates can range from $45 to $150. Others restorers, however, charge by the piece. Costs can vary depending on the condition of the piece and how much work needs to be done. In the case of per-piece fees, request an itemized estimate that clearly explains where each charge comes from. Be sure you receive a written contract for the amount of work agreed upon and the cost. If additional work is needed, the professional should notify you before taking action and a new fee should be agreed upon.

Choosing the Right Specialist for You

No licensing bureaus or governing boards regulate furniture restorers, so it is crucial that you take the time to find the right professional for your particular piece. Although furniture restorers tend to be well-versed in all styles and periods, each has a specialty. You wouldn't take a broken toe to an allergist, nor would you want to take your japanned armoire to a caning specialist. Inquire about the professional's area of expertise. For example, if your dining room table needs to be refinished, be wary of a craftsman who wants to use French polish and says you'll be eating from your table within a day or two. French polish is typically saved for show pieces, such as game tables and armoires, and is not used on surfaces that are prone to spills or burns. If you do want French polish, know that applying it is a time-consuming process that requires numerous layers of shellac and alcohol to be applied, dried and rubbed before being reapplied. Keep in mind that moisture captured between the layers can cloud the surfaces irrevocably, so humid weather will prolong the process. Be patient because a good professional will not want to rush the job.

Also, be wary of someone who is eager to refinish your Federal bureau, or any of your antiques. Much of the value of any antique derives from its rarity, quality and condition, and an original finish is an important part of this. A real craftsman knows that a furniture's original patina is what gives an antique much of its character. Be sure to find a professional who is as interested in preserving the unique qualities of your piece as you are.

QUESTIONS TO ASK A FURNITURE PROFESSIONAL

Although your main contact will most likely be the firm's principal, most firms have numerous employees, each with a different area of expertise. Ask who is working on your piece and what that person will be doing. The person who re-creates the leg of your table may not be the person who finishes it.

Don't be afraid to ask about the firm's expertise, including whether individuals have been trained in a particular style or period. Ask where they've worked and with whom. Also, ask to see their portfolios and to speak with numerous references. Make a point of speaking with the references. They know the work and will tell you if actual fees exceeded the estimate, if the work took twice as long as expected or—the best scenario—if the work was beautifully done.

FURNITURE CARE TIPS

✧ Protect furniture from direct sunlight, which fades colors, bleaches wood and clouds polished surfaces.

✧ Avoid exposing furniture to excessive heat—do not place it near a radiator or set hot objects upon it, as this damages surface coatings, veneers and underlying adhesives.

✧ Place coasters on surfaces to protect them from liquids, which can stain.

✧ Wipe up water-based spills with a towel, but dab alcohol spills carefully to prevent spreading the spill— alcohol breaks down finishes.

✧ Invest in a humidifier/dehumidifier to minimize large fluctuations in humidity.

✧ Use a buffer when writing on a table top. Pens and pencils can cause unsightly indentations.

✧ When moving furniture, lift by the strongest units or rails—never drag!

	Quality	Cost	Value	Recommend?
	+	$	◆	★

FURNITURE REPAIR & REFINISHING

🛍 FIRMS WITH PORTFOLIOS 🛍

LA Stripping & Finishing Center 🛍   **3.5   2.5   4.5   4**
1120 North San Fernando Road, Los Angeles, CA 90065
(323) 225 - 1073   www.lastripping.com

Refinishing and stripping of furniture and interior woodwork

From repairing carousel horses in San Francisco to restoring family heirlooms in Hollywood, LA Stripping & Finishing does a solid job the first time, every time. The small shop is run by the Lukasiewicz brothers, Rand and Zenon. The precocious Rand bought the shop in 1991 at the age of 21 and later recruited Zenon to be a partner.

We hear the two do a good deal of refinishing of mid-century modern furniture, although they have been known to work on fine antique pieces. Dabbling in everything from architectural restoration to cleaning up aging hardware, Rand and Zenon stay busy. On rare occasions, they will travel for projects. Sources tell us LA Stripping has recently taken on the interior restoration of a number of bungalow and Craftsman style homes in the city, as well as the job of refurbishing the passenger cars of the San Bernardino Southern Pacific Railroad. As of last year, the firm also began a distribution business for stripping and refinishing products such as paint removers and lacquer.

"A couple of nice guys who have a great attitude and like people." "Totally devoid of ego in a business that can be very snooty. And their work is solid."

FIRMS WITHOUT PORTFOLIOS

ALS Stripping & Refinishing   **4   4   4   4.5**
8860 Exposition Boulevard, Suite A, Culver City, CA 90232
(310) 559 - 4953

Refinishing, repair and waxing of fine antique furniture

Adolfo Lopez trained with some of the area's best refinishers, including Caesar Medina, before branching out on his own in 1984 to create ALS Stripping & Refinishing. Specializing in fine finishes, Lopez is said to be skilled with any kind of stain, color, crackle or antique finish. He also does antique repair, hand waxing and stripping, for projects that range from a small Italian desk to an entire wood-lined library. ALS maintains a low profile and is described as "a well-kept secret" by some, but this firm is well known within the industry.

Lopez is the sole principal of this firm, which has seven employees. We're told that the company can handle any size project in its 2,500 square foot shop. While he works primarily with decorators on large projects, Lopez will work with the public on small ones. The company services an elite Angeleno clientele from Brentwood, Beverly Hills and Pacific Palisades. ALS will also make house calls with a crew and one of two master finishers. Sources say that the firm charges by the piece and can be expensive. But the investment is reflected in the company's great craftsmanship.

	Quality	Cost	Value	Recommend?
	✚	$	◆	★

"To be that talented at that many finishes really is a testament to his passion for the craft." "I wasn't sure I'd ever be able to get my piece back to its previous beauty, but Adolfo pulled it off with flying colors."

Brady Wicks   5   4   4.5   5
84A Industrial Way, Buellton, CA 93427
(805) 686 - 2425
Conservation and restoration of fine antique furniture

Lynn Wicks has been the insider's choice for conservation and restoration of fine decorative arts, antiques, fine furniture and miscellany (fixtures, sculptures and candelabras) for more than 32 years. A crafts and design major at Cal State/Northridge, Wicks got his start building sets and props for a magic company. Since then, he has painstakingly taught himself the art of restoration. His extensive experience encompasses eighteenth- to twentieth-century furniture of French, English, American and Chinese origin.

In 1971, Wicks teamed with longtime friend Mike Brady to launch the firm. Today, Brady Wicks is helmed solely by Lynn Wicks, and the three-person staff now includes Wicks's son, Chris. The firm works with interior designers, museums, insurance companies, auction houses, educational institutions, collectors and homeowners of discriminating taste. The company's pristine work has appeared in the pages of *Design West* and *Forbes*.

About 25 percent of Brady Wicks's work consists of on-site maintenance at large estates. The staff goes to each home once a year to "tune up" a collection. The rest of its business consists of smaller projects, dealing mainly with French furniture. The staff has been known to travel to jobs throughout Southern California, but primarily stays in the LA and Santa Barbara areas. The company offers free estimates (except for insurance purposes, for which they charge) and provides bids on projects. Brady Wicks's prices are high end, but so is its reputation, which is rated by clients as "the highest imaginable."

"They have such a diverse practice that they can handle just about anything." "It's hard to say what their specialty is—they do it all so very well."

Cane & Basket Supply Co.   4   2.5   5   4.5
1283 South Cochran Avenue, Los Angeles, CA 90019
(323) 939 - 9644
Detail-oriented caning and recaning for chairs

Nearly all of Cane & Basket's business is devoted to restoring aging chairs to their former glory. But current owner Bill Fimpler does occasionally cane new chairs for small manufacturers and has worked on as many as 40 pieces for a single showroom. The shop is busy, handling up to 150 jobs per month. All work, including wicker repair and rush seating, is done on-site in Cane & Basket's workshop/store by the company's nine employees.

Cane & Basket has been in business since 1964, with Fimpler at the helm. Fimpler learned the basics of furniture from his father, but sources tell us he also takes a highly intellectual approach to his subject. Fimpler has read a tremendous amount about caning, as his shop's many books make clear.

Fimpler works closely with some designers, but pricing is the same for the trade and the public. Fimpler gives free estimates based on a self-devised pricing chart. Although caning is known to be very labor-intensive, Fimpler keeps his fees manageable and serves everyone "from Venice Beach to Beverly Hills."

"I can't imagine that the work he does was actually done by hand—it's so intricate." "I'm glad there's someone out there like him to do this stuff, because there's no way I could begin to figure it out." "He's a character, no doubt about it."

	Quality	Cost	Value	Recommend?
	✚	$	◆	★

Charles S. Poer Inc.   4   3.5   4.5   4

4910 West Jefferson Boulevard, Los Angeles, CA 90016
(323) 731 - 2935

High-quality painted finishes and antique reproductions

Some families hand down a love of cooking, others pass on a talent for sports. Charles Poer's family was partial to the genteel art of painted antique finishes. Poer learned the skill from his father, who in turn had learned it from his sister 40 years earlier. Today, Poer is respected by the city's decorators and architects for his 22-karat gold and chinoiserie finishes and his 30-plus years of expertise in antique reproductions.

Applying finishes to new furniture makes up about 90 percent of Poer's business, and he's able to take on jobs involving anything from a single piece to 50 pieces. Sources say Poer is also known to do architectural finishes for entire rooms, such as kitchens and libraries. Poer usually works on two to three estates each year, filling his time in between projects with numerous showroom commissions.

We hear that Poer "prices things to get jobs" and is flexible in his estimates. Many of his clients tend to be from Beverly Hills, Bel Air, Aspen and San Francisco. He's been published in *Architectural Digest* and has worked on pieces for television and movie sets, including *Dallas* and the *Father of the Bride* movies. He was recently commissioned to create the soda fountain sculpture in the soon-to-open Disney Store in Hollywood.

Cliff May of Mays of London   5   4   5   4.5

6567 Sheltondale Avenue, West Hills, CA 91307
(818) 377 - 4343

Fine French polishing, furniture restoration and period reproductions

"It's a dying trade," insiders say of the craft of Old-World finishing. Indeed, there are only a few remaining local artisans trained in the European style of antique restoration. Cliff May is one of that rare breed. We're told May will finish everything from chairs to mirrors in all styles, all periods.

After fifteen years' experience working with his father in London, May brought his expertise in French polishing to Los Angeles in 1987. He studied antique restoration at London's College of Furniture, where he learned gold leaf and other styles. Clients appreciate May's knowledge of French polishing as well as his ability to restore badly damaged pieces. He is also noted for his uncanny ability to maintain valuable pieces without leaving so much as a trace that someone has worked on them. Sources tell us that in addition to his many skills of preservation, he can also make new pieces appear as authentically old as a piece from the eighteenth century.

Many of May's significant projects come to him via decorators and contractors, although he will deal with the public for projects as small as a single piece. May has been known to take his skills on the road, traveling to Zurich, New York City and Florida at his client's behest. All work is done on location. May personally oversees each project, working with a crew that fluctuates between four and twelve

Quality	Cost	Value	Recommend?
✚	$	◆	★

members, depending on how busy he is. We're told he works seamlessly with decorators in coordinating and finishing a project. While some may have to endure a short wait for his services, clients applaud his extraordinary work.

"Exquisite craftsmanship." *"I wouldn't think of going to another person for French polishing."* *"This kind of work is in his blood, and it shows in the care he puts into each piece."* *"A charming old soul. A pleasure to work with."*

Don Cribb   5   4   5   4.5

1016 1/4 North Sweetzer Avenue, West Hollywood, CA 90069
(323) 650 - 1737

Highly customized surface finish restoration and leather antiquing

Don Cribb got into the furniture finishing business by chance when he helped unload a truck full of furniture on his day off as a volleyball teacher. As he was taking the last piece from the truck, decorator Rose Tarlow offered him a job in her workshop. After a long apprenticeship at area showrooms and decorating firms, Cribb started his own business in 1975. Today, Cribb expertly restores and refinishes all kinds of English, French, Russian and Italian furniture dating as far back as the seventeenth century.

We're told Cribb "likes a tough customer" and strives to make each project glow with high quality and taste. Cribb's fan base even includes other refinishers in the area, who often refer work to him. Cribb is known for his "gallery treatment," in which he inspects and delicately treats a piece of furniture as if it were a museum piece, keeping the original surface intact. Cribb's specialties include working with leather and wood, and applying "therapeutic finishes" involving different types of wax. He believes conservation is key, rather than constant refinishing, which diminishes the furniture's original patina and takes away most of its "character."

We're told Cribb approaches each project very scientifically and seriously, going as far as studying the air quality of a home. Sources say that he has a thorough knowledge of fumigation techniques and understands how sunlight affects different kinds of furniture. He charges strictly by the piece. While he's not the most expensive in the area, Cribb's fees are definitely up there. But sources tell us they are justified due to the care and skill he brings to a job.

"He's the guy I go to when the situation exceeds even my expertise." *"The consistency he applies to entire collections is unimaginable. And he does it all by eye."* *"Trained by the best and it shows."* *"The work looks like the original finish. That's the highest compliment."*

Joseph P. Reardon Antique Restoration   4.5   3.5   5   4.5

2275 Huntington Drive, Suite 125, San Marino, CA 91108
(626) 355 - 1840

Highly customized French polishing and in-home furniture restoration

Treasured for his ability to salvage existing finishes on exquisite antique English, French and Italian furniture, Joe Reardon has amassed a devoted clientele after less than a year. He went into business for himself in early 2002 after an eighteen-year tenure with a well-known Los Angeles furniture refinishing firm. Clients applaud Reardon's kind demeanor and professional attitude as well as his "impeccable" French polishing techniques and cosmetic touch-ups of interior architectural woodwork. Sources say that Reardon's specialty is the house call, and customers report that working with him is like "having an enthusiastic teacher in your house to answer any questions you might have."

Reardon is able to do gilding, but we're told he's most at home with wood finishes, veneer repairs and structural repairs to fine pieces. When a finish cannot be salvaged, Reardon is adept at re-creating almost any finish in any color. He will take on jobs of up to 80 pieces. Nearly all of his commissions are in-home

restoration calls that can last anywhere from an hour to two to three weeks, although he does do some work in his 600 square foot workshop. Reardon currently has two full-time employees and personally oversees each project.

"On top of being a really easygoing guy, he's about as talented as they come."
"There's no way you can tell his reproduction finishes from a 300-year-old original."

Kevin Brown and Co.   5   3.5   5   5
26 Brooks Avenue, Venice, CA 90291
(310) 399 - 0997
Custom furniture design, period restoration and reproductions

After 37 years in the business, Kevin Brown's dry wit is almost as famous in the industry as his skill as a restorer and manufacturer. Many of Los Angeles's most highly sought decorators swear by his skills at designing custom furniture and restoring valuable furniture of centuries past. Industry insiders rave that Brown "makes things look authentic, never mass-produced." Between his superior craftsmanship and his celebrated sense of humor, clients are pleased as punch with Brown.

Brown hails from the UK, where he studied architecture at London Polytechnic. After deciding against becoming an architect, he "learned by doing" at his father's furniture shop. Now he has his own 3,000 square foot workshop, where jobs range from designing a single custom piece to restoring a roomful of English and French furniture from the eighteenth and nineteenth centuries.

Brown is known for taking great care on each project, and clients appreciate his diligence and attention to detail. We hear Brown executes all the designs and drawings for his custom furniture himself and can recreate woodwork from any period or place. Of all of his fine attributes, Brown's preoccupation with creating a beautiful patina is considered the most notable. The majority of Brown's commissions come to him through decorators. We're told that due to his low over-head, Brown's fees, while not cheap, are a bargain for the quality of his work.

"He's a really funny guy once you get to know him, and there's no doubt he's one of the best." *"He studies each piece thoroughly before even touching it."*
"Quality, quality, quality. Enough said."

Luis Pirir Antique Furniture Waxing Service   4.5   2.5   5   5
161 South Berendo Street, Los Angeles, CA 90004
(213) 385 - 6453
On-site French polishing for the trade and public

Insiders tell us Luis Pirir is one of the most talented antique waxers in Southern California. Though he specializes in French polishing, Pirir will take on any kind of furniture, from the seventeenth century to modern pieces and reproductions. For polishing, touch-up and repairs, reports say Pirir can handle it all—and with the highest-quality craftsmanship.

Pirir started his own company seven years ago after working for an antiques showroom, where he got to know many of the area's interior decorators. Today, more than half of his work comes from designers. Clients often call Pirir to their homes to wax entire collections, which can take up to a month. The rest of his work comes from furniture collectors and showrooms, but we're told that Pirir is always willing to take on new clients and can do small projects at his shop. Pirir and his staff of three offer free on-site estimates, and sources tell us his prices are moderate, making his services an even bigger draw. Sources say Pirir is a pleasure to deal with and has a friendly, approachable personality.

"He's fast, neat, friendly and talented. What else can I say?" *"Takes the greatest of care with every single piece."* *"His hourly rate is more than fair."*

	Quality +	Cost $	Value ◆	Recommend? ★

Master Finish
6826 Crenshaw Boulevard, Los Angeles, CA 90043
(310) 877 - 3537

Antique finishing with a specialty in all forms of faux finishes

Insiders delight at the artistry of Luis Villegas, principal of Master Finish. We hear Villegas applies antique finishes to new furniture so well that it's virtually impossible to tell that a piece isn't hundreds of years old.

Villegas started his firm in 1987 and has carefully trained his staff of seven in the secrets of antiquing. With more than 22 years of experience, Villegas developed his skills working for some of the city's best-known refinishers. We're told that the firm works on any kind of furniture, whether it is a new line from a showroom, or a bona fide French piece from the seventeenth century.

With his expert eye, Villegas can perfectly match the color of any Old-World finish, as well as apply crackle, whitewash and faux finishes to nearly any piece. Villegas's 9,000 square foot workshop can handle projects ranging from a single piece to a collection of 50. We hear that he works closely with decorators and will make house calls. Pricing is by the piece and is considered high end, as is the quality of the craftsmanship.

"For the untrained eye, it would be impossible to tell the difference between Luis's work and that of a seventeenth-century Frenchman."

Master Finish — Quality 4, Cost 4, Value 4, Recommend 4

Murphy's Touch
2029 Pontius Avenue, Los Angeles, CA 90025
(310) 268 - 8285

High-end furniture restoration and ebonizing

Murphy's Touch — Quality 4.5, Cost 4, Value 4, Recommend 4.5

Paul and Stacey Murphy are partners in life and work. Together they founded Murphy's Touch in 1987: he practices the craft, she runs the business. With their staff of five, the couple handles the custom finishing and restoration of all kinds of fine antiques. Murphy's skilled restorers are said to keep antique pieces looking antique—but they also have a knack for making new pieces look old. Having worked for a king, museums and the Hollywood crowd, Murphy's Touch can pretty much replicate "whatever kind of finish you can come up with."

Paul is a third-generation custom refinisher who worked for restorers in LA and in England before setting up his own shop. We're told that "his ebonizing is truly amazing" and that the company "turns jobs around very quickly." Murphy's Touch works largely through decorator referrals, doing in-home projects and workshop jobs finishing up to 100 pieces. Decorators will often ask the firm to work on all of the furniture in a house. Murphy's Touch also does architectural finishing for libraries, floors and paneled rooms. The company's fees are priced per piece, based on the time and amount of work put into each. Prices are said to be on the higher end, but "you don't pay until you're happy with the work" and all work is guaranteed.

"Absolute professionals, both of them." "Paul is an artisan, no doubt about it."

Noel's Fine French Refinishing
4912 West Jefferson Boulevard, Los Angeles, CA 90016
(323) 731 - 2566

Old-World refinishing and antique restoration

Noel's Fine French Refinishing — Quality 4, Cost 3.5, Value 4.5, Recommend 4

Veneer work, high lacquer, gold and silver leaf finishes—Noel Ochoa is said to execute them all at the highest level. Noel's Fine French Refinishing, which was opened in 1992, generally takes on four to six large residential collections annually and has sent artisans to Florida, Germany and Italy. Though he has been called on to restore all kinds of antique furniture, the majority of Noel's projects involve applying Old-World finishes to brand new pieces.

The company charges by the job and is on the high end of the scale. We're told Noel's Fine French Refinishing works with a wide variety of clients, from younger professionals with modern tastes to the more classically influenced, older Hollywood crowd. About 75 percent of the company's work comes from decorators and architects. The rest of its projects come from showrooms and private clients. Noel's was recently one of the featured firms in the city's popular showhouses: The Brentwood House, The Pasadena Showcase House and The Designer Showhouse in Sherwood. The company's exquisite work has been seen in many magazines and was recently featured in three straight issues of *Architectural Digest*.

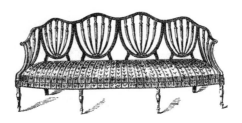

Philippe Graf Design 4 4 4 4.5
8927 National Boulevard, Los Angeles, CA 90034
(310) 839 - 4560 www.philippe-graf.com
Furniture restoration and refinishing with a strength in French pieces

Philippe Graf "doesn't waste his time on junk," say loyal customers. Born and trained in France, Graf specializes in repairing and building furniture—traditional, Art Deco, Art Nouveau, contemporary—you name it, he can build it. Clients say they admire his refined taste and his uncanny abilities with lacquer. While most of his work comes by way of decorators and architects, Graf does work with the public and is able to take on new customers. His fourteen-year-old firm deals with a young client base, who "appreciate high-end quality and have no problem paying for it."

Working closely with decorators and architects, Graf has recently come into his own as a custom furniture designer. Insiders tell us that he and his staff of four make exquisite armchairs and sofas. He will design and restore everything from one piece to an entire collection. Graf occasionally takes his talents on the road and has worked in San Francisco, Phoenix, New York City, France and parts of the Caribbean.

Graf is a favorite among decorators and architects, who say he can see a project through "from A to Z"—from the design process to the building to the actual installation (if required). All work is done in his studio. At any given time, his company works on as many as ten projects in its 2,500 square foot shop. Graf is flexible about his fee structure, either pricing by the piece or by the project.

"Philippe is a gentleman and a wonderful designer." "He's so flexible. He'll do almost any kind of project—as long as it's high quality."

	Quality	Cost	Value	Recommend?
	➕	💲	◆	★

Reborn Antiques

	4	4	4	4

853 North La Cienega Boulevard, Los Angeles, CA 90069
(310) 289 - 7785

Restoration, reproduction and design of custom lighting and fixtures

Customers rave that Mark Dierickx and Victor Hernandez are "unbelievable when it comes to rewiring old lamps." In six years, they have grown Reborn Antiques from a small company focusing on restoration to a 25-person concern that designs custom fixtures, sells reproduction lighting and refurbishes antique iron furniture, sconces, chandeliers and lamps. The company's philosophy is to work with the original finish to "bring the piece back to life." Reborn Antiques deals most often with the trade, a great number of jobs coming directly from interior decorators and antique dealers who need old pieces rewired.

Both Dierickx and Hernandez got their training by working for years with another mainstay of the Los Angeles antique lighting scene, Paul Ferrante. Reborn charges by the piece and insiders tell us prices range from reasonable to very expensive. In line with its costs, we're told the company produces a truly high-end product. The firm recently designed a new line of furniture and lighting fixtures with a "slight vintage flair" which can be viewed in their newly opened second showroom in the Valley.

"It's almost impossible to tell their reproductions from a 200-year-old piece. It's amazing." "Even with their large volume, you still won't find a flaw in their work."

Terrence Leiker Restoration

	4	3	4.5	4.5

4333 Dixie Canyon Avenue, Sherman Oaks, CA 91423
(818) 906 - 8831

Precision matching of finishes and fine furniture restoration to the trade

Terry Leiker began working in furniture factories and custom finishing shops more than 40 years ago. He also has eighteen years of experience as an architectural finisher. But Leiker's true love is antique repair and restoration, and over the last ten years he has built up a solid following for his work on some of the most extraordinary European and Asian antiques in the Los Angeles area. Specializing in house calls, Leiker currently services more than 60 homes annually. Sources report that an average on-site project involves 30 to 40 pieces and takes up to five days to complete.

The rest of Leiker's commissions are restoration projects that take place in his workshop. Clients say Leiker's greatest strength lies in his precise matching of finishes. He is also praised for his French polishing and varnish work. Working exclusively with decorators and designers, Leiker is said to have reasonable fees, especially given the decades of experience and knowledge he brings to the table.

"How can you question the skills of a guy with 40 years in the business?" "He doesn't take any foot traffic, and he shouldn't have to." "I was really impressed with his perfect match of my armoire's 200-year-old finish."

Valerie Newcomb Woods Antique Restoration

	4.5	4	4.5	5

3579 East Foothill Boulevard, Suite 226, Pasadena, CA 91107
(626) 791 - 4718

In-home restoration, repair and refinishing

Clients praise house-call specialist Valerie Woods for her artistic eye and appreciation for fine furniture. When Woods established her company more than 22 years ago, the idea of in-home restoration was a novelty. Today, 85 percent of Woods's work is house calls. Working like a mobile surgical unit for furniture, Woods and her staff do patinas and Old-World finish restorations on-site. We're told that crews arrive at homes equipped with their own lighting, tarps and sheets to ensure that no mess is left behind. When a job is done, the only proof of a crew's appearance is the perfectly restored piece of furniture.

Woods is sought after not only for her refinishing skills, but also for her knowledge as a teacher. She frequently leads discussions about furniture preservation and restoration. Given her expertise, it's no surprise that Woods's staff excels in French polishing. Though the firm is most often approached to work on English and Continental furniture from the eighteenth and nineteenth centuries, it has also worked with pieces of Portuguese and Asian origin.

In-home projects usually begin with the restoration of a single piece, but impressed clients often ask Woods to stay on for the maintenance of entire collections. The company takes on about one in-home project per week and it has been known to travel to Puerto Rico and New York City at a client's request. Sources tell us that Woods works with a privileged clientele that includes former presidents and entertainment royalty. While the company's prices aren't shy, clients say "you get what you pay for."

"She really is a teacher in every form." "A well-kept secret, but I guess she won't be anymore." "Her staff takes the job so seriously, it really is like an operating room when they get to work."

Hiring an Interior Designer or Decorator

The decoration of homes has captivated people throughout recorded history. In 67 BC, Cicero commented, "What is more agreeable than one's home?" Interior designers put their style, creativity and experience to work to help a home reach its full potential—be it a canyon bungalow or a multi-million dollar spread.

The Franklin Report has uncovered over 80 design firms in LA that clients consistently praise for their abilities and professionalism. Clients believe that these firms saved them considerable time and money by finding uniquely creative objects and avoiding costly errors. Each practice has its own style and personality, which is described on the following pages. Due to page limitations, we have tended to highlight the most well-regarded, beloved designers, which often translates into higher quality, costs and minimums. Remember, a "3" rating in quality is still "strong" and a "4" is "outstanding" with excellent references and skills. Also, a "5" quality often carries with it a "5" cost—over the top and unnecessary for most clients. Additional firms and the most current information may be found on our website (www.franklinreport.com).

Finding a Match

After you fully assess your needs and your budget (see *What You Should Know About Hiring a Service Provider*, page 5), we recommend that you gather photographs from magazines and books to share with potential design candidates to communicate your preferences. Through our research, we have found that the best interior decorator-client bonds are founded on common ideas of style and taste. Even the best designers can falter and lose interest in a project if they are not excited by the end goal. So as you gather potential names from *The Franklin Report* and from friends, focus on the preferred style of the designer and ask to see their portfolio (or view it on our website)—even if they say they can do anything.

As you narrow down your list and begin the interview process, think about your working relationship with the interior designer who, for better or for worse, will become a big part of your life. Will you be seeing the principal or the project managers on a regular basis? Are you interested in a collaborative process or are you looking for strong direction? Will you be offered a wide range of budgetary choices? Finally, the prospect of working with this person should feel positive and enjoyable. Given the amount of time and money you are about to spend, it ought to be fun.

On Cost

Only a client can determine the worth of an interior designer's services. The "great masters" of interior design are considered exceptional artists who may charge whatever the market will bear. No one ever valued a Picasso based on a markup over the cost of his materials. That said, the vast majority of designers are not masters, but competent professionals looking for a reasonable profit.

Interestingly, very few designers earn huge sums, due to the inherent unscalability of the process. Since clients generally want to deal with the Name on the Door and not a senior associate, a design firm can only handle so many projects a year, usually about eight. Therefore, even with an average job size of $300,000 including a markup of 33 percent, annual pretax profits to a designer working with eight clients equal only $67,500—a good living but not a fortune (especially compared to their clients).*

Just a handful of designers have the clout to make serious money. This can be done by charging unusually high markups or hourly fees, employing multiple senior project managers, selling custom products (which carry very high, undisclosed markups) and/or accepting only clients with very expensive purchasing habits. While you should know standard industry pricing practices, many clients are willing to pay more for additional service or amazing talent.

STANDARD INDUSTRY PRICING

There are three fundamental services for which interior designers receive fees: 1) up-front design plans 2) the purchasing of products (new and antique) and 3) "hourlies" for the oversight of construction and installation. While there is a different formula for each design firm using these basic elements, the total amount you pay should add up to the standards outlined below. A few LA designers charge one flat fee for all services (Rose Tarlow, for example), but most bill you separately for the three functions. The following pricing indications described are what you can expect from a very competent, experienced Los Angeles design professional—neither a part-time designer nor a grand master.

UP-FRONT DESIGN FEES: Ninety-nine percent of Los Angeles interior designers will charge an up-front, non-reimbursable design fee. This fee may be a flat negotiated price (recommended in most situations) or may accrue hourly. If you are using a flat rate for a four- to six-bedroom house, the price should be about $5,000 to $10,000 for a minor fluff job and up to $30,000 for a renovation with some structural changes. If you are adding a wing or starting from the ground up, design fees may come in anywhere from $30,000 to over $75,000, depending upon the involvement of the decorator.

If calculated on an hourly basis, the cumulative design fee should add up to about the same amounts as above. Some people put a cap on the hourly fees, but that can be unfair to the decorator if you change your mind a hundred times and never commit to a fabric. Alternatively, if you think you have a good plan in mind and are clear about your preferences, you can save money with hourlies by being a quick decision-maker.

Either way, you should have a clear agreement with the decorator about what the design fee covers. Does it cover all shopping with markups? All the rooms in the house? How many schemes? Are all discussions with the architects and the contractors included? What happens if you add a closet or a wing later? Are drafting fees included? For this payment, you should receive a specific furniture layout and the major fabric selections. The extent of these plans can range considerably, from loose sketches to extensive architectural drawings with coordinating furniture

---

*Assumes net/wholesale cost of products before the markup of $225,000 with a designer markup of 33 percent, totaling $300,000 of retail product cost to the client and $75,000 of markup/gross revenue to the designer. With a 15 percent profit margin (after all operating costs) net profit to the designer is only $11,250 for a client, or $67,500 for six clients (before tax).

memos, swatches and a detailed electrical plan. Qualify these expectations before you sign on.

Certain designers will charge a smaller design fee to repeat customers, and a select few designers have no design fee but larger product markups instead. Some providers, but not many, will operate on an hourly consultation basis, with the client doing all the subsequent shopping, purchasing at net and implementation.

NEW PRODUCT FEES BY PERCENTAGE: Designers earn most of their fees by delivering products, such as upholstery, case goods, window treatments, rugs and accessories. The vast majority charge clients a markup over the net (or wholesale) price. Designers who search high and low for the lowest-cost materials might charge a substantial markup, but still offer a very good value to clients.

⬧ **Product Markup Over Net:** Almost all the design firms in LA charge a flat 30- to 35-percent markup over net cost on all new products, including workroom costs. This pricing is considered "standard" in *The Franklin Report*'s designer reviews. The net price is often 40 percent below retail. So even with the decorators' 35 percent mark-up, customers ares still paying about 20 percent below the suggested retail price on fabrics—not a bad deal.

⬧ **New York Retail:** A few established, "old-line" designers charge "retail" on products, or what the showrooms state as retail. This is generally 50 percent above net cost on fabrics, 66 percent on new furniture and 33 percent on new rugs. For example, if the decorator were charged a net price of $100 per fabric yard, the client's retail price would be $150. Workroom costs are usually marked up 25 to 50 percent at NY retail (this is a very squishy number that should be clarified). This type of retail pricing is considered "high" in *The Franklin Report*'s interior designer reviews.

⬧ **Pricing Structure:** Remarkably, virtually no one charges under any other price structure—it is either retail or about one-third up for new products. This is an interesting unifying principle in an industry that contains so many variables.

⬧ **Points to Watch:** While the price may be clear, it is important to understand if the designer is charging an hourly shopping rate on top of the materials cost. Most do not if a design fee has been taken. Many do not even without a design fee if they are getting their one-third markup (unusual). Some may charge for shopping time, but stop the hourly clock when a product is officially chosen (lots of hours are put in, beyond shopping, for administrative ordering and installation).

⬧ **Another Consideration:** Understand if the designer is getting a markup on the subcontractors. Any artistic endeavor for which the designer plays a role may come with a fee (rightly so). But know what you are getting into. Is there a twenty-percent markup on the decorative painter? The mosaic tile layer? There may be a product markup or hourlies for overseeing this work (see hourly and oversight fees below).

ANTIQUE PRODUCT FEES: Antiques are fairly tricky. First, the retail price is usually negotiable with the dealer. Once a retail price is established, most dealers offer designers a further discount of ten to twenty percent. This presents a conundrum. For the designers to make their normal 30 to 35 percent markup, they may have to charge the client substantially above new retail price (which could be above or below the original retail price). This is further complicated by the fact that most antique dealers are happy to sell directly to the public.

The most satisfactory solution used in many successful client-designer relationships seems to be full disclosure with a sliding scale. These designers charge a markup over the new negotiated net price, their usual 30- to 35-percent markup for lower-priced items and a smaller markup for larger items (price breaks start at $25,000 to $50,000). Many designers further guarantee that clients will never pay over the original or new retail price. A few prominent designers appear to be able to hold to a set markup and/or not disclose the net prices. For expensive antiques, an independent appraisal may be warranted (see our listing of Appraisers).

There is an additional point that needs clarification between a client and the designer on antique purchasing. If a client happens to walk into an antique dealer on Melrose or an auction at Sotheby's and finds the perfect sideboard that has been eluding the decorator for months, should the decorator get a fee? Arguments may be made both ways, especially if that piece has been specified in the design plans, the decorator has spent time shopping for it (educating the client along the way) or the client seeks approval from the decorator before making the purchase.

Most decorators have a strong enough client bond to withstand these issues, and the client will not balk if, in fact, the designer deserves the fee. But specific contracts help in these times. An elegant solution that some of the more sophisticated designers have is to charge an hourly consultation fee under these circumstances or to take a much larger up-front design fee to cover all antique and auction purchases.

HOURLY FEES: Most LA decorators will charge an hourly fee for the time they spend on product procurement for which they are **not** receiving a product markup. A good example is when the designer picks out the kitchen tile or the marble floors but the contractor buys it. This is a standard practice in Los Angeles, and considered "standard pricing" in the interior-designer reviews, assuming the amount charged per hour is in line. Also, some designers will charge hourly for every meeting and "look-see" outside of their immediate product areas, and some will not. There should be an understanding of exactly what is covered in the design fee and what is not before you go to contract.

Hourly fees generally range from $75 per hour for a design assistant to $250+ per hour for a grand master, with $150 to $200 as the typical, well-established Name-on-the-Door designer rate. A few designers will charge a standard hourly fee for all or most hours and a standard markup on product, but this is unusual in LA. A compromise is occasionally reached where a decorator will charge a lower hourly fee for all hours (about $100 to $125) and a lower product markup (20 to 25 percent versus the standard 35 percent), which add up to about the same overall fee.

A very small but growing minority of designers charge clients on an hourly basis for all product procurement, including antiques, and pass the net prices through to the client with no markup. This methodology eliminates confusion and uncertainty on pricing, but introduces debates on how long it can take to order all the trims and fabrics for a sofa (it takes longer than you think). Hourly fees are particularly popular with architecture-trained designers (since that is how architects usually charge).

OVERSIGHT FEES: Rarely, designers will ask for fifteen to twenty percent of the general contractor's net product costs to coordinate the artistic direction of the entire project. While possibly appropriate if the designer has a very large role in the architectural direction or is the project manager, usually these services are covered in the up-front, flat design fee. Anything beyond the agreed-upon design fee scope is usually charged on an hourly basis (see above). Also, it is usually unnecessary to pay this oversight fee if you are using an architect who takes on the project manager's role.

FLAT FEES AND OTHER NEGOTIATED TERMS: As mentioned above, a limited but increasing number of designers will consider an overall flat fee for all of the services listed above. This fee would remain stable within a specified expenditure and scope, and go up or down if the product costs far exceeded or came in significantly lower than the estimates. But the key lesson here is that most interior designers are fairly negotiable on pricing and other terms, within reason.

CONTRACTUAL AGREEMENTS

Given the wide fee choices, it is highly recommended that you and your designer agree upon an explicit price scheme for each type of product and service before embarking upon a project. While not normally necessary, it is not unreasonable to ask to see all bills and receipts.

Also, before you sign, it is customary to speak with of one or two past clients (and occasionally, see the projects first-hand). Once the contract is signed, a retainer is often paid to be used against hourly fees. The design plans will be drawn and purchases will be made. Timing expectations should also be addressed in the contract, but in many cases the timing of materials is out of the control of the designer. Therefore, if you have specific deadlines, the designers should be directed to order only in-stock items.

LICENSING OF INTERIOR DESIGNERS

The debate over the potential licensing of interior designers has been spirited. Currently it is not necessary to hold any type of degree or license to legally practice interior design in California. While the American Society of Interior Designers (ASID) and the National Council for Interior Design Qualification (NCIDQ) administer qualifying examinations to become an Allied or Professional ASID member or certified by CCIDC (California Council for Interior Design Certification), only a minority of the top residential interior designers have complied. Most designers describe these tests as having more to do with health and safety issues (generally handled by architects) than with design competency and creativity. In fact, the tests do include sections on space planning, historical styles, fabric selection and all the necessary algebra, but do not really test creativity.

All this may change with a bill that could be introduced in the not too distant future. The bill would limit the use of the interior designer title to those with certain educational, experience and testing credentials (including the passing of the two-day NCIDQ exam). Those who are not certified would be classified as interior decorators rather than designers.

From a residential consumer viewpoint, there seems to be little correlation in *The Franklin Report* data between the passing of the NCIDQ exam and the satisfaction of the customer. However, so few residential designers in our list of the top 80 have taken the exam that the sample size is just too small to judge. As discussed in *What You Should Know About Hiring a Service Provider,* it is incumbent upon the homeowner to do a thorough investigation of the competency of any potential service professional through extensive interviews, referral information and a competitive analysis.

FINAL CONSIDERATIONS

As further described on the following pages, an overwhelming majority of the countless clients we talked with had very positive feelings toward their interior designers. While it may be possible to purchase "trade-only" fabrics and furnishings in other ways, truly successful decorating is about creating an intangible upgrade in mood and lifestyle that an expert can accomplish. Professional designers also have the creative energy and resources to manage projects in a cohesive manner from start to finish, realizing clients' dreams effectively and efficiently.

WHAT YOU SHOULD NOT EXPECT FROM
YOUR INTERIOR DESIGNER OR THE DESIGN PROCESS

- ✧ That the designer will maintain interest in the project if you cannot make any decisions.
- ✧ That you will attend each shopping trip or will be shown every possible fabric.
- ✧ That the designer can read your mind.
- ✧ That there will be no misunderstandings or mistakes along the way.
- ✧ That the designer will bid out every subcontractor. There is a reason that the designer has been working with the same upholsterer and decorative painters for years. On the other hand, if you have a favorite supplier, the designer should be accommodating.
- ✧ That the designer will supervise others' work without an hourly fee. (The designer should be there, however, to oversee the installation of their products at no additional fee.)
- ✧ That the designer will become your new best friend.

WHAT YOU SHOULD EXPECT
FROM YOUR INTERIOR DESIGNER

- ✧ That the designer will have a full understanding of your lifestyle and use of your living space.
- ✧ A full consideration of your interests and opinions.
- ✧ That some of your existing furnishings will be integrated into the new design, if you wish.
- ✧ That you will be shown a full range of options and products—creative ideas well beyond the Blue Whale. However, you should not feel forced to take whatever they purchased on their last worldwide jaunt (and pricing is really fuzzy here).
- ✧ That the designer will stick to a budget (and not tempt you with "the best" unless that is encouraged).
- ✧ That the designer will provide you information about the net cost of every item, if you desire.
- ✧ That the designer will be accessible and make a proactive effort, taking the initiative to complete the job to your satisfaction.

INTERIOR DESIGNERS & DECORATORS

🛍 FIRMS WITH PORTFOLIOS 🛍

Alisa Smith Design   4   3.5   4.5   4.5
By Appointment Only, Los Angeles, CA 90065
(213) 910 - 3491   coloursmith@gmail.com
Understated, reflective, graceful interior design

"Design enabler" Alisa Smith listens well and delivers a "personal and enchanting" product. Smith is also noted for her sensitivity to historic restoration: she intently follows the architectural lines of a structure, adding complementary interiors. Her use of color and light lets the space itself control the atmosphere, with furniture playing a subtler role. Often taking a cue from the client or the local environment, Smith prominently features vibrant colors and exotic themes.

Upon graduation from the Parsons School of Design in New York City, Smith launched her creative career as an art director in advertising. She moved to Los Angeles in 1989 and began doing color consulting for historic preservation projects, which, in turn, led her into interior design. One of her most notable projects was the transformation and restoration of Charlie Chaplin's old studio lot into the creative services department for A&M Records. More recently, Ben Stiller's Hollywood duplex was done in quiet, unpretentious elegance, emphasizing architectural detail.

As a sole practitioner, Smith generally takes on one major project and a multitude of color consultations and kitchen/bath renovations each year. Producers, business professionals and lawyers are her most frequent customers, most often doing one room at a time. Smith works on a standard hourly rate with no product markups. Reports cast Smith as a fiscal realist with projects starting at $30,000. References are pleased to recommend the good-natured Smith to friends for her patience and her ability to bring out the best in her clients and their homes.

"Her East Coast restraint results in a stunningly elegant product. Ends up meeting the budget, too." "The lines are simple, yet so well placed that the architectural details shine through." "Contractors really enjoy Alisa's professional nature and wonderful spirit." "It is amazing how Alisa inherently knows which paints work best in which light. She can even do this over the phone." "She is sweet and there is never any pressure." "I spent months trying to figure out the proper layout for my kitchen, and she came in and magically figured it out instantly." "Alisa was highly sensitive to our environmental concerns." "She understood the essence and soul of the house." "Alisa is a very special and caring person. As a therapist, I can say she would make a great therapist."

Annette English Interior Design   4   4   4   4.5
6230 Wilshire Boulevard, Suite 1775, Los Angeles, CA 90048
(323) 285 - 5180   www.annetteenglish.com
Handsome, harmonious, collaborative interior design

With her deep belief that the home should be a sanctuary, Annette English works most sincerely to find each client's hidden design persona. As English and her clients develop and create together, rooms evolve with a quiet dignity of character, usually in homogeneous hues, tempered by characteristic highlights. For some, this means acrylic and white leather, for others, deep woods and silk. But all of English's interiors offer a restrained reflection of the personality of the owner.

At the age of nineteen, English left her native Perth, Australia. For the next eight years she explored the world, experiencing New York, Turkey, Morocco and most of Europe and Asia. She eventually landed in San Francisco, where she designed and opened a dining hot spot. The decor received rave reviews, so—ever the entrepreneur—English embarked on a design career. English started her firm in 1996 in San Francisco, moving her operation to Los Angeles in 1998. Currently there are three on staff, working on about five projects at a time. English is amenable to doing a few rooms for new clients, and mostly works in Hancock Park, Beverly Hills, Holmby Hills and Westwood.

Noted for her clear project management skills and her straightforward, business-like approach, English charges a standard up-front fee which is applicable to later product purchases, lower product markups and hourlies. Product choices are wide, with reasonable replicas and alternatives to the standard course. Clients enjoy the process and applaud the final result.

"She took my vision and expanded on it, surprising me with the excellent results." "Flexible, accessible." "Services rendered with efficiency and promptness." "Great personality and wonderful taste." "Does what she promises." "Annette English created my dream home." "Annette is both creative and warm—a rare commodity in the world of interior designers." "A pleasure to work with. Annette understands her clients and leads them to creating a truly beautiful home that suits their every need." "She fulfills her mission statement—'to find the client's unexpected yet perfect choice.'" "Annette is a real find."

Antonia Hutt & Associates Inc.   4   4   4   4
755 North Kilkea Drive, Los Angeles, CA 90046
(323) 782 - 4949 www.antoniahutt.com

Color-infused, classic yet glam interior design

Creating her own trends, Antonia Hutt continues to design rooms with distinct verve and personality. Hutt loves to juxtapose unique forms with classic architecture as their foil, and saturated colors play off the most chic tonal surfaces. An independent yet realistic thinker, Hutt develops a magical composite of the client's concept and her own original thought. Ideas tend to evolve in phases, as Hutt considers the interplay of day-to-day necessities and theatrical possibilities. Clients feel they have been educated by the process and rewarded by the result.

Hutt grew up in England and began her design education in silversmithing and then antiques. Moving to Los Angeles, she opened an antique shop on Melrose that showcased her years of European "furniture-picking" expertise. She also worked for Vincent Jacquard. Going to school in the evenings, she completed UCLA's four-year design course in two-and-a-half years (under the tutelage of Rose Tarlow). She founded her own office in 1992, whose staff of three is said to be highly organized and effective. Clients are most often actors, producers, writers, musicians and other creative souls, including Debra Messing, Courteney Cox, Sandra Bernhard and Sean Connery.

Reportedly never over budget, Hutt's plans are quite detailed. Either a flat design fee or a retainer is taken up front with a deductible against higher hourly fees. Standard product commissions are taken on purchases. Hutt is known to gravitate toward the "top end" but offers choices. Many clients become converts and friends. HB Top Designers, 2000, 2001, 2002.

"Antonia is smart and dedicated—she is on a mission to create something that sings." "She will only buy things that she loves and that really make a difference." "She can do the most robust colors or a toned-down version, but it always has a point of view." "Somehow she can make various centuries rest easily together, but at times you have to tell her no." "Antonia did an amazing job using what we already owned—she is a perfectionist and realistic at the same time." "Every piece is clean and vibrant, like gemstones in my house." "She marches to her own stylistic drummer." "She took my basic concept and turned it around brilliantly— I am amazed at the result." "A straight shooter." "She remembers every color she has ever seen and is a terrific problem solver." "A high-level performer and a real professional." "A Mondrian in a world of soft Impressionists."

Arch-Interiors Design Group Inc. 🛍   3   3   4   4.5

275 South Robertson Boulevard, Beverly Hills, CA 90211
(310) 652 - 7600   www.archinteriors.com

Tailored, innovative, diversified interior design

Employing earthy tones and warm practicality, Christopher Grubb and his team develop urbane, textural environments that clarify the client's desires. Typically working in a modern sensibility with clean lines and subtle colors, outdoor grilles may be highlighted in African masks while bedrooms may be done in multiple patterns of gold-infused hues. Furnishings are generously proportioned and the rooms are dramatic.

Grubb is commended for his design guidance and business acumen—he offers an optional "turnkey" approach where the firm handles everything from design inception to choosing and overseeing the contractors and subs. Focusing simultaneously on residential, commercial, trade shows and retail/hospitality, the firm parlays the knowledge of one design discipline into innovative ideas for another. While Grubb has successfully undertaken many extensive ground-up projects, he is also quite willing and able to do single-room redos, and kitchen and bath renovations are a specialty.

Arch-Interiors was established in 1994 when Grubb left ArcForm Design, where he had managed multimillion-dollar Las Vegas hotel constructions and high-end residential projects. Previously, Grubb studied interior design in Milan and at the San Francisco Academy of Art, and worked on a number of commercial design projects for Bally of Switzerland, Apple Computer and Disney. We hear that his staff of seven is among the most articulate and competent in Los Angeles and now includes a landscaper. Responsible project managers supervise each job, with Grubb collaborating.

Arch-Interiors works on a standard hourly rate for up-front design and shopping, and it charges a standard product markup. The firm is said to be good about working within a budget, collaborating and keeping a realistic perspective. Clients often start small and grow with the firm in phases, as funds allow.

"Technology is a strength—but they know not to get carried away." "Christopher spent a lot of time up front understanding our lifestyle." "A metamorphosis occurred in my bathroom. After that I hired Christopher to do the whole house." "They think outside the box—maximizing space with continuity and creativity."

"While they offer a number of economic choices, they encouraged me to make an investment in my space. I now fully agree." "Process is their forte." "They are consistently professional and courteous." "Christopher imagines fantastic possibilities and implements them with control and patience." "They are so practical on price and know of so many options."

Atelier AM   4.5   4   4.5   4.5

8265 Marmont Lane, Los Angeles, CA 90069
(323) 654 - 6401 www.atelieram.com

Sophisticated, restrained, graceful interior design

With strength of character and sophistication beyond their years, Alexandra and Michael Misczynski have already completed commissions for some of the biggest names in town. Bridging the traditional and contemporary, Atelier AM has that undefinable magic that sublimely suffuses a room. Restraint is a critical factor—both in the calming, neutral palettes and the highly edited number of pieces that grace a room. Enthusiastically recommended by clients and peers alike, Atelier AM looks to be one of the great up-and-coming firms in LA design.

It's apparent from their impeccable work that this husband-and-wife team trained with the best. Alexandra graduated from Hamilton College in fine arts and then worked with Naomi Leff for four years and Michael Smith for three. Michael graduated from USC in architecture and then trained with Rose Tarlow for two years and Richard Meier for three. Their firm, established in 2000, has a few on staff and takes on about five projects at a time (recently, Michael Eisner and Eli Broad). The principals are intimately involved in every design decision while the firm is developing its distinct imprint.

Antiques are important to the look and the process of creating rooms with a finely honed patina. Budgets can be set up front or evolve, but they are commensurate with Atelier's high quality. The firm's flat fee is set up-front based on scope. Thus, the finest antiques or (rarely) Crate & Barrel may be used, with no differentiation in design fee. Clients remark that great care and attention are lavished on the project, with extraordinary results.

"Each item is stunning in its own right and then looks impeccable in its chosen location." "They are clear in their own design focus and simultaneously clear as to who the client is." "They are totally in control of the process and the subs— when they say a fixture will be here by 9 AM, you can bet on it." "Incredibly responsive." "We had an architect of necessity, but hired Alex and Michael for their taste." "Consistent in look and in deed." "They both look like they could be in the movies, but have no attitude." "Expensive, with a strong preference for antiques, but the pieces do not have to be the highest end. They are not snobs about it." "They are dedicated to details: doorknobs, little accessories. All the things you take for granted, but actually transform the look." "Catch them while you can."

Audrey Alberts Design   4   4   4   4.5

11664 National Boulevard, Los Angeles, CA 90064
(310) 477 - 8315 www.albertsdesign.com

Contemporary, clean interior design

Audrey Alberts is best known for her ability to sensitively complement contemporary architecture with responsive interior design. While conversant in many design styles, leading-edge architects often recommend Alberts as "the only decorator I know who will not mess up the aesthetic." Alberts adheres to the clean lines of form with unadorned furnishings in tranquil shades of pale or earth tones. Modern artwork often factors into the picture, adding depth and interest. For more traditional venues, Alberts does streamlined neutrals and mid-century calm. Clients report that they prefer their new, reflective homes to any imaginable spa or travel location.

After graduating from the Art Institute of Chicago, Alberts worked in textile development at Jack Lenor Larsen and then with a prestigious residential design firm. After moving to LA, she designed retail shops, worked with several commercial architect and interior designer firms and formed Audrey Alberts Design in 1986. We hear she encourages an open design forum with her group of four in-house designers. Clients mention the entire staff is "professional and friendly." Today, her well-heeled audience is mostly residential. Alberts will take on smaller projects for young couples, appreciating their enthusiasm for design.

The firm takes pride in its comprehensive project management skills, including scheduling, coordinating, purchasing and installation. Charging by the hour, Alberts takes a retainer up front and invoices the client twice a month, based upon scope. There are no markups on product. Overall, the pricing is in line with other high-end designers.

"Audrey saved the day. We moved from Westchester to LA, and she guided us through the process." "She has a strong vision, but is also completely collaborative." "Right on the mark with her color palettes, they work so well with the minimal forms." "I never knew how much thought could go into choosing the right shade of gray." "She convinced me of a metal table, though I was skeptical. It is now my favorite piece." "Audrey was also so helpful with the millwork." "I love the entire staff who returned all my calls immediately." "Audrey totally took control when the painter had a mental breakdown." "Very professional and friendly, I wanted to stay connected to her after the project was completed."

B. Jordan Young Inc.   3.5   3.5   4   4

4121 Wilshire Boulevard, Suite 101, Los Angeles, CA 90010
(213) 305 - 1273   bjyla@aol.com

Evocative, warm, theatrical interior design

Believing that a home is the stage for the theater of life, Bettye Young seeks to deliver the dramatic. Rooms are designed to fulfill the dreams of the client, whether they be sleek Art Deco dreams with panache, artful early Californian ones or ornate Louis XVI fantasies complete with antique Flemish tapestries. Statements are made with strong palettes, layers of detail and a certain dash of fun.

Raised in Georgia, Young's 30 years in the design profession took her to Atlanta, New York and finally Los Angeles. A one-woman show, Young impresses clients with her patience and willingness to design—right down to the soap in the dish. Young is known to have a broad perspective and a broad clientele. From CEOs to artists to young marrieds, projects may range from a 21,000 square foot mansion in Brentwood to a modest makeover. Similarly, living rooms can go from $50,000 to over $1 million.

While most say Young defines clear schedules and budgets, others say things tend to evolve. References compliment Young for using their existing furnishings and for introducing a range of economic choices, albeit for generally intricate designs. An hourly design fee for non-product time and a lower-percentage markup on products is the norm, but Young can also work on an hourly consulting basis for smaller projects. She recently opened a Palm Springs outpost.

"Bettye absolutely spends the time to understand what is the ultimate for her client." "The inlaid floors were modeled after the Roseland Ballroom. They are incredible." "My gossamer cloud drapes cheer me every morning." "She has been so gracious. We have gone in waves with her following a master plan." "She has a good knowledge of antiques, and what little she does not know she figures out." "When we decided to put an agenda together before every meeting, the time was spent more effectively." "Over the top for my friends but I love it." "Her rolodex is deep and she is very kind about sharing it." "Bettye loves custom everything and lots of trims." "We gave her free reign and she did not take advantage of it." "I have great respect for Bettye and her whole team."

Brad Dunning 💼   4.5   4.5   4   4.5
8935 Dicks Street, Los Angeles, CA 90069
(310) 385 - 0006   braddunning@earthlink.net
Aesthetic, rakish, modern interior design

After first being knighted by Tom Ford and most recently by Demi Moore, Brad Dunning is now firmly ensconced as the leading edge of modernism in Los Angeles. In fact, Dunning has moved beyond modern and is developing a lighter touch, working with textural materials and a contrasting palette. Part artist, part intellectual, always forward-thinking, Dunning is noted as "the real thing" by his clients who are often fashion icons themselves. Rooms of clean edges, luxurious fabrics and modern materials are sparely complemented by handsome counterpoints of form. Clients also applaud Dunning for his business sense and the unflagging initiative that keeps his projects on track.

After two years with the Museum of Contemporary Art in LA, and another two with Roy McMakin, Dunning was working in set design when he was called into interiors by his associates. He opened his doors in 1995 and now handles about five major gut renovations at a time with a staff of four. Clients say that Dunning is extremely straightforward and that his back office is very effective. His recent run as a contributing editor to *GQ* has only added to the appeal. Clients include photographer Steven Meisel, Eric and Lisa Eisner, Sofia Coppola, Courteney Cox Arquette, Spike Jonze and Bryan Lourd, principal of CAA.

With a clear budget in mind, the firm works on standard hourlies and a standard product markup. Furnishings range from the very best antiques to quintessential Paris flea-market finds. Besides the well-heeled notables above, customers include young bachelors on a tight rein, for whom living rooms can cost as little as $40,000—of course, other living rooms can go for well over $500,000. Furnishing fees are taken at standard markups or on an hourly consulting basis with a smaller design fee.

"Brad stays true to the style of the house and the vision, without that feeling of being a slave to the sensibility." "Brad is incredibly gifted. He just sees the issues and crafts the answer." "Thank goodness we caught him at the beginning—now he is the hottest ticket in town." "There is a cerebral focus to Brad's work that makes you want to take it to the next level." "Brad is intent upon delivering a crystalline vision, true to its historical roots." "Not a shabby chic kind of guy, but not a snob either. It just has to look clean and handsome." "It is all about elegance and quality." "He has expensive taste, but so do I." "I would not change a light bulb without asking Brad first." "He is the only person I would ever want."

		Quality	Cost	Value	Recommend?
		+	**$**	**◆**	**★**

Brown-Buckley Inc. 🛍   3.5   3.5   4   4

9036 Vista Grande Street, Los Angeles, CA 90069
(310) 274 - 7652   brnbuckley@aol.com

Characteristic, comfortable, caring interior design

Clients commend Tom Buckley for his knowledge of various design periods and details, his stylistic flexibility and his gentlemanly nature. In the interior design business for almost 50 years, Buckley is an established presence in LA. He most often works in the traditional mode, but in recent years, he has produced simpler, edited, relaxed versions of his eclectic past. Brighter colors are still favored, either as the main palette or as strong bit players. He is most often cited for his sincere interest in working with patrons to achieve their design objectives.

Buckley established his firm in 1969, after working in New York with the legendary Mrs. Brown at McMillen Inc. for fifteen years. The firm has a notably strong staff of four with Buckley as the primary client contact. Buckley does most of the shopping himself and takes on about four major projects each year. Many clients have been working with Buckley for over twenty years, but are now updating in a less formal style.

Budgets tend to evolve, with antiques used regularly. Buckley usually works on rooms from the raw walls all the way up to the last accessory. A sizable retainer is taken up front, half of which is applicable toward future fees. Standard product fees are charged, with higher hourly rates for non-product consulting. Products of higher cost and quality are most often favored, but clients do not feel pressured. Buckley's many fans appreciate his good humor and responsiveness.

"Tom still understands the value of a handwritten note." "Such a likable person." "His original presentation gave me great confidence up front, and he never pushed." "He considered every idea that we suggested." "The minute you walk in the door you are 'hugged' by the design and drawn to sit down." "His color palette and melange are not for everyone." "My husband wanted the house to look like a Savings & Loan and I wanted an English Cottage. Tom graciously figured out a way to make us both happy." "Tom works from sunup to sundown to get it right for the client." "Tom likes the high end, and we really did not have a budget." "Three other designers came and went. He was the only one who listened to my ideas and had the patience to work it through." "I invited Tom and his staff to my son's wedding. They have become part of the family."

C.M. Wright Inc. 🛍   5   5   4   5

700 North La Cienega Boulevard, Los Angeles, CA 90069
(310) 657 - 7655   cmw@cmwright.com

Sumptuous, detailed, historically derived interior design

Adroitly developing the archetypical California design vernacular, Craig Wright creates rooms with a dazzling sense of wonderment. Building on the client's interests, Wright most often delivers spectacular, lavish, continentally influenced panoramas on a grand scale. For others, more understated "oases of calm" may be realized. Featured in *Architectural Digest* 38 times, Wright has developed a celebrated following. Described as both sharp and genteel, Wright is said to have "patience beyond belief" and the deepest interest in making the client's dreams come true.

A native Angeleno, Wright studied architecture, fine arts and art history at USC and UCLA. Soon after his first decorating project in 1966, he began making regular shopping forays to Europe for clients, igniting a lifelong passion for antiques. In 1977, Wright founded Quatrain, his antiques (and more recently, reproductions) gallery. Today, most of Wright's interior design business serves many business luminaries in the local area, with a sprinkling of celebrities (Michael Douglas, Dan Aykroyd, James Coburn and assorted barons and baronesses).

A staff of nine assists Wright with about eight large projects at a time, but references feel that Wright develops all the design decisions. Shooting for the finest quality, Wright will often show clients the best first and try to hold the line. Vendors confirm that Wright has an exacting eye, but further mention that he seeks good value for his clients. Drawing rooms make the strongest statement, often boasting curtains "likened to the finest couture gowns." Markups are standard, fine antiques much lower, and there are standard hourlies for non-product time. Clients are unanimously delighted with the process and the result. AD 100, 2000, 2002, 2004.

"The project was about our lifestyle. Craig really listened—it was never about him." "He opens doors, throughout the US and Europe." "Craig can take care of every interior and exterior detail, but he also welcomed me to become involved." "We would not buy a doorstop without him." "Craig can somehow be both really direct and also incredibly nice." "He will go to any length to make something as small as a welt just right. Days have been spent on a welt." "Craig takes on a good workload, but it is not overwhelming, so we always felt there was sufficient time for us." "His only weakness is that he needs another ten hours a day, because we so enjoy his company." "He is a classic workaholic—getting in and out expeditiously." "When you hire him, you get Craig, not an assistant." "Most of the homes are new, and filled with a dramatic mélange of the magnificent and the comfortable." "While bills can be quite high, late and complicated, you absolutely get what you pay for." "We did not have a budget." "Craig creates his own sense of history—which is the classic California dream."

Chris Barrett Design, Inc.   4   3.5   4.5   4.5

1640 Nineteenth Street, Santa Monica, CA 90404
(310) 586 - 0773 www.chrisbarrettdesign.com
Confidently comfortable, genial interior design

Bringing a familiar calm and warmth to each project, Chris Barrett is known for her designs of down-to-earth elegance. There are usually a few well-loved antiques that invite you into the room, complemented by clean lines and soothing textures. Intriguing vintage accents enhance the appeal. Recently, Barrett has worked on a tremendous variety of homes—from a formal yet soothing 18,000 square feet in Bel Air to a homey Cape Cod cottage in Santa Monica to comfortable Spanish glam in Hollywood Hills. She is currently working on the restoration of the 28 cottages of the San Ysidro Ranch, where JFK and Jackie honeymooned.

A former actor, Barrett graduated from UCLA's interior design program and formed her practice in 1984. She now has a group of four working on about three major and several smaller projects at a time. Commissions include the homes of Charlize Theron and *Scooby-Doo* star Matthew Lillard, as well as the office of Jerry Moss. The back office is noted to be highly efficient. In addition to her residential work, Barrett recently designed a line of tableware and rugs.

Most commissions are of entire homes, but smaller kitchen and bath rejuvenations are often undertaken. Living rooms can be done with exquisite antiques or with product sourced from Pottery Barn, as long as there is a mix of style and provenance. The firm charges a standard design fee and a standard commission. Time and economic benchmarks are set realistically and met, with strong lines of communication throughout the life of the project.

"While other designers might consider a piece too worn and funky, Chris loves to ground a room with such warmth." "She is constantly on the move, but amazingly effective." "She really valued our perspective." "Chris encouraged us to use forgiving fabrics like linens and chenilles which wore so well over time." "Chris just makes sense to my husband: she is good with Kohler's and Maytag." "I learned to trust Chris's vision." "You have to exercise a certain amount of self-restraint because Chris finds the most wonderful things. But she is always

	Quality	Cost	Value	Recommend?
	✚	$	◆	★

good if you say no." "She is not shy, but quite collaborative." "Chris was always on call and dealt with the architect and contractor very well." "She has a very calming effect on everyone." "We loved everything she did except for one chair, but we did not tell Chris. Somehow she knew and magically had the chair reupholstered while we were on vacation."

Christopher Coleman   4   3   4.5   4.5

55 Washington Street, Suite 707, Brooklyn, NY 11201
(718) 222 - 8984   www.ccinteriordesign.com

Graphic, bold, witty, contemporary interior design

Clients appreciate Christopher Coleman's confident mix of geometric shapes, clean lines, exuberant colors and warm undertones. They also applaud his enthusiasm, wit, warm personality and willingness to take design risks. Following five years with Renny Saltzman, Coleman founded his design practice in 1993.

Based in New York, Coleman recently made his Los Angeles debut with residences in Pacific Palisades, Westwood and *House Beautiful*'s showcase in Brentwood. Coleman's modern, intelligent forms are perfectly suited for California living and have been very well received. Past clients include *Harper's Bazaar* editor Kate Betts, Helen Henson (Jim's wife), Time Inc. chairman Don Logan, many established professionals and also young couples decorating their first homes. Clients credit Coleman for taking the time to educate them about the design process—including classical historic styles, economic alternatives and timing. Other strengths include a sensitivity to family living, a flair for mixing the old with the new and Coleman's contacts with highly creative artisans. References say Coleman is available, attentive and lots of fun.

Coleman works with a smaller up-front design fee, lower percentage over net for products and no hourlies. He is known for his ability to make the most of less with high-style excitement on a modest budget. Clients report that Coleman is extremely professional and straightforward: all bills and the background paperwork are presented on a regular basis. A new line of Coleman's carpets was recently introduced by Doris Leslie Blau. HB Top Designers, 1999, 2000, 2001, 2002, 2003, 2004.

"Christopher designs fearlessly with class and coherence." "Such a joy to work with." "Whatever he cannot find at a reasonable price he gets made. His upholstery people can do the highest-quality sofas for half the price of what we expected, and deliver in half the time." "He is overtly modern without being rehashed retro." "We so enjoy his creativity. Anything can become an interesting design motif to him—country, ethnic, old maps." "He is the only guy in the business who can do red vinyl successfully." "When I was after a particular, very expensive Italian look, he found a very good match at Crate & Barrel." "We interviewed twenty decorators over the phone and five in person, and feel so lucky to have found Christopher." "He has a wicked sense of humor and a hip design sensibility to match."

	Quality	Cost	Value	Recommend?
		$	◆	★

Dale Carol Anderson Ltd.   4.5   4.5   4   5

2030 North Magnolia Avenue, Chicago, IL 60614
(773) 348 - 5200   www.dalecarolandersonltd.com
Classical, sophisticated, flawless interior design

Setting new industry standards for client service, Dale Carol Anderson and her team are said to know more about clients' homes than they do. Delivering strong, timeless designs with a brushed patina, Anderson is considered a master by her patrons. Rooms often include fine French furniture or English antiques expertly mixed with modern, comfortably sized upholstered pieces in calm, warm hues. Accessories and dramatic lighting figure largely in the designs. Clients remark that no detail is too small for Anderson to do to perfection.

While based in Chicago, several recent substantial projects have been on the West Coast. Most clients are established business leaders, many with multiple homes all done by Anderson. With five employees, Anderson takes pride in working closely with clients, and manages long-distance relationships very successfully. Alternatively, Anderson will do turnkey projects where she has carte blanche, especially for vacation homes. Her staff is consistently praised as extremely professional and discreet, with a willingness to "pitch in any way they can."

We hear that the value of the chosen items can be as high as the client wants but is balanced with more reasonable product. The firm works with an up-front retainer, standard markups on products and high hourly rates (lower for design associates). Anderson is considered to be a well-kept secret, passed among close friends. ASID.

"Dale always exceeds our expectations." "She was able to complete our West Coast project very successfully with her usual custom designs and personalized service." "Dale has the most amazing Old-World craftsmen and antique sources." "She will pull out all the stops for the client. What may appear compulsive to some, is a big plus for the right client." "The day before a big party, she made the electricians move the sconces so they were exactly centered, just as they should have been." "Dale redesigned the windows and chose all of the materials, including the flooring and cabinetry, from afar. I was amazed at how cost-effectively it was done, with her flying out here only once." "All the upholstery is big enough for long naps." "California was our fourth project with Dale, who continues to please us as much with the process as with the outcome." "She is the consummate professional with the client's interests at heart."

David Desmond   4   3.5   4.5   5

1360 North Crescent Heights Boulevard, Los Angeles, CA 90046
(323) 650 - 0492   www.daviddesmond.com
Streamlined, classical, fusion interior design

Roundly applauded for his professionalism and educated point of view leaning toward classical modernism, David Desmond has built a devoted clientele. A man who excels at whatever he does, Desmond graduated from Williams College with honors in French, after spending his junior year at the Sorbonne. After college, he returned to Paris for four years where he formally studied art, architecture and design. Temporarily changing his course but not his drive, Desmond received a law degree from UCLA, passed the California bar and practiced law for five years. Returning to his creative passion, Desmond studied design at UCLA by night while handling class-action suits by day. Soon his UCLA professor, the respected Antonia Hutt, convinced Desmond to quit his day job and work with her. Since launching his own firm in 2000, Desmond has been known to present alternatives until receiving an "A+" from the client.

Desmond's years in France forged the essence of his design style, which is classically based and continentally influenced. Appropriate scale, bountiful color and the harmony of light are at the foundation of his work today. Supporters say that Desmond's cleaner, more modern elements beautifully offset the historically fabulous. Alternatively, rooms may be created with more saturated layers from diverse sources, commingling the fine and the personally meaningful.

The firm often takes a phased approach—smaller projects often become larger as budgets allow. Rooms can be developed with a mix of the great and the good, many incorporating owners' collections. A small design fee is taken up front, with lower product markup and hourlies only for non-product time. Desmond appreciates the fine but considers all. Clients also laud Desmond's effectiveness and easy manner. As a very small firm, Desmond can ensure highly personalized service and a polished finished product.

"David is by far the most competent and responsive interior decorator we have ever seen." "He never pushes costly options when more reasonable alternatives make sense." "Delightful and charming personality." "David is a great listener, a quick study and an effective communicator, making everything crystal clear to us along the way." "Working at a major antiques house, I have seen lots of decorators come and go. David will rise to any occasion." "David has a passion that is only possible in a second career born of a love for his subject." "David's presentations are stellar—he gave us room-by-room furniture charts." "He can be a bit focused." "David is not at all a snob. He works with what you have and is hugely collaborative." "While not cheap, a bargain at any price. We would not consider using anyone else."

David M. Plante Interior Design LLC 🏠 4 3.5 4.5 4
533 North Huntley Drive, West Hollywood, CA 90048
(310) 659 - 5058   www.dmpid.com
Classic to modern, streamlined interior design

Whether designing the inside of a yacht or a young author's home, David Plante favors sultry contrasting forms and worldly accents against strong cream-colored architecture. With a design education from the masters, Plante can execute minimal classic to modern cosmopolitan with a proclivity toward elements of the 1930s, 1940s and 1950s. With a sophisticated eye but a realistic sensibility, Plante strikes a balance, shifting with ease from formal dining rooms to functional home offices. Plante is well known for his excellent communication skills and professional business practices.

Rising from librarian to senior designer at John Saladino's firm in the mid-1980s, Plante learned the trade from a true master. He then worked with top New York designer Peter Carlson before forming his own practice in 1995. Together with business manager Christian Militello (formerly of Raoul Bennessya), Plante takes on a maximum of four projects at a time. This allows for excellent client service and a focused approach. Long-term relationships have become the norm—patrons starting small and soon asking for more. Exterior areas are considered as important as the interior and often become the client's favorite space.

Fully specified budget planning is a specialty with choices at all levels. One-of-a-kind vintage chairs are balanced against lesser-priced objects. The redesign of one or two rooms for $30,000 is not unheard of, but rooms are usually somewhat more. A small up-front retainer is taken against lower hourlies for everything up to product purchase, for which there is a standard product markup. Clients see and appreciate the firm's practice of full disclosure on all transactions. ASID.

"For David, the quality of the relationship is just as important as the quality of the design." "He taught us the difference between standard and fine upholstery, and had us invest in the quality. But we made up the difference with great, reasonable finds elsewhere." "He was able to tie together a random array of my possessions with uniform elements throughout, such as floors and curtains." "Consistency is critical to David and he really created an earthy calm." "You would

not go to David for frills." *"He did my 1,800 square foot condo with diligence and warmth."* *"David created an entire new world with my outdoor space."* *"Always offering at least four different choices, he is thoughtful and reasonable."* *"I would refer anyone to David, from a young person to a gazillionaire."* *"He can turn a deficit into a jewel of an asset."* *"The bills are timely and clear."* *"Beauty through harmony and balance."*

David Phoenix Inc. 📷

3.5	3.5	4	4

8485 Melrose Place, Suite A, Los Angeles, CA 90069
(310) 657 - 6577   www.davidphoenix.com

Easy, casual, traditional interior design

With a conservative bent that reflects his established clientele, David Phoenix delivers updated, neutral designs for comfortable living. Taupes and creams, mixed with warm woods, black highlights of leather and buffalo plaids often factor in. With Phoenix's streamlined, classic forms, clients say there is always a light where you need one, usually with a fine silk shade. Textures, patterns and layers are blended casually, the expensive mixed with the good and solid. Each room has a historical base, while accommodating the client's preferences and personal finds.

Beginning in the Brunschwig & Fils sample room in LA, Phoenix truly learned the business from the inside out. After working in Ralph Lauren's interiors department for several years, Phoenix began doing interiors on his own in 1994. Now a staff of four supports him in about six major installations per year. Phoenix is reported to be very speedy and very hands-on, picking every fabric and sitting in every armchair. Clients include many notable "bankers, politicians and celebrities," including Dick Reardon, Maria Shriver and Arnold Schwarzenegger, *Will & Grace's* Sean Hayes and GAP CEO Paul Pressler. Phoenix is currently overseeing the renovation of the governor's office in Sacramento.

Working on whole houses or in a few rooms, Phoenix discusses budgets up front and quickly delivers a finished product. A retainer is taken at the outset with standard markups on product. Supporters feel that Phoenix is very committed and do not hesitate to highly recommend him.

"It is not showy or fabricated—the designs are straight and solid." *"Meat and potato designs for real people."* *"The house is completely ours and ours alone."* *"My friends are green with envy."* *"David can be adamant sometimes, but backs down."* *"He tends towards the expensive."* *"He was always there for me."* *"We interviewed others that were just as talented, but David is so much fun and intelligent, too."* *"Paperwork is not his strength."* *"He works with lots of biggies, but was very responsive to us."* *"He pulls off very big jobs."* *"David was actually way ahead of schedule, shocking the architect and the contractor."* *"David tries to develop long-term relationships with clients. He became our friend."*

Digs By Katie 📷

4	4	4	4.5

523 Euclid Street, Santa Monica, CA 90402
(310) 394 - 7524   digsbykatie@mac.com

Layered, personalized, understated interior design

With caring, focus and soul Katie McGloin has designed homes from Brentwood to Maine to New York. Intimately involved in the process, she works very collaboratively with the client, creating a rich, understated panorama that "not everyone would get." There are layers of thought and personal details, highlighted by antique rugs and textiles. Traditional homes get a modern edge and modern homes get a softened patina.

McGloin was raised in Midland, Texas, graduated from Andover and was a theater arts major at Dartmouth. She became an equity actor in New York, joining a respected repertory company doing off-Broadway and then moved to LA to pursue acting. McGloin was pulled into the design business by a friend who asked for help on her Bel Air home. Others soon caught on, and McGloin has been quite busy since 2002. There is a small but highly effective back office.

Budgets tend to evolve, with clients reporting that McGloin is very clear about costs and offers lots of choices. There is a flat design fee per room and a lower-than-standard fee on product. Clients describe the process as a "delightful design journey" and highly recommend McGloin.

"Katie is doing it for the love of the aesthetic pursuit, not for the economics." "She does not gravitate to the highest-cost products, but she is not really aware of the price/yard either." "Katie is so attached to the quality of her work." "She really wants to sit around and have dinner with you to better understand your lifestyle before she shops for your dining room chairs." "She is so respectful of the client and so lovely to be with." "I am a tchotchke girl, and Katie taught me that everything has to be special to be included." "Always available by cell—I talked to her twice a day even when she was in New York." "Katie was wonderful about working directly with the kids and they just adore her." "We had so much fun together."

EBS Design 🛍   4   4   4   4.5
8811 Alden Drive, Suite 6, Los Angeles, CA 90048
(310) 203 - 0333   ebsdesigngroup@aol.com

Thoughtful, personalized, engaging interior design

Edward Bacot Scott enjoys the design process almost as much as clients enjoy working with him. Aiming for elegance, warmth and classic beauty, styles range from chic stainless to Edwardian chintz and toile—but a single piece always anchors the room. Scott has been known to wade through clients' clothing closets, asking dozens of questions to better understand their personal styles. Noted for his intelligent approach and innovative nature, Scott spends much of his time researching options and creating the unexpected.

Raised in historic Charleston, South Carolina, Scott studied commercial art and design before taking up residence in the internal store design departments of Ralph Lauren—and then Saks—for eighteen years. He struck out on his own in 1992 and remains a one-man band, offering highly personalized client services and taking on one or two major projects at a time.

The firm charges a low up-front design fee, an hourly fee for all hours and lower product markups. Alternatively, a flat fee may be implemented. Scott will outfit public spaces with higher-quality product and children's areas with Pottery Barn. Clients say his experience on the commercial/business side makes him an economic realist. Customers often become his friends and highly recommend him to others. Praising his work as "beautiful and imaginative," some of the most established designers in Los Angeles say they expect Scott to become a force.

"Anyone can create beauty on an unlimited budget, but Edward can create magic on a very reasonable one." "My house is completely different from my friend's, but he did both in a way that is timeless and beguiling." "Edward is a doll." "He made it easy and fun." "Edward can even get involved in creating architectural strength where there is none." "He understood me from the beginning and never pushed." "Edward's sensibilities extend beyond traditional interior design and include sounds and smells—clocks ticking and the perfect candle fragrance." "He is up at 4 AM thinking about the color of my bathroom." "He also has the most wonderful design ideas for parties—what was already special becomes amazing." "Edward will do anything to elicit a 'wow' from the client."

Elizabeth Dinkel Design Associates Inc. 4 4 4 5

8544 Melrose Avenue, West Hollywood, CA 90069
(310) 278 - 3700   elizabethdinkel@aol.com

Tailored, spirited, urbane interior design

While many designers like to make this claim, Dinkel really does create classically enchanting rooms with traditional bones and modern ambitions. Dinkel was raised by one of the mainstays of traditional design—her mother is Leta Austin Foster of Palm Beach. Now Dinkel has awakened the expected with her own distinctive purity, wit and charm. Clients say Dinkel uncovers their design style, then makes it infinitely more chic.

After graduating from Georgetown and working in New York, Dinkel opened a shop in San Francisco in 1991 and moved to Los Angeles in 1995. Her small four-person firm undertakes about four major projects at a time. Recent commissions include work on Andrew Getty's (the 35-year-old grandson of J. Paul) seven-acre Hollywood Hills estate, including a fantasy sleeping loft. The firm dwells on the details, right down to plumbing fixtures and specifically recommended cleaning products. Dinkel is said to be a workaholic, taking great pleasure in completing projects effectively, efficiently and assuming a strong leadership role when appropriate.

Many projects are started with a few rooms, a phased approach and no minimums. In the past, $10,000 powder room beginnings have led to whole-house renovations. The firm takes a higher markup on products, standard hourlies on non-product time and oversight commissions on services, but no design fee. Antique purchases (a favorite) are never overstated retail. Clients feel that Dinkel goes "above and beyond the call of duty" and creates tremendous value in the process. HB Top Designers, 2004.

"Lizzie's designs are classy, clever and extraordinary." "An influential preppy look." "I did not know how much fun it could be. Lizzie has such upbeat energy." "While I know that Lizzie is doing serious work for a prominent Texas family and moguls in Telluride, she makes us feel just as important." "When we had to fire our crooked contractor, Lizzie took up the reins and led us home. The project would have fallen apart without her." "While offering a mix, she really wants a few good pieces in each room." "The budget evolves." "She gears it up and gets it done." "The house is worth twice as much due to Lizzie's creativity." "She has tremendous resources, which she is quite generous in sharing." "She works so well with family 'treasures,' and also incorporates the dogs and children quite sensibly." "Lizzie turned the project around and made it happen."

ERGO Design Works 4.5 4 4.5 4.5

8112 1/2 West Third Street, Suite D, Los Angeles, CA 90048
(323) 658 - 8901   www.ergodesignworks.com

Exuberant, luxurious, high-style interior design

Lory Johansson and June Robinson Scott are applauded by clients for pouring their hearts and souls into every project, making each one an ultimate, individualistic statement. From silk-tented Marrakesh fantasies to proper English country perfection to a Spanish hacienda in the Yucatan, all creations are lovingly detailed and expertly executed. Mixing historic relevance with excessive fun is ERGO's modus operandi.

After studying mathematics in college, Johansson apprenticed for nine years—first with Anthony Machado and then with Brian Murphy at BAM. Meanwhile, Scott graduated from UCLA in design, earning her NCIDQ. The partnership was formed in 1991 and now has six employees. Projects tend to be expansive, extensive and expensive. Jeff Goldblum, Laura Dern and Sir Richard & Lady Branson are all clients. For the Bransons, ERGO completed three projects: a vacation home in the Caribbean, the V2 Records offices and a home base in London.

Traveling to Thailand and China for the finest silk, Nepal for carpets and Paris for the flea markets, ERGO literally searches the world for the most appropriate options. Linen draperies at fifteen dollars a yard are considered as readily as $250,000 carpets. ERGO takes a flat monthly fee over the course of the project. Clients feel quite comfortable with the economics, since the designers are paid the same regardless of the actual costs of the purchases (the flat fee is based on standard rates of the mid-priced budget). References would absolutely use them again, saying they are inspired, diligent and always go the extra mile.

"Hire ERGO and your world will be a far better place." "Brilliant, charming, delightful, visionary, gifted." "A little funkier, but they work for the 'Who's Who' in town." "Lory and June will tear the contractors apart if they don't maintain their high standards, but they are always incredibly sweet." "These two give everything they have, but better assistants might help them leverage their time." "They took over when the architect flagged." "You have to want to take design risks." "They think of every project as a research and development effort." "They aim to create a house you are totally thrilled with. You just have to be sure not to get carried away monetarily in the treasure hunt." "Sometimes I had to rein them in, but they are totally fine with that. No ego." "We could not imagine bringing this project to reality without the help of ERGO." "My house was transformed—a gigantic, earth-shattering revelation!"

Frank K. Pennino & Associates 🛍️   4.5   4.5   4   5

8654 Holloway Plaza Drive, Los Angeles, CA 90069
(310) 657 - 8847   frank@frankpennino.com

Inviting, full, honest interior design

With a worldly view and the warmest demeanor, Frank Pennino has been part of the quintessential California look for the last 30 years. Pennino is roundly acknowledged as a consummate professional, an acclaimed designer and an all-around nice guy. With clients like Bruce Springsteen, Steven Spielberg and Chris Columbus, it might be hard to remain modest; but Pennino has done just that and takes a sincere, focused and personalized approach to each project. Interiors are described as honest, enriching, comfortably full-sized and appropriate for family life. Fulsome in detail and strength, the compositions feature complimentary, layered and patterned neutrals highlighted with unique touches.

While providing clients with a historical perspective, thanks to his trips to Paris, Pennino is a Wisconsin native who did graduate work at UCLA. The firm is comprised of seven full-time workers, including three draftsmen. The staff is noted as highly professional and always helpful. Very competent project managers are assigned to all jobs, with Pennino making the major design decisions. The vast majority of his work is in Los Angeles.

While Pennino clearly uses the best materials, clients report he does not stretch for the ridiculous but prefers the sublime. The interior architecture often is transformed to complement the designs and develop depth. Living rooms run the gamut from $50,000 to considerably more. Most projects are for homes well over 10,000 square feet with up-front design fees and standard product markups. Clients cannot imagine using anyone else and have brought Pennino to New York and elsewhere for many repeat performances.

"Frank is of the old school—he looks and acts the part of a well-honed design professional." "Frank is not the least bit aloof, not a prima donna. He is a team player." "He has all the respect in the world from the design community." "Frank is a chameleon—he will respond to the client with darker Arts & Crafts or oversized Palm Springs. His own house is more refined." "Frank knows how to listen, but holds firm when needed." "As a high-end contractor, I commend Frank and his staff for doing a remarkable job with the details needed to get things done effectively and efficiently." "He is a genius and knows everything." "Working with Frank was like taking a design course at UCLA." "Very sensitive to the kids' rooms with an appropriate budget." "As wonderful a friend as he is a designer." "Will do repro, but really prefers the real thing." "While Frank can be out of reach sometimes, the project managers are great." "He never pushes and really makes it fun." "He is is out of central casting as the debonair designer."

Hendrix/Allardyce  4.5 4.5 4 4
8721 Beverly Boulevard, Los Angeles, CA 90048
(310) 659 - 8721 www.hendrixallardyce.com
Grand, original, evocative interior design

Illya Hendrix and Tom Allardyce have established themselves among the elite of Los Angeles's design circle. Their unique look mixes high style with innovative furnishings and customized backgrounds to create intoxicatingly dramatic settings. All styles and periods are called upon, but the most frequently featured are eighteenth- and nineteenth-century English, French and Italian antiques and recreations of the highest quality. Quintessentially Californian, the pair develop oases of generous luxury, with no expense spared.

Allardyce, a Texas native, studied business, while Hendrix, hailing from Arizona, studied psychology. Partners since 1980, clients describe the two as "incredible bookends," balancing business and design. Typical residential commissions are from 20,000 to 30,000 square feet and are generally fully embellished with plaster moldings, rich textiles and exotic woods. The firm employs a staff of thirteen, including four full-time draftsmen, and most projects include substantial architectural reconfigurations. The finest craftsmen are employed, from "magnificent marble fabricators" to "the ultimate ironworkers." The designers charge a very substantial up-front design fee and standard product markups. Not unusual are budgets in the $1 million range, with clients reporting that the firm assumes "an open checkbook." *Architectural Digest* has featured the firm twenty times (including a recent cover story on Rod Stewart), solidifying its position in the industry. Many clients are very loyal, several having completed multiple projects, exclaiming that they "felt privileged to work with Tom and Illya." AD 100, 2000, 2002, 2004.

"Offering the crème de la crème." "Everything they touch is of the finest quality." "The office staff is the best in the business." "As if you were living on a highly stylized set." "Not much patina, but a lot of panache." "I liken their furnishings and extensive accoutrements to fine jewelry." "We were quite overwhelmed by the level of quality and cost." "It is like living in the world's finest

hotel." "The client list is incredible, and the client service is impeccable." "As an architect, I appreciated their detailed and accurate drawings." "We fell in love with Tom and Illya. The ultimate result for the ultimate price."

Jackie Terrell Design ▪   4   3.5   4.5   5

400 South Burnside Avenue, Suite 12H, Los Angeles, CA 90036
(323) 571 - 1622   www.jackieknows.com

Joyful, fresh, refined interior design

With a design style that is described as "oxygenated, fresh and refined," Jackie Terrell has impressed both clients and peers. Her clean, spare interiors strongly reflect an educated perspective. Rooms are awakened with a clean stroke of livable, obtainable style: some more modern, others more traditional. Bauhaus or Shaker influences are enlivened by beautiful, engaging murals or sections of amusing trompe l'oeil drawn from Terrell's painterly imagination. Terrell works closely with each client, discovering personal design preferences together.

Terrell's various artistic endeavors have come together in interior design. Graduating with a degree in fine art and design, Terrell painted realist works and created gouache Indian miniatures for fifteen years. She then worked as a clothing designer for Nancy Heller, and more recently she assisted Kathryn Ireland in her line of printed hemp fabrics. In 1994, at a friend's insistence, Terrell ventured into interior design. With an excellent staff, she is making waves, working on about seven new projects at a time. Clients tend to be younger, including several TV writers in their 30s, and more recently, some established movie stars.

Budgets can evolve or be set up front. The firm charges a lower hourly rate and a small markup on trade products only. Terrell is known for her wonderful resources, especially her access to outstanding mural painters. Clients further add that there are clever (and economically practical) juxtapositions of color and light, utility and entertainment, and the expensive and the cheap. But all comment that each room comes together as a well-composed, thoughtful mural. HB Top Designers, 2003, 2004.

"Jackie turns the most mundane rooms into pleasurable, desirable vistas." "Jackie is so easy to work with, yet shows the necessary strength with contractors and vendors." "Responsible and responsive." "She transforms the impossible into the doable, with a lampshade to match." "This is our second divine job together. For the next one I plan to take a long nap and let her go for it." "Jackie comes up with really practical and helpful storage solutions." "She easily works with the most expensive fabrics to Ikea. She is not a snob." "We cannot recommend her strongly enough."

James Swan & Company Inc. ▪   3.5   3.5   4   4

201 North Robertson Boulevard, Suite 201, Beverly Hills, CA 90211
(310) 659 - 3488   www.jamesswanco.com

New-wave traditional with warmth

Clients laud Jim Swan's ability to work in a range of vernaculars and create a lighter take on the traditional. Taking his cue from the architecture, Swan has recently completed homes in English Georgian, Nantucket cottage, urbane contemporary, and French revival styles. Swan is praised for his accommodating nature and warm personality, as well as for the care he takes to consider the homeowner's lifestyle. The firm offers an "after-care" program to assist in the maintenance of the home.

After working with an architecture firm for ten years and training with Frank Pennino for two, Swan opened his office in 1999. A Boston satellite office supports his fairly frequent East Coast shopping expeditions and client engage-

ments. With five on staff in LA and Boston and only a limited number of projects taken on each year, Swan is the clear client contact. Patrons include CEOs and young professionals.

Swan is reportedly sensitive to the budget, offering choices and sticking to the bottom line. Repro is justly blended with excellent finds. The firm works with a flat or percentage fee for design services and interior architecture, and a standard markup on products, with administrative hourlies.

"Jim adds a young touch while also staying traditional." "So easy to get along with." "He manages many tasks and jobs at the same time and remains quite cool and collected." "Unique and original ideas." "Less sensitive to child-friendly wear and tear." "I totally trust Jim." "The staff is very easy to work with." "Jim listens well and does not impose his wishes on you." "Works well within a budget." "I never refer anyone to my friends, but I felt comfortable referring Jim."

Jane Eschen 🏠   4.5   4   4.5   5
11301 West Olympic Boulevard, Suite 493, Los Angeles, CA 90064
(310) 479 - 5780   jeschen@earthlink.net

Understated, radiant, alluring interior design

Bespoke, brilliant elegance is her signature, and Jane Eschen is making a mark on some of the finest homes in Los Angeles. Trained by the city's great masters, Eschen worked side-by-side with Rose Tarlow for ten years (during the renovation of the Geffen estate), and for Kalef Alaton for two years. On her own, Eschen has developed a design sensibility that emphasizes fine lines, extraordinary woods and affable colors, offering uplifting livability. Interiors vary in mood from tranquil to dramatic.

A few years ago, Eschen began taking on her own clients. Limiting the business to only a few select commissions at a time, Eschen carefully, discreetly and rigorously considers all creative options. A perfectionist, Eschen has only two part-time assistants, preferring to do it all herself. Eschen will do small commissions for just a few rooms provided she has a full budget and full control.

While the standards of the product are quite high, and thus the jobs quite expensive, there is no design fee. Product markups are at the standard percentage, lower on major items and an hourly fee on non-product time. Living rooms are generally filled with the finest, but Pier 1 may be used in the kids' rooms. References report that Eschen is good about creatively rehabilitating their existing possessions—if they're worth saving. Eschen encourages her clients to take their time to collect "just the right things."

"Jane is deliberate in thought and in deed. Other designers look slapdash in comparison." "I am set in my ways. Against my will, Jane brought me up-to-date— and I could not be happier about it." "I inherently trust Jane." "Jane will not let me get away with lesser major pieces, but she will mix it up with minor items." "Jane dipped our ordinary antique French lantern in silver and created magic." "She will sit in a room for an hour envisioning all that it can be." "She is so dear."

	Quality	Cost	Value	Recommend?
	✚	$	◆	★

"As a top antiques dealer, I see that Jane never pressures her clients. She is very sensitive." "While I did not really want to spend as much as I did, I am thrilled with the result." "A rare asset in the design marketplace." "There is no one better in LA right now." "She cares as much about my house as I do."

Jeffrey Alan Marks Incorporated   4   4   4   4.5

7012 La Presa Drive, Los Angeles, CA 90068
(323) 850 - 8828 www.jam-design.com

Chic, comfortable, English-inspired interior design

Said to be one of the more talented young designers in town, Jeffrey Alan Marks has a fresh, breezy style. Allergic to clutter, Mark's rooms are elegantly spare, yet joyfully playful. Timeless English armchairs with silk striped pillows sit contentedly beside glam chrome and glass. Architecture often plays a starring role in projects, to which Marks contributes greater vision from the start. Landscape also receives a good amount of attention from Marks, who thoughtfully integrates the inside with the outside—furniture frames windows and verdant fabrics highlight views.

After completing a five-year program in architecture and interior design in Arizona, Marks studied and apprenticed in London for another five. He formed his own firm in 1992 with an outpost in London. Willing to do a few rooms or a ground-up operation, Marks's budgets run the gamut. With just Marks and a back office of one and about five major projects a year, he is said to be quite responsive. Marks divides his time between Southern California and London, which unquestionably influences both his hip Euro-chic and his more stately compositions.

The firm works on a flat, standard design fee and a standard markup. Marks has developed a line of furniture based on favorite client designs. Innovation impresses clients and comfort draws them back, as Marks is often used again and then referred to friends. HB Top Designers, 2004.

"Jeffrey's designs are original, imaginative and inspired." "Jeffrey demonstrates resourcefulness at every turn." "He is supportive and cooperative with the client and with subs and vendors." "Jeffrey truly cares about his projects and his clients." "He adds panache, elegance and color as appropriate for the situation." "He does a really wonderful stately traditional as well." "A real professional, and Jeffrey maintains a witty sense of humor throughout." "He might show up in bright green plush trousers and suggest the same for your living room sofa." "The budgets have been reasonable, and his fees comparable to others." "He respects the architecture, building upon its heritage." "A super friendly, easygoing guy, which is the best style you can have."

Jeffrey Hitchcock Enterprises Inc.   4.5   4.5   4   4.5

511 North La Cienega, Suite 206, Los Angeles, CA 90048
(310) 659 - 7053 www.jeffreyhitchcock.com

Traditionally based, all-encompassing, luxurious interior design

Exquisitely filling cavernous new mansions with a mix of the grand and eclectic, patrons hail Jeffrey Hitchcock for his impassioned love of the design process. Hitchcock has developed a clear preference for more formal settings, but one that can embrace sleek steel set against velvet, gilt alongside a third-century vase. Rooms are filled with a multitude of treasures from lands near and far. Clients tend to be well-traveled, well-heeled and to appreciate his all-encompassing approach.

After apprenticing for eleven years in interior design, Hitchcock struck out on his own in 1987. About ten substantial projects are taken on per year by this group of four, which is noted to be exceptionally organized. Hitchcock does all the shopping, which is generally based on high-end repro and a few great antiques. Clients trust Hitchcock to find a balance between the very best and the very good.

While the cost of the furnishings is generally quite high, the fees are moderated on the larger items. A standard product commission is charged along with hourly fees. An overwhelming percentage of current clients are repeat customers.

"I see them all and I know that Jeffrey works exceptionally hard for his clients." "He has the utmost integrity." "He is not sending his assistant out to go shopping—he does it all." "While expensive, you get excellent value with Jeffrey." "As an antique dealer I can see that he spends the time to make sure that a fabric historically, physically and practically makes sense for the chair." "Jeffrey listens very well, but is not swayed by bad taste." "As East Coast as a West Coast guy can be." "Jeffrey can be a bit focused and obsessive, but he works extremely hard and makes it happen." "Jeffrey held my hand through the entire process." "He speaks directly and will take as much care with a regular guy as with a huge client." "He has a wonderful sense of humor and really embraces the profession." "While it is all quite expensive, he gives you alternatives." "We have done over ten major projects with Jeffrey."

Joe Nye Inc.   4   3.5   4.5   5

9239 Doheny Road, West Hollywood, CA 90069
(310) 550 - 7557   www.joenyeinc.com
Crisp, comfortable, traditionally based interior design

Joe Nye is adored by clients for his excellent taste, can-do attitude and personable demeanor. Usually done in an updated traditional genre, Nye's designs are appreciated for their comfortable sophistication and family friendliness. Said to be highly resourceful and up-to-date on the latest fabric and furniture, the designs are a mix of the familiar, the fashionable and the suitable. Nye's clear aim is to please the client, both in process and in result.

A Midwesterner by birth and by personality, Nye graduated from the University of Nebraska and first went into the floral business for ten years. After years of furniture retail management, Nye joined the inimitable Suzanne Rheinstein at Hollyhock for nine years. Currently, Nye helms an experienced staff of nine. Two teams take on about fifteen total jobs at a time. The firm will start with a lampshade or with 16,000 square feet, and officially offers "interior design, party planning and lifestyle consultation." This includes an optional maintenance program where the silver is polished, the linens are pressed and the china is washed on a regular basis.

Nye is known for happily placing an Ikea table next to a priceless antique and making the composition "look fabulous." A standard up-front design fee and a standard product markup is charged by the firm. Clients consistently report that Nye meets schedules and budgets, and they happily refer him to friends. HB Top Designers, 2003, 2004.

"Joe is just so charming and fun, I would be happy to work with him in any field that he pursued." "Joe pulled off a small miracle—incorporating my American and Victorian furniture successfully into my Spanish-style home." "Unflappable energy and enthusiasm." "He not only designs a room, but he actually finishes it with details. I have not found anyone else who cares that much in the interior design world." "A determined decorator who stays on task until it is done correctly." "Joe prides himself (as he should) in coming in on budget and on time." "He makes quick decisions and is very budget-conscious." "Just what I asked for." "Very honest with his opinions." "Extremely resourceful and knows everything imaginable about house cleaning, flowers, etc., and loves to share his information." "Going beyond great design, Joe offers world-class service and flawless bookkeeping." "All who see our home want to hear about Joe because his level of taste is fantastic." "He will become your friend for life."

		Quality	Cost	Value	Recommend?
		+	$	◆	★

John Barman Inc.

4.5 4.5 4 4

2411 Briar Crest Road, Beverly Hills, CA 90210
(310) 948 - 1070 www.johnbarman.com

Mid-century modern interior design with a kick

John Barman has staked out a unique, seductive look that incorporates mid-century design icons and historical references. While others may attempt "eclectic," Barman delivers it with success. Vibrant arabesque taffeta nestles against sleek woven leather daybeds, and antique French curves converse with acrylic and Andy Warhol. Barman intensifies and enlivens. In his more discreet mode, Barman can do a toned-down version with mellower colors, still using bold accents to freshen a more traditional composition.

The firm of seven was established by Barman about twenty years ago. He takes on about 30 assignments annually, six or eight of which are major. Clients say Barman is backed by a "first-class" support staff who keep meticulously detailed budgets and status reports. Additionally, Barman is said to work extremely well in collaboration with architects and contractors to ensure that the final product is the client's true vision.

Barman spends most of his time in Manhattan, where he recently has done renovations for the likes of Wynton Marsalis, Bryant Gumbel, Sean "P. Diddy" Combs, and Leonard and Allison Stern. An LA satellite office opened in the summer of 2003. The firm charges a standard up-front design fee and standard product markups. Budgets can be set or evolve, but Barman is trusted by clients to stay relatively sensible. ASID. AD 100, 2004. HB Top Designers, 2000, 2001. KB 2000, 2001, 2003.

"The designs are showstoppingly hip." "Snappy, with vision." "John's designs move with the times." "You have to see his portfolio to believe it. We love him, but he would not be for everybody." "He loves shopping in London and Paris, and is great about organizing trips." "He rescued the architect and the contractor from what could have been a disaster on the house we built in the country." "Timing can be an issue, especially if the project is not focused." "John is an earnest and straightforward character with a bottomless pit of untapped creativity." "After wandering in the design forest, John has really found his groove." "He respected issues of economics and authenticity, and was very understanding about my choices." "As long as it looks good, he will go to Crate & Barrel." "He selects fabrics and furniture with such character. He would not settle for anything less."

Kerry Joyce Associates Inc.

5 4.5 4.5 4.5

115 North La Brea Avenue, Los Angeles, CA 90036
(323) 938 - 4442 www.kerryjoyce.com

Suave, restrained, stately interior design

Operating at the top of his form, Kerry Joyce delivers subtle expressions of handsome harmony. His appeal is in his crystalline focus, resolute professionalism and accountability. Joyce's work consistently features cream, white and beige with undeniably genteel contrasting forms of mahogany and ebony. Recently, luxurious linen velvets, shots of moderate color and intricate tapestries have crept into the profile. While modern in hue, the designs are imbued with historical references. Believing strongly in the integration of architecture and interior design, Joyce is highly involved with every detail.

Raised in Massachusetts, Joyce trained at NYU in set design, for which he later received an Emmy. He moved to Los Angeles in 1973, and in the 1980s ran Designer Resource, an architectural elements shop. Joyce pursued interior design beginning in 1992, making quite an impression in a relatively short time. Commissions include work for actors Jami Gertz and Paul Hogan, Clipper coach Mike Dunleavy, and design-savvy CEOs like Ian Schrager and Tom Freston, CEO of

MTV Networks. Joyce and his team of ten do just three to six projects at a time, about half of which are from the ground up. Homes tend to be over 10,000 square feet with product ranging from Rose Tarlow to Paris flea market treasures to retail finds. Manufacturers have called upon Joyce for his fine lines, which can be seen in lighting from Palmer Hargrave and Joyce's own line of furniture, displayed in LA at Dessin Fournir.

Joyce's design fees range substantially depending upon scope, but they are in line with peers. There are standard product commissions, and oversight fees are charged for ground-up architectural projects, with which Joyce is quite involved. More complicated custom furniture may see hourly fees. While clearly expensive, clients tell us Joyce always sticks to the timetable and budget, and he offers economic alternatives. Adoring clients say Joyce is "sincere to the core" and "incapable of doing anything less than perfectly." HB Top Designers, 1999, 2000, 2001, 2002, 2003, 2004.

"Extremely thoughtful, tranquil rooms." "You get exactly what you expect." "He's absolutely the best at what he does." "He focuses on every small element, clear in his view that it makes a difference." "An artist's approach with an artist's specific point of view." "Thank goodness he reworked the architect's plans and made the house flow." "Architecture is his forte." "Such a fine person." "He demands that the vendors' quality and timeliness match his own standards, or he will use someone else." "Kerry's designs are stellar, but the aesthetic can occasionally conflict with function." "He said it would be ready on July 1, and on July 1 all the beds were made and the candles lit." "While known for his tone-on-tones, he had great fun with our colorful Hawaiian theme." "Not the guy for you if you do not have a full budget." "I know of at least three people who hired Kerry immediately after they saw what he did in our house."

Kim Alexandriuk Interior Design 🛍   4   3.5   4.5   4.5
1047 12th Street, Suite 9, Santa Monica, CA 90403
(310) 394 - 8100   kadesign@aol.com
Clean, interwoven, updated continental interior design

Whether overhauling a bungalow in Santa Monica or classically restoring a Paul Williams estate built by Vincent Price, Kim Alexandriuk's unique appeal shines through. Rooms are resonant with clarified color, or more neutral palettes may be expertly highlighted with mid-century jewels. She happily does traditional or modern, but each family is presented with a fresh idea, using a softer version of streamlined style and assimilating alluring organic materials. Mixing periods, provinces and paragons with a deft hand, the interiors speak to the clients' time, travel and intentions.

Raised in Germany and educated in Lyon in fine arts, Alexandriuk worked for the Getty Museum for two years and Michael Smith for six before opening her own firm in 1999. The team of three takes on about six projects at a time and Alexandriuk is the main contact. The office receives kudos from clients for its effectiveness.

A standard design fee is taken up front as is a straight lower percentage on products. Alexandriuk delights clients by mixing items of extraordinary heritage together. Patrons also speak well of her access to a wide array of interesting international resources as she frequently travels home to Europe. Bills are said to be clear and reasonable. Many clients who have used other decorators in the past become advocates, stating that they will never use another. HB Top Designers, 2004.

"She has incredible taste and has the rare ability to tailor the look to my sensibilities." "Kim gives so much of herself and really cares that you love your home." "One of the few people left out there who cares enough to drop you a handwritten note." "Paint colors are a focus. She goes way beyond the norm here using international companies or couture brands." "She gets it done. When I wanted to freshen up the pillows afterwards she was here the next day." "She can deliver extraordinary quality as she was trained to do, or she can be creative with a lower budget. And there is never any attitude." "I hired three 'known' decorators before I found Kim, and will look no further." "My house would have looked like Winterthur if it were not for her. She took us to a whole new level." "It might cost more and take longer, but I now have a much more sophisticated version of myself." "My husband has nicknamed her 'the goddess' because her taste is really that good and the budget is not excessive." "She is the only person on our remodeling team we would hire again without a second thought."

Kolanowski Design Inc.   4   4   4   4.5
8569 Holloway Plaza Drive, West Hollywood, CA 90069
(310) 652 - 2411   www.kolanowskidesign.com
Soft, streamlined, personal interior design

Kevin Kolanowski is compiling a cadre of grateful clients based upon his transitional clean lines, integrated approach and responsible and accommodating nature. Mixing the fine and the found, Kolanowski creates comfortable, personalized homes with the client's interests at heart. Casual, relaxed atmospheres abound, most often with warm-colored backgrounds and neutrally hued upholstered forms.

After heading up Marshall Field's furniture display group, Kolanowski received a design degree from Chicago's respected Harrington Institute, then moved to Los Angeles and started his own firm in 1985. With two on staff, Kolanowski takes on about five major interiors projects at a time. Because he's open to new endeavors, younger clients with just a few rooms often turn to Kolanowski, with budgets evolving as the situation allows. Kolanowski also spends about a third of his time with his well-regarded lighting line, www.fuselighting.com, which is favored by some of the best names in the trade.

Kolanowski charges a small, flat monthly design fee with a standard product markup and a supervision fee. Clients report that he is always available, does detailed sketches and is diligently prepared. He is also known for scouting out excellent products in unexpected territories, often finding comparable concepts for half the cost. Clients plan to hire Kolanowski again with the confidence that he will get the job done.

"The first thing Kevin did was to ask me what pieces I owned that meant something to me. I so admired that. Was about me not him." "I was working 80 hours a week, and we had invested a ton of money with another decorator. None of it looked right at all. Kevin came in and saved the day." "He is not a nine-to-fiver. He will always fit you in, even on weekends." "He took the gloss off my favorite 30-year-old Asian piece, which now looks like a valuable 300-year-old antique." "He can get anything made at half the cost of a fine antique." "Takes me to warehouses with excellent pricing, not the easy Melrose stuff." "Kevin would inspect everything before it came into the house, so there were never any

glitches." "There are incredibly detailed sketches. He deals with size and scope up front, so no surprises." "Always prepared, always well dressed, a real professional." "We showed him how we wanted to see the invoices and he presented them that way." "Kevin is a breath of fresh air." "I did seven houses on my own, but now will always use Kevin." "Always has the client's best interests at heart."

kwid/Kelly Wearstler   4.5   4.5   4   4.5
317 North Kings Road, Los Angeles, CA 90048
(323) 951 - 7454   www.kwid.com
Adventurous yet regal interior design

Daring and captivating, Kelly Wearstler is cutting a sparkling path through the Los Angeles design community. Feminine, glamorous and alluring, her designs felicitously integrate Lucite, Murano glass, mirrorized surfaces and traditional English furniture and fittings. She is best known for updating the Avalon and Maison 140 in Beverly Hills, the Estrella in Palm Springs and the oceanfront Viceroy in Santa Monica. Wearstler brings this same fusion of noble past and present allure to her residential work, which constitutes about half of her practice.

Born in South Carolina and raised by an interior-designer mother, Wearstler studied graphic arts and architecture. She then apprenticed with the luminary Milton Glaser at Pushpin Studios and worked on movie sets before forming an interior design practice in 1995. Wearstler currently works on about ten residential projects per year and receives project requests from all over the world. The back office is noted to be very organized in keeping with the demands of the commercial process. The title of her book, *Unexpected Style: Designing and Decorating with Drama*, speaks for itself.

Happily mixing flea-market finds with the very best antiques, Wearstler stretches the evolving budget without compromising the look: Louis XIV lives happily next to high-styled Italian and 1960s mod finds. The firm starts with a retainer applicable against hourly design fees (or scheduled as flat) and charges standard product commissions. Many clients are repeat customers. HB Top Designers, 2000, 2001, 2002, 2003, 2004.

"A wake-up call—she is pushing the glam envelope." "Kelly finds things in every style that she loves." "She is always exploring new things and strongly encouraged us to do so as well." "An incredible fashion sense." "The designs are incredible fun, but one wonders if they are timeless." "She will not budge on certain points with the subs—as the client, I appreciate that." "Kelly makes it easy." "While much of the hotel work is in partnership with her fiancé, it's the beauty and innovation of the designs that are harkening the press." "All of her projects are totally different, tied together with upper-crust nostalgia." "Kelly has a comprehensive view which has a major impact on the landscape and the exteriors." "She listened to what we wanted and brought it to a whole new level."

Lafia/Arvin   5   4   4.5   5
741A 10th Street, Santa Monica, CA 90402
(310) 587 - 1141   www.lafiaarvin.com
Articulate, luxurious, classic interior design

Discreet and calm, Lafia/Arvin has raised the concept of client service to an art form. Their clear goal is to make decorating easy and fun for the customer, while creating unassuming, classically beautiful homes. Interiors are graciously appointed in the finest antiques and some repro, with every possible comfortable detail considered. Designs range from formal traditional with sparks of leather to comfortable relaxed clubby looks using dark woods, light fabrics and eloquent antiques. Monique Lafia takes the lead on design while her husband, Chris Arvin, heads up the business end.

Lafia graduated from UCLA's design program, worked in commercial interiors and designed with legends Waldo Fernandez and Hendrix/Allardyce. Arvin is an attorney with a passion for design. Established in 1997, the business is rounded out by six others who supporters say are on top of every detail. Clients seem to truly be "in love" with Lafia's design sensibility and her kind manner. Many have signed on for multiple projects, including four for Victoria Jackson (including, currently, the Buster Keaton Estate), three for Courtney Thorne-Smith, two for Josie Bisset and several for Andy Conrad. Other clients include Sylvester Stallone, Wayne Gretzky, Rob and Sheryl Lowe, Bernadette and Sugar Ray Leonard and Lilly Tartikoff.

Perfection comes at a cost when the best products are used. Fees are standard, including up-front design fees and product markups, with no hourlies. The pair is said to be good about recovering the old and finding a home for many of the client's current possessions. NCIDQ, CCIDC.

"Monique learned from the masters and applied her own understated elegance." "There is a controlled calm to their style that works with Gap and also with Prada." "Lots of accessories, lots of work." "Millions of questions are asked of everyone, including the kids and the housekeepers." "They bend over backwards to make sure that everything is perfect." "I just hope they do not get too big, as their charm is in their individualized attention." "They do expect a certain high level of quality, but can work with you if you set limits." "I totally trust Monique. She saved my life on our last project, taking it from humdrum to amazing, yet it was still comfortable." "Right after I had my baby she was there, making everything easy." "They have become indispensable and also friends." "They came highly recommended and fulfilled our expectations."

Lane-McCook & Associates Inc.   4   4   4   4.5

926 North Orlando Avenue, Los Angeles, CA 90069
(310) 657 - 7890   lanemccook@aol.com

Traditional yet comfortable, timeless interior design

For the past 35 years, clients and peers alike have depended upon Bill Lane for that perfect, relaxed, multigenerational warmth. Classic forms, softened woods and timeless dignity anchor his work, which is then altered to fit the interests and lifestyle of the client. K.C. McCook (Casey) joined Lane about eight years ago, and continues the firm's tradition of excellence and high standard of client service.

The firm's team of six takes on about five major new commissions each year. Clients seem to become clients for life—many of them are on their fourth or fifth renovation. Projects may be extensive—recently, a 737 was outfitted along with its fully decorated hangar. The Disney family and Dolly Parton are longtime patrons. Projects tend to be at the high end of the range, with substantial antiques.

The firm charges a relatively low design fee, standard markups on products and no hourlies. Budgets seem to evolve with the progress of the work. Lane and McCook work in close collaboration with clients, taking them shopping throughout the process. "Making it easy for the client" is the hallmark of the firm's business, and the key to its success.

"Bill's clients have not used anyone else for 30 years." "Bill is a pro, one of the founders of serious LA interior design." "If your lamp is broken they will loan you one." "So collaborative—they are happy to take you shopping." "They are a dream—I call upon them for advice on everything, including pool tiles and landscaping." "A granddaddy of LA design, the firm is less active." "If the slipcovers are not just right they will magically whisk them away and fix them." "While technology is not a strong point, their transitional designs are moving with the times." "They understand what is comfortable, attractive and proper."

Lisa Pak 🛍️   4   3.5   4.5   4.5

36 25th Avenue, Venice, CA 90291
(310) 439 - 2343   www.lisapakdesign.com

Serene, cohesive, enticing interior design

Lisa Pak designs rooms that exude a reflective classical modernism, an educated perspective and a balance of form. Using a more neutral palette, clean lines and a consistent plan, spaces are both soothing and beguiling. A mid-century American farm table may be surrounded by 1940s Italian chairs, Asian grass cloth walls and linen Roman shades. Clients are delighted with the mix, which they proclaim is fresh, young and uplifting.

After twelve years as a graphic artist for New York City advertising firms, Pak decided to direct her creative talents to the home. While working toward a degree at Parsons, Pak secured prestigious internships with some of the best names in NY interior design, including Laura Bohn, Victoria Hagan and Bruce Bierman. Soon thereafter, Pak went out on her own, doing both lofts in TriBeCa and homes in the Westchester County suburbs. Recently, Pak moved to Venice, where she just finished a design project on the beach.

A one-woman operation, Pak keeps the clients happy and is able to keep the fee structure quite modest. Standard design fees are taken up front, with low product commissions and no hourly fees. References are impressed with her thoughtfulness, organization and resourcefulness.

"She makes it work." "While I know she would rather do fine antiques, Lisa is very accommodating and creative with custom and repro." "Everyone asks who helped me, and I am always pleased to refer Lisa." "Her inherent sense of proportion and restraint leads to a sophistication well beyond my capability." "Not only are the designs fabulous but Lisa is so professional and good natured. She makes it a pleasure."

London Boone Inc. 🛍️   4.5   4.5   4   4.5

8687 Melrose Avenue, Suite G168, Los Angeles, CA 90069
(310) 855 - 2567   www.mimilondon.com

Characteristic, luxurious, organically influenced interior design

Mark Boone is now taking the lead, corralling a wide spectrum of globally influenced product into sophisticated arrangements. Adding to his signature predilection for organic materials and quiet palettes, Boone is focusing more attention on a dialogue between the antique and the modern, rounded out by a streamlined approach. His work is no longer rustic, but you can still put your boots up. With partner Mimi London centered on the overall atmospheric gesture and Boone spearheading the firm's excellent client service, the pair continues to impress clients.

Recognized in the early 1970s for her log-and-tree-trunk furniture built in collaboration with Michael Taylor, London brought the beauty of natural formations to her interior design. Boone, raised in Virginia, received a degree in architecture from Virginia Tech and trained with some of the best, including an esteemed interior design firm in Virginia and the renowned Baker, Knapp & Tubbs. In 1989, he joined London, and about a decade ago London Boone Inc. was formed. While there are fifteen on staff (most in product design), clients say they enjoy excellent attention from Boone. About half of the commissions are in LA and half in resort communities, such as Aspen, Indian Wells, La Jolla and Sonoma County. London Boone's favorite couture creations for clients form the inspiration for its furniture line.

The firm generally takes on whole houses, either from the ground up or complete renovations. The designers are open to all economic price points—if the look suits—including calico curtains at $3 a yard. Flat, standard design and product fees are most often arranged to avoid any conflicts on product pricing, and budgets are said to have meaning. Many patrons start with a country house that is more relaxed yet elegant, finding themselves so happy with the result that they move on to the more formal house in town. AD 100, 2000, 2002, 2004.

"Giants in the industry. Everyone respects them." "Mark is clear and specific. It is a pleasure dealing with the team." "He completely gets it. Very thoughtful and personable." "A Western attitude with wide open spaces and broad gestures, but now done for silk stockings." "He helped me stage a 'clutter intervention program' for my husband's endless collections with grace." "While they are celebrated for their Western log homes, they did a stunning country home for me that is like a little piece of England." "They tend to use unusual objects in unusual ways." "While much of the furniture is new, it looks antique with a wonderful patina." "Mark agilely combines the rough-hewn with the elegant creating glamour." "It magically all came together and looked like it had been there for years."

Lowrance Interiors Inc.   4   4   4   4.5

707 North Alfred Street, Los Angeles, CA 90069
(323) 655 - 9713   lowranceinteriors@sbcglobal.net
Luxurious, tradition-based interior design with vitality

Representing the authentic look of the "Hollywood old guard," Jack Lowrance has very loyal patrons, some of whom he has led through a half-dozen projects. And nowadays, he's working with their children and grandchildren. With a professed love of the contemporary and a client base to the right of traditional, his interiors are most often a bona fide mix, centering on neoclassical, highlighting satins and gilt. Antiques play a central role, and generally there are one or two major stars in every scene. Architectural backgrounds are also of great importance, with Lowrance encouraging flow and balance.

Clients commend Lowrance for his common sense and accommodating nature, which is said to flow naturally from his Texas upbringing. Lowrance practiced commercial art and design after receiving training in the field from the University of Texas. His interests led him to interior design, and he opened an office in Palo Alto in 1963, moving to LA nine years later. Lowrance is noted to be especially good about stylishly bringing the accumulated objects of his customers' 50 years of marriage into a coherent whole. With two highly competent staffers, about ten major projects are run a year. Most of his clients are successful businessmen who appreciate the straightforward process and can afford the quality.

Entire homes are usually undertaken and, more recently, large Westwood condos. Living rooms often feature extensive draperies and elaborate trims. The firm charges a low design fee, no hourlies and standard product markups (lower on auction and antiques). Lowrance is said to be insightful about judging the client's scope and setting a realistic, detailed budget that is usually met. Time and again, we hear that Lowrance really enjoys his clients and his clients really enjoy him.

"I have been using Jack for over 25 years. I depend on him." "He is as honest as the day is long." "A seasoned pro, he knows everyone and knows how to get it done." "He can be a busy dude, sometimes in France, but he is good about returning your calls." "Established society guy with very loyal, old-money clients." "In all these years, he has never delivered anything I did not like." "Jack works best when taking notes." "If anything is ever damaged, Jack will do all that

is possible so you are not caught in the middle." "He really knows his fabrics and can always offer you a range of choices, both stylistically and economically." "Jack is not a snob, nor is he finicky." "The bills are always very clear." "You could not do any better."

Luis Ortega Design Studio   4.5   4.5   4   5
6030 Wilshire Boulevard, Suite 300, Los Angeles, CA 90036
(310) 358 - 0211   luis@lods2000.com

Purposeful, poetic, contemporary interior design

Clients are effusive when it comes to Luis Ortega's distinguished, sinuous work, original contemporary thinking and sincere manner. Ortega's holistic approach makes patrons feel they are rewarded with homes of spiritual warmth, homes that embody their dreams and enhance their lives. A few purposeful pieces are harmonically incorporated with comfortably sized leather seating, rich woods and unusual marbles. Clients feel as if they are taking an enriching course in design, which culminates in the ultimate benefit—the perfect home.

After receiving an architecture degree from USC and interning for a few years, Ortega established his own firm in 1977. There are two assistants with several years of experience each, contributing to about four major projects at a time. The back office is noted to be "marvelously well organized and efficient." Contractors and millworkers comment that the architectural drawings are immaculate, making everything flow more smoothly.

Viewing each project as a unified piece, Ortega carefully considers each item. Anchor pieces are bigger investments than some would like, but are not regretted. The firm's architecture and design fees are at a flat rate based upon standard product markups. Ortega strives to have outstanding relationships with his clients—and succeeds.

"Renowned contemporary architects who generally bristle at the thought of working with an interior designer, embrace Luis." "Given his reputation, we were amazed at how approachable Luis was." "Luis is incredibly sincere, trustworthy and delightful to boot." "No one compares for that look." "The uniformity of the inside and out is poetic." "My wife and I have wildly different tastes, and Luis was able to gracefully please us both." "While he gritted his teeth about redoing the design for one room three times, he absolutely nailed it." "In the middle of construction, Luis had a dream about the dining room. And it looks just like he envisioned it." "He is a genius, but best for those with an unlimited amount of time and money." "We set up a loose budget and he more or less stayed within those parameters, giving us choices." "We continue to have lunch after all these years. I even met his mother. We will unquestioningly use him again."

m. design interiors   4   3.5   4.5   4.5
7421 Beverly Boulevard, Suite 10, Los Angeles, CA 90036
(323) 933 - 2981   www.mdesignla.com

Sassy, refreshing, clean interior design

With wit, focus and expression, Molly Luetkemeyer has emerged on the LA design scene. Bold colors, strong moldings, Palladian balance and flea-market finds play upon each other to create rooms of intelligence and character. Items are often used in an innovative manner, and rarely for their intended purpose. While better known for her irrepressible retro, the firm does a more timeless swank with equal aplomb. Clients are effusive about the easy process and the end result.

An aspiring actress in New York, Luetkemeyer went to LA to join the production side of Mike Nichols's film, *Primary Colors*. Her stay in LA revived a long-held passion for interior design. After receiving her masters at UCLA—during which she landed two very prestigious internships, one with Kelly Wearstler and one with

Antonia Hutt—Luetkemeyer began her own firm in 2001. With the recent addition of designer Farrah Dragon, the firm takes on several large projects at a time. Commissions take them to Hancock Park, Beverly Hills and New York City, with clients such as Academy Award-winning screenwriter Akiva Goldsman, *Gilmore Girls'* Lauren Graham and *Ed*'s Julie Bowen (Luetkemeyer's sister). There is also a solid group of happy bachelor clients.

Luetkemeyer deals with a wide variety of budgets—the very smallest for one of her media plays with TLC's hit show *Clean Sweep,* where she miraculously turned a wreck of two rooms into highly workable home/office for $2,000 (and in two days). The firm takes a flat design fee, standard product markups and no hourlies. Budgets tend to evolve. Luetkemeyer is reportedly good about freshening up the old, using what clients possess. We're told she takes the initiative in preempting any lurking issues, a strength particularly admired by references. HB Top Designers, 2002, 2003, 2004.

"Quite simply, Molly and Farrah get it." "This design duo is young and hip, but also incredibly professional and easy to work with." "When we could not find the right entry hall piece, Molly designed one at a great price." "She introduced unexpected pops of color into our chroma-phobic lifestyle, and we just love it." "There are no preconceived notions, but an openness of attitude." "Molly does not expect us to say yes to Scalamandre and call it a day." "If I hesitated, she had a Plan B 24 hours later. And then I usually went with Plan A." "She asks all her clients to name five adjectives to describe the way they want to live." "They also can expertly execute an elegant, modern and yet not industrial trendy." "Celebrating pop culture as an art form." "I would not recommend her for period-pure, but for innovative, exciting, fresh design, she is the best."

Madeline Stuart & Associates Inc.   4.5   4   4.5   4.5

630 South La Brea Avenue, Los Angeles, CA 90036
(323) 935 - 3305   www.madelinestuart.com

Agile, measured, eloquent interior design

Madeline Stuart embraces a distinct design intention that incorporates quiet elegance, a reverence for historic beauty and honest simplicity. The hip and chic mingle easily with the comfortable and the more refined. Fortuny fabrics play against lovingly detailed nineteenth-century custom millwork, which in turn dances with 1940s French Lucite-and-glass chandeliers. While less is more, it's clearly enough to add warmth and character—with a glimmer of what is to come.

Raised in Beverly Hills by a film-director father and an interior-designer mother, Stuart started her business in 1990. Working with a staff of six, Stuart undertakes about five major projects at a time. Many clients are in the entertainment and political world, including Jason Alexander and Fleetwood Mac's Lindsey Buckingham.

While budgets may evolve, Stuart gives the client lots of time and lots of choices. She has been known to sit clients down with armfuls of books and ask them about their preferences. Shopping together is the norm. Standard design fees are charged, with standard product markups and rare hourlies. Employing mostly custom-made furniture, Stuart pours her heart into every detail. Her search for perfection on one project sometimes leads her astray from others and may drive the staff to its wits' end, but clients are euphoric about the final results. HB Top Designers, 1999, 2000, 2001, 2002, 2003, 2004.

"A lot of people say they work 24/7, but Madeline really does." "She is smart and articulate. I enjoyed every minute with Madeline." "While she did a more traditional setting for us, she did an amazing modern home for my friend. Madeline's only design conviction is that it be comfortable for you." "She never makes you feel uneasy if you do not step up to buying something." "Never a 'fait accompli'—there are always choices." "She is a true artist, taking her trade very seriously—it is a real business." "She thinks through each detail, making her own

knives to manufacture-specific, historically accurate millwork moldings." "She is best with clients who are really involved, otherwise she can get frustrated." "Madeline gets it done, and you can depend on her." "Lots of turnover in the back office." "She always attended our weekly meetings." "We would definitely do another project with Madeline."

Magni Design Inc. 4.5 4.5 4 4.5
8060 Melrose Avenue, Los Angeles, CA 90046
(323) 866 - 0600 www.magnidesign.com

Sleek, modern interior design with spice

James Magni has built a strong reputation with his signature, dramatic global modernism schematic. Sinuous simplicity is achieved with strong organic contemporary architectural backgrounds. This simplicity is juxtaposed against furnishings from all times and heritages: eighteenth-century French and Italian, Chinese, Indian, Art Deco and fine-tuned contemporary pieces from his own Magni Classic line. The mélange is usually enhanced by clients' amazing modern art collections. While this might sound too complicated, it falls beautifully into place due to the spare selection of product, each item appearing as a work of art in a delineated, stunning gallery.

Magni received a B.S. in architecture in Nebraska, then worked in commercial interiors with many of the top corporations in Dallas. Soon these corporate clients also wanted Magni's style at home, and a residential practice was born. Founded in 1990, the firm takes on about five major projects at a time, generally ranging from the large to the larger. The hyper-competent staff of seven includes two project managers and a most effective MBA, who runs the business end. Clients include Steve Wynn of Mirage Resorts, Dorothy Lay of Frito-Lay, and many top 200 art collectors.

The firm works most often on a flat fee, billed out over the course of the term. This fee is comparable in magnitude to the standard product pricing policies of most other LA design firms, but avoids the inherent designer-fee conflict issue. European shopping trips with clients abound. While much of the product is the very highest, patrons comment that Magni makes the best use of the architecture without requiring major reconstruction and always offers "chicken, filet and lobster" product alternatives. Magni has many loyal fans, one of whom has done four projects with the firm and another who has done seven. AD 100, 2000.

"Dealing with Jim is like dealing with the CEO of a corporation. He is intelligent and gets it the first time." "Jim's mantra is 'global modernism' and he is strict in his view of contemporary architecture. You know what you are getting." "It is not unusual to find Robert Rauschenberg, Ed Ruscha, David Hockney, Andy Warhol, Robert Ryman, etc., hanging near pieces of Etienne Meunier, Louis XV's personal furniture designer." "He spent an entire day asking us about every aspect of our life: Who does the cooking? What time do you eat? What was your favorite vacation? Favorite hotel? All before embarking on the project." "Since he also studied architecture for six years, he really understands and can design any custom piece." "To Jim, furniture is really sculpture that you happen to sit on." "Nothing is out of reach. In one recent project there is a 3,500 square foot entrance way and a 40-foot handmade silk rug that took more than a year to make." "Can do 'million-dollar' work on a limited budget, but usually doesn't." "A perfectionist, sometimes to a fault." "His dedication is unbounded." "We interviewed twelve designers and feel privileged to be a client." "A real gentleman who became a friend."

Mark Cutler Design Inc. 　　　4　　3.5　　4.5　　4.5

8656 Holloway Plaza Drive, West Hollywood, CA 90069
(310) 360 - 6212　www.markcutlerdesign.com

Streamlined, stylish, tradition-edged interior design

Maintaining a classical European-American tradition while inviting the charm of modern interplay, Mark Cutler offers an updated take on the expected. With the greatest respect for historical lines, Cutler takes a space and molds the concept to create a personalized portrait of the client. This translates into a modern take on traditional or a "soft and warm" take on modern, depending on the client's preferences. Distressed woods may be used to create a more formal cadence, or modern fittings may be used in a farmhouse to create balance. In all cases, Cutler has won the confidence of his clients, who consistently compliment his professional and personal skills.

Raised in Australia, Cutler received a degree in architecture at the University of Queensland. Starting his career in New York, he was soon lured to LA. Working under the tutelage of Bill Hablinski in the interiors department for nine years, Cutler struck out on his own in 2000. Now with his own very competent team of six, Cutler takes on about six major commissions a year. While several projects are quite substantial, including a house for Tom Skerritt, the budgets can be quite moderate. The firm is also willing to take on smaller projects, and has had great success with excellent kitchen and bath rejuvenations. Most commissions are on the west side, in Orange County or the Montecito/Santa Barbara area.

Clients and contractors credit Cutler for his comprehensive CAD floor plans, which detail every item. The company is also commended for "value engineering" budgets and its reasonable, businesslike approach. Standard design fees are taken up front with standard product fees taken on purchases. There are fairly regular shopping hunts across Europe to find unexpected, well-priced alternatives.

"Mark really has a special ability to get inside a client's head and understand their vision." "All my rooms are my favorite." "The nicest guy in the world to work with. And humorous to boot." "Extremely hands-on." "A genuine team player with the remodeling staff." "My husband is a builder with exacting standards. He is very pleased with Mark's professional, knowledgeable, creative skills. I never thought it would be this easy." "Mark also developed wonderful exterior details that made the house special." "If we said 'go for it' the costs would be too much, but he is excellent about meeting a specified budget." "He saved us tons of money in potential plumbing mistakes." "I never felt pressured in any way." "He would always come back with alternatives if we asked, which was the case with the practicality of the children's fabrics." "We are really opinionated and Mark always respected our viewpoint." "While Mark is a busy guy with lots of clients, he was always accessible." "He made it so easy."

Mark Weaver & Associates Inc. 　　4　　4　　4　　4

519 North La Cienega Boulevard, Suite 12, West Hollywood, CA 90048
(310) 855 - 0400　www.markweaver.com

Calm, content, traditional interior design

A gentle warmth is reflected in Mark Weaver's work, a glow that invites the onlooker to come and take a seat. The firm prides itself on active collaboration with the client, finding a seamless balance between the traditional and the more contemporary, with comfort as a primary goal. California forms in soothing neutrals are most often favored, with punches of graphic art that reflect Weaver's association with the LA Museum of Contemporary Art. Italian influences also may be seen with frequent trips abroad. References report that not only are the rooms calm, but so is the process.

Raised in Southern California, Weaver moved to LA to attend Woodbury College, and soon thereafter worked with respected old-line designer Frank Austin. In 1969, he set up on his own and soon had a society editor client. There are five members of the team, including Darrell Wilson, who received a master's of architecture at Princeton and a master's of fine arts at the Otis School. The firm can do the most complete jobs, down to placing the clothes in the closet and lighting the fireplace, but it is also open to refurbishing a few rooms.

Clients report that the process is quite clear, with a specific letter agreement. The firm charges a standard up-front design fee and standard markups on product. Weaver has maintained the loyalty of clients over his 35-year career, now doing several children's and grandchildren's homes.

"As a dealer, I see them all. Mark is really a terrific person." "He gave us the confidence to take on a new look, but never pushed us beyond our comfort zone." "Mark has a very clear-cut approach. There is continuity in his work." "He absolutely helped us avoid trendiness and errors in judgment." "Mark can do everything in Crate & Barrel, bring in the finest Pompeiian artifacts or get an antique Grecian bed reproduced." "Everything is so well defined with an excellent road map."

Martynus-Tripp Inc. 📷   5   4.5   4.5   4.5

658 North Crescent Heights Boulevard, Los Angeles, CA 90048
(323) 651-4445   www.martynus-tripp.com
Unabashedly pedigreed, layered yet refined interior design

While others say they do eclectic, Martynus-Tripp is creating a bold new consciousness with compositions of extravagant fantasy and clear refinement. Most rooms contain heavy continental influences, exotically layered into a fusion of color and drama. Ornately turned French, English, Indonesian, Spanish colonial, Middle Eastern, Moroccan, Italian and especially quirky Portuguese antiques and ornaments lay side by side. Remarkably, other interiors are stunningly classic traditional, and yet others are disciplined modern with an unspoken air of history established by fine antiques or a luxurious rug. Clients and peers alike have stood up and noticed.

Ralph Haenisch majored in business at the University of Kansas, and co-owns Waldo Collections along with Waldo Fernandez. Martyn Lawrence-Bullard, a classically trained actor, moved to LA from London hoping to become a movie star. When he was anointed to do Cheryl Tiegs's massive home, Lawrence-Bullard called in Haenisch for help, and Martynus-Tripp was formed (the name signifies a Greek god's journey, Martynus being the Greek god of war). Thus, they became decorators to the stars, including Christina Aguilera, Edward Norton, William H. Macy and Felicity Huffman. Since 1996, there have been six on staff doing about eight large projects at a time. Lawrence-Bullard and Haenisch tend to work on most jobs together, including, currently, a 25-bedroom château in the Loire Valley and a massive hunting lodge in Cape Town.

Lawrence-Bullard, an antiques dealer from the age of twelve, has a special fondness for all things with a warm patina. The firm often mixes the old with the new (especially from their own line, Martynus) to modernize the look. Fabrics may be used from the $10 to $400 range. The up-front design fee is actually low and the product commissions are low, but the cost of product can certainly add up. Clients are overwhelmed with the beauty of the finished product.

"Martyn will get involved with so many of the architectural details, like the alignment of the antique limestone floor—which took the project from just very good to amazing." "He would shop with me and clearly refined my taste, but did it in such a gracious way." "Tripp not only considers hue but has a wonderful innate sense for the interplay of texture, which is what makes the rooms come alive." "They absolutely understood our vision, turned up the volume and created

a masterpiece." "As a photographer for AD, I see it all. Great things can be expected from this design team." "Clients often become friends." "Becoming an influential part of the design community in LA."

Mary McDonald Interiors   4.5   4   4.5   4.5
By Appointment Only, Los Angeles, CA 90069
(310) 246 – 1307   mmi1548@aol.com
Unabashedly warm and classical interior design

    Taking on just a few privileged clients a year, Mary McDonald has made a big impression. Recent commissions have included a home for actress Renée Zellweger and the revitalization of Buster Keaton's Italian villa, a 10,000 square foot, 1925 Mediterranean fantasy. McDonald is one of the last great holdouts in LA who admits to a love of pattern, color, layers and chintz. With restraint, warmth and charm, McDonald transforms ordinary spaces into atmospheric oases, melding the best of hip modern with the glamour of the ages. Romantic yet never sentimental, her designs are stylishly retro and inspiringly progressive.

    A third-generation Angeleno raised in Brentwood, McDonald inherently understands understated glam. Educated at Boston University and Parsons School of Design in New York, McDonald contemplated acting and then designed hats at the now-defunct but renowned Madeleine Gallay. Following her design instincts, McDonald then pursued interiors. Her small office is said to be extremely competent. Recently, she redesigned the rooms and public spaces of the Luxe Hotel on Sunset.

    Mixing up fine antiques and nineteenth-century Persian rugs with generational heirlooms and Pier 1 Imports, McDonald keeps an eye on costs while delivering the dynamic. There is a standard up-front design fee, standard product commissions and no hourlies. HB Top Designers, 2002, 2003, 2004.

    "Mary's rooms are the epitome of elegant restraint, yet are bursting with joy." "Mary was born with taste that you cannot learn." "She is classic, old school, but never boring." "She is so funny. It is like Chris Rock's humor in Kate Spade's body." "Mary does not want to take on a lot of jobs, just enough to keep it going." "Clients love working with her—she is so sweet and so much fun." "We call her Zippy McDonald, because she has such great creative wit." "It is all about warm, comfortable cheerful rooms, and yet they are also so sophisticated." "She has respect for the client's histories and what is meaningful to them." "Mary will fight for what she believes in—in a good way." "The designs are timeless and appealing—Mario Buatta in stiletto heels."

Michael S. Smith Inc.   5   5   4   4.5
1646 19th Street, Santa Monica, CA 90404
(310) 315 - 3018   info@michaelsmithinc.com
Opulently casual, refined interior design

    Though he's the media-pronounced king of the LA interior design world, Michael Smith is not resting on his laurels. Intensely involved with his clients and their projects, Smith delivers an instant pedigree of understated, timeless elegance hearkening to a more innocent era. While Smith disparages designs with a "staged, theatrical vibe," each Smith project is a finely tuned, multilayered theatrical performance involving substantial architecture, investment antiques and layers and layers of paint. While clients gush, many others just don't get it. Smith basks in the limelight, most often enjoying the company of movie-star clients and customers with open checkbooks.

    Stylistically, Smith's designs are refined and polished versions of historically classical motifs: English country, Art Deco, 1940s French moderne. Smith has the energy to attend to clients in New York, Hawaii and LA all in the same week—often just after shopping in Italy. Jobs are usually over $1 million, sometimes less for patrons with household names. Past and current clients include Rupert Murdoch, Sir Evelyn and Lady de Rothschild, Richard Gere (2 projects), Dustin Hoffman (3), Cindy Crawford (6), Michelle Pfeiffer (4) and Steven Spielberg (5).

Smith charges standard design fees as a percentage of the job, no hourlies and standard product markups. However, the products tend to cost a lot and the architects are often parachuted in from New York. The staff of 24 is said to be exceptionally efficient and the reimbursables are not marked up. Smith is known to doggedly pursue the perfect piece for a client, sometimes using his clout to force a dealer to place an antique on trial in the client's home for longer periods than normal and then negotiate hard on price. While vendors appreciate his sensibility and dedication, he is not their favorite customer. Similarly, he will go to an auction house's rug warehouse to inspect the quality of goods not yet on sale. Clients clearly appreciate the effort and the result, saying that Smith tries very hard to create his effortless perfection. AD 100, 2002, 2004. HB Top Designers, 1999, 2000, 2001, 2002, 2003, 2004.

"I still do not know how he does it. The rooms are impossibly beautiful but also very livable." "With tongue firmly implanted in cheek, he never takes himself or the decorating too seriously, although it is clearly serious decorating." "Michael finds it highly amusing to use fabric from Urban Outfitters and priceless antiques in the same room." "Michael cancelled our interview. I know he did not think the job was big enough." "Michael is now trying to be more a part of the design community." "He gets completely jazzed about an idea and it is contagious." "Michael's gigantic staff really helps to leverage his time so he can be there for the client." "He has a warehouse of product that he has taken back when the client says no. It just magically disappears." "Does not suffer fools gladly." "You won't believe how much you will spend, but it will be your fault, not his." "He brought life to our home."

Molly Isaksen Interiors ◼   3.5   3.5   4   4.5
9920 Durant Drive, Beverly Hills, CA 90212
(310) 556 - 3624   molly@mollyisakseninteriors.com
Polished, warm, transitional interior design

Offering a calm, appealing aesthetic, Molly Isaksen is finding a harmonious balance for her clients. In her capable hands, the traditional will take on a more streamlined view and the modern a warmer hue, but all are distinguished in their comfortable ease. Clients are extremely fond of Isaksen, as she guides them through the design process and doesn't stop until every last detail is finalized.

With a background in fashion design, Isaksen was pulled into interior design when her movie-star fashion clients asked for help at home. The firm was officially established in 1998, and there are currently two assistants working on about four projects. Clients are often established professionals in the entertainment and corporate world, who are effusive about the personal attention received from Isaksen. Despite the short life of the firm, one client is already on a third project. Isaksen is also said to have a special sensitivity to family living.

Budgets tend to evolve with fabric choices from the very reasonable to reasonably high. There is either a flat design fee or standard hourlies taken for design conception. Product sees a lower markup. Isaksen is known for her excellent attention to detail, going well beyond the normal scope, including designing customized phone pads and stationery and choosing the books in the library. Similarly, Isaksen will assist with client entertainment, providing menus, flowers and calligraphy place cards.

"Not only did Molly design an incredible screening room, but the details are so special. She found the perfect antique box to house the remote." "She has an excellent feel for family life, making sure all the fabrics were washable." "She has helped us continually over the years." "Molly can take what you have, move it around, add some accessories, and voila, you have a new room." "Not always the fastest, as it is a smaller firm." "She mixes the treasured, some lower-end and some select pieces to create an ideal setting on a reasonable budget." "The staff is also terrific with great taste."

Orsini Design Associates   4.5   4.5   4   4.5
865 North Figueroa, Los Angeles, CA 90017
(213) 955 - 0166 www.orsinidesignassociates.com
Updated traditional, high-end interior design

Susan Orsini is commended for her acute attention to detail, professional manner and excellent customer service. She leans toward updated, traditional designs, reflecting the interests of her client base and the pleasures of the English countryside (she is Joint Master of Foxhounds for the Rombout Hunt Club). The firm has also successfully completed Art Deco and more contemporary projects. Designs are appreciated for their suitable, tailored lines and livability. The majority of the firm's work is residential, mostly for prominent business executives (including their boats and planes), though Orsini is open to new clients with smaller projects. The firm also does office, commercial and hospitality work, including projects for Chanel, GTE, Goldman Sachs, Forstmann Little, NYNEX and Disney's first two cruise ships.

Orsini is reputed to deliver exactly on budget and on schedule. New customers are charged a design fee and products are purchased for a standard percentage over net. The firm spends a great deal of time with clients doing research and planning, often recommending complete reconfigurations. A wide range of products are considered, from the finest French silks to Crate & Barrel. No one says the project costs are a bargain, but all agree that Orsini makes the process as easy as possible. The firm often implements detailed winter and summer maintenance programs for its patrons and has embraced new home technologies, such as state-of-the-art home theaters.

Although she employs a "very capable" staff of 23 with offices in New York and Los Angeles, Orsini oversees all client relationships. She spends about one week a month in the LA area. Many clients that started with Orsini 25 years ago are still with her today. HB Top Designers, 1999, 2000.

"Susan's style reflects the ease and comfort necessary for busy people who often have several houses to keep up." "She has a strategic plan for everything, which was very appealing to my husband, who is used to that sort of thing." "There are lists and lists of things she reviews. You have to be prepared." "She can get it done anywhere—even in Mexico." "They are open 24/7 and can make things happen faster than a speeding bullet, even if Susan is out of town." "Very demanding of her employees." "She wants the facts and gets them." "Fortitude and persistence are her watch words." "She works well with business managers and corporates because she does not waste time, but she is not a hand-holder." "Susan's designs work. There is always an electrical outlet where you need one." "She has gotten to know my design preferences so well, she will send me the same photo in this month's AD that I planned to send her." "Susan checks every penny the contractors spend and will always win a debate with them." "The details overseen by her office are remarkable, right down to the place mats and paper napkins."

	Quality	Cost	Value	Recommend?
	✚	$	◆	★

Peter Dunham Design 🛍

	4.5	4	4.5	4.5

909 North Orlando Avenue, Los Angeles, CA 90069
(323) 848 - 9900   www.peterdunham.com

Atmospheric, friendly, classical interior design

With a preponderance of charm and the stylistic intelligence to successfully balance class against edge, Peter Dunham has developed an outstanding reputation. Catering to families and to the stars, industry peers say he is star bound himself. Using classical forms and warm colors—highlighted by objects of character with a nod to pedigree—Dunham creates rooms that are livable and joyous. The quirky lives happily side by side with the sublime. Currently, about half the work is traditional with a modern bent, and the other half is contemporary with an educated view of the past.

Dunham grew up in England, France and Spain. After studying language at Oxford and business in Paris, he moved to New York City, landing in high-end residential real estate sales for sixteen years, remodeling several of his own homes along the way. Friends wanted the same, and a design career was launched. Moving to LA in 1998, he set up shop. There are now five on staff to assist with about four major projects at a time, but references say they have Dunham's unfettered attention. With a European sense of scale, a strong point of view and a practical outlook, Dunham now has a stable of clients who report that their design visions have been realized. A fabric line of hand-printed linens was recently launched, reflecting Dunham's cosmopolitan perspective (at Thomas Lavin in LA).

The firm is willing to take on a few rooms, with antiques and family heirlooms employed as much as possible for a "comfortable, lived-in look." Budget is usually focused on the most important elements, with Crate & Barrel and salvage-yard goods used to supplement appropriately. The firm takes no design fee, but will charge a standard product markup and lower hourly rates for non-product hours. For more complex operations, a percentage of construction fee may be taken. Clients are as impressed with Dunham's businesslike approach as his design skills. HB Top Designers, 2001, 2002, 2003, 2004.

"Peter has a very educated and erudite point of view, but makes it work for day-to-day living." "One of the very few people who can use strawberry red and make it work." "He does the unexpected with ease." "Peter really considers the place and time of the house. He would never do Louis XV in a contemporary setting." "Peter takes a tremendous amount of pride in his work, as it is a second career and he is doing what he loves." "There are great presentation boards and he will do the whole dog-and-pony show over until everyone is perfectly satisfied." "Peter has strong opinions, but he is good about adapting to the client's desires." "While he really prefers the $20K mirror, when I say no, he finds excellent alternatives." "I am hooked. I can never go back to overstuffed upholstery. Peter's look is much more sophisticated." "While he does not focus on bargains, it is overall a good value." "It will never look like a hotel." "There is no attitude." "He gets it done." "It is a pleasure working with Peter because he is clear, concise and professional."

Robert Couturier & Associates 🛍

	5	5	4	4.5

69 Mercer Street, Third Floor, New York, NY 10012
(212) 463 - 7177   www.robertcouturier.com

Dramatic, stylish, lush interior design

Robert Couturier's interiors are simultaneously voluptuous and tailored, a marvelous sleight of hand pulled off by a true master of the craft. Influenced by his years spent studying in Paris, a French spirit infuses the creations. While known in New York for compositions of continental grandeur, in California,

Couturier's work is given to fanciful explorations of the finest twentieth-century French aesthetic. Consistently inspiring his peers, Couturier creates visions of historical resonance that are infused with the presence of today.

Couturier spent six years with Adam Tihany before starting his own firm in 1986. Many projects are undertaken for the international elite (compounds in Mexico, chateaux in France), but younger clients also enjoy working with Couturier. He is willing to begin with just one room at a time, knowing that the budget-constrained will return when they are able. Alternatively, he is capable of assembling an entire village of workers in a remote location to get the job done correctly. In either case, references report Couturier is an attentive listener and effective implementer.

While some balk at his prices and uncompromising taste in expensive fabrics, all find him honest, and his staff helpful and responsive. Well-heeled references credit Couturier for helping them to make wise design investment decisions. He readily admits and absorbs any mishaps, and most feel the high costs are clearly worth it for the ultimate in upscale chic. AD 100, 2000, 2002. HB Top Designers, 1999, 2000, 2001, 2004.

"Pure pleasure—the process and the epic result. But you have to have an abundant budget." "Robert can do crisp, sleek modern with the best of them. But his designs are based upon my history and the history of design. They make referential, aesthetic and intellectual sense." "Robert captured exactly what I wanted, even though I didn't know how to express the thought myself." "Works with the most influential people in the world, and with my friends, who own rather small homes." "He is an ingenious master, but he does not take himself too seriously." "Robert composes harmonic design symphonies. He is the real thing. Others try to do this and it just looks like a hodgepodge." "If there is ever an issue, he says, 'Don't worry about it,' and magically finds a solution." "Facile— all is coordinated for you. Brilliant results." "They obviously so enjoy the work and friendships emerged."

Ron Wilson Designer   4   4   4   4
1235 Tower Road, Beverly Hills, CA 90210
(310) 276 - 0666 www.ronwilsondesigner.com
Sumptuous, dramatic, dashing interior design

Best known for his nineteen opulent extravaganzas for Cher, Ron Wilson delivers the dream. For those less dramatic, Wilson's designs can be more moderate but are still imposing, with at least one sensational aspect per room. Be it a 700 AD Roman statue, an overscaled, turreted ceiling or a gigantic limestone mantelpiece, all preside over generously scaled furniture and luxurious details. Suede, mohair, silk, satins and velvet are fabrics of choice, while collections of prints, porcelains, panels and bronzes fill in the gaps.

Wilson oversees a small staff of three and is personally involved with each project. About ten commissions are done at a time, the vast majority of which have been in the LA area (including an estate for the late Princess Diana of Wales), and about half for the entertainment industry (Kenny Rogers, Tom Selleck, Johnny Carson, Michael Landon). Typical projects are over the million-dollar mark, with living rooms ranging from $120,000 to "the sky is the limit." Complete drawings are usually created before embarking upon purchasing. There is a high, flat design fee billed out over the course of the project, and standard product markups. While some clients feel they are offered a breadth of economic and stylistic choices, others feel that Wilson is limited to the gallant. AD 100, 2000.

"Ron is comfortable with the largest of projects and easily takes charge." "He is very articulate and explains the process to us step by step." "Ron has a big personality, but is candid and honest." "Even the pot racks are overscaled." "I needed pictures of every purchase along with the bills, and the office has been excellent about providing this." "There is a good mix of fab antiques and repro. Not everything is over the top." "Ron is not the most sensitive to economic constraints." "He really wants to create something unique and beautiful." "His visions are spectacular, but the details do not always follow." "I always felt confident that he was on track." "He is a super professional—as a lawyer, I appreciate this."

Samperton & Hackathorn   4.5   4   4.5   4

134 North Sweetzer Avenue, Los Angeles, CA 90048
(323) 655 - 6603   www.sampertonhackathorn.com
Timeless, sophisticated, accessible interior design

Making the most of their sterling training with Michael S. Smith, Schuyler Samperton and Anna Hackathorn are creating resplendent, joyful interiors turned down half a notch. Rooms look as if created over a lifetime of experience, thought and travel. The colors are rich, the upholstery is elegant, the case goods are well-worn and all is threaded together with the fine details of the craft.

Samperton, a Washington, DC, native and the daughter of an architect, studied art history at Trinity College in Connecticut and New York University. After seven years in PR with Fox television, Samperton went to Smith's firm to do PR and was quickly brought over to the design side, working there for almost five years. Hackathorn was raised in LA, studied in Paris for her junior year and graduated from Tulane. She then worked in New York, doing store design with Calvin Klein and consulting for Ralph Lauren Corporate, returning to LA to join Smith. Samperton & Hackathorn was founded in February of 2003, and is currently doing about six major projects at a time with two design assistants. Clients include young families, established business professionals, and Ron Howard and Brian Grazer for Imagine Entertainment. The designers are happy to start with just a few rooms. They recently acquired Broadbeach Lighting Company and soon will be adding their own creations to the line.

While the basis of their work is the inspiration of Michael Smith, intriguingly, their take comes with a lot more repro, a few less details and a more realistic budget. Sideboards may range from $5,000 to $100,000. There is a flat up-front design fee, a standard markup and no hourlies.

"It is Michael with a reality check." "Rarified and beautiful, but not over the top." "Lovely attitude. They keep their appointments and get back to you within hours." "Recently arranged flowers and tables for a big party." "Willing to work with you. Will bring a whole new batch of samples if you did not like the first batch." "Fabrics all price ranges." "A pragmatic, fresher look. Not overdone."

Studio Sofield   5   4.5   4.5   4.5

2044 Laurel Canyon Road, Los Angeles, CA 90046
(323) 650 - 6309   design@studiosofield.com
Nonchalantly extravagant interior design and architecture

With insouciant elegance, William Sofield confidently and uniquely stimulates the senses with interiors that are hip, glamorous and slightly decadent all at once. Floating ceilings, polished-concrete floors, columns with gilded fluting and the maximization of natural lighting are signature elements of his work. These forms and aspects dance together in a paradigm of great aesthetic theater. Nothing is considered too much of a challenge. Not for the faint of heart.

Sofield is best known for his worldwide redesign of the Gucci, Bottega Veneta, Boucheron and Yves Saint Laurent stores, many boutique hotels and the executive offices at Disney. The firm is about 40 people strong and takes on a wide variety of residential projects—ranging from metropolitan apartments to expansive estates with extensive landscaping, and including homes for Ralph Lauren, Tom Ford, Giorgio Armani and Martha Stewart. The LA satellite office of six was opened in 1999, and Sofield spends about one week a month operating out of his sprawling "pan-exotic" home, formerly the haunt of Douglas Fairbanks. Sofield is reportedly just as content working on the first home of young newlyweds as for the estate of a very established figure. But, we understand every detail must be precisely designed and executed for all.

Sofield graduated from Princeton with degrees in architecture, urban planning and European cultural studies. His early career years were intellectually tumultuous: a Whitney Museum fellowship, interiors consulting for Ralph Lauren, apprenticing with an 89-year-old wood craftsman on the Upper East Side of New York City for three years and designing for several mega-architectural firms. Finally, he formed his own practice in 1989. In 1992, he co-founded Aero Studios with Thomas O'Brien, and in 1996, he established Studio Sofield. The firm prides itself on its original looks that often demand a redefinition of a project's structural under-pinnings. Project costs may also be greatly affected by the acquisition of pricey artifacts, which are mixed with the client's existing collections. Firm fees are by the hour, with Sofield's falling at the high end of the spectrum. Clients find the resulting decor to be of personal importance as well as excellent value. HB Top Designers, 1999, 2000, 2001, 2002, 2003, 2004. ID Hall of Fame.

"A self-described 'rigorous modernist,' his work in LA is much softer—and drawing on popular glam culture and mixing it up with the best of the fine arts." "He is dedicated to bringing the finest craftsmanship to interior design—inlaid leather, Italian carvings—and nothing is too much to pursue." "Sofield's main interest is the successful marriage of functionality and fine detailing." "Despite the fact that there might be over twenty residential projects, during the critical design times, Bill was making the major design decisions and was on the job about ten hours a week." "While he is triple booked, his focus is so intense, you get all of him." "He has the most amazing way of being self-effacing and a star all at the same time." "When new owners buy a 'Sofield' house, they often bring Bill back to modify it, not considering anyone else." "Bill is a true artist and a legend in his own time."

Suzanne Rheinstein & Associates   5   4   4.5   5
817 Hilldale Avenue, West Hollywood, CA 90069
(310) 550 - 8900

Luxurious, classical interior design with verve

A leader in the LA design community, Suzanne Rheinstein eloquently introduces new design concepts while embracing classical traditions. Prints, patterns, silks and toiles are dominant players but are clarified to distinction. An indomitable force of creativity and function, her spaces are known to be elegant without being pretentious, heightened with joie de vivre and grace. She does sprawling Virginia horse farms and Hancock Park homes with equal ease, balance and charm, and her work is always geared to family traditions.

Rheinstein's classical New Orleans heritage taught her to appreciate the beauty and comfort of patina. Working collaboratively since 1994, Rheinstein is involved with every project, regardless of size, offering good balance and full coverage. About six major new projects are taken on each year, many from the ground up, with Rheinstein adding great insights to architectural plans. Hollyhock, a hot retail destination spot for many other designers and the public at large, carries her choice array of eighteenth- and nineteenth-century antiques and several exclusive home design lines.

As Hollyhock is the financial engine of the operation, the design business is priced quite reasonably, albeit with expectations for a certain level of quality. Standard design fees and product commissions are charged by the firm, with no hourly rates. Clients return regularly for a remix or a complete renovation, and highly recommend the team to friends. HB Top Designers, 1999, 2000, 2001, 2002, 2003, 2004.

"This is the real thing; not faux glamour." "She is one of the very few in LA who understand what genteel really means." "You have to understand and appreciate the look." "There is an incredible warmth of character with Suzanne that builds with the relationship." "She understands that I had a life before I met them, and graciously integrated my possessions with the new." "By reupholstering and changing the furniture around, much from room to room, we got a whole new look without buying much." "So creative with something as simple and economic as a grosgrain ribbon." "You get Suzanne, not a junior associate." "She aligns the grand and the humble." "Suzanne challenges you, yet she is remarkably understanding and practical." "While known for inspired traditional, she can also do Asian-zen fabulously." "We would go nowhere else."

Thomas Callaway Associates Inc. 🖼 4.5 4 4 4.5

2920 Nebraska Avenue, Santa Monica, CA 90404
(310) 828 - 1030

Interior designs of elegant simplicity and warmth

Thomas Callaway accomplishes what many others attempt: creating homes of inherent strength of character and grace. While he's best known for his elegant Spanish colonial designs, clients report that Callaway is equally adept at gabled Nantucket shingle, French Provençal, Moorish Alhambra and 1940s contemporary retro. Regardless of the style, Callaway takes an exacting approach to make the work look inexact, as if it evolved over time. He fastidiously focuses on the architecture and details of the period first, then adapts his designs for comfortable living. Formal touches lie calmly beside the practical and utilitarian, all with thoughtful restraint. The outside is considered as important as the inside, with hedges and exterior courtyards creating private havens.

After receiving a bachelor's in architecture and fine art, and doing post-grad work in painting and printmaking, Callaway spent 25 years as an actor. Called upon to do family and friends' homes from coast to coast, Callaway officially launched his LA-based interior design career in 1988 after his own Spanish bungalow was widely published. Early clients included actors Peter Horton and Michelle Pfeiffer, and he has been swamped ever since. More recent patrons include Miami Heat coach Pat Riley, Seinfeld creator Larry David, CAA head Richard Lovett, Warner Brothers' Peter Roth and many more from the entertainment industry.

Callaway is said to proceed like a "general in a war campaign." He has twelve in his camp, including several experienced project managers and three architects. The firm has about fifteen projects in process, ten of which are major. Callaway (noted as "very hands-on") or a project manager visits local job sites daily. Budgets are extensive and may be highly detailed up front or evolve over time. In renovations, architectural changes are usual, as Callaway is said to insist on getting the structure right first. Using unusual and smaller sources, Callaway finds better pricing than most on many pieces, saving the budget for a few really good items. The firm charges a standard product markup and a flat percentage on any structural changes. Many returning clients feel that no one else will do. HB Top Designers, 1999, 2000.

"As a peer of Tom's, I find his work inspiring." "Tom made our boathouse the most romantic place in the world. It is just magic." "Even his storyboards are like little jewels." "Each one of the three homes Tom has done for us has a completely different flavor." "My husband has very strong opinions and Tom managed around that with flexibility and confidence." "Tom only presented stuff he knew we could afford." "The bills are all clear, but he only works at the highest quality level." "Everyone's mouths drop open when they see how beautiful our living room is." "He was good about using our furnishings and renewing." "He pushes in areas only where he knows he is clearly correct, and he is." "Tom is excellent at returning calls, and he has a really competent back office." "As a top dealer in LA, I can vouch that Tom is very fair, even if the client is impossible." "At the end of the project I told Tom that is was so much more than I ever imagined. He retorted 'Well, it is exactly as I imagined it.' What more can you say?" "He is operating at the highest levels."

Thomas Jayne Studio Inc.   5   4.5   4   4.5

136 East 57th Street, Suite 1704, New York, NY 10022
(212) 838 - 9080   www.thomasjaynestudio.com

Historically based, spirited American interior design

Heralded for his American preservationist expertise and design integrity, Thomas Jayne has won the respect of clients and peers. While retaining an enlightened historic mood, he adds levity and a modern perspective with spirited colors and updated accents. His designs run the gamut from fun to serious, but all references say they are gorgeous. Though he's based out of New York, Jayne's commissions take him all over the United States and Europe, mostly to clients who are generally well-funded, and often art and antique collectors. Several projects have recently been completed in Southern California, incorporating a softer, more Californian sensibility warmed with excellent antiques, a measure of comfort and a truthfulness of spirit.

Born in Santa Monica and raised in Pacific Palisades, Jayne studied architecture in Oregon. He went on to receive a master's degree in American architecture and decorative arts from the Winterthur Museum. Later, Jayne trained at the Cooper-Hewitt, Christie's and the famed Parish-Hadley. Clients say he takes his training seriously and believes in "period-pure" rooms without "gimmicks" or reproductions, though he will mix styles for a comfortable, sophisticated touch. Most clients note that Jayne is captivating company, and others say he can be charmingly intent.

Many clients are repeat customers. One or two own five residences, all decorated by Jayne. By the time the fifth house is completed, it's time to do the first one over again. Jayne reportedly has a hard time saying "no" to a client, sometimes accepting more jobs than he can handle. All, however, remark that he meets the important deadlines and is extremely conscientious.

The firm charges retail on products and a standard markup on antiques. Customers say the designer has a strong preference for high-end fabrics (some quite over the top) and serious rugs. Living rooms can start lower for "guerrilla decorating," but can go as high as the imagination with fine antiques. All believe that Jayne is quite earnest and honest. He is highly recommended by serious collectors of American antiques and others looking for intelligent quality with a modern twist. HB Top Designers, 1999, 2000, 2001, 2002, 2003, 2004.

"No one knows how to make historical American furnishings sing more joyfully than Thomas." "Working with Thomas is like a really good addiction—it is hard to stop once you get going." "He knows when he is right, but patiently waits for you to come around." "Timing used to be an issue, but now he has a hyper-efficient back office." "He is clearly worth waiting for. He is always direct about timing and treated us with the utmost respect." "He has a passion for doing things the right way, starting with the architectural bones." "When the rectory of his church was

in disrepair, he took it upon himself to refurbish it." *"He has amazing common sense, great judgment and an original, dry wit."* *"Thomas reflects the embodiment of place in a thoughtful, artistic and amazing way."* *"One of a kind."*

Tim Clarke Design 💼   4   4   4   4.5
2110 Main Street, Suite 100, Santa Monica, CA 90405
(310) 452 - 8374   www.timclarkeinc.com
Unique, understated, luxe interior design

Uniting romance and realism, Tim Clarke creates individualistic spaces full of personality, warmth and grace. For Allen Allen clothing founder Jules Allen, he did a "young, hippie surfer-girl style" (in ten days, no less). Matthew Perry got Mies van der Rohe, an indoor-outdoor reflecting pool and a descending screen for video games. For himself, at his 1930s Spanish revival house, Clarke chose "inherited ease," a multigenerational patina.   Clients consistently remark on Clarke's collaborative approach, wide stylistic range and entertaining juxtapositions.

After receiving a degree in marketing and working in the fashion industry, Clarke followed his passion into interior design, first apprenticing with Waldo Fernandez for three years and then with Michael Smith for three. Forming his own firm in 1997, Clark now has a team of five doing roughly six major projects a year, about half from the ground up. Clients tend to be younger, and interested in Clarke's new twist on fun and functional luxury. Clarke will start with just a few rooms, but these usually lead into a much larger project. There is now an "old-fashioned decorator shop" at the above location with a mix of unique pillows, lamps, and vintage and antique finds.

The firm takes a flat design fee, which depends upon scope, and low product markups with no hourlies. Clients report that Clarke insists upon a few great pieces and then fills in with the good, which can "quickly add up," but never disregards the budget.   Supporters appreciate Clarke's practical, organized, "connected" and hip approach, and highly recommend him. HB Top Designers, 2002, 2003, 2004.

"Tim has gotten a lot of attention lately, especially with the hip, young crowd." "He could not be more pleasant and he makes it happen. A rare combination." "When you are dumbfounded at how rude the architect has just been, Tim is your advocate and makes it work." "My husband is a micromanager who never saw the need for a decorator, but now he is having Tim do his office." "He is so nice, but knows when to hold ground and when to step back, without ruffling any feathers." "Tim will bring you an endless stack of swatches and help you sort." "Calls are returned within minutes." "Tim was never anything but positive, even when I asked him to redo my yoga pillow three times." "Very generous with his time, he takes the stress out of the building process." "I was stunned to see magazine clippings of his recent work, which is nothing like my English country. He can do it all well."

	Quality +	Cost $	Value ◆	Recommend? ★

Timothy Corrigan/Landmark 🛍 Restoration/Belcaro Fine Arts

4.5   4.5   4   4.5

8225 Fountain Avenue, Los Angeles, CA 90046
(323) 525 - 1802   landmarkrestor@aol.com

Substantial, luxurious, European-inspired interior design, interior architecture and construction management

Thriving on a global scale, Tim Corrigan is in the midst of projects in LA, Boston, England, France, Spain and Egypt. Building on this breadth of scope and knowledge, Corrigan specializes in the epic restorations and renovations of magnificent older estates, retrofitting them for today's lifestyles. Corrigan is known to do it all—from helping clients locate a property, doing the interiors, rehauling the landscaping and managing the process through his two firms— Belcaro Fine Arts (interior design) and Landmark Restoration (all the rest). About half of the projects involve both companies, and half use only Belcaro for notably extravagant interiors that look as if they had evolved over a lifetime.

Corrigan left the world of advertising in 1995, after bringing Dorothy Chandler's white elephant estate to life on his own account. Now there is also a satellite office in Paris, where Corrigan spends one week a month purchasing and working on grand European projects. Clients have included the Mars candy dynasty, the Hambros family of banking fame, Sarah Jessica Parker and Matthew Broderick, Casey Wasserman of the LA Avengers and actor David Schwimmer. Madonna reportedly offered to buy Corrigan's own home when she saw it, but eventually settled on becoming a client and purchasing another.

While often seriously expensive, Corrigan is praised by clients for finding good investments, be it rugs in Rotterdam or armoires in Antwerp. Digitized and e-mailed to the clients, many items are purchased from afar. Budgets are extensive. Nevertheless, clients say they never feel pressured by Corrigan, who always has alternatives and never exceeds the high end of the interior design plan. The firm starts with a smaller concept fee, takes a standard markup on product and a smaller one on larger items. Hourlies are added for consulting and interior architecture, including kitchen and bath design.

"Exemplary in his field." "In over 40 years, going through many decorators, I have never been happier and received more compliments." "He is a real decision maker." "I knew nothing. He asked me a million questions. I left town and it was done in six months." "He interviewed each one of my kids and made them all feel important." "I felt as if I received a degree in design going through this with Tim." "I get all the credit because it doesn't look like a decorator did it." "Always available through e-mail." "He took pride in our home as if it were his own." "Don't go there if you do not have a full budget." "Always strives to find the best with the client's financial situation." "The first decorator who did not try to throw out all my existing furniture." "He added several rooms and did it all." "Tim is so exceptionally professional: decent, helpful, clear, reliable and dependable, with no ego. Why go anywhere else?" "Best of class."

Tommy Chambers Interiors 🛍

4.5   4.5   4   5

1146 North Gardner Street, Los Angeles, CA 90046
(323) 436 - 7565   www.tommychambersinteriors.com

Eloquent, updated, traditional and contemporary interior design with charm

Tommy Chambers is known for his reflective twist on the expected, offering a heightened awareness of the view at hand. In his twentieth-century moderne there might be a zen-like pillow. In his polished American farmhouse you may find a fabulous leafy crystal chandelier. In a traditional guest room there could be a Craftsman toolbox nightstand. Clients say he delivers their particular vision, but with the added sparkle of design charm and wit.

Chambers grew up in west Texas, receiving a degree in architecture at Texas A&M. After studying architecture and the arts from Assisi for a year and apprenticing with Joan Axelrod for five years, Chambers and a classmate, William Murray, established the successful Chambers and Murray in 1997. Recently, Chambers formed his own firm, and now takes on about five major projects at a time with four on staff. Clients have included director/producer Todd Holland, Cindy Costner and Norman and Lyn Lear. Chambers will work collaboratively or on a turnkey basis, aiming to please.

With nothing period-pure, Chambers has an open, creative mind as to the economic possibilities. It is the clear consensus view that he enjoys being cost effective and working a deal for the client. Pottery Barn is happily used in the guesthouse (but not the living room). There is always a professional working budget early on in the process, with every item accounted for. Delighted clients say these budgets prove to be quite accurate at the end of the day. The firm charges standard product markups (less on the art), a flat design fee for ground-up or hourlies for non-product time. All item bills are shown as the normal course. ASID. NCIDQ.

"There is a warm feeling of individual inspiration in the work." "Committed 110 percent, punctual, open minded, lovely, flexible, honest, caring and patient." "He knows the economic constraints and does not try to pressure you." "There is always a low/middle/high choice and it is up to you to make the decision." "Tommy's way of interacting with staff and industry contacts shows great character." "If there are any issues he will fix them. He stays awake at night making sure everything is right." "Tommy is very straightforward. Business managers love him." "He does it because he loves it and takes joy in transcending the obvious choices." "Tommy really, really listens and understands your idea of comfort." "There is a lot of art to help express the client's point of view and mix it up." "Every day in every season in every light my home looks magical, thanks to Tommy."

Vincent Jacquard Design   4.5 4 4.5 5
9663 Santa Monica Boulevard, Suite 881, Beverly Hills, CA 90210
(310) 657 - 3463   www.vincentjacquard.com
Exuberant, comfortable, enticing interior design

Vincent Jacquard's spirited mixture of stylish design reflects his rich, resonant past. Raised in France, trained in Paris and the Middle East, and loyal to LA for the past twenty years, Jacquard offers a worldwide view of the very best. While better known for his modern style, Jacquard works in all genres, including extravagant classic continental, as long as the fabrics and furnishings are esteemed. All looks as if it evolved over time, effortlessly and with panache. Clients say that after over 30 years in design, Jacquard is still a man "ahead of his time."

Growing up in Lille, France, in the family's eighteenth-century manor home, Jacquard joined a prominent Parisian architectural firm, rejecting his family's expectation of a career in the clergy. After several years, he moved to Beirut, doing design for the royal families of Jordan and Saudi Arabia until the civil war forced him to leave. Settling in LA, Jacquard later created the design arm of Galerie Michael on Rodeo. At one time the resident of Bela Lugosi's former Hollywood Hills home, Jacquard clearly leans toward the dramatic. The firm employs a staff of three, including an M.B.A. business manager, and about three major jobs are taken a year.

Generally, projects consist of gut renovations or ground-ups. The firm charges a standard product markup with a percentage design fee and hourlies for plan verification. Travel and expenses are all first class. Plans are highly detailed with "acres of documentation." While demanding excellent quality, Jacquard is also pragmatic regarding the client's budget. Clients roundly say Jacquard is a "complete dear" and dedicated to his craft.

Quality	Cost	Value	Recommend?
✚	$	◆	★

"Vincent is the ultimate deluxe designer." "His creative and artistic nature touched our hearts and intellect." "His certain charisma of understanding transformed our ideas into divine and mythical designs." "So impressed with Vincent's daring compositions." "Exciting conversations and visits to art and antique galleries." "Vincent has very strong opinions and everything needs to be perfect." "Vincent is quite flexible with clients, but not with architects and contractors. He forces them to his level of quality." "He is practical as well as amazing. While he showed me gazillion-dollar fabrics, we reached a happy compromise and remained on budget." "He is not a snob. We are just regular people and he made our house look incredible with limited funds." "He is an LA secret." "He is like one of my best girlfriends—we have had so much fun."

Waldo's Designs 🛍   4.5   4.5   4   4

620 North Almont Drive, West Hollywood, CA 90069
(310) 278 - 1803   www.waldosdesigns.com

Clean, robust, signature interior design

A master of his genre and a forerunner of the well-recognized modern California streamlined style, Waldo Fernandez is known by all. Consistency of design is a trademark, and clients appreciate that they will understand the end product before the first fabric is chosen. Luxury is created with a few, simple, bold strokes. Neutral colors, classic overstuffed and overscaled upholstery, fine European antiques, Roman antiquities and French-modern accents meld together in rich harmony. Fernandez is also known to be a pro at implementation, unquestionably capable of pulling off the most complicated or substantial jobs.

The Cuban-born Fernandez came to LA penniless and ended up in set design, working on such films as "Hello Dolly!" and "Doctor Doolittle"—until director John Schlesinger asked him to do his home. Now Fernandez lives in a Mediterranean-style mansion on Sunset Boulevard complete with ancient statues, extraordinary antiques and a few Picassos. Summers are spent in Malibu East—aka the Hamptons—with other members of the Hollywood elite. Past clients have included Jennifer Aniston and Brad Pitt, Burt Bacharach, Warren Beatty, Goldie Hawn, Will Smith, Sean Connery, Tobey Maguire, Merv Griffin (a 59,000 square foot spread) and continuous projects for Elizabeth Taylor.

Budgets are not generally a factor in Fernandez commissions. It is said that the minimum is well over $1 million, with Fernandez encouraging clients to buy the very best they can afford. Clients are happy to let Fernandez take control, which is his favorite modus operandi. About three major projects are taken on at a time with a small staff. Fernandez's trademark furniture line may be seen at his shop at the address above. While there are many repeat and very satisfied clients, customers who want a different spin may next head toward another designer. HB Top Designers, 1999, 2002, 2003, 2004.

"What you see is what you get. And it is truly inspired." "Waldo believes that less is more, encouraging you to buy a few truly great pieces." "It can take five phone calls before his office will call you back." "I was left holding on the line for four minutes, and they were calling me with a question." "Waldo is a very decent person, but clearly a control freak." "He fulfills his clients' fantasies—Elizabeth got white shag rugs and others got an eighteenth-century Italian villa." "He is an

original master of the California look, and while he has modified and refined that look, he is true to his hallmark." "Not big on organizational management." "He can somehow create subtlety and greatness in the same room." "Waldo is a design icon—he brought all of California to the next level."

William Hefner Architecture

5820 Wilshire Boulevard, Suite 500, Los Angeles, CA 90036
(323) 931 - 1365   www.williamhefner.com
Residential architecture

See William Hefner Architecture's full report under the heading Architects

Windsor Smith Home   4   4   4   4.5

9899 Santa Monica Boulevard, Suite 377, Beverly Hills, CA 90212
(323) 851 - 4822   www.windsorsmithhome.com
Traditional, spirited, familial interior design

Adding joyous verve to traditional lines and expectations, Windsor Smith creates comfortable and becoming interiors. Particularly adept at understanding and accommodating the client's interests, the firm adds charm and panache "that celebrate family living." Classical sensibilities are their forte, recently completing the historical renovation of an English manor home, designing a Cape Cod estate (for actor Michael Chiklis) and furnishing a New England farmhouse.

Raised in Houston, Smith moved to LA in the 1990s to pursue musical theater. She soon became an antique dealer, traveling the world to find treasures. Smith segued into interior design in 1995, while continuing to run her thriving antiques and custom furniture business. With a staff of four, including an in-house architect, about eight to ten projects are taken on at a time. A good part of the work centers upon the classic old estates of Brentwood and Bel Air, with Smith involved in all aspects of the process.

Smith presents her clients with a detailed budget up front, and takes a standard design fee, standard product commissions with no additional hourlies. Clients very much enjoy the process and applaud the result.

"Windsor has first class antiques that she incorporates into the designs, which really makes the process and the result so special." "Such creativity, such vision—we love every space she touched." "Windsor goes above and beyond." "Great spirit and enthusiasm." "The staff is also highly professional and hands-on." "She turned our home into a grown-up home." "Windsor stayed right on budget and on time—way better than I expected." "Not only incredibly talented, but so much fun to be around." "We can't wait to hire her again."

FIRMS WITHOUT PORTFOLIOS

Annie Kelly Art & Design   4.5   4   4.5   4.5

By Appointment Only, Los Angeles, CA 90068
(323) 876 - 8030   streetkelly@earthlink.net
Enticing, worldly, refined interior design

Taking her cue from the World of Interiors, Annie Kelly composes eloquent, sophisticated rooms with a global view. Intelligently composed and carefully moderated, each interior is a thoughtful treasure, never overdone. Andalusian is distinct from Spanish, English distinct from continental, with each stylistic element playing its role at the appropriate moment. The existing architecture is critical to Kelly's strategy—it must be of significant stature to balance the personality of the furnishings.

Trained as an artist in Australia, Kelly began as a color consultant, then segued into interior design. But it was after images of her own home were published that clients began flocking to Kelly, telling her they wanted that same becoming, European-chic in their lives. A sole proprietor, Kelly takes on a limited number of projects at a time. She has a strong preference for antiques and fabrics with heritage, but we're told she is also good about reworking existing pieces into the creation.

Architects have a particular fondness for working with Kelly, who is said to respect and incorporate a home's structural bones. She is often called upon to develop millwork that is sympathetic to the form. The firm charges a flat fee for the design concept, standard on product markups and hourly for non-product consulting.

"Annie is so clear of intent and fascinating to be with." "She honors the views of the client and imagines what life will be like in the house after she is gone." "Annie can get anything made if you do not find something available. Great resources." "She can go from Moroccan exotic to layered, laid-back aristocratic, and it is always captivating and hip." "As an architect, I am generally terrified of working with decorators, but Annie was a pleasure." "She captured the spirit of my intent and made it better than I ever could have imagined."

Barbara Barry   4.5   4.5   4   4.5
9526 Pico Boulevard, Los Angeles, CA 90035
(310) 276 - 9977   www.barbarabarry.com
Disciplined, timeless, alluring interior design

Admired as one of the guiding lights of design in Los Angeles and around the globe, Barbara Barry consistently creates unassumingly beautiful furnishings and rooms. Profiles of simplicity and quiet reflection belie a glamorous Hollywood allure. Her profound belief in the home as a sanctuary leads to works of clarity, unity and strength. Currently, Barry devotes the vast majority of her time to her many branded manufactured lines.

Born in Northern California, Barry studied at the Academy of Art College in San Francisco but was essentially self-taught in interior design. In 1985, she began working from her dining room table. The business soon flourished, and commercial commissions ensued, including Manhattan's Avon Spa and The Savoy Grill in London. A multitude of product manufacturers have now partnered with Barry to bring her distinctive look to the retail market. Co-branding with Ann Sacks tile, Baccarat crystal (the first American designer to design for the French company), Bagni Volpi Noemi linens, Baker Furniture, Bloomingdale's Bed and Bath, Boyd Lighting, Haviland Limoges china, Hickory Business Furniture, Kallista bath, McGuire Furniture and Tufenkian Rugs, Barry's influence can reach into just about every corner of the home.

Barry works with a staff of twenty professionals, including architects, interior designers, graphic artists and product designers. Barry herself takes a few interior design projects of significant interest per year, with project managers playing a large role. Clients very much enjoy the process, saying Barry has her own point of view but lots of patience. Past clients include Eli Broad, Michael Ovitz and cinematographer John Bailey. AD 100, 2000, 2002, 2004. HB Top Designers, 1999, 2000, 2001, 2002, 2003, 2004. ID Hall of Fame.

"You absolutely know what you will get, and it will be fabulous." "She uses her residential clients to help clarify her design trends. If she is interested in celadon green that year, you will get celadon green. Now she is predominantly into periwinkle." "Her sense of style is unequalled." "She is a whirlwind. Her mind is incredible." "She will cut a lighting design to shreds in three minutes, and she will be right." "Barbara's ideas are not new, just perfect." "The client work is all reviewed by Barbara." "The designs are consistent to an extreme within one home—the leitmotif is chosen and replayed. Usually in creams and pales."

	Quality	Cost	Value	Recommend?
	+	$	◆	★

"Barbara's work transcends the mere mortal. You are working with a master." "She is a visionary, and you really get her vision." "In the business myself, I think that Barbara is the most brilliant designer I have ever met. Her thought process is unparalleled and her productivity mind-blowing."

Christopher Teasley Interior Design   3.5   3.5   4   4.5
1201 De La Vina Street, Santa Barbara, CA 93101
(805) 969 - 4005   info@ctinteriordesign.com
Uplifting, streamlined traditional interior design

Crafting solid, well-respected designs for a very traditional following, Christopher Teasley envisions rooms of restraint, balance and polish. Working primarily in the Montecito/Santa Barbara area (generally with a more relaxed look), references say Teasley takes designs one step beyond, reaching unexpected sophistication. His insightful and accommodating nature is also mentioned consistently by clients, who love the fact that his homes do not look "decorator done."

Raised in Los Angeles and schooled in Santa Barbara, Teasley apprenticed in design in San Francisco after college. Moving back to Santa Barbara in 1979, Teasley worked with Richard Byers Interiors before starting his own firm in 1983. With a staff of four, his office is said to work "like a tight-fitting glove." About three blockbuster projects are run at a time with smaller reruns for many. Clearly entrenched in the regional market, Teasley has over 30 repeat clients and has decorated three major country clubs: Valley Club, Birnam Wood and La Cumbre.

The firm works on the New York retail basis, which is 40 percent below retail for new products and less on antiques. Hourlies are charged for architectural consulting, but there is no design fee. Living rooms tend to be in the moderate price range, for which the client's existing goods can be retrofitted. References are very pleased with Teasley's budgeted mix of period vernacular and originals, and they greatly appreciate his flexibility in all matters.

"The organization is run beautifully by wonderful people who speak politely to everyone they meet." "You can depend on Christopher for the correct look: not too much, not too trendy, but comfortable." "Christopher helped me execute what I wanted." "He is very well liked and respected at the Blue Whale. Makes shopping fun." "He is here in a minute if I need him." "Chris is very generous with his sources. He really taught me the market." "He gives you the feeling that he is not working for a living. He is more than fair." "He also comes up with better ideas for the contractors." "I give him the keys and it is magically done while I am away." "He never makes you feel like a piker if you do not want something." "I have worked with fancy New York decorators, but I never will again. Chris is so easy." "He ends up becoming a friend."

E. Ferucci Designs   3.5   3   4.5   4
13955 West Tahiti Way, Suite 167, Marina Del Rey, CA 90292
(310) 745 - 1300   eferucci@aol.com
Classical, modern, swank interior design

Always keeping it friendly and comfortable but still unique, Erin Ferucci does beach bungalows, Sun Valley retreats, Beverly Hills homesteads or fabulous wedding events with pizzazz. Her young and hip client base turn to her for fun "decorating adventures" that are practical, organic and unique. With a terrific sense of what makes an interior fun and inviting, Ferucci uses exotic woods, unusual stones (found on trips to Italy and Brazil) and indigenous products, usually on a more neutral background.

A self-described beach aficionada, Ferucci grew up in California, studied in New York and moved to Paris in 1991, where she organized antique tours for decorators and other Americans. In 1993, Ferucci returned to Los Angeles and set up shop as an interior designer and antiques consultant, following in the footsteps of four previous generations. With the help of several freelance assistants, the firm takes on about a dozen projects each year. Commissions have included glam projects for the Marciano family of Guess Jeans and six projects for Bruce Willis. While there is no minimum—living rooms typically range from $25,000 to $150,000+.

Whether shopping for rare Sotheby's antiques or lamps at Ikea, Ferucci enjoys the challenge of a budget. The firm charges a flat design fee, standard product markups (lower on art and antiques) and good hourly rates for non-product time.

"I hardly had to tell her anything. Erin makes everything look amazing." "Erin is a true artist. Shades of beige, which I can barely differentiate, come alive in her hands." "Erin was good about balancing the budget: she stuck to her guns on the important stuff and filled in with shabby chic." "She can drop everything and be there." "She speaks French quite well and can easily negotiate St. Tropez or Paris." "While she is fairly available when she is in LA, she can be out of town for a week and unreachable." "The projects had fits and starts, but I am crazy about the end result." "Erin had great resources to get things made when we could not go for the original." "She even helped with the landscaping."

Kathryn M. Ireland Inc.   4   4   4   4
1619 Stanford Street, Santa Monica, CA 90404
(310) 315 - 4351   www.kathrynireland.com
Understated, comfortable, continental interior design

Bringing familial warmth, calm and stylish ease to her interiors, Kathryn Ireland has a clear viewpoint. With breezy elegance, she makes a house an inviting home for all—including the children and the dogs. Ireland finds unique furnishings of character in Los Angeles, New York and Europe (spending her summers in the south of France). Clients clearly sign on for the lifestyle appeal and comfort Ireland provides, knowing that much less will get done in the summer, but that tranquil beauty will emerge come fall.

Born in Britain, Ireland used her creative talents in a number of callings— public relations, fashion, acting, and styling and producing music videos—before entering interior design. Starting with a home furnishings store in Santa Monica, Ireland took on her first full-scale interior project in 1993. She now has a group of ten to help her with her multifaceted business, including her successful signature line of printed hemp fabrics shown at Hollyhock in LA and a newly opened show-room in London.

For past clients, Ireland will do a single sheer in a bedroom, but for the uninitiated project budgets start high. There is a mix of the antique, the new and the well-worn. Clients have included Steve Martin, Caroline Kennedy Schlossberg, Fran Drescher, Julia Louis-Dreyfus and Lady Annabel Goldsmith. The firm charges a flat monthly design fee and standard product commissions with evolving budgets. Ireland is known to convince clients to keep their current furnishings, just adding a new slipcover or a complementary pillow. Her fabrics make regular appearances in her rooms, offering a quite consistent theme. Clients tell us they know at first sight that they want Ireland's timeless compositions. HB Top Designers, 2002, 2003, 2004.

"Kathryn is a celebrity in her own right, but she is incredibly down-to-earth to work with." "I love what she did to our house—it is so easy, happy and unpretentious." "You know exactly what to expect." "Provence feel is the theme with pattern on pattern or toile—always quite similar and always beautiful." "Kathryn was good about doing one room at a time with us, as the budget allowed." "A wonderful sensitivity for family life." "She understands that decorating should be fun, and should not be taken too seriously." "I adore her institutional haphazardness." "A razor edge to her humor." "Not the kind of person that works with a strict budget." "She will always take it back if it doesn't work." "Bits and bobs are pieced together." "Kathryn is thoughtful, clear and specific." "A great decorator and a great dinner party guest."

McCormick Interiors   4   4   4   4
1721 East Valley Road, Santa Barbara, CA, 93108
(805) 969 - 1110   penelopebi@cox.net
Traditional, warm, bucolic interior design

Weaving together centuries of European savoir-faire, Penny Bianchi develops dioramas of "life in the country." Her signature style is one of bucolic good breeding, effortlessly linking highbrow with the more relaxed. Influenced by the late twentieth-century British interior designer Nancy Lancaster, Bianchi adds similar whimsical touches. Fine dining chairs may be slipcovered in striped cotton for the summer and large porcelain parrots may stand guard. Clients say they love the Old-World ease of printed fabrics that live cohesively with patterned rugs, often in lush colors.

After reading *House In Good Taste*, Bianchi put aside her English literature degree and launched a decorating business in the early 1970s. Originally from Pasadena, she formed an excellent reputation in the neighborhood that still resonates today. Her longest and most over-the-top project lasted twelve years when Warren Buffett's right-hand man, Charlie Munger, gave her carte blanche to decorate condos in Montecito. With one assistant, Bianchi now balances several projects at a time mostly in and around Montecito where she lives with husband Adam, who handles the business side of the firm. She is delighted to do one room, as much as she likes to lavish attention on an entire house. Customers are quick to return for new projects, as well as smaller cosmetic tasks.

Bianchi charges a standard up-front design fee and standard product commissions, and there is no hourly fee. Estate sales, flea markets, auctions and eBay items are purchased to keep costs down. We hear clients are very pleased with the experience and the finished product.

"She really knows traditional style and with my existing furniture turned a masculine home into an Italian masterpiece just by changing colors, rugs, adding tiles and wallpaper." "Penny has an amazing sense of what is comfortable for family life." "She uses antiques that make sense, not anything over the top. All else is found at very reasonable sources." "The tiles were left unglazed to allow the moss to grow. That is so classy, and so un-LA where everybody here tends to be shiny and new." "She has an amazing collection of antique textiles, which adds such character and warmth to the rooms."

McGee-Mitchell Design   3.5   3.5   4   4
222 South Bedford Drive, Beverly Hills, CA 90212
(310) 788 - 3978   mmdsn@earthlink.net
Classic, chromatic, harmonious interior design

Blending a timeless design style with robust color and whimsy, Lisa McGee works collaboratively with clients to reflect their vision. With an East Coast sensibility, a worldly perspective and a love of the tropical palette, she offers original and refined designs. References appreciate McGee's cooperative spirit, responsiveness and her ability to get the job done.

Raised in Bermuda, part of the family fashion business from her teens, McGee acquired an eye for the stylish early on. After working professionally in fashion in New York and then Europe in the 1980s, McGee launched her LA interior design business in 1990. With an assistant, McGee works in a very hands-on manner with several clients per year, mostly in LA and Bermuda.

A few rooms may be done at a time, with very reasonable budgets. A smaller flat design fee is taken up front or hourlies taken for all hours, and products receive a standard markup. McGee is said to present clients with products out of the budget spectrum, but then have good alternatives. While this practice can lead to budget inflation at the direction of the client, references are delighted with the end result, often referring McGee to friends.

"We worked for four years with Lisa and sold the house at a considerable profit." "She really gets a feel for who you are. My girlfriend's house is completely different." "Lisa has expensive taste. We had to rein her in several times, but then she was good about offering a proxy." "She took the time to understand the interests of each of us individually, including my two kids." "She would guide me to make decisions I could do on my own without a fee." "Very buttoned-up. She listened to my thoughts and made them better." "It was really a group effort." "Lisa was also great about directing the painting, lighting and carpet crews." "We have hired her again for our next project."

Orlando Diaz-Azcuy Designs   5   5   4   4.5
45 Maiden Lane, San Francisco, CA 94108
(415) 362 - 4500   oda@odadesigns.com
Thoughtful, urbane, spare yet sumptuous interior design

Letting the artistry speak for itself, Diaz-Azcuy creates unparalleled, understated drama with accessible luxury in a minimalist mode. Employing architectural simplicity and shots of vibrant color, Diaz-Azcuy assiduously limits each design to its essential elements, which are executed with exacting beauty and comfort. Based in San Francisco and New York, but with a worldwide following, Diaz-Azcuy does several projects in Los Angeles each year. Clients feel as if they are graced with the thoughts of a legend, and trust his judgment implicitly.

With an undergraduate degree in architecture and master's degrees in landscape architecture and city planning, Cuban-born Diaz-Azcuy has an expansive view. After working with landscape icon Lawrence Halprin and then with Gensler Architects in San Francisco for twelve years, Diaz-Azcuy founded his own firm. There is an effective staff of fourteen (all clothed in white lab coats in their neutral office setting), including several licensed architects and senior designers who manage about twenty major ongoing projects. Diaz-Azcuy sets the direction for each design and approves each presentation. Commissions have included hotels in Hong Kong, Thailand, Japan and the States, but most of the interior work is residential. The firm has designed furniture, fabrics and accessories for a range of companies, including McGuire, Hickory Business Furniture, Stow Davis, Steelcase, Schumacher and Boyd Lighting. Diaz-Azcuy travels and lectures extensively, and teaches a summer session at the Graduate School of Design at Harvard.

Undertakings are generally for the seriously committed with strong budgets. While most of the furnishings are custom crafted with exacting details, Diaz-Azcuy has been known to appropriately incorporate Ikea and Gump's. The firm charges lower to higher hourly rates, meaningful travel costs and a lower product markup. HB Top Designers, 1999, 2000, 2001, 2002, 2003, 2004. ID Hall of Fame.

"As a contractor, I see that his clients hang on his every word. They will not do anything without Diaz-Azcuy's approval." "There are never any issues." "He gets involved with every detail." "He has only one distinct look, but it is done to perfection." "He creates drama without saying 'look at me'." "To Orlando, simple lines speak volumes." "We were unrealistic in our budget, and were enticed into better quality." "The house and the landscape are symbiotic." "Orlando is a master. He is intelligent, thoughtful and clear—it is a wonderful experience." "There is such a mystique about Orlando." "After over 30 years in design, Orlando is still on a minimalist mission, but it is a softer one."

Rose Tarlow   5   5   4.5   5

8454 Melrose Place, Los Angeles, CA 90069
(323) 653 - 2122   www.rosetarlow.com

Refined, timeless, effortless interior design

Rose Tarlow's every design movement is taken as a sign of what is to come. Heralded as the most insightful interior designer in LA, each new line of fabric in her Melrose House showroom brings on waves of redesigned homes and product knock-offs. Tarlow is said to have initiated the concept of the historically referential as applied to the unique California look, resulting in an increased West Coast design awareness.

While most of her time is spent on the extensive product line, Tarlow currently works with two assistants on a few homes, most for friends or those of significant note. Several years were spent with David Geffen on his $47.5 million spread, after reportedly turning him down several times. While no one can predict how or why her famously discerning eye alights upon a certain object and declares it perfect, all agree that she is undeniably correct. Tarlow will try at least twelve paint colors on a wall before even considering a decision. Some say her perfectionism can be trying and sovereign, but most look on adoringly, intently watching a masterpiece being born. Tarlow, on the other hand, appears to take this all in nonchalantly, clear in mind and purpose.

Melrose House was opened in 1975, when there were very few fine-antique dealers in LA. From the very beginning, Tarlow offered an intriguing mix of the old and the new. When European antique prices went sky high in the mid-1980s, Tarlow determined that it was a lot easier and a lot more profitable to create her own originals. Currently, the vast majority of her product is very fine reproduction. Melrose House (trade only) is credited by all for its exemplary products and equally exemplary staff and customer service. Tarlow teaches a master class at UCLA and published a book in 2001, *The Private House*, detailing her design philosophy. AD 100, 2000, 2004. HB Top Designers, 1999, 2000, 2001, 2002, 2003, 2004. ID Hall of Fame.

"Rose is always learning and growing, intellectually pursuing the next level." "She is never just evolving in one direction—recently she did a boat, a rustic estate, a Meier minimalist and a Georgian manor. But there is definitely a common, purist view." "She has such an astute mind, no one can match her design acumen." "With the most minor tweaking of the splay of a leg, she turns the ordinary into the extraordinary." "Rose is highly demanding of herself and of those around her, but simultaneously warm and approachable." "She can be quite insistent with the client, and they always see that she was right all along." "The key to Rose's success with her furniture is in the quality of the wood. Nothing but the best will do." "She is on the cutting edge, continually reinventing her look." "Rose is full of life."

	Quality	Cost	Value	Recommend?
	+	**$**	**◆**	**★**

Stamps & Stamps   4   4   4   4.5

318 Fairview Avenue, South Pasadena, CA 91030
(626) 441 - 5600   www.stampsandstamps.com

Delightful, thoughtful, traditionally based interior design

Awash in charm and elegance, the rooms of designer Kate Stamps and her architect husband, Odom, enchant clients with their imaginative concepts, genteel design approach and can-do attitude. Homes are created to look as if they could have evolved naturally, full of generational personality and covered in lush oleander, bougainvillea and wisteria. While the Stamps often emphasize the Mediterranean with an Andalusian overlay, other styles are done equally well. Whether it be formal Brentwood neoclassical, a relaxed Malibu cottage or a take on Turkish yali, rooms are created with traditional bones, quirky treasures and memories.

Kate and Odom met at Tulane, where she majored in English and art history, and he in architecture. Before opening their joint partnership in 1991, Odom worked in commercial architecture with Johnson Fain Partners for several years. Currently they have fourteen on staff, including six architects and draftsmen, and they take on about ten substantial projects at a time. Clients have included Ellen DeGeneres, Ron Underwood, Geena Davis and Mrs. Frank Zappa. Commissions go anywhere from 3,500 to 35,000 square foot homes. No matter how big or small the project may be, the Stamps ask the client to fill out a 50-page questionnaire that quantifies everything from their plate diameters to the way they fold their underwear.

The firm favors taking on all three aspects of home design: the architecture, interiors and gardens to create a coherent structure. Clients often bring the two Stamps on as a team, and Odom also does a fair amount of architecture independently. Several yearly shopping trips across the United States and Europe yield the most interesting and well-priced pieces. Living rooms and product range widely with fabrics falling anywhere from $5 to $300 per yard. Standard architecture, design and product fees on all purchases are taken.

"While we had a strong sense of what we wanted, Stamps really took the time to understand." "Odom integrated seamless extensions of the existing property." "I started at Laura Ashley and Kate took us way beyond." "The architectural aesthetic can sometimes take precedence over function." "The Stamps take a vested interest in their work and create an emotional response. It is way more than just a job for them." "There is no such thing as 'off duty' with the Stamps." "There is much attention to detail and, thankfully, not much to fashion." "It is an ongoing process with Kate. She encourages you to wait until you find the perfect piece." "When they work together they're wonderful—unified flow and vision." "They can visualize what you want from a little swatch and make it happen."

The Warner Group Architects Inc.

1250 Coast Village Road, Suite J, Santa Barbara, CA 93108
(805) 969 - 5074   www.wgarch.com

High-end residential and commercial architecture and interior design

See The Warner Group Architects Inc.'s full report under the heading Architects

Trevor Goff   4   4   4   4

458 North Orlando Avenue, Los Angeles, CA 90048
(323) 651 - 0424

Traditional, timeless, reliable interior design

Clients appreciate Trevor Goff's pleasant demeanor and timeless, classic designs that look good "over the long haul." With many repeat customers asking Goff to work with a variety of architectural styles in a variety of locations, Goff has successfully done indigenous Cape Cod, Arizona, French Burgundy, Mexican, Hawaiian and American Country in a log cabin. All are done with a quiet ease of reassured confidence.

The firm was established in 1979 and remains quite small, taking only about three projects at a time. The designer grew up in Malibu, going to UC San Diego. Goff usually works with a combination of mid-priced antiques and repro. A flat design fee is taken up front, and standard product fees on purchases along the way. There are no hourlies. Clients find Goff calm and discreet, and very helpful in getting the project "across the finish line."

"Trevor is delightful and easy to work with." "At his suggestion, we met every Friday." "His strengths are his color sensibility and his style at pulling it all together." "Will not waste your time." "Trevor learns what you like and takes you right to it." "Any delays, and he is right on it." "Guarded, but open to your design style." "As a dealer, I think he has very good traditional designs and will get better known over time." "Was able to handle our East Coast look with ease." "I am now bringing Trevor to Virginia to do our house there. I would not want anyone else."

Valerie Pasquiou Interiors + Design Inc.   3.5   3.5   4   4

1855 Industrial Street, Suite 608, Los Angeles, CA 90021
(213) 402 - 1500   www.vpinteriors.com

Warm, intriguing, modern interior design

Inventively presenting interiors that are striking, relaxing and nourishing all at once, Valerie Pasquiou has warmed clients' souls. Pasquiou blends earthy colors and diffuse textures with a polished hand and a professional head. Yards of raw silk complement burnished woods, oriental screens and silhouetted velvets. Unique Craftsman pieces with French accents often appear, highlighting Pasquiou's wonderful Gallic connections and her offices in Paris and New York.

Pasquiou began her creative career in set design with Ben Stiller, then moved to video art direction with Sheryl Crow and Tom Petty. After a chance meeting with K.D. Lang in a Japanese antiques store, one thing led to another, and soon Pasquiou was doing interior design for Lang and her friends, officially setting up shop in 1997. Pasquiou does about four major projects a year, with the help of freelance staffers. Clients have included Serge Azria (BCBG owner), Lisa Kudrow and Sharon Stone.

With great finders in Europe—especially Paris—Pasquiou offers unique and interesting elements at reasonable prices. Budgets are quite reasonable and guidelines are established up front. Large projects carry a flat fee and smaller ones an hourly rate, both with a lower product markup. Product design is at retail. References are thrilled with the results and recommend Pasquiou to any who share her unconventional sense of style.

"Valerie is fresh, fun and very French." "Our beach house is far more sophisticated and eclectic than I expected or envisioned, and I love it." "Valerie is passionate about her work, happily meeting on Sunday mornings." "Extremely sensitive to both our tastes, which were not always the same." "She has a cast of French characters at the ready who provide Old-World product, goods and services." "There is great respect from vendors, who often find unique items just off the boat for her, for less." "Valerie can be tenacious when she knows that a certain piece works. I disagreed, but then woke up the next morning and loved it." "While we went a bit over budget, I got more than I ever paid for." "I think it is pretty rare to find a decorator like Valerie, who has both the vision and management skills to make it all come together." "She was always available, explained every change before it occurred and produced a house we could live in forever."

Hiring a Kitchen & Bath Designer

The perfect kitchen won't make you a great cook, and a decadent bathroom will still need cleaning, but the fact remains that a kitchen or bath remodel can make your life at home much more pleasurable on a daily basis. They are often the two rooms that see the most use, so their planning and construction deserve careful thought. A good kitchen and bath designer will listen attentively to a client's desires and incorporate them into rooms that are as functional as they are beautiful.

Finding a Designer

Some architects, interior designers, space planners and certified remodelers dabble in kitchen and bath design. There are even "designers" who work for manufacturers and home improvement stores. But if your sights are set on a specialist, you'll want to look for a Certified Kitchen Designer/Certified Bath Designer (CKD/CBD). To get certified, the designer needs at least seven years of hands-on experience in addition to coursework, and must pass a series of tests administered by the National Kitchen and Bath Association (NKBA), the field's main professional organization. Even after certification, continuing education will enable a designer to stay abreast of current styles and the latest advances in equipment.

Most designers have either a showroom or portfolio to give you a sense of their particular style. You may think you are on the same page when you talk on the phone, but when you see the ideas embodied in a room you may find that you have very different takes on what a word like "contemporary" or "traditional" means. You'll be a giant step closer to getting what you want if you can find a designer whose style is similar to your own. Take a look at your prospective designer's recent work history while you're at it. At the very least, a designer should be able to produce three current references, and a history of two or more projects per month shows a healthy demand for the professional's work. Another good idea is to ask if you can go see a project that is in progress (which lets you see if the workmen are neat and clean in the house).

Finding someone with whom you feel compatible will make the whole process more pleasant and productive—especially if you see eye to eye on budgetary considerations. It will also help to alleviate some of the inevitable stress. With the right designer, you'll be able to openly discuss such issues as project cost, time frame for completion, product information and warranty issues. You should feel comfortable asking for advice on the logical and functional placement of appliances, how to make cabinets child-proof, lighting alternatives, your storage needs, personal preference for gas or electric stoves, the upkeep involved in tile kitchens vs. stainless steel and other design considerations. Also, do you want to work with the appliances you have or completely replace them? If you want new appliances, the designer may or may not coordinate their purchase. Don't assume that a designer can read your mind and know that you will not, under any circumstances, part with your matching canary-yellow refrigerator and stove.

On Cost

There are generally two ways in which designers can charge for their services. The first type of pricing structure is a percentage—generally about ten percent—of the project's total cost. This type of fee schedule is common when the designer coordinates the entire project as well as supplies the artistic template. Coordinating the project includes ordering all materials and finding and managing the workers to install everything. This approach is often a good value. It also relieves you of having to find someone else to carry out the project or immerse yourself in the hassles of ordering and overseeing.

The second method of pricing is an hourly fee called a pure design fee. Your money buys only the designer's ideas and plans for creating the kitchen or bath of your dreams. The price will depend upon the designer's experience, education and general reputation. Hourly charges range from $75 to $200 or more per hour.

It is imperative to discuss total cost prior to starting the job, of course, so you know what to expect. If you have your heart set on a new kitchen layout that requires new plumbing and electrical work, for example, know that this will be a more expensive renovation than one that involves existing systems. If the cost of such a renovation is more than you'd like to spend, work with the designer to match your dreams with your budget.

Once you've chosen a designer, you'll need a contract to protect both parties. No professional will be offended if you request one. The contract should spell out the services you're expecting and include a timetable for payment. Expect to part with a down payment of 40 to 50 percent to secure a good designer.

Many designers are sole proprietors, which means that the designer may be the only employee of the company. Others are part of a large firm with designers representing a range of specialty areas. Deciding whether or not to use an individual or a firm is a choice that depends upon your own style and the scope of your project: a firm's diverse collection of talent may come in handy if your project is especially complex. Some clients prefer dealing with one person, while others may feel more confident having a number of designers available. If, after speaking to a few of the vendors in this book, designers from both large and small firms interest you, make some comparisons, such as their availability to begin work and how long they anticipate it will take to complete it. Their answers may help you narrow your search.

As with any major home project, you'll go through a period of upheaval when everything—including the kitchen sink—gets overhauled. But the result will be worth the trouble, whether your fantasy is to cook dinner for twenty with ease or to sink into a tiled Roman bath.

Open Your Mind—Trend Ideas

 ✧ **Pay Close Attention to Lighting:** Talk to your designer about the latest lighting trends (use glass tiles as a backsplash to reflect the light).
 ✧ **In the Bathroom:** California living often means bringing the outdoors inside. Many designers are adding large windows and doors and opening this space up to a sanctuary garden or small terrace.
 ✧ **In the Kitchen:** Use an open cabinet for storing your everyday dishes and glassware. This will break up the monotony of all-doored cabinets and come in handy when washing dishes—you'll duck beneath open doors less frequently. Placing your everyday dishes in open cabinets may also motivate you to clear out any mismatched pieces and to better organize your frequently used tableware.

Quality	Cost	Value	Recommend?
	$	◆	

KITCHEN & BATH DESIGN

FIRMS WITH PORTFOLIOS

Alisa Smith Design
By Appointment Only, Los Angeles, CA 90065
(213) 910 - 3491   coloursmith@gmail.com
Understated, reflective, graceful interior design

See Alisa Smith Design's full report under the heading Interior Designers & Decorators

Arch-Interiors Design Group Inc.
275 South Robertson Boulevard, Beverly Hills, CA 90211
(310) 652 - 7600   www.archinteriors.com
Tailored, innovative, diversified interior design

See Arch-Interiors Design Group Inc.'s full report under the heading Interior Designers & Decorators

Cross Interiors   3.5   3.5   4   4
6712 Colbath Avenue, Van Nuys, CA 91405
(818) 988 - 2047   www.crossinteriors.com
Kitchen and bath design

Cheryl Casey Ross boldly spans a startling array of services and specialties. She helms Cross Interiors, which specializes in practical kitchen and bath design of any style, from a boy's nautical bath to a country kitchen. However, the firm also custom designs and constructs indoor and outdoor furniture, birdhouses, fountains, light fixtures, glasswork, pillows and window treatments.

Founded in 1975, Cross Interiors employs six assistants. Ross offers consulting services on design plans, and frequently receives "rescue" projects from clients. She is a certified interior designer, Member of ASID, IIDA, Professional Associate of SFV/AIA. Fees are calculated on a project by project basis, which we hear gives clients "more value for their money." Clients report that they feel well taken care of by Ross, who keeps in very close contact with her contractors and is on-site every day of a project.

Dream Kitchen Designs   4   4   4   4
7055 Pellet Street, Downey, CA 90241
(562) 928 - 5388   www.dreamkitchendesigns.com
Kitchen and bath design

Owner and lead designer Leslie Eib-Neubauer is a self-declared cooking *afficionada* and loves to entertain. Her commitment to fulfilling the needs of the chef and entertainer sets Dream Kitchen Designs apart. For over 25 years, Dream Kitchen Designs has provided full-service designs, specializing in kitchens, baths and libraries. With her designs, Eib-Neubauer attempts to "carry the flavor of the architecture throughout the house into the kitchen with grace."

	Quality	Cost	Value	Recommend?
	✚	$	◆	★

Although the company is a representative of Poggenpohl's progressive cabinets, they are not tied to any one style and carry many other popular cabinetry lines. The firm is also said to stay current with the latest trends in kitchen and bath design, incorporating elements such as glass countertops and backsplashes. Depending on the scope of the project, Eib-Neubauer either charges a flat project fee (ranging from $2,000 to $30,000) or an hourly rate of $120 for consulting. The firm has designed kitchens all over the world, including projects in Italy, Mexico and Korea. Almost all of the company's work comes from word-of-mouth referrals, which speaks to Eib-Neubauer's talent for making her clients' very specific dreams come true.

Plush Home 🛍   4   3.5   4.5   5
8323 Melrose Avenue, West Hollywood, CA 90069
(323) 852 - 1912 www.plushhome.com
Kitchen and bath design

Designer Nina Petronzio softens the edges of modern life with her classic, understated designs from Plush Home. Her star-studded clientele values her intuition and her razor-sharp aesthetic. They also appreciate her creativity: Petronzio is the kind of designer who can turn an antique Chinese vase into a unique, charming desk lamp.

The firm offers custom cabinetry for kitchen and bath, as well as upholstered and wooden furniture, lighting, window treatments, fine art and accessories. Each piece of cabinetry is custom designed and fitted to its surroundings. We hear Petronzio's discerning eye often spots "just the thing" for a space.

"Nina is a one-woman powerhouse." "I just can't say enough about her."

FIRMS WITHOUT PORTFOLIOS

Ann Sacks Tile & Stone Inc.
8483 Melrose Avenue, West Hollywood, CA 90069
(323) 658 - 8884 www.annsacks.com
Handcrafted tiles and luxury bathroom fixtures

See Ann Sacks Tile & Stone Inc.'s full report under the heading Tile, Marble & Stone

Bay Cities Kitchens & Appliances   3.5   4   3.5   4
1412 14th Street, Santa Monica, CA 90404
(310) 394 - 2025 www.baycities.net
One-stop shopping for kitchen and bath design and installation

Whether you just want to check out the latest and greatest Miele dishwasher or want your entire kitchen redesigned, sources say that Bay Cities is a great place to start brainstorming. The firm carries a broad selection of high-end cabinetry, such as Wood-Mode and Brookhaven, and a wide array of plumbing products and fixtures.

A member of the NKBA, Bay Cities Kitchens & Appliances has been in business for twenty years, offering design and drafting services as well as installation. Sources say its 15,000 square foot showroom has something for everyone, and its experienced salespeople are incredibly knowledgeable. Although the firm works with all kitchen styles, clients particularly appreciate the company's traditional and country kitchen designs. Completed projects from Bay Cities range from $60,000 to $150,000.

"Their showroom is phenomenal, and they have every high-end appliance you can think of." "The helpful staff always returns my calls within minutes."

| **bulthaup** | 4 | 4 | 4 | 4 |

153 South Robertson Boulevard, Los Angeles, CA 90048
(310) 288 - 3875   www.bulthaup.com

Sleek, minimal, contemporary German cabinetry

bulthaup's superbly crafted contemporary cabinetry has earned it the nickname "the Mercedes of kitchens." Founded in 1949 in Bavaria by Martin Bulthaup, the company has long been a household name in Germany. Since its arrival in LA in 1990, it has been winning over architects and designers who often turn to the firm for sleek, minimalist designs.

But according to clients, there's a lot more to bulthaup than its trademark minimalism. The firm offers a broad array of styles, from ultra-contemporary industrial looks to muted kitchens with more traditional appeal. Most of the company's business comes from the trade, but its much-praised staff members are more than happy to work with retail customers.

"Not only did I find the look that I was searching for, but the quality was amazing." "The best in Los Angeles for kitchen design, and a great staff to boot."

| **Clive Christian Beverly Hills** | 4.5 | 4.5 | 4 | 4 |

8687 Melrose Avenue, Suite G295, West Hollywood, CA 90069
(310) 854 - 3862   www.clive.com

English country kitchen and bath design

Internationally esteemed by clients and members of the industry, Christian designs and installs top-quality kitchens, bathrooms, bedrooms and dens in the English country tradition. The firm offers a complete range of oak, pine and mahogany cabinetry, and specializes in painted furniture. Clients include many high-profile media and entertainment figures, as well as top designers and architects in search of beautiful traditional interiors.

Sources say that the quality and detailing of Christian's designs are comparable to custom made, but its prices are lower. Its showroom is located in the Pacific Design Center. References praise the company's professional and knowledgeable staff, calling the process of designing a kitchen with the firm "luxurious."

"Not the cheapest, but the outcome was gorgeous." "Gives you that Old-World custom look with modular packaging and pricing." "While there is less flexibility, what you see is what you get."

| **Cooper-Pacific Kitchens** | 4 | 4.5 | 3.5 | 4 |

8687 Melrose Avenue, Suite G299, West Hollywood, CA 90069
(310) 659 - 6147   www.cooperpacific.com

Kitchen and bath design

Cooper-Pacific Kitchens has been designing and installing kitchens for LA architects and designers for 25 years, and customers and industry leaders are impressed. Everything this firm installs is of superior quality, from state-of-the-art SieMatic and Wood-Mode cabinetry to Sub-Zero, Miele and Viking appliances.

Cooper-Pacific's showroom is located in the Pacific Design Center, and we hear that its display is hard to beat. The firm does most of its work in the Los Angeles area, but its services have been requested and delivered in locales as far away as Canada, Mexico and Asia.

"The sales staff made the kitchen the heart of my home."

Countertops by Olive Mill

4247 East La Palma Avenue, Anaheim, CA 92807
(714) 528 - 3789   www.olivemill.com

Granite and solid surface fabricator

See Countertops by Olive Mill's full report under the heading Tile, Marble & Stone

Downsview of Los Angeles   4   4   4   4

359 North Robertson Boulevard, Los Angeles, CA 90048
(310) 858 - 1008   www.downsviewkitchens.com

One-stop shopping for kitchen and bath design

Downsview's showroom has something for everybody, our sources report. Part of a 38-year-old international chain, this Los Angeles showroom offers a huge selection of kitchen cabinets, hardware and countertops as well as design and installation services. This Canadian firm specializes in finding "just the right piece"—right down to that perfect doorknob or handle. Styles range from the contemporary minimalist to French country. Downsview's LA showroom has been open since 1989 and serves architects, designers and the general public.

"Their showroom gave me some great ideas about what to do with my kitchen."
"They were able to combine appearance and function to create our favorite room in our home."

Elizabeth Graham Kitchen and   3.5   3.5   4   4
Bath Interior Design

PO Box 50616, Santa Barbara, CA 93150
(805) 969 - 6630   elizabeth.sb@verizon.net

Kitchen and bath design

Insiders laud Elizabeth Graham for her hands-on approach to kitchen and bath design. We hear that for eleven years Graham has not only been giving clients the rooms of their imagination, but also showing them how to make the most of their small and large spaces.

Always on-site during the construction process, Graham makes sure that her kitchen designs work for each individual's needs. While Graham does not have a signature style, sources say that she always stays architecturally true to the home itself. She charges an hourly rate of $185 plus a percentage of product. Graham's projects range anywhere from $5,000 to $20,000.

Ferguson   3.5   3.5   4   4

8532 Melrose Avenue, West Hollywood, CA 91605
(310) 657 - 1750   www.ferguson.com

Wholesale distributor of kitchen, bath, plumbing and HVAC supplies

Coast-to-coast distributor Ferguson has all the bases covered. With over 700 showrooms and 2,300 outlets across the United States, Mexico and several Caribbean countries, Ferguson is the nation's largest wholesale distributor of plumbing supplies; pipes, valves and fittings; waterworks; building materials; and heating and air conditioning products. Seven Ferguson outlets and two showrooms dot the LA area from West Hollywood to Pasadena. They carry a dizzying selection of faucets, fixtures and waterworks, including high-end lines such as Moen, Bach, Newport Brass and Hans Grohe.

Founded in 1953 in Washington DC, Ferguson has expanded steadily, doubling in size every five years. Despite being an international company, Ferguson prides itself on being "full service" from manufacturer to warehousing to sales. Their commitment and supply channel integration have made them a "go-to" player in the contracting and plumbing industries. Clients say that Ferguson's appointment-only showrooms, staffed by informed consultants, prove to be a great stimulus for new kitchen and bath ideas.

Hub of the House Kitchens and Interiors   4   3.5   4.5   4
420 North Robertson Boulevard, Los Angeles, CA 90048
(310) 652 - 2332
Kitchen design

Clients appreciate Hub of the House's intimate approach to kitchen design. From its customer service to its distinctive designs, Hub of the House exudes an inviting warmth. Owners Carla Smith and Karen Harautuneian take on only a select few projects, which allows them to concentrate on clients' individual needs. While Smith and Harautuneian do not adhere to a specific kitchen style, they are praised for basing their designs on the style of the home.

Hub of the House works all around the United States, but its projects are concentrated in Beverly Hills, Brentwood and Malibu. Depending on the size and scope of the project, design fees average between $3,000 and $6,000. Sources say this small, relaxed and friendly showroom is just what the doctor ordered if you are tired of high-pressure salespeople and cookie-cutter kitchens.

Kathleen M. Rogers Design   4.5   4   4.5   5
274 Ashdale Place, Los Angeles, CA 90049
(310) 440 - 1125   kmrogers@gte.net
Kitchen and bath design

Sources tell us that Kathleen Rogers' kitchens are so good, they should be studied in design schools. According to clients, Rogers' "attention to detail, brainstorming and troubleshooting" enable her to design a house down to the tiniest detail. A member of the NKBA and a certified bath designer, Rogers takes the hassle away from her clients by acting as the middleman and dealing with sub-contractors. Clients describe Rogers as a sharp thinker who rapidly picks up on key factors—like the fact that kitchen storage requirements vary for every family.

Rogers discovered her love for kitchen and bath design working as the West Coast designer for Smallbone, a prestigious English cabinetry company. She went solo in 1996 and quickly established a following. Depending on the complexity of the design, Rogers charges an hourly rate of $120 to $150. On large jobs, Rogers will consider a fixed monthly fee. A completed project from Rogers ranges from $75,000 to $100,000. Expensive prices don't faze her clients, who speak glowingly of her hands-on work and invaluable advice.

"Ms. Rogers' knowledge of planning and state-of-the-art appliances ensured us an extraordinary kitchen." "I love that Kathleen gives options for her designs so that you can select the one that best suits your budget." "She was able to incorporate and showcase our existing furniture and collections into wonderful new settings." "When it became necessary to fire my contractor (whom I found and selected against Kathleen's advice), she stepped in and found all the subcontractors necessary to complete the job. Everyone she chose was excellent." "Without Kathleen, we never would have realized our dream project so joyously."

Le Gourmet Kitchen   3.5   3.5   4   4
2015 South State College Boulevard, Anaheim, CA 92806
(714) 939 - 6227   www.legourmetkitchen.com
Kitchen design

Le Gourmet offers soup-to-nuts kitchen design, from cabinets and countertops to appliances and lighting. The firm comes by its gourmet status honestly: the Laguna Culinary School is located in its 3,000 square foot showroom.

Established in 1993 by G. Townsend Bradner, Jr. and Bruce Colucci, Le Gourmet Kitchen carries high-end cabinetry, such as Wood-Mode and Brookhaven, and represents hundreds of other high-quality manufacturers and suppliers. The company's certified kitchen designers offer expert advice. Sources say the firm's staff is helpful and knowledgeable and will assist you in establishing a budget for anything from a small kitchen remodel to a large-scale construction project.

Poggenpohl Los Angeles   4   4   4   4
8687 Melrose Avenue, Suite B188, West Hollywood, CA 90069
(310) 289 - 4901   www.poggenpohl-usa.com
Innovative German kitchen design

Poggenpohl has been in the vanguard of high-end German kitchen design and cabinetry for more than 100 years. Since opening one of its worldwide showrooms in LA at the Pacific Design Center in 1999, the firm's name has become synonymous with cutting-edge quality.

Customers visiting the showroom are greeted by stunning wood veneers and high-gloss lacquers, along with elegant stainless steel and glass accents. Poggenpohl's countertops are also available in teak, exotic granite and limestone. Industry leaders laud Poggenpohl for its slick, hyperfunctional German designs: drawers that close quietly by themselves and "magic" corner cabinets that offer extra storage.

"I was impressed with the overall appearance of the designs in their showroom."

Smallbone of Devizes   4.5   4.5   4   4
220 Brompton Road, London, UK SW3 2BB
(020) 7589 - 5998   www.smallbone.co.uk
English kitchen design and fine hand-painted cabinetry

English farmhouse kitchens are the hallmark of Smallbone of Devizes, a London-based firm with an elite following in Los Angeles, New York and other cosmopolitan hubs. Smallbone's quintessentially British kitchens have been described as warm and cozy. Its fixtures, made of oak, olive, ash, sycamore, pine, teak, maple and chestnut, have the air of fine furniture. The firm offers a wide color palette for furniture painting and will paint and stain each piece by hand, using artisanal finishing techniques. Raised-panel doors, glass-front hutches and built-in drawer organizers are company trademarks. Smallbone also designs custom furniture and wall paneling.

The company operates out of London, so using its services represents a substantial commitment in terms of communicating with overseas and local staff. To insure optimum client relations, the firm assigns a team to each project, consisting of designers, a draftsperson and a professional installation manager. Some clients report that the quality is not quite up to the price, while others are completely satisfied, praising the designs as "free-flowing, stately and elegant." In the end, for those who want a proper English kitchen designed as only the British can, Smallbone is the natural choice.

Solistone

5974 West Pico Boulevard, Los Angeles, CA 90035
(323) 931 - 0444   www.solistone.com

Tile importer, distribution and installation

See Solistone's full report under the heading Tile, Marble & Stone

Specialty Hardware and Plumbing

283 South Robertson Boulevard, Beverly Hills, CA 90211
(310) 659 - 9351   info@specialtyhardware.net

High-end kitchen/bath showroom

See Specialty Hardware and Plumbing's full report under the heading Plumbers

Waterworks   5   4.5   4.5   5

8715 Melrose Avenue, West Hollywood, CA 90069
(310) 289 - 5211   www.waterworks.com

Bath design, sales and installation referral

Clients say that visiting one of Waterworks' five area showrooms is "like being a kid in a candy store." The national high-end outfitter offers "gorgeous tubs and fixtures" that are classic, clean and crisp—plus top-quality product support and service. Used by both the trade and private clients, this is the place for people who are serious about creating sophisticated bathrooms regardless of price.

Qualified Waterworks sales associates are able to guide you through the design and spec phase. However, we hear that the company does advocate bringing an interior designer or architect on board for any involved project. Waterworks does not install, but it will refer clients to a stable of trusted professionals. Its service associates coordinate and track delivery of materials, and will even go on-site to troubleshoot during installation. Tips on the design process and commentary by featured decorators can be found on the company's handsome, helpful website.

Waterworks works closely with contractors, providing tile and stone samples, facilitating quotes and bidding packages, and providing technical support for installations. The company's products include fittings, fixtures, tubs, bath accessories, lighting, furniture, sinks, textiles and personal care and apothecary items. The company maintains a complete parts department and offers a lifetime warranty on its product. Additional showroom locations can be found in Pasadena (626) 568 - 3301, Los Angeles (310) 246 - 9766, Santa Monica (310) 393 - 9197 and Newport Beach (949) 717 - 6525.

"A truly phenomenal selection of kitchen and bath products." "The salespeople have always been informative, polite and more than helpful." "Cutting-edge design."

HIRING A LANDSCAPE ARCHITECT/DESIGNER

In the mild Southern California climate, where homes are more a celebration of nature than a refuge from it, the need for thoughtfully designed exterior space is as important as any architectural element. Garden designers, horticulturists and landscape architects use plants and masonry on the canvas of your property like a painter uses brush strokes, invoking various moods with composition, color, texture and light. Experts in both art and science, these professionals can conjure up natural havens that provide shelter from the hustle and bustle of everyday life.

More Than Planting

Planning a garden paradise for your property is a job for professionals because many technical elements are involved. Garden designers create water and soil systems that are unique to each city, suburban and estate landscape. Their craft requires a complex blend of botanical knowledge, construction expertise and creativity. Projects can be more or less involved, incorporating large trees and bushes, masonry and rock formations, ponds and streams. Due to the harsh and dry weather conditions of Los Angeles, extensive knowledge of irrigation systems is also quite important.

Service providers included in *The Franklin Report* reveal a common thread—artistry combined with a passion for creating the ultimate natural space to suit each client's unique habitat.

Where Do I Start?

The first thing to ask yourself when planning a landscape is, What purpose will the space serve? Are you a cook who loves using fresh ingredients and longs for an herb, vegetable or cutting garden? Have you discovered the joy of exotic plants and wish to install a greenhouse for your orchids? Or are you an observer who dreams of a superbly designed terrace with benches and several layers of growth? With your overall purpose in mind, take stock of the space available in and around your home. If you want to create an outdoor oasis, are you primarily interested in shrubs, trees and vines or particular colors and species of flowers and plants? Are you considering adding hedges to separate your yard from your neighbor's because privacy is an important issue? Do you prefer the informal charm of an English cottage garden or the elegance of a neoclassical French one? Keep in mind that the more complicated the design, the more maintenance is involved. Explore your ideas by looking through home, garden and architecture magazines before you contact a garden designer.

Foremost in a landscape designer's mind is creating a setting that can be enjoyed year-round. The designer will have many ideas for you, but if you have done some research and fallen in love with specific plants and flowers, you will be a step ahead in designing your perfect escape.

ON COST

The pricing system for landscape design varies from firm to firm. Some designers charge an hourly rate—others determine a flat fee after analyzing the job. The average hourly rate in Los Angeles is between $75 and $100, translating into a baseline of 3 for Cost in our book. Like other professional services, garden design companies will produce a written agreement for the client that lists what will be done and at what cost. It is not unusual for these agreements to leave room for flexibility in scheduling and pricing, should unforeseen circumstances, such as bad weather delaying the work, affect the job.

WILL A DESIGNER ALSO MAINTAIN MY GARDEN?

Services provided by garden designers vary from firm to firm and depend on the scope of your project. Many companies provide a complete package of design, installation and maintenance, and thus strive to establish a long-term relationship with the client. Other professionals are limited to design and consulting, and subcontract for installation and maintenance. Landscape projects can vary dramatically in size and detail, and therefore in degrees of maintenance. Discuss these aspects with your designer and make sure you're aware of the amount of attention your yard or garden will require. Like interior designers, garden designers, horticulturists and landscape designers work closely with clients on a one-to-one basis to bring their creative ideas to fruition.

PERMITS AND PROFESSIONAL CONSIDERATIONS

A garden design project that includes structural hardscape will require permits. Permits for softscape (plants) depend on the scope and visibility of the work. Designers are well schooled in this process. A license is not required to be a garden or landscape designer, and these green specialists have a variety of educational backgrounds, including degrees in horticulture, study programs affiliated with arboretums and botanical gardens, degrees in sculpture and other studio arts, and lifetime experiences with plants and nurseries. Landscape architects, many of whom focus primarily on the hardscape aspects of garden design rather than on horticulture and maintenance, have degrees in the field and are licensed.

There are organizations, such as the Association of Professional Landscape Designers (APLD) and the California Landscape Contractors Association, that continually educate the landscaping field by offering classes and conferences. Although it is not necessary for a landscape architect or designer to be a member of such an organization, it certainly enhances their qualifications. All those drawn to the garden design profession undoubtedly share the view of Thoreau, who wrote, that "in wildness is the preservation of the world."

LOW MAINTENANCE PLANTS FOR A "CLASSIC" SOUTHERN CALIFORNIA GARDEN

- ✧ **Bird of Paradise:** Although native to South Africa, this tropical looking plant with its exotic orange, blue and white flowers is the official flower of the city of Los Angeles.
- ✧ **Citrus Trees:** Orange, lemon and grapefruit trees all make excellent small scale ornamental trees that can be grown in large pots as well as in the ground. They have attractive, deep green leaves, which they hold year-round, and they bear small white flowers that are immensely fragrant.
- ✧ **French Lavender:** This is one of many varieties of lavender that flourish in this region. An evergreen perennial with gray-green aromatic foliage, the leaves of this species are distinctive for their square-toothed edges. The plant produces short rounded purple flower spikes almost perpetually.
- ✧ **Iceberg Rose:** Roses play an important role in the Mediterranean garden tradition and are well-suited for cultivation in Southern California. Iceberg is a vigorous modern landscape rose that is remarkable for the profusion of white flower clusters it produces practically all year long.
- ✧ **Mediterranean Foxgloves:** Small leaves and brown flowers that flourish in dry rocky terrain.
- ✧ **Rosemary:** A versatile and tough evergreen shrub with narrow, dark green leaves, this plant is available in upright forms that are suitable for clipping into low hedges as well as prostrate forms that make good groundcovers for sunny locations.

Quality	Cost	Value	Recommend?

LANDSCAPE ARCHITECTS/DESIGNERS

FIRMS WITH PORTFOLIOS

All Phase Construction   4   4   4   5
6737-B Variel Avenue, Suite B, Canoga Park, CA 91303
(818) 340 - 2095   www.allphaseconstruction.com

Landscape design/build and swimming pool design/build

We hear there's no aspect of Mother Nature that All Phase Construction can't tame. Satisfied Angelenos say that All Phase Construction is the firm to call if you need anything created in your backyard—from a swimming pool to a kitchen.

The husband and wife team of Harriett and Richard Peardon has been designing and building some of the most elaborate and creative outdoor spaces in Los Angeles since 1973. Clients say that Richard's background as a general contractor, combined with Harriet's background as a landscape contractor, makes for a strong partnership. Supported by a crew of twenty, Harriett and Richard eagerly pursue projects where they can work with the "bones of the house," giving landscape the spirit of extant architecture. References report that not only is their design phenomenal, but their knowledge of the process is unparalleled—allowing projects to be completed without hassle, within budget and on time.

"An excellent team of professionals who can work closely with their clients to create a beautiful and practical living environment." "This was the second major remodeling project that this company has completed for me in the past five years, and they were gloriously creative and responsive." "Reliable and dependable." "Ultimate high-end work, but worth the price for the spectacular results." "Translated our ideas into exactly what we wanted." "All Phase is a family business that stands behind their work. We have recommended them to friends, who were just as thrilled as we were."

Appleton & Associates Inc.
1556 17th Street, Santa Monica, CA 90404
(310) 828 - 0430   www.appleton-architects.com

Comfortable, contemporary, appropriate residential architecture

See Appleton & Associates Inc.'s full report under the heading Architects

C&K Landscape Design   3.5   3.5   4   5
PO Box 0441, Tujunga, CA 91043
(818) 353 - 7030   www.candklandscapedesign.com

Environmentally conscious landscape design, installation and maintenance

Clients tell us that C&K's designs are not merely gorgeous, but also responsible—incorporating drought-tolerant plants that thrive in native California soil. Founders Cassy and Kirk Aoyagi offer a full menu of landscape services from design through maintenance. Both "C" and "K" have degrees in environmental horticulture, and their blend of science and personalized service has proved a winning combination. Established in 1997, the firm has grown quickly to a team of twenty.

We're told the company charges a reasonable design fee reflective of the size and scope of the project. Maintenance is a flat hourly rate of $75 an hour for a highly qualified three-man crew, while project costs average between $30,000 and $70,000. C&K's gardens have won awards from the California Landscape Contractors Association, appeared on HGTV and been featured on tours by the National Garden Conservancy, Santa Monica City College and Eco-Home Networks.

"Cassy and Kirk are a helpful and engaging team." "They obviously love what they do." "C&K maintains our landscape to perfection." "They created a thrilling wonderland for us to enjoy and they did it with sensitivity to our environmental and ecological concerns." "The entire team is extremely professional, courteous and responsive, which is exactly the tone that the owners, Kirk and Cassy, set when you meet them the very first time."

Double Green Landscape, Inc. 🖼   4.5   4   4.5   4.5

315 Washington Boulevard, Suite 4, Marina Del Rey, CA 90292
(310) 448 - 4220   www.dglandscapes.com

Artistic landscape design, installation and maintenance

Double Green Landscapes has been "carefully sculpting each yard to echo the design of the home as well as the unique and individual desires of the homeowner" since 1991. Insiders and industry leaders consider the firm a trusted resource for design, installation and maintenance. Owner Tom Levi and his team of over 30 work closely with architects, designers and homeowners to create the perfect outdoor space.

Located in Marina Del Rey, Double Green has planted palm trees in Culver City, Beverly Hills, Santa Monica, Bel Air, Pacific Palisades and Brentwood. Projects range anywhere from $10,000 to $500,000. An impressive client roster includes Tom Ford and Mossimo.

"If any problems crop up they will always get someone out to the job." "We literally cleaned out the entire yard, except for the two main trees and started from scratch. Walkways, grass areas and gardens were all designed by Double Green. We worked with Tom and found him to be creative, innovative and a wonderful collaborator. The result is an asset to us as well as the entire neighborhood." "Prices are quite competitive. I have recommended to many others and all have stated that Double Green exceeded their expectations."

Greentree Landscaping 🖼   4   4   4   5

1015 Gayley Avenue, Suite 1125, Los Angeles, CA 90024
(323) 935 - 9470   www.greentreela.com

Landscape garden design and installation

Clients credit Michael Baer and his field and office staff of 22 with fostering a customer service-oriented atmosphere at this excellent landscape design firm. With a solid referral base, much of it concentrated in the Hollywood Hills and Pacific Palisades, the company produces beautiful work tailored to the customer's desires. Baer is said to listen closely to his clients, and he takes his design cues from the architecture of the house.

Born in Southern California on an orange and avocado ranch, Baer received a degree in international business and worked as a journalist while adding landscape design to his already full resumé. A stint as a fireman schooled him in the delicacies of water pressures and hillside irrigation to avoid erosion. Just like their hard-working boss, staff members are said to accomplish things swiftly and diligently, completing anywhere from twelve to fourteen large jobs a year. In addition to his reasonable hourly consulting fee, Baer charges a minimum of $5,000 to produce project drawings.

"Michael restores faith in the concept of customer service in particular, and the human race in general. His initial estimate was well beyond our budget, but without a hint of the Beverly Hills indignation one comes to expect, he focused on the essentials and adjusted accordingly." "We had such an essential vision for our garden, and Michael was able to quite literally bring that to fruition." "He suggests and embraces other points of view, and works diligently to make the final result a masterpiece." "Great company, crews and knowledgeable. First to arrive, last to leave." "He delivers on his mantra, 'creating beautiful surroundings'."

JN Land Maintenance

4	3	5	5

12483 Wagner Street, Los Angeles, CA 90066
(310) 577 - 9378   www.jnlandmaintenance.com
Landscape maintenance and design

For those who want a reliable and capable landscape maintenance company, we hear that Jeff Nord and his team at JN Land Maintenance are the only choice. JN offers unique and creative landscaping design for their residential and commercial clients, as well as a broad spectrum of maintenance services and programs. They perform weeding, quarterly fertilizing, mowing, lighting and irrigation. Nord established the firm in 1998 and began by mowing lawns. Today, the firm has a total of ten employees and pleased customers say that Nord's impeccable attention to customer satisfaction is on par with the best in the business.

Complete landscape projects can range anywhere from $10,000 to $100,000, depending on the size and scope of the project. Maintenance fees are $75 an hour, and that includes three people. JN can take on a few landscape design projects at a time along with about 40 ongoing maintenance clients.

"You really don't need to hire a designer if you can use JN. Their creativity and breadth of knowledge was extensive." "We receive the finest quality of professional service, in addition to receiving wonderful personal attention. We have found that our children enjoy following the workers around the yard, learning along the way! We have no other option for landscaping. We have been spoiled."

KAA Design Group Inc.

4201 Redwood Avenue, Los Angeles, CA 90066
(310) 821 - 1400   www.kaadesigngroup.com
Highly intellectual, well planned, site-specific contemporary residential architecture

See KAA Design Group Inc.'s full report under the heading Architects

Patricia Benner Landscape Design

4.5	4	4.5	4.5

135 North Orange Drive, Los Angeles, CA 90036
(323) 933 - 1091   www.benner-design.com
Classical gardens and swimming pool design with a California twist

Clients admire Patricia Benner's sophisticated home gardens, which are skillfully adapted to the California climate. Clients say Benner's landscapes are visually appealing even when the gardens are not in bloom, because she pays special attention to foliage design in terms of color, texture and scale. The flexible Benner will create anything from a small garden gem to an estate-size project.

Benner's eye for exteriors comes from her mother, a landscape architect, and from her studies at the USC landscape architecture school. Since 1996, Benner's firm has provided a full range of services for exterior landscapes. With an added focus on garden furnishings, Benner's gardens feature well-appointed garden rooms for outdoor family enjoyment and entertaining. Both *Town & Country* and *House Beautiful* have featured Benner's work. She offers quarterly maintenance consultations for two years following the completion of a project.

"Pat is able to manage a project to a defined budget which is more than I can say for my wife and myself." "She ensures satisfaction and comes back often to make sure our gardener prunes and pampers our plants." "Pat was extremely knowledgeable about plant suggestions for my specific design needs." "She did a great job with the spatial design and layout." "Pat is good at incorporating our thoughts and ideas into a well thought-out plan." "We are constantly surprised and pleased to see our garden change over the seasons."

Proler Garden Antiques Inc.   4 4 4 4
528 Palisades Drive, Suite 501, Pacific Palisades, CA 90272
(310) 459 - 0477   www.garden-antiques.com
Garden antiques

At any given moment, Proler Garden Antiques likely has agents patrolling Europe in search of the finest in statues, fountains and antique garden accoutrements. "And if it can't be found," adds principal Lynette Proler, "then we'll hand-carve it." That kind of dedication to aesthetics has propelled this firm, founded in 1993, from a Swiss import-export business to a darling of West Coast celebrity gardens. Most of Proler's antiques are purchased directly from European villas and chateaux, but they also employ a team of master carvers based in Italy.

Working with a staff of ten, Lynette Proler provides full service installation, including museum crating, shipping, installation and coordination with landscape architects. Proler Garden Antiques keeps an "up-front" attitude with customers on pricing, a trait that surfaces in reference reports that call the firm "frank and friendly."

Rios Clementi Hale Studios
8008 West Third Street, Los Angeles, CA 90048
(323) 634 - 9220   www.rchstudio.com
Contextual contemporary residential architecture with mid-century modern appeal

See Rios Clementi Hale Studios's full report under the heading Architects

Tichenor & Thorp Architects
8730 Wilshire Boulevard, Penthouse, Beverly Hills, CA 90211
(310) 358 - 8444
Traditional residential architecture and landscape design

See Tichenor & Thorp Architects's full report under the heading Architects

FIRMS WITHOUT PORTFOLIOS

A. Lee Shelbourne and Associates 3.5 3 4.5 4
15904 Strathern Street, Suite 24, Van Nuys, CA 91406
(310) 854 - 1916   www.gardens-pools.com
Landscape design/build and swimming pool design/build

Clients praise A. Lee Shelbourne and Associates for its classic garden and swimming pool designs. Shelbourne takes on jobs throughout Southern California, primarily in the high-end heart of West Los Angeles, where it has been pleasing residents and industry pros for more than 40 years. While the company offers design/build services, it does not perform maintenance duties.

The firm has steadily increased in size since its inception in the 1960s. Long-standing clients applaud the firm's quality and individualized customer service as "superior" and "outstanding." The company charges a flat design rate that clients tell us is more than fair for the ease of one-stop shopping Shelbourne offers.

"My experience with Shelbourne has always been pleasant." *"Lee and his team were always customer-service oriented."* *"No matter how many people were working in my backyard, Lee was always overseeing every aspect of the project."* *"Anybody who has been in the business as long as Lee has got to be good."*

Art Luna   4   4   4   4

8930 Keith Avenue, West Hollywood, CA 90069
(310) 247 - 1383

Garden design—terracing and outdoor living rooms

Move over, Edward Scissorhands: former hair dresser Art Luna is now wowing Los Angeles with his top-notch garden designs. Interior designers and architects throughout Southern California praise Luna for transposing the design and structure of classic English and Italian gardens to a more desert-friendly California key. We're told Luna's favorite flourish is to "redecorate existing gardens" using containers and potted plants.

Luna's landscape design adventure began a few years ago. The courtyards he created at his successful hair salon so impressed his clients that they decided to put their gardens in their stylist's capable hands. In a town where famous former hairdressers include a major movie producer, Luna's transition didn't raise many eyebrows.

We hear Luna employs the same two crews he used on his first job to implement his original outdoor living room and terrace designs. The firm charges an hourly consultation fee of $150 with a three-hour minimum, and a flat design fee with a 25 percent product markup. References insist that Luna's garden designs are well worth it. His work has been published in *House Beautiful* and *Elle Decor*.

"Art is fabulous for people who want to upgrade and redesign their gardens." *"Has an unbelievable talent for working around existing structures."*

California Landscapes   4.5   4   4.5   4.5

1212 South Stanley Avenue, Los Angeles, CA 90019
(323) 930 - 0808   www.californialandscapes.com

Low-maintenance Mediterranean-style garden design and installation

Fans throughout greater Los Angeles praise California Landscapes' consistent show of professionalism, integrity and responsibility, which principal Gayle Martin has maintained for over a decade. The firm offers Mediterranean-influenced landscape design, installation and quarterly assessments. Clients are pleasantly surprised by the low-maintenance aspect of Martin's creations, saying it's relatively easy to keep them looking good as new.

Martin has a strong background in sculpture, giving her an eye for detail and aesthetic beauty that is said to inform her unique landscapes. In addition to her artistic training, Martin also studied garden design and horticulture at UCLA. We're told her firm produces amazing designs at very reasonable prices. Although most of California Landscapes' jobs fall between $35,000 and $60,000, we understand Martin will take on any project she views as a challenge.

"Gayle is a southern gem. Her charm and creativity were only surpassed by her phenomenal performance in transforming my overgrown backyard into a tropical,

tranquil retreat featured on HGTV." *"Excellent designs with a keen ear to what you want as well as being conscious to the environment and toxic sprays and pesticides."* *"Gayle is an experienced and very creative artist."* *"The best of all compliments: my neighbors want her to do work for them."* *"She is on the job in the mud with her crew."* *"Gayle has a fabulous sense of design."* *"They replaced grass patches that did not take root at no additional expense."* *"Gayle always showed up exactly as planned and kept her word. I wish every contractor was as conscientious."*

Christine London Limited   5   4.5   4.5   5
2370 Bowmont Drive, Beverly Hills, CA 90210
(310) 273 - 5660   clondonltd@aol.com
Classical European landscape design

Insiders inform us that Christine London and her small five-person firm are responsible for designing some of the most elegant gardens in Los Angeles over the past decade. Although the firm does not install or maintain its landscape designs, London enlists only the best landscape contractors in the business for the dirty work, and she stays closely involved in the oversight and realization of her aesthetic. Clients praise London's refined taste and appreciate her engaging manner, an attribute that really matters, considering that an average landscape project takes two to three years.

After receiving her undergraduate degree in art history, London returned to school to study horticulture. Architects and interior designers are routinely impressed by London's feel for the character of a property and instinct for riffing off its architectural elements. We hear London takes her clients' needs to heart, creating gardens that allow fluid motion between the interior rooms and their exterior counterparts. The firm charges an hourly design fee of $150, and the budget for the average London-designed project is around $80,000.

"Christine transformed an ordinary site into the most beautiful garden in Southern California." *"She is extremely imaginative, highly creative and a pleasure to deal with in every way."* *"She inherently gets it."* *"Christine is incredibly talented. We're extremely impressed with her designs."*

Clark & White Landscape Inc.   4   3   5   4
2930 Westwood Boulevard, Suite 203, Los Angeles, CA 90064
(310) 453 - 3766   www.clarkandwhitelandscape.com
Landscape design, installation and maintenance

Jim Clark and Dana White helm this dependable and well-regarded landscape architecture firm. With Clark's strong contracting experience and White's background in architecture, the duo have become known for their skilled execution of striking landscape designs. We're told that the firm takes care to ensure that designs are always well-suited to the client's needs.

Established fifteen years ago, this burgeoning firm has grown to 42 employees and counting. Fees are standard for the high-end market. Clark & White charges a design fee ranging anywhere from $500 to $2,500, depending on the scale of the project. The firm's installation estimates also vary in cost according to the scope and complexity of the designs.

"Jim has proven himself to be an amazing landscape contractor."

	Quality	Cost	Value	Recommend?
	✚	$	◆	★

Daniel Busbin Landscape Architect

4.5 4 4.5 4

PO Box 17823, Beverly Hills, CA 90209
(323) 876 - 8300   danielbusbin@aol.com

Historically related landscape architecture and design

Appreciative clients say that the versatile Daniel Busbin can conjure up a landscape to surround a Moorish villa or the formal gardens belonging to a Georgian townhouse. Since 1992, Busbin and his small, talented team have been creating atmospheric landscape designs primarily for high-end residential estates in Bel Air and Beverly Hills. Whereas some landscape architects are known for a singular style, Busbin's curiosity drives him to take on any style house, then focus on generating the appropriate surroundings for it.

Busbin's designs combine plantings and lighting elements to develop and improve landscapes. Clients applaud his efforts, saying that his historically based design is a perfect complement to the architecture, creating a harmonious composition. In addition to the initial design work, Busbin provides ongoing assistance to clients, recommending installers and suggesting maintenance companies. Acting as the owner's agent, he will also assist with the bidding, negotiation and oversight of a job.

Deborah Nevins & Associates

5 5 4 4

270 Lafayette Street, Suite 903, New York, NY 10012
(212) 925 - 1125   info@dnalandscape.com

Classic, high-end landscape design

Deborah Nevins is based in New York City, but her coveted designs have been commissioned by savvy designers across the United States, including Los Angeles. In business since 1983, her legend has grown as brilliant as the flowers and plants she so painstakingly selects.

Celebrated professionals and A-list clientele place her small company of six at the top of the heap, which, in the world of horticulture, is a high honor. Among Nevins's many virtues is her ability to create a garden that is equally spectacular in spring and winter. For projects in LA, Nevins will travel to oversee the execution and maintenance of her designs by local contractors herself.

"She is about the best there is at conceiving classic at a larger scale." "Debbie is absolutely marvelous. I use her all of the time."

Earth Patterns/Holdenwater

729 East Chapman Avenue, Fullerton, CA 92831
(714) 626 - 0333   www.waterarchitecture.com

Integrated swimming pool design/build and landscape architecture

See Earth Patterns/Holdenwater's full report under the heading Swimming Pools

G. Grisamore Design Inc.

📁 📁 📁 📁

412 31st Street, Newport Beach, CA 92663
(949) 673 - 0411   www.ggrisamore.com

High-end residential landscape design

Gannon Electric Light

3033 South Kerckhoff Avenue, San Pedro, CA 90731
(800) 443 - 2466   johngannon@cox.net

Architectural landscape lighting

See Gannon Electric Light's full report under the heading Electricians

	Quality	Cost	Value	Recommend?

Garden View Landscape Nursery & Pools 3 3 4 4

70 East Montecito Avenue, Sierra Madre, CA 91024
(626) 355 - 3541   www.garden-view.com

Landscape and swimming pool design/build

For those who don't know a perennial from a pagoda, references recommend Garden View as a great place to go for a preview. Launched in 1978 by Mark Meahl, the company has evolved into a large design/build firm delivering a wide selection of services. Specialties include landscape maintenance, swimming pool design, boulder work and even Koi ponds. Clients tell us that they are pleased with Garden View's strong customer service and impressed by the selection of plants in the company's nursery. Most of its offerings are locally grown and acclimated to the California climate, making for healthier landscapes.

Garden View professionals take on most tasks without subcontracting. Clients say that Meahl strives to play an active role in every project, no matter the size. We hear the firm's competitive prices offer just one more reason to check out this firm—or at least stop by the nursery.

"Great for people who need one-stop shopping." "A pleasant staff willing to go the extra mile."

GDS Designs 4.5 3.5 5 5

6547 Homewood Avenue, Los Angeles, CA 90028
(323) 466 - 4266   www.gdsdesigns.com

Contemporary landscape design, installation and maintenance

GDS Designs earns customer kudos for creating landscapes with character on budget and on time. For seven years Greg Sanchez and his team of four have been designing, installing and maintaining gardens throughout Brentwood, Beverly Hills and Santa Monica. Sanchez does not stick to one particular style of garden and landscape design, but is known to take a "contemporary approach to the garden, incorporating a unique range of plants selected for contrast, structure and drama." Regardless of the strategy, we hear Sanchez realizes the landscape the client wants.

The firm's wide range of services include hardscape, masonry and lighting. While the company does not offer weekly maintenance on its projects, it does offer quarterly check-ups to gauge overall growth and to advise on proper upkeep. Fees are thought of as reasonable, and are calculated as a percentage of the project's total cost, which varies according to the scope of the project.

"Greg was able to visualize and create a garden that totally represented my concept." "An original and attractive design for a very tight site." "The final product came in under my original budget and on a very fast schedule."

	Quality	Cost	Value	Recommend?
	+	$	◆	★

Inner Gardens Inc. 4 4 4 4

6050 West Jefferson Boulevard, Los Angeles, CA 90016
(310) 838 - 8378 www.innergardens.com

Antique garden containers and interior plant design

Stephen Block's popular container and interior plant design company is housed in a dazzling 10,000 square foot showroom stocked to the ceiling with more than 1,000 antique containers. Called a must-see by insiders, Inner Garden's warehouse also includes orchids, interior and exterior plants, and specimen trees.

Block's fancy for foliage took root while he was studying horticulture at the University of Florida. He founded Inner Gardens in 1990, and already the company has more than fifteen employees and an unbeatable reputation among those in the know. Though Block specializes in interior plant design, he also tackles the outer garden—often integrating containers into poolside or patio designs. The firm offers a free consultation to serious prospective clients, charges a flat fee for design and bills hourly for installation. Both Block and the Inner Garden showroom have been featured on Martha Stewart's show.

"I have seen a lot in my life but I have never seen such a selection of high-end garden products in one place." "Steve was always more than willing to help me make a decision when I had no idea what I wanted."

Isabelle Greene & Associates 4.5 4 4.5 5

2613 De La Vina Street, Santa Barbara, CA 93105
(805) 569 - 4045 iga@isabellegreene.com

Sustainable landscape design

Interior designers and architects describe Isabelle Greene's landscapes with one word: exquisite. Emphasizing native plants and sustainable designs, Greene has been transforming residential, commercial and institutional landscapes since 1964. The firm oversees the installation and support of its creations, and Greene is known to maintain close personal relationships with her clients.

Though most of Greene's projects are in California, she has worked all over the country. Her landscapes, designed in close collaboration with the project architect, are reputed to honor the character of each individual site. Greene's belief that design is a very small part of a larger whole brings an environmentally sensitive element to her work.

The granddaughter of Henry Mather Greene, an early pioneer of the Craftsman movement in Southern California, Greene has a natural eye for detail and proportion that is informed by over three decades of experience. She holds a bachelor's degree in botany from UCLA, and she also studied art extensively at the University of California Santa Barbara (UCSB). References report her knowledge of drought-tolerant plants is unparalleled and her original and practical designs require little upkeep. Design, management and support fees for the small five-person firm are charged by the hour. The company's impressive resume includes the master planning for the Santa Barbara Botanic Gardens, as well as residential projects ranging from $15,000 to $1 million. Greene's work has been published in *House & Garden, Vogue Decoration* and *House Beautiful*.

"Very enjoyable to work with." "Remarkably good at coordinating all the other participants, accepted as the leader and admired by all." "The garden has been a constant source of pleasure to me for twenty years."

	Quality	Cost	Value	Recommend?
	✚	$	◆	★

Jay Griffith Landscape   5   5   4   5

717 California Avenue, Venice, CA 90291
(310) 392 - 5558   www.jaygriffith.com

Vibrant landscape architecture design/build

Clients tell us landscape architect Jay Griffith "goes for the bold stroke." His vibrant personality, straightforward attitude and pizzazz for plants put his firm on everybody's list of favorites. We hear three factors account for the company's popularity: great clients, great architectural sites and great budgets. While Griffith admits that his company is not for everyone, clients who have worked with him call the experience "phenomenal" and "fun."

A native Californian, Griffith was born into a family of gardeners and has over 30 years' experience. He now helms a firm of 35 employees, but despite the large size of the company, we're told Griffith invests himself in the most minute aspects of design and installation. Architects and interior designers marvel that Griffith seems to have a way of "staying on top of everything." No job is too big for Griffith and company, with projects averaging a pricey $200,000. If money grew on trees, clients roundly say they'd call Griffith to plant them.

"I love his craziness." "I did a huge job with him and the guy has such a sense of fun." "One of the best in the business, no question." "Whimsical designs . . . you gotta love it."

Katherine Spitz Associates Inc.   4   4   4   4

4212 1/2 Glencoe Avenue, Marina Del Rey, CA 90292
(310) 574 - 4460   www.katherinespitzassociates.com

Landscape architecture and design

Katherine Spitz's delicate and serious approach to landscape architecture makes her a darling of Los Angeles' most discriminating architects, designers and contractors. She has quite a resume, having first received a B.A. in painting from the University of California, Santa Barbara, then a Master of Architecture from the University of California, Los Angeles. She was a principal in the landscape architecture firm Burton & Spitz from 1985 to 1993 before striking out on her own.

Sources say Spitz is mindful of the nuances and complexities involved in imposing a humanist aesthetic on natural beauty and the natural environment. A fine example of this sensitivity is her proclivity toward using native drought-tolerant plants. For those who share those values, Spitz is the natural choice.

Katie Moss Landscape Design   4.5   4   4.5   4

2001 Mandeville Canyon Road, Brentwood, CA 90049
(310) 569 - 5333   mrszimmer@aol.com

Landscape design, installation and maintenance—English-style gardens

Katie Moss's proper, cozy English gardens have been turning heads in Los Angeles for the last decade. The child of parents who loved their classic English borders and a graduate of UCLA's landscape architecture program, Moss initially put her talents to use in her own yard. Friends and passersby were soon recruiting her to design their gardens. Since then, Moss has built a flourishing business one neighbor at a time, as good word of mouth spreads her designs from yard to yard. Working throughout the Palisades, Brentwood, Westwood, Beverly Hills, Santa Monica and Bel Air, Moss quickly garnered attention—both for her gardens and for her clients' homes.

Sources tell us that Moss's look, described as "gorgeous, soft and pretty," can also be tailored for a masculine appeal. After the design phase, Moss subcontracts installation out to well-trained crews and supervises the progress of each project. Satisfied clients tell us they are enchanted with the simple beauty of the designs, and are willing to pay a premium for her services. A two-hour consultation is $250.

"Her gardens have a huge amount of curb appeal."

Knibb Design Corp.　　　　　4　　4　　4　　5
141 South Barrington Avenue, Los Angeles, CA　90049
(310) 440 - 0101　www.knibbdesign.com
Colonial-inspired modern garden design

Clients applaud Sean Knibb for his contemporary, urban landscape design and his enthusiasm for spending time in the field. His firm provides all design and installation services, seeing projects through from inception to completion. Those clients who have snared the firm's rare maintenance service consider themselves a privileged few. The company takes on two to three major projects (over three acres) and twenty to thirty minor projects (under one acre) annually. All are residential landscapes in such upscale enclaves as Bel Air and Beverly Hills.

After working as a furniture designer for a couple of years, Knibb opened his doors and stepped out into the world of garden design in 1992. The response has been tremendous. Sources report that though business is brisk, Knibb himself retains a hand in each and every landscape. The firm charges a design fee and hourly consulting rates, with budgets for completed landscapes ranging anywhere from $80,000 to $160,000.

"Creative, knowledgeable, flexible, enthusiastic—and focused on doing a first-rate job." "Sean is expensive, but he is absolutely worth it to me." "Wonderful to work with! Our garden is beautiful." "Sean has worked very well with my wife and I. He presents his design plans clearly, he listens to our desires, our needs, and through spending time with us, he has learned the type of people we are, how we live and how we intend to use the space."

Mia Lehrer + Associates　　　　　4.5　　4.5　　4　　4
3780 Wilshire Boulevard, Suite 1100, Los Angeles, CA　90010
(213) 384 - 3844　www.mlagreen.com
Residential and commercial landscape architecture

Clients recommend Mia Lehrer + Associates for a host of landscape architecture services. Mia Lehrer herself is known to collaborate famously with world-class architects and interior designers throughout Los Angeles, working with big names such as Ricardo Legoretta. The firm's work has been published in *Architectural Digest, House Beautiful* and *Town & Country,* and Lehrer has lectured in South and Central America.

	Quality +	Cost $	Value ◆	Recommend? ★

Mitchell Pest Control, Inc.

4   4.5   3.5   4

305 Agostino Road, San Gabriel, CA 91776
(626) 287 - 1106

Plant disease and insect specialists

Solving disease and insect problems, the "tree doctors" at Mitchell Pest Control have been serving the Los Angeles area since 1947. Don't let the name fool you: this firm is not an exterminator service. The company specializes in restoring health to trees and plants outside the house—they won't go near any household pests.

Owned by a professional arborist and employing a staff of ten, the firm has over 200 years of cumulative experience in agriculture, horticulture and entomology. A favorite with both homeowners and landscape architects, Mitchell Pest Control's specialists have a reputation for being professional, experienced and highly educated in their fields. Clients say the excellent service is worth the considerable expense.

Nancy Goslee Power & Associates

5   5   4   4

1660 Stanford Street, Santa Monica, CA 90404
(310) 264 - 0266

Bold, innovative, elite garden design

Insiders and industry leaders gush about Nancy Goslee Power's versatile, innovative, stunning designs. A former interior designer, Power now lends her exquisite eye to the home's exterior. Admirers say Power's designs have Italianate contours—her bold strokes of color create landscapes that are essentially works of art. It does not surprise us, therefore, to hear that Power is protective of her canvasses.

Shot to international prominence with her design of the 79,000 square foot sculpture garden at the Norton Simon Museum in Pasadena, Power has since collaborated with luminary architects Frank Gehry and Steven Ehrlich, to name but two. As Power's reputation has grown in legend, we hear she has become about as difficult to pin down as any mythological character. Featured in *Breaking Ground: Portraits of Ten Garden Designers,* Power is also the author of *The Gardens of California.*

"I have not worked with her but I have attempted many times. As an interior designer, I have always thought her projects were phenomenal." "Considered a giant not only of landscape design but design in general." "Big time, high-end and outstanding vision." "She blows you away with her designs. They're simply breathtaking."

Nick Williams & Associates Inc.

4.5   3.5   5   5

18751 Ventura Boulevard, Suite 200, Tarzana, CA 91356
(818) 996 - 4010   www.nickwilliamsdesigns.com

Natural landscape design and swimming pool design

Clients tell us they like nothing more than planting themselves near Nick Williams' work. Recommended by the best architects in the business, Williams has been designing landscapes and swimming pools throughout Los Angeles for more than 40 years. Although the firm doesn't bow to one specific style, insiders tell us Williams is partial to the natural look and tends to sprinkle his designs with boulders and other hardscape elements, including outdoor fireplaces.

Williams' personal approach wins glowing reviews from references. We hear he goes to great lengths to involve himself and his clients in every aspect of the process. Williams will even take his clients to nurseries to get their feedback on plant selection. Although the company does not offer maintenance, it will check on the progress and upkeep of a project every three to four months if needed. With Williams' reasonable design and supervision fees, we're told you can look forward to rationing water, not greenbacks.

"As a long-standing member of the green industry, I believe my expectations are relatively high. In my experience, Nick provides an excellent level of service and good value." "It is difficult to describe how happy we are with our pool and yard. It would be hard to move and leave this incredible place." "Nick and company bring a fresh perspective as an overlay on the client's personal preferences and expectations." "They transformed an area into a natural gathering place, inviting for both friends and family." "Nick Williams put us in Sunset *magazine. The before and after photos speak for themselves."*

Pamela Burton & Company   4.5   4.5   4   4
1430 Olympic Boulevard, Santa Monica, CA 90404
(310) 828 - 6373   www.pamelaburtonco.com
Award-winning landscape design and architecture

Insiders tell us the widely published Pamela Burton is an "impressive talent," noting the roster of A-list celebrities on her resumé. Over the course of a twenty-year career, Burton has earned the highest praise from residential and commercial clients for her award-winning landscape design. Burton's spaces (which are part displays of passion, part intellectual exercises) are said to satisfy even the most demanding Los Angeles powerbroker.

Burton established herself in the late 1970s after receiving a master's in architecture at UCLA. She now oversees a staff of eleven and plays a decisive role in each project. She is known to lecture worldwide, touching upon topics such as Garden as Sanctuary, Memory and Landscape, Balance and Uncertainty, Civil Landscapes and Poetics of the Garden. Despite this heavy public schedule, private clients tell us Burton, whom they describe as pleasant and reserved, doesn't put them in the backseat. References report her residential commissions are as ambitious as her major commercial offerings, and her budgets—well, as healthy as her landscapes.

"Pamela pays close attention not only to the plants that she uses, but also to keeping the architectural integrity of the building." "I love her designs—both residential and commercial." "She is a lovely and genuine person to work with." "An intellectual marvel."

Paul Robbins Garden Design Inc.   4.5   4.5   4   5
517 North Plymouth Boulevard, Los Angeles, CA 90004
(323) 933 - 3490   robbinsgarden@aol.com
Informal, naturalistic garden design and installation

Clients applaud Englishman Paul Robbins for some of the most beautiful naturalistic landscapes in the greater Los Angeles area. Robbins' creations, which are acutely sensitive to the architectural and environmental character of the site and to the client's lifestyle, have been featured in *Architectural Digest* and *Traditional Home*. While the firm specializes in romantic naturalistic creations, clients note that Robbins shows equal talent in orchestrating formal gardens that, not surprisingly, have an English air.

Robbins was formally trained as a horticulturist in England, receiving a diploma in garden design from The College of Garden Design in Pershore. He came to the United States six years ago and has since designed some of the hottest properties in Brentwood and Beverly Hills. The firm takes on twelve to fifteen new clients a year. Robbins designs, installs and maintains his projects in-house with a staff of six. We understand Robbins and his team will not accept a project for under $30,000 and that they charge a design fee starting at $5,000.

"I was most impressed with Paul's unrelenting patience and follow-through."
"When I asked for a garden that would withstand the abuse of a labrador retriever, Paul understood what my reality required and he acted accordingly." *"He completely transformed my home gardens from a barren wasteland of cement and dying grass to a truly serene haven."* *"Paul kept me apprised of every aspect of his design and installation."* *"He is very very honest, with tremendous integrity."* *"Paul's work crew was very polite, reliable, punctual, honest, neat and efficient."* *"A pleasure to work with, Paul skillfully interpreted our home's architecture and created the perfect garden."* *"Very precise. Methodical."*

Peridian International Inc.   4   4   4   4
28th Street Marina, 2600 Newport Boulevard, Suite 130, Newport Beach, CA 92663
(949) 675 - 2445   www.peridian.net
Landscape architecture and planning

Peridian International offers a wide range of professional services, including industrial, residential, commercial, community and urban planning. The firm has over four decades of professional experience and was established in 1951. In 1989 Peridian established a regional office in Guadalajara, Mexico to better serve its expanding operations. Despite the large breadth of the company, Peridian fosters a close personal working relationship with both their residential and commercial clients.

"As a contractor I can honestly say that Peridian not only has the ability to take on large projects, but they also do the best job."

Peter Vracko
2005 North Sycamore Avenue, Los Angeles, CA 90068
(323) 883 - 0022   vracko@pacbell.net
Challenging residential commissions

See Peter Vracko's full report under the heading Contractors, General & Job

Rob Steiner Inc.   4.5   3   5   5
6415 Moore Drive, Los Angeles, CA 90048
(323) 931 - 4425   www.robsteinergardens.com
Landscape architecture, design and project coordination

We're told Rob Steiner will design everything from the skin of a house out, accepting projects that range in scale from Zen courtyards to multi-acre estates. Steiner's diverse palettes include Mediterranean, native, South African and Australian flora. While industry insiders hold his modern and Mediterranean gardens in particularly high regard, Steiner has proven his expertise with a wide range of architectural styles. Clients agree that he succeeds in his effort to "create spaces of privacy, refreshment and reflection."

Steiner received his formal training in Landscape Architecture at Yale and Cornell. After working with Peridian International and partnering with LA landscape luminary Jay Griffith, he struck out on his own in 1999. Despite the firm's micro-size (two), Steiner is known to be a very conscientious and professional macro-manager, shepherding ten to twenty projects at a time. He charges a design fee as a percentage of the total landscape construction costs and will occasionally work at an hourly rate. It's clear that Steiner is the real deal, which may be why clients are surprised to discover that his prices are a real deal.

"Rob Steiner is an artist who happens to use plants, earth, stone and water as his media, but all the while he retains a practical sense of how his projects will be used by the clients." "My architect recommended him and I decided to use him the day we met." "He was fabulous to work with." "Rob was very conscious of my budget and my goals on the project. He was a pleasure to work with and I recommend him highly." "Great design ideas, highly accommodating to client's tastes and needs." "Good supervision of subcontractors."

Robert E. Truskowski Landscape Architects 📁 📁 📁 📁
1110 North Coast Highway, Laguna Beach, CA 92651
(949) 494 - 6650
High-end traditional landscape design

Rodriguez & Satterthwaite   4.5   4   4.5   4
1424 Old Topanga Canyon Road, Topanga, CA 90290
(310) 455 - 1919   rodsatt@earthlink.net
Semi-formal landscape design/build

This landscape design/build company is in high demand for its stunning semi-formal landscapes that ooze Old-World charm. Established in 1992 by principals Martin Rodriguez and Jade Satterthwaite, the company of twelve is praised for taking a landscape project from design through installation and on to maintenance.

Satterthwaite, who manages the firm, holds a master's degree in landscape architecture from USC. His education backs up Rodriguez's more idiosyncratic, artisan-like approach. This winning combination has made the duo one of the most highly sought after landscape design teams in the area—a fact that's reflected in the firm's upper-end prices. The company charges a design fee based on the size of the project—installation and monthly maintenance fees are additional.

Schwentker Watts Design   4   3.5   4.5   4.5
3829 Udell Court, Los Angeles, CA 90027
(323) 664 - 4336   schwat@pacbell.net
Landscape architecture and design

We hear this firm treats landscape as an extended architectural element of the house from day one. For those who prize designs that richly complement the existing architecture and the site's integrity, they are said to be a great find.

Jamie Schwentker trained and worked as an architect before tapping into his lifelong love of horticulture. Harvey Watts brings his own architectural acumen, making the team doubly attractive. We're told the firm views each job through the prism of its unique site, no doubt a reflection of the duo's respect for architecture.

Although much of the firm's work is in Los Angeles County, it has accepted projects from Santa Barbara to Orange County. Landscapes are said to be professionally executed and delicately rendered. With only one other employee, we hear the two principals remain involved in every aspect of a project, from design to overseeing installation. The firm annually takes on approximately ten landscape projects, budgeted between $30,000 and $500,000.

"He heard us—every detail right down to details we forgot." "Very reliable and dedicated." "Excited by the execution of a difficult project." "Jamie gets my vote for creating an exciting yet peaceful palette of colors."

	Quality	Cost $	Value ◆	Recommend? ★

Sylvan Design   3.5   3   4.5   5

5414 Newcastle Avenue, Suite 25, Encino, CA 91316
(818) 609 - 1972   smsylvan@aol.com

Landscape architecture and design

Clients turn to Sherman Sylvan for his distinct brand of understated elegance in landscape architecture. Praised for listening to his clients, Sylvan carefully tailors his design to their preferences. At the same time, he carefully considers the project environment, using plants known to mature best in the extreme California climate.

Sylvan has steered his sole proprietorship for over a decade, averaging between fifteen and twenty projects annually. The firm works throughout the region, from Beverly Hills to Pasadena. Upon project completion, Sylvan offers a quarterly maintenance plan under which he will oversee grounds professionals/gardeners. With standard prices, the firm makes landscapes look dynamite without blowing your budget.

"Will do and suggest things based on your own ideas." "He makes it work."

Todd Hall Design   4   4   4   4

7614 Hampton Avenue, Los Angeles, CA 90046
(310) 704 - 4998   toddhalldesign@adelphia.net

Landscape design and installation

Todd Hall's penchant for nurturing strong client relationships keeps his team of six quite busy. For more than a dozen years, his firm has been producing complex architectural landscape drawings and contracting the installation out to pros. Most of Hall's projects are in Brentwood and Beverly Hills, but he will work as far away as a job takes him. Although Hall does not do landscape maintenance, sources say he "always remains on call." Hall's lifelong interest in landscape design informs landscapes from Mediterranean to Zen. The firm is not bound by any particular aesthetic, but whatever style Hall works in, clients say he always arrives at a "sense of magic." While Hall can be hired in a consultancy role at $100 an hour, in most cases the firm's fees are calculated on a per project basis, with budgets averaging $100,000.

"Extremely creative, very talented." "Goes above and beyond." "Todd's work was so good, I'm using him to completely redo our backyard."

Hiring a Millwork, Cabinetry or Custom Windows & Doors Service Provider

In any renovation, millwork buttons up the newly pressed suit of your home. The integrity and artistry of Old-World craftsmanship hasn't been lost on today's generation of woodworking professionals, who create cabinets, moldings, doors, mantels, staircases and furniture. These service providers can tuck a plasma TV into architectural detail of a custom design/built library—or reproduce antique furniture.

Choosing a Millwork Firm

Not all millworkers are cut from the same piece of lumber. The right service provider must fit plumb with your project and personality. Some firms relish working directly with homeowners, taking an idea from concept to completion. Others are more comfortable realizing the defined plans of a designer or architect. In either case a millworker will produce detailed, or working drawings for you to sign off on. Significant projects that involve the coordination of other trades (like electrical and plumbing for a serious kitchen remodel) or that involve complex structural elements (stairways) should always have a designer or contractor involved. In this case, finding a millwork firm that collaborates well with other design and construction professionals is essential.

Service providers range from a single talented craftsman with a few helpers to a large full-service woodworking firm with retail showrooms. Where you may get a more businesslike approach and greater capacity, you may lose that artisan appeal and personal touch. Visit the shops of those firms you are considering. You'll not only get a good idea about the vibe of the place, but see the product being produced, whether by highly precise, computer-controlled (C&C) machines or by skillful hand and eye. Last but not least, check out the finished result and talk to references. You should be as concerned with the quality of the work—tight joints, pristine finishes and plum doors and drawers—as with the style. Finally, consider the craftsman's style. Don't go with Mr. Euro-style sleek when you're looking for someone to hand-carve a built-in window seat at your Spanish hacienda.

Three Levels of Quality

Once you've determined the scope of your project, it is wise to determine the caliber of workmanship and quality of wood that is most appropriate for your needs. There are essentially three tiers of woodworking quality to choose from, each with its own standards for materials and craftsmanship.

Economy is the lowest grade of woodwork and may be chosen for projects that will not put a lot of demand on the structure or materials. For example, a built-in desk and shelving unit in a guest room that gets very little use could be constructed at the economy level. Although the work must be attractive, it need not be made from exotic wood or constructed with intricate joinery.

The next grade is custom woodwork, the level of craftsmanship most frequently requested. Custom woodwork ensures good quality wood and workmanship and is suitable for such popular projects as household cabinetry and moldings. A beautiful kitchen makeover with glass-paneled cabinet doors and a new butcher-block island could be constructed using custom woodwork.

The highest grade is premium woodwork, top-of-the-line millwork that delivers the highest quality of craftsmanship, wood and finishing. Premium jobs include outfitting an entire room with elaborately carved wall and ceiling panels made of top-grade wood, or building a grand staircase using imported wood and marble.

On Cost

Due to the specialized, diverse nature of the millwork business, there is no standard pricing structure. Most firms determine their fees based on the materials that are being used and the complexity and scope of the project, which is why it is important to collect several bids for your job. When requesting bids, it is also important to note whether or not the cost of installation is included. Some firms subcontract the installation process. Before you sign a contract, be sure that you know exactly who will install the work you ordered in its intended place in your home.

What to Expect From Your Millwork Company

Your millworker should be as familiar with the actual installation space as he is with his client's lifestyle needs. A good millworker, like any service provider, should prove meticulous in the planning stages: asking questions, massaging the design and triple-checking measurements—from the opening width for appliances in kitchen cabinets to the knee-height of a custom built desk for a taller client. You must also plan ahead, as lead times for fabrication and delivery are usually six to sixteen weeks.

The quality of any end product is only as good as the installation. However, not every firm installs or finishes what it fabricates. If the shop milling the pieces isn't the one assembling the puzzle, know who will be before you spill any ink on the contract, and qualify them as well. The same goes with finishing, a messy process that can effectively shut down the job site. A great deal of product comes pre-finished, however, so the dirty work is completed in a controlled environment off-site.

If the structure of your home will not be altered by your millwork project (as with replacement kitchen cabinets, for example), the job will not require a permit and can probably be done without a contractor or architect (if the millwork shop does detailed drawings.) This work is very much a craft in the Old World sense, where skills are often passed down from master to apprentice. As such, there are no license or permit requirements for millwork firms, nor are there any trade associations through which millworkers are generally certified. Before you sign a work agreement, request proof of the company's insurance and warranty policies, which vary from firm to firm. If craftsmen will be working in your home, you'll want to be sure they are covered by the company's workmen's comp policy. You don't want to be held responsible for a misguided nail or toppled ladder.

Millwork Mastery Tips

❖ It's your millworker's duty to measure! If you do it yourself and give him the dimensions, you're only asking for trouble.

❖ Plan the electrical and plumbing layout meticulously or you may have to rip up fine work, send it to the scrap heap and pay to have it redone.

❖ Don't install millwork too early in a renovation project. Your millworker should be the last person in so that other workers won't scratch your beautiful new wood finish.

❖ Hire excellent professionals for the entire renovation. Millworkers must have a level surface on which to work, and shoddy workmanship from carpenters, drywall or plastic contractors will haunt the millwork.

❖ Remember to design backing structures where necessary. You don't want a cabinet that will store heavy cookware fastened to a mere half-inch of drywall.

❖ Don't be afraid to reject a panel or piece of molding that doesn't match the quality of its brothers and sisters.

Quality	Cost	Value	Recommend?
✚	$	◆	★

MILLWORK, CABINETRY & CUSTOM WINDOWS & DOORS

🛍 FIRMS WITH PORTFOLIOS 🛍

Centinela Cabinet Company 🛍   4.5   3.5   5   5
6020 West Boulevard, Los Angeles, CA 90043
(323) 778 - 1787

Intricate cabinetry, moldings and paneling; historical restoration

From intricate eighteenth-century moldings to a cutting-edge "floating" staircase, Centinela Cabinet Company can execute the most exacting jobs. Established in 1951 by Edward Arzouman, the company is now helmed by his son, Michael, who learned the skills of the trade from his father and grandfather. For 33 years, this amiable craftsman has been delighting clients, who describe his work as "exquisite," "innovative" and "precise." Most of the company's commissions are high-end residential kitchens and libraries, but Arzouman and his five-man team are also willing to do smaller projects and loose furniture pieces. Centinela also does meticulous historical and landmark work. The firm is frequently called upon to replicate architectural details in churches, schools and residences. The company works with designers, architects and homeowners from Beverly Hills and as far away as Capistrano. Quality is said to be extraordinary, while prices are described as "competitive."

"In a town full of imagination, Mike and his team raise the bar by creating conservative yet liberal and liberating work." "Really comes up with creative solutions to problems." "His work is impeccable—the craftsmanship beautiful." "I get so many compliments on my kitchen cabinets!" "Excellent work with a high degree of professionalism." "The whole crew was thoroughly engrossed in making sure that every detail was right." "Would use them again in a heartbeat."

J W Custom Woodwork Corp.   3.5   2.5   5   4.5
12627 Foothill Boulevard, Sylmar, CA 91342
(818) 834 - 0194

Casework, stairs, cabinets and hardwood floors; custom furniture specialists

Jose Wawrik hails from a family of Polish craftsmen transplanted to Argentina during WWII. It was there that Wawrik got his start, first building wagons with the family, and then, at the age of fourteen, working alongside German carpenters to help support his relatives. Today, Wawrik runs a studio of his own in Sylmar, overseeing eight employees. The firm builds stairways, kitchens, casework and hardwood floors. He's even been known to mix sawdust with stardust, building millwork in both home theaters and stars' trailers.

Wawrik's passion and the firm's increasing focus is custom furniture. We hear he studies older pieces, looking for distinctive elements to replicate. Crafted with old-fashioned elbow grease and advanced technology, each JW creation is said to have a hand-hewn uniqueness of character that machines just can't match. Although JW doesn't like to stray far from LA, designers in New York have approached the firm about its good work, and some pieces have found their way to Nevada and Arizona.

	Quality	Cost	Value	Recommend?
	✚	$	◆	★

Clients say Wawrik has an open mind, and his eye for detail is appreciated by designers, who praise his fine sense of proportion. Wawrik is said to consider the existing architectural canvas. He will even go so far as to adjust a design for an especially tall client. For such personalized attention, one might expect to pay upper-end prices, but JW's rates are said to be quite affordable.

"Beautiful detail work. The craftsmanship is superb." "A pleasure to work with. I learned a lot just from talking to him."

LoPresti Millworks   3   3   4   4
14621 Titus Avenue, Suite A, Van Nuys, CA 91402
(818) 782 - 5888   www.loprestimillworks.com
Custom window and door specialists; prefabricated millwork

Insiders tell us that LoPresti Millwork, an off-shoot of LoPresti Construction, measures up to the standards of its highly discerning parent company. Jerome Hampton oversees a 10,000 square foot shop that specializes in custom windows and doors. It also produces furniture, cabinets, countertops and custom moldings.

In addition to its custom work, the firm offers a prefabricated line of product. LoPresti supplies windows, doors and millwork at various price points for its own slate of high-end construction projects as well as for other quality-minded contractors and homeowners in the area. This "one-stop shop" designs and creates both contemporary and traditional windows, doors and door hardware. Their newly opened showroom at The Pacific Design Center will house their new line of entry and interior doors as well as an inventory of excellent door hardware, molds, surrounds and other architectural details by Baltica Hardware and Enkeboll.

Principal Peter LoPresti, a former jeweler, brings his sharp eye for detail and sparkling persona to each project. His office is said to be "obsessively efficient."

"Peter is a delight to work with." "Dependable and level-headed." "I could not recommend anyone more highly for doors, windows and millworks." "Peter understands the needs of his highly discerning clients." "He has a great eye and an amazing artistic sensibility." "They are always enthusiastic and friendly."

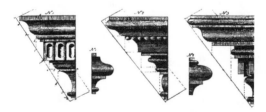

Silver Strand Inc.   5   4.5   4.5   4.5
9535 Owensmouth Avenue, Unit D, Chatsworth, CA 91311
(818) 701 - 9707
Expert high-end cabinetry and millwork

The best contractors in the business say Silver Strand meets the gold standard. Supported by a full 10,000 square foot shop, Silver Strand has been milling and installing high-end carpentry and cabinetry since 1987. The company is also entrusted with the delicate task of installing precast interior plaster and compo molding. Most Silver Strand jobs are in massive 15,000 to 30,000 square foot homes and start at $100,000. The firm works mostly with contractors and with some homeowners on major jobs, but it will not accommodate single-piece projects.

Principal David Meador's efforts have been lauded as far back as his days as junior high Craftsman of the Year in Malibu Park. He heads a large crew of more than 50 employees. All Meador's men come with cell phones and are supported by a well-tended office and prolific millshop. This gives Silver Strand the ability to turn out jobs quickly and to adapt nimbly to mid-course changes. The firm dabbles in design beyond mere shop drawings and will present mock-ups to clients for approval. Whether it's a mahogany-laced bathroom or exquisite Tuscan woodwork, we hear Silver Strand's sumptuous work is worth its weight in gold.

"Dave is an incredibly organized fellow." "Keeps on it until you are satisfied." "Definitely one of the biggest and best out there." "Very well-run company, but not cheap." "Excellent attention to detail." "Use them if you want the real thing."

Triumph Fine Cabinetry & Millwork 📖   3.5   3   4.5   4

7430 Fulton Avenue, North Hollywood, CA 91605
(818) 765 - 1389

Detail-oriented original and restoration millwork

The brainchild of Triumph Construction honchos Bill Rosenberg and Steve Ferguson, this firm specializes in standard custom millwork, from a single room to an entire apartment or home. Fabrication and design are handled in-house, while all finish work is farmed out. The firm is also experienced in all manner of restoration work; it once plucked wainscoting from England to revive an original twenties-style bungalow.

With designs in hand or concepts in head, professionals and homeowners approach Triumph to make their ideas come to life. References report that Triumph's consideration of every little element—be it door glides, box construction or drawer hardware—produces a durable end product at reasonable standard prices. The company recently moved to a new location in the San Fernando Valley.

"Terrific detail work." "Excellent turnaround." "Always responsive, very professional. A pleasure to work with."

Universal Craftsman Incorporated 📖   5   4.5   4.5   5

15155 Califa Street, Van Nuys, CA 91411
(818) 779 - 7966

Extraordinary cabinetry and millwork

Clients say Universal's 30 years of experience are evident in an extraordinary level of custom millwork for high quality designers and architects. Universal really does cover a universe of options, from traditional to contemporary, residential to corporate, domestic veneers to exotic veneers. Its work spans built-ins, libraries, custom bars, screening rooms and furniture—but does not include kitchen cabinets.

The firm takes projects from shops to punch, including finish and installation. Jobs run from $25,000 to $500,000 and are overseen in Universal's 12,000 square foot shop. The firm's international team of craftsmen hail from Greece, China, Hungry, Germany and Latin America. Each has a staggering fifteen to thirty years of experience. Clients say the remarkable staff bring unique, Old-World knowledge to the process.

Renowned architect I.M. Pei's firm, Pei Cobb Freed & Partners, signed Universal to craft "high-tech and beautifully crafted" custom boardroom furniture pieces for an LA client. On occasion, the firm has been commissioned to create pieces for East Coast clients. In 2005, one of the principals was passing through New York City and decided to drop in at the Four Seasons Hotel. He was pleasantly surprised to find that the pieces he'd created fourteen years earlier were still being used in the hotel's lobby, bar and restaurant.

The four partners at Universal are actually two teams of brothers: John and Paul Agrios and John and Steve Sarris. Each man learned his trade in Europe. The partners are very selective about the projects the firm assumes, out of concern both for quality and for not overextending its talents. John Agrios shepherds the design phase, playing intermediary with the designer/architect, while the other partners split field installation and shop supervision duties. One of the four will have his eye on a project at all times, say our sources. Reflecting the quality of its "fabulous product," the firm's prices come in at the top of the top tier.

"Extraordinary. Very much of the past generation." "Takes more responsibility and care than anyone else I've met in this field." "Hard to get in touch with, but worth the wait."

FIRMS WITHOUT PORTFOLIOS

11:11 Architectural Products Inc.   3.5   3.5   4   4
628 Pacific Avenue, Oxnard, CA 93030
(805) 487 - 4142   www.1111architectural.com
Blueprint-derived millwork and cabinetry; primarily to the Trade

11:11 Architectural Products is well known for its furniture, paneling, staircases and cabinets. The firm is geared toward architects and designers who come prepared with strongly defined conceptual blueprints. None too keen on designing from scratch, the company rarely works directly with homeowners who aren't previous customers. The firm splits its time between commercial and high-end residential projects, ranging from $7,000 to $200,000.

11:11 is cleverly named for the company's logo, a screw with two straps on either side. The firm employs a staff of seven who manufacture, install and occasionally finish its work. The company has been commissioned by clients as far away as San Diego and Denver, but it typically works within the boundaries of Los Angeles County.

Owner Carlos Gentile learned the trade in his native Buenos Aires. He came to the States in 1968 and worked for a German company before striking out on his own 25 years ago. References report Gentile still measures each job and lays everything out personally. We hear the firm's methods are firmly steeped in the old-school tradition, and Gentile does not cut corners. Costs, which are slightly above mid-range for the high-end market, are described as more than fair.

Artisans du Bois   4.5   4   4.5   4
1291 West Center Street, Lindon, UT 84042
(801) 785 - 9998
Artisanal millwork and cabinetry; custom door specialists

Du Bois artisan Nick Bruford learned his trade under the tutelage of Swiss master craftsman Andre Liardet nearly 25 years ago. Today, his work is still informed by timeless European design and a respect for structure and functionality. We're told that Artisans du Bois' fine cabinet work and its fabulous Old-World custom doors make a stunning impression.

Though the firm recently moved to Utah, Artisans still maintains all of its Los Angeles clients, including high-end builders, top designers and savvy homeowners. For these loyal customers Bruford will accommodate requests ranging from a single door to an entire estate. While Artisans du Bois is called upon to custom design much of its product, it also offers a selection of traditional door designs.

While Bruford favors French and Italian designs, he works effectively in most styles. Artisans now works with a computer numerical router, which makes measurements more accurate without tinkering with the authentic, Old-World

Quality	Cost	Value	Recommend?
✚	$	◆	★

craftsmanship, for which the firm is known. Clients clamoring for Bruford's services are thankful for the shorter lead times the computer system has produced. While the firm's work is in the expensive range, we hear prices are backed up by excellent quality and an admirable door replacement program.

AVM Woodworking Inc.   3.5   3.5   4   5
15818 Arminta Street, Van Nuys, CA 91406
(818) 994 - 4614

Creative custom cabinetry and millwork

AVM Woodworking boasts a small company atmosphere and big company resources. References turn to the "well organized shop" for creative cabinetry for high-end residences. Project budgets fall between $5,000 and $400,000. Owner Alex Mendelis immigrated from Ukraine 25 years ago, where he worked as a mechanical engineer in the aerospace industry. He has since launched his cabinetry company into the high-quality stratosphere with the help of a talented crew, a state-of-the-art shop and glowing referrals.

Mendelis manages all aspects of millwork production and installation closely, from programming machines in the shop to monitoring quality control in the field. Mendelis is considered a design-oriented millworker, but he's not the difficult artiste type: clients say he works well with both professionals and homeowners.

AVM serves the West LA, Santa Monica and Encino areas. Clients say that while the firm strives to keep costs earthbound, it goes out of its way to improve the integrity of design, finding unique hardware to complement its cabinets. AVM also offers a menu of finishes, performs veneering and presents samples and mock-ups for approval. With eight full-time craftsmen, the company produces computer-generated drawings that architects and contractors appreciate. We hear the firm always stands behind its work.

"Whatever you want, he works with you." "Beautiful cabinetry." "He has done five high-end homes with me." "Higher-end jobs, tighter schedules." "Methodical. I can rely on him way more than the other guys."

Basile Cabinets Inc.   4.5   4.5   4   5
7701 Densmore Avenue, Van Nuys, CA 91406
(818) 786 - 0350

Cabinetry and millwork building specialists

Clients crow that this company "builds like no one else." Owner Gaetano "Guy" Basile joined his brother's woodworking operation in 1960 and, after four decades of rave reviews, has built some of the most prestigious residential projects in Los Angeles. Despite the firm's standing among the elite, we hear Basile will attempt to reasonably accommodate any size project—be it for a contractor or homeowner—as long as he can squeeze it into his schedule.

References say Basile delivers stellar service with "absolute integrity." Basile drafts shop drawings personally but rarely designs from scratch. He makes himself available on site each day and addresses issues with a smile. We're told Basile's sizable shop is as reliable as its product is excellent. While the firm's go-the-extra-mile attitude might cost an extra buck (or three), clients say it's worth it.

"Guy's work—from custom doors and windows to cabinetry and custom millwork—cannot be surpassed in quality." "At the top of his field." "Responsive, always does more than expected." "A team player." "Basile Cabinets has done top quality work for us for years. We highly recommend them."

	Quality	Cost	Value	Recommend?
	✚	$	◆	★

bulthaup

153 South Robertson Boulevard, Los Angeles, CA 90048
(310) 288 - 3875   www.bulthaup.com

Sleek, minimal, contemporary German cabinetry

See bulthaup's full report under the heading Kitchen & Bath Design

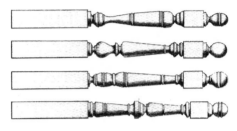

CCA Woodworks   4   4   4   5

1641 South Magnolia Avenue, Monrovia, CA 91016
(626) 303 - 6068

Cabinetry and millwork with design expertise

The CCA crew "all take such pride in their work," clients say. "It's a joy to see them in action." We hear these craftsmen display such enthusiasm for what they do—it rubs off on everyone involved. Even the most demanding and finicky of LA designers get along well with the folks at CCA.

CCA is a working partnership formed nine years ago by three experts who already owned their own millworking firms: Tom Calnon, Kevin Chakerian and Fred Anderson. Today, the firm has a total of seven employees, and a typical CCA remodeling project starts at $50,000. Past projects have included kitchens, libraries, walk-in closets and even furniture—along with a few new homes and a hopper of smaller projects served up by past clients who just can't get enough. In addition to offering fabrication and installation (but no finishes), CCA will also offer as much input at the design stage as requested. Designers know CCA as the firm that "can make things work," while clients tell us they value its design acumen.

We hear the partners complement each other's abilities: Kevin keeps the books, Fred oversees the shop and detail work and Tom controls bids, design and installation. References report this firm is frank about timelines, keeps everyone in the loop, is always available to field questions and follows through. CCA adapts well to shifting job conditions and takes pains to satisfy the client completely, which explains why clients are more than happy to pay upper-end prices for its services. Sources agree that Tom, Kevin, Fred and crew are "genuinely nice" people and a "pleasure to work with."

"All in all a great experience." "Tom is really good at redefining design and adding on aesthetic details while fitting the jigsaw puzzle of what we wanted into the space we had." "I'd recommend them to anyone for anything." "The men are nice to have around. You can just leave and everything will be okay." "I don't think they're cheap, but they're worth it." "Just as responsive with the little things."

Cliff May of Mays of London

6567 Sheltondale Avenue, West Hills, CA 91307
(818) 377 - 4343

Fine French polishing, furniture restoration and period reproductions

See Cliff May of Mays of London's full report under the heading Furniture Repair & Refinishing

	Quality +	Cost $	Value ◆	Recommend? ★

Concepts by J

3.5   3   4.5   4.5

834 East 108th Street, Los Angeles, CA 90059
(323) 564 - 9988

Solid, unpretentious cabinetry, furniture and millwork

For old-fashioned quality products without establishment attitude, clients recommend Concepts by J. They tell us Konrad Pichler upholds the tradition of the company's late founder: to best serve the varied tastes and needs of each individual. The company fabricates, installs and finishes both contemporary and traditional styles of furniture and cabinetry for kitchens, baths, entertainment rooms and libraries. Concepts by J will also assist in design when necessary.

We're told that the firm's appreciable skills at high-end, custom-built woodworking are applied with the same integrity to middle-end and volume assignments. This is one of the rare firms that is as approachable for homeowners as for Los Angeles's discriminating design and building pros.

Formerly the shop manager, Pichler brings seventeen years experience to the role of president of the firm. Pichler learned traditional woodworking through apprenticeships and a master craftsman school in his native Germany. Clients are delighted by the reasonable prices that accompany the excellent results.

"Many can do one well, but not all like Pichler." "They are expert at supervising design, production and quality control." "Pichler brings a deep understanding of wood technology to every project."

Continental Fireplace Mantel

4   3.5   4.5   5

(323) 461 - 6567

Hand-carved millwork, cabinetry and furniture

Los Angeles's top designers turn to Colombian-born Hever Sanchez for handmade cabinets, furniture, built-ins and, of course, fireplace mantels. Described as an "understated craftsman" and "master carver," Sanchez has been at it for more than twenty years, and his small firm has been steadily gaining word-of-mouth steam since he established it seven years ago.

Along with two other craftsmen, Sanchez personally builds and carves every creation, whether custom or a reproduction. He does installations himself and subs out the finished work. Sanchez's elegant woodworking skills are routinely called upon by the best, such as Paul Ferrante. From a single piece of furniture to a wholly commissioned residence, Sanchez delivers exceptional work. He comes highly recommended for his skills and his attitude—he's only happy if a customer is happy and will do what it takes to get to that point.

"Shows a delicate hand and restraint." "A bit difficult to reach, but worth the wait." "Always a masterpiece."

DPC Woodwork Incorporated

5   4.5   4.5   4

5714 West Pico Boulevard, Los Angeles, CA 90019
(323) 954 - 2272

Historical restoration and design of detailed millwork and cabinetry

This high-end, full-service finish carpentry and cabinet shop is noted for taking existing architectural features and restoring or reproducing them to the exacting standards of their original makers. Whether engaged in restoring architecture, making historical reproductions or creating something new, DPC Woodwork designs, produces, installs and finishes all of its work.

Owner Dennis Parry learned his trade under apprenticeship in England. He struck out on his own at 23 as a journeyman carpenter and joiner. He's handled just about everything a woodworker can, including crafting furniture, swinging doors and hanging windows. After a stint on the West Coast supervising the restoration of a seventeenth-century European-style home, Parry decided to call Los Angeles home.

Today, his firm produces a product insiders say is outstanding yet cost-conscious. Quality is checked through close coordination with the architect, Parry's office staff, project supers, workshop foremen and, of course, himself. The firm's resumé boasts an impressive range of projects, including the re-creation of an operating windmill from elements brought back from Europe and the reconstruction of a special paneled room at the Ritz Hotel in Paris. Most projects run north of $50,000.

"High quality stain and paint-grade finishes." "Beautiful craftsmanship and excellent turnaround." "The whole process was smooth and stress-free. I couldn't be happier."

Garrett Woodworking   3.5   3   4.5   4
7348 Deering Avenue, Canoga Park, CA 91303
(818) 888 - 2740
Original and reproduction millwork and furniture design

There are no boundaries, geographical or creative, when it comes to Garrett Woodworking's furniture and casework. Though the small shop is often enlisted to do unique, technically sophisticated jobs in locations ranging from Santa Monica to Colorado, it is also happy to take on classic projects, such as the custom duplication of doors for a 1920s restoration. The firm is an experienced hand-holder of high-maintenance clients and can work remotely on far-flung projects. Garrett Woodworking is fearless about taking on inexperienced customers and designers, as long as said novices prove willing to invest the time and money required to get it right.

Owner Mark Garrett has been active in residential construction since 1978. Formerly a general contractor, he's well versed in the expectations of designers and builders, and is sensitive to schedules and the integration of his work with other trades. About 30 percent of Garrett's commissions are for furniture, starting at $4,000 to $5,000 per piece. Casework for a small kitchen starts at $15,000. The firm provides shop drawings and samples in addition to what has been praised as sound aesthetic advice. Installation and finish work are subcontracted out.

Gary Schultz Custom Cabinets   4   4.5   3.5   5
3515 Helms Avenue, Culver City, CA 90232
(310) 204 - 3407   www.gschultz.net
Sleek contemporary cabinetry, millwork and furniture

"Clean," "precise," "sleek" are some of the words used to describe Gary Schultz's creations. One of the trade's best-kept secrets, Schultz is frequently called upon by designers, architects, contractors and homeowners alike to design, create and install cabinets, furniture, moldings and other intricate architectural details. With a preference for contemporary millwork, Schultz honed his skills on the job at some of the most respected furniture and woodworking shops. Since officially opening his business in 1983, Schultz has slowly but surely built an impressive client base in the Los Angeles area. Although the firm mostly works in Beverly Hills, Santa Monica, Malibu and other parts of metropolitan Los Angeles, it has taken on projects as far away as Singapore and Bermuda.

Schultz works mostly with wood but will create in any medium, from leather to metal to glass. While commissions are usually for whole rooms or bigger installations, Schultz and his four-man team are happy to take on smaller projects or craft individual pieces. Though insiders say his prices are on the expensive side, the quality keeps them coming back for more.

"Professional, pleasant and great quality." "Always accurate measurements—makes installation process a breeze." "Hard to get a hold of, but worth the wait." "Super-fine work and top-of-the-line equipment."

Gemeiner Cabinets   4.5   4   4.5   4.5
3201 B Exposition Place, Los Angeles, CA 90018
(323) 299 - 8696

Experienced, solid cabinetry, millwork and furniture

Charles Gemeiner tells us he began tinkering with wood more than 22 years ago. These days a good number of Los Angeles' best building professionals "fight tooth and nail" to obtain his services and urge their clients to do the same. Gemeiner takes on a tremendous variety of high-end projects, from fashioning a single table to outfitting a monster estate. Depending on the job, he may take his cue from a fully realized blueprint or assist in the development of a customer's idea. With eighteen workers on staff, the firm fabricates and installs—but does not stain—all its own creations. Gemeiner totes around a laptop and inspires clients with a digital slide show of his work.

"A big guy" at six-foot-four, Gemeiner is also said to "build that way—sound and solid." Noted as a real problem solver, he tackles projects that those with less experience pass up, inspiring builders to return to him for job after job. The firm's sturdy, well-conceived work is produced in a 10,000 square foot shop with computer-controlled equipment. We're told Gemeiner's prices are in the zone of other top-tier millworkers.

"Anything you need." "He will work to make a project perfect." "His work is not minimal or delicate, but substantial." "He's a traditionalist and will follow designs." "Works with the best people." "He is the nicest and will make it work." "Not too expensive."

Hirsch Custom Cabinets Inc.   4.5   4.5   4   4.5
16129 Wyandotte Street, Van Nuys, CA 91406
(818) 947 - 0067

Reproduction and original cabinetry and millwork; designer furniture production

This versatile firm continues to earn kudos for its high-end custom cabinetry and millwork for contractors and architects and its production furniture for the very top brand-name designers. In addition, the firm creates wall units and kitchens for homeowners, and does reproductions. Principal Russ Hirsch tells us he will consider a project of any size, as long as the prospective homeowner is serious about a professional job. Clients report that the firm actively contributes to design. Sources rave about Hirsch's contemporary veneer work.

Hirsch's sound Midwest work ethic and technical foundation are noted by clients. Growing up in Wisconsin, he pursued a formal education in woodworking.

Hirsch then built and sold furniture on his own under the tutelage of a veteran cabinetmaker who emphasized precision and integrity. Upon moving to California, he gained experience in the high-end sector, trimming out corporate jets and homes in Aspen.

Hirsch's partner Lane Sanderson has an art background and brings an added aesthetic dimension to the firm's solid wood cabinetry and finish work. We hear that whether a job is in the shop or on site, one of the two partners keeps an eye on the project at all times. However, this executive-level quality and service comes at a higher price. Always striving to perfect its product and adapt to new techniques, the firm now employs a computerized CNC router to cut pieces with precise measurements, improving quality while increasing productivity.

"Wonderful range of work." "Responsible." "Reacts quickly to any mistakes." "Congenial to work with." "The quality of work is unsurpassed. We had only positive experiences with them." "The honesty and speed is incredible."

Joseph Schneider   3.5   3.5   4   4
17601 Tarzana Street, Encino, CA 91361
(818) 784 - 2353
Millwork, cabinetry and furniture; hand-carving specialists

If you think Joe Schneider is a piece of work, wait until you see what he can do with wood. The self-taught Schneider has been at it for 50 years now, inspiring fervent supporters in industry circles who say they just love his cabinets and furniture.

Schneider, who specializes in hand carving, can and will do just about anything with wood. He designs/builds for homeowners and assists interior designers in achieving their visions. Schneider and his son form a two-man band, and together they will take on everything from building a contemporary entertainment cabinet to outfitting a full traditional kitchen. Clients say Schneider "tells it like it is and builds it even better," keeping busy with work from Montecito to Manhattan Beach and charging slightly-above-standard rates. All pieces are built in the shop and taken to the site for installation.

"A real craftsman of the old tradition." "A master of intricate architectural details."

Mt. Washington Woodworks   4   3   5   4.5
4080 Sea View Avenue, Los Angeles, CA 90065
(323) 225 - 6311
Artisanal custom furniture, millwork and cabinetry

For buttery, beautiful and elegant furniture and cabinets that are also utilitarian, clients recommend Mark Feinberg's small firm. A furniture maker at heart, Feinberg takes inspiration from feats of proportion and simplicity. His custom cabinets are considered an inventive hybrid between Craftsman and modern styles. References tell us he can reproduce high-end European designs for a fraction of the cost of originals. Mt. Washington will produce a single piece of furniture for a homeowner—or complete cabinetry for a multimillion-dollar home for a top designer.

As his word-of-mouth business has grown, Feinberg has remained determined to stay focused, overseeing only a couple of craftsmen. He lives above his workshop and takes his customers as seriously as his aesthetic. Feinberg begins each job with a visit to the client's home to size up his or her lifestyle needs. Clients tell us his attention to layout and design is rivaled only by his dedication to hand-holding and strong service. We're told he can execute fully realized blueprints or conjure up his own schematics from an idea on a napkin with equal aplomb. Feinberg is also said to be very flexible about pricing.

"The boutique feel of the company assures me that my pieces won't get lost in the crowd." "A great eye for detail." "Refuses to overbook himself so each piece gets his undivided attention."

Nolan Arnold Furniture   4.5   4.5   4   5
3942 West 147 Street, Hawthorne, CA 90250
(310) 644 - 0366

Lavish custom cabinetry, millwork and furniture

The much sought-after Nolan Arnold hand-selects logs for the perfect result, whether fashioning a single nightstand or an entire library. Over the past twenty years, his firm's work has been sought out by clients from coast to coast—and admirers in Japan, England and Israel. Arnold services many marquee-name designers as well as a cast of famous homeowners. Insiders report this millworker satisfies a very discerning clientele.

A staff of five assist Arnold in the fabrication and installation of his creations. In realizing a design, Arnold fleshes out the technical aspects with shop specs so detailed that references report he leaves zero room for error. However, if trouble enters the room, we hear Arnold deals with it tout de suite. Finishes are outsourced and usually applied in a controlled environment before the product is delivered on site, typically to rave reviews.

Sources say Arnold's service is as impeccable as his craftsmanship. He uses only the best materials, and while clients say the firm delivers on all counts, the final bill is substantial.

"There is no comparison." "Clean, crisp, precise work." "Everything is always under control." "Never a problem other than the cost." "He builds the most beautiful cabinetry and is a delight to work with. He won't let me make a mistake." "Works through every aspect before construction thereby avoiding problems at installation."

Pacific Woodworks   4.5   4.5   4   4
5320 Derry Avenue, Agoura Hills, CA 91301
(805) 531 - 9238

Custom cabinetry and millwork; staircase and mantel specialists

This large, oft-used firm creates and installs high-end custom millwork for designers and creates production pieces for big builders. Pacific specializes in exquisite staircases and fireplace mantels. Cabinets and cased paneling are also produced in its 10,000 square foot shop. Furniture and other designer pieces can be produced in the context of a larger job.

Principals John Long and Steve Gonsalves stepped to the helm of this firm seventeen years ago. Long brings twenty years of woodworking experience to the business; Gonsalves, who got his start in the restoration of old San Marino estate homes and has done everything from mill cabinets to swing doors, contributes his hands-on know-how and spearheads all custom work.

The firm is equipped with CAD, and while it is primarily oriented toward contractors, it also works well with designers, helping them develop their concepts. Pacific's fabrication and design team was recently featured in *Extreme Makeover* and in the *LA Daily News*, generating even more positive buzz for this highly regarded industry stalwart.

Pacific charges a minimum of $25,000 for a custom project such as a kitchen or library.

"Such nice guys." "They turn around a terrific product on time."

SDM Company   5   4   5   4.5

5738 West Washington Boulevard, Los Angeles, CA 90016
(323) 936 - 0295

Expertly crafted millwork, cabinetry and custom furniture

"The old-fashioned way" is still the motto—and the method—of SDM. The design community swoons with delight over the firm's carving department, which produces very high-end custom furniture and built-ins. A favorite for kitchen cabinets, SDM is fluent in any wood, from butternut to bird's-eye maple, and even has its own veneer machine for finish work. SDM can also reproduce anything antique, thanks to its keen eye for scale and proportion. This in-demand company will install furniture pieces as far away as Santa Barbara. Recently, the company has started incorporating ironwork and upholstery in its repertoire, much to the delight of its clients.

SDM is a 30-year-old family affair. Siblings Mike and Sandy Cohen have followed in their father's footsteps. Clients tell us the next generation shares dad's affection for the Old-World style of furniture making. Customers say the firm can create anything the client can imagine. The consensus is that SDM proves "very eager" to please at a "very good price" for its quality.

"They made a piece that blew my mind." "I showed them a picture of what I wanted, and SDM's contribution only added to the wonder of the piece." "It's important to Mike and Sandy that the client is getting a good job." "Always very pleasant."

Showcase Cabinetry   4   3   4.5   4

14813 1/2 Oxnard Street, Van Nuys, CA 91411
(818) 781 - 7337   www.showcasecabinets.com

Full-service cabinetry and millwork

Owner Peter Scholz and company are as experienced in creating modern European-style cabinets with special veneers and laminates as they are in matching or restoring ornate old moldings. Recently, this expanding firm has been featured in episodes of *Redesign* on HGTV and done a number of loft projects in the West Hollywood area. In response to demand, Showcase recently added another 1,000 square feet to its workshop and opened a showroom to house its line of cabinets, sample doors, kitchen & bath products, countertop materials and veneers.

Scholz is a second-generation cabinetmaker who got his start sweeping the floors in his father's shop at age twelve. Today, he manages a crew of six and orchestrates the day-to-day preparation and planning of projects at Showcase Cabinetry. A hands-on guy, Scholz also does the estimates and field measuring himself. His firm takes on jobs of every size, from design to installation, and will work with homeowners as well as contractors and architects.

We're told Scholz asks a lot of questions and makes sure all options are known at the outset, ensuring the customer stays happy in the long run. The firm is at its best, clients say, when given some creative leeway to execute a design. Indeed, Showcase's reasonable pricing gives clients some leeway as well.

"Excellent value for the price and quality of work." "Always on target with his interpretation of the clients' needs." "Extraordinarily organized and efficient."

	Quality	Cost	Value	Recommend?
	✚	$	◆	★

Signature Millworks 4 4 4 4.5

2060 D. Avenida de Los Arboles, PMB 478, Thousand Oaks, CA 91362
(805) 497 - 4701

Large-scale cabinetry and millwork projects

From fabrication to finish, this company puts its John Hancock on large, high-end projects in 6,000 to 20,000 square foot homes with taste and style. Signature Millworks will create interior panels, windows, doors, moldings and cabinets—as well as exterior structural woodworking.

Owner John Prichard has been in the millwork business for more than twenty years. Designers appreciate his attention to detail and ability to interpret a set of plans, refining crude information into beautiful reality. We hear Prichard spends most of his time in the field, always seeking to elevate a project. The firm complements its own shop resources with collaborations with other quality-minded millworkers. This enables Signature to tailor each project to the client's desire, by tapping a particular shop's strength.

There's a great deal of continuity in the quality of work provided by Prichard's crew of 25. His office, run by his wife, Liz, is said to be responsive and organized. In the end, satisfied clients find Signature simply outworks its competitors. This Thousand Oaks firm will travel, and has accepted commissions in New York City and Las Vegas.

"A respected clan of professional craftsmen." "Well managed. Great cabinets and service."

Smallbone of Devizes

220 Brompton Road, London, UK SW32B
(207) 581 - 9989 www.smallbone.co.uk

English kitchen design and fine hand-painted cabinetry

See Smallbone of Devizes's full report under the heading Kitchen & Bath Design

Stewart's Woodworking 4.5 4.5 4 4.5

83 Thomas Road, Buellton, CA 93427
(805) 688 - 8903 www.swi-usa.net

Architecturally sensitive millwork, cabinetry and furniture

Over the course of his twenty-year career, Mark Stewart has graduated from building chairs to outfitting yachts in Spain. The ultimate "can-do guy," Stewart now produces some of the highest-end casework, coffered ceilings, doors and cabinets around. His seasoned 25-member firm offers complete finishing capabilities in the state-of-the-art environment of Stewart's 12,000 square foot shop—but they are equally adept at field finishing.

Stewart takes on $100,000+ jobs for homeowners, GCs and designers. Design pros tell us Stewart can take a sketch and run with it, contributing valuable input on both aesthetic and technical levels. They count on him to work out the kinks and deliver exactly what the client conceptualized. Stewart is known to work well with "very particular and difficult" designers and clients. The firm has been exposed to a level of architecture that most woodworkers have not experienced, and clients say this experience further informs its work.

Stewart looks for challenges, among which has been the eye-popping detail of a number of Gwathmey Siegel commissions. Inspired by the firm's experience restoring old Montecito estates, Stewart has collected a number of cabinet profiles and is currently reproducing them in a "Santa Barbara Collection" cabinet line that will shortly be available at Eagle KitchenWorks. Contracts are mostly negotiated, while design services are offered on retainer, which is credited back if the firm is selected to execute the project. Stewart's full-service excellence comes at a substantial premium.

"Mark is extremely professional and very bright. He makes everyone look good." "His guys are my favorite to work with." "Will be there any way he can." "He's fun to work with. There is an exchange of ideas there."

T&R Carpentry   4   4   4   4
1629 Fremont Drive, Thousand Oaks, CA 91362
(805) 496 - 8854

Cabinetry and millwork; large estate specialists

If vast 10,000+ square foot estates qualify as a niche, that's T&R's spot in the Angeleno market. Working primarily for building professionals, T&R mills, installs and finishes cabinetry, finish carpentry and millwork, including custom windows and doors. The firm has been recruited to work on such prestigious projects as the restoration of a Frank Lloyd Wright home. Modest in size, T&R works mainly in Malibu and Beverly Hills. Clients tell us they continue to come back to the firm because it tackles tasks with urgency and is diligent about tying up loose ends.

Principal Bob Talbert, a carpenter since he was fifteen, established the company in 1985 and ultimately partnered with Tim Redmond to create T&R. The firm accepts only four to seven jobs concurrently, and we hear one of the partners drops by each job site every day. The firm's costs fall in line with most high-end millworkers.

Zook Woodwork   4.5   4.5   4   4.5
570 Madrid Avenue, Torrance, CA 90501
(310) 379 - 4300   www.zookwoodwork.com

Artisanal cabinetry and millwork; custom furniture specialists

Richard Zook got his start crafting the woodwork of boat interiors, but soon moved on to cabinetry and furniture. Hired by some top-flight interior designers, Zook carved out a niche in high-end residential projects. Today Zook's specialty is said to be creating custom entertainment consoles and pop-up mechanical TV cabinets, though some reports say he's also fantastic with furniture.

Zook runs a very versatile shop with six employees, taking on large and small jobs. Using computer design software, the firm can narrow down conceptual ideas into precise drawings that dazzle clients. Currently, the firm is working on a library in Manhattan Beach, a large house in Venice Beach and law offices. For larger projects, Zook prefers to have a designer attached, but he will work directly with a homeowner.

Clients tell us Zook won't let something leave the shop unless it's perfect, and that he works well under deadline. Zook himself splits his time between the field and the shop, and is backed by a foreman who has been with the company for fifteen years. Much of the firm's work encompasses the West LA area, but it has completed projects in Hawaii, New Mexico and New York City. The firm proves to be on the more expensive side, due to its painstaking attention to detail.

"Amiable and pleasant to work with." "One of the old-timers in the business, really knows what he is doing." "Excellent quality." "Super busy but worth the wait."

HIRING A MOVER

Whether relocating to a beach-front bungalow across the neighborhood or rebuilding a new life across the country, the mere thought of moving can cause even the fittest Angelenos to hyperventilate. Even more worrisome than organizing the process is the thought of placing all of one's worldly goods into the hands of a truckload of burly strangers. The less-than-sterling reputation of the moving industry doesn't help either. According to the Better Business Bureau, moving companies consistently make the list of the top-ten industries consumers complain about. Even moving companies themselves admit that three in ten moves result in a complaint against the mover. While those odds don't sound promising, the moving industry in California is highly regulated. There are several precautions you can take to ensure that you are one of the satisfied customers who end up providing glowing references about your moving company to your friends—and to *The Franklin Report*.

WHERE DO I START?

Hundreds of moving companies are listed in the Los Angeles Yellow Pages. Consider four main factors in making your choice: reputation, reliability, cost and availability. Begin with an assessment of your needs. According to most movers, if you are a single city apartment dweller you will probably need 15 to 20 boxes for all your possessions. A family of two adults and two children will require approximately 120 to 200 boxes.

You should request a written estimate from several movers to compare prices and services. Written estimates are binding for the mover. All estimates must be based on a physical inspection of your possessions and must show the total estimated charges (be sure to get these in writing). Keep in mind that a verbal rate quote is not an estimate—movers must see what needs to be moved to prepare a fair estimate. When getting estimates from companies, be as consistent as possible—you want to compare apples to apples. In any event, be prepared with the requisite information before you call movers for estimates. Keep in mind that some movers only perform in-town moves while others are licensed to do nationwide and international moves as well.

Most movers provide packing services in addition to transportation. Packing, of course, incurs additional cost. If you choose to have your items packed by a mover, you'll need to schedule packing days. Be sure to take inventory of what gets packed into each box, noting any existing damage. Keep a copy of the inventory list handy as you unpack to ensure that all your items have arrived safely. While movers assume liability for damage incurred by any items they packed themselves—they will not accept responsibility for items packed by you. Be sure to get estimates both with and without packing services to ensure that you opt for the services best suited to your needs and budget.

RULES & REGULATIONS

The organization that regulates moving companies in California is the California Public Utilities Commission (CPUC, online at www.cpuc.ca.gov). It has a helpful telephone line (800-366-4782) that can tell you if a company is licensed to perform moves in California. While the CPUC does not provide consumers with information on complaints, the Better Business Bureau does. Accessible by phone (909-825-7280) or online (www.bbbsouthland.org), the organization will also tell you how long a company has been in business and provide a principal contact person should you need to speak to someone in a position of authority.

The CPUC requires moving companies to provide an information booklet to customers prior to a move within the state of California. Included in this booklet is every bit of information you would want and need to know about your rights and obligations as a consumer, and what to expect from your mover. If your mover does not provide you with this booklet, you are eligible for a $100 refund. As you can see, the state of California takes moving very seriously.

On Cost

Once you select a moving company and you have agreed upon a moving day and time, the mover must prepare an agreement, which includes the moving company's name, PUC license number (aka CAL-T number), telephone number, an address and phone number where the mover can contact you, location where your belongings are being moved, date of pickup, date of delivery, a summary of goods being moved, declared value of goods being moved, rates upon which the charges are based and any minimum the carrier may have, and the "Not To Exceed" price.

The moving company must complete the agreement (except for the "Not To Exceed" price), sign it and give it to you no less than three days in advance of the moving date. This gives you time to review it and ask for an explanation of any unclear items. Before your move begins, the carrier must fill in the "Not To Exceed" price on the agreement and you and the mover must sign it again.

If you have been given an estimate, the amount of the estimate is the highest price you can be charged and should not go above the "Not To Exceed" price written on the agreement. If there are any changes, a change order form should be written up (these are additional items or services added by you after the estimate), and these charges will be added.

In general, local moves (defined as any move within 100 miles) are billed at an hourly rate, ranging anywhere from $80 per hour (a 3 on our Cost scale) to $200 per hour (a 5 on our Cost scale). This rate generally includes a truck and the labor of two men. For the most part, moving companies will stipulate a minimum number of hours of moving time (usually two hours), and sometimes a minimum amount of travel time. You should plan to factor in a gratuity of at least $5 per man per hour.

Weight-rated fees are usually for long-distance moves (anything more than 100 miles). The charges are based on the weight of the goods and the distance they are moved. The truck is weighed before it is loaded with your household items and furniture, and then again after. The difference between the two weights will determine how you are charged. Again, get the best estimate you can before the move, but realize that the actual cost will be calculated after all the goods are loaded on the truck and weighed.

To keep costs down, budget-minded consumers should consider boxing up their own books and clothes, but leave the packing of breakable items to the movers. That way the cost of moving can be contained, and the cost of breakage and any other kind of damage can be absorbed by the moving company.

Contracts, Insurance and Licenses

As with most business relationships, make sure that you negotiate a written contract before you move. As with any agreement, scrutinize it carefully before signing it. If it doesn't contain every foreseeable detail of the move, insist on adding these details. Ensure that any agreed-upon terms, such as mileage, packing, standard charges, additional costs and insurance, are all included. The contract should state that the men will stay after 5PM to finish the move if it takes longer than expected. If possible, attach a copy of the inventory, as well. Retain a copy of the signed document well after the move has been completed to ensure that all of your possessions are delivered in the manner that the contract dictates. Be aware that most standard agreements require that the movers be paid before they unload their truck at your new home.

For interstate moves, basic insurance usually provides $.60 of coverage for each pound of goods transported ($.30 for local moves). While there is usually no additional cost associated with this kind of protection, you do need to sign an additional contract to activate it. Unfortunately, the coverage itself is less than adequate: for instance, if your $500 television weighs ten pounds, you can collect only $3. Several other insurance plans are provided at additional cost, and protecting the value of that TV might require purchasing one. Optional plans come at varying costs and provide different degrees of coverage. The American Moving and Storage Association (www.moving.org) can provide you with greater insights about moving insurance—they also supply guidelines to follow when planning a move.

COST-SAVING MOVING TIPS

✧ Packing items yourself will save you a bundle. However, movers are only liable for damage resulting from *their* packing, so limit the do-it-yourself items to unbreakables, such as books and clothes.

✧ Packing materials cost significantly more when purchased from the moving company. If you're doing your own packing, buy the materials at an office product or packing product store.

✧ Insurance may seem like an expensive frill, but it can save you a lot of money and headaches in the event of damage. There are many types of coverage, so check out all your options before choosing one.

✧ The time of year and/or week during which you move will affect the cost. Since movers are typically busiest on weekends and in the summer, many companies offer discounts on jobs that take place during the week—and between Labor Day and Memorial Day.

MOVERS

🛍 FIRMS WITH PORTFOLIOS 🛍

Bevard Delivery 🛍   3.5   3.5   4   4
8350 Melrose Avenue, Suite 6, Los Angeles, CA 90069
(323) 653 - 2273
Residential and commercial moves; delivery and logistics for design trade

"Laidback" and "efficient," this boutique moving company will get expensive furnishings and fine art there "with no fuss." Favored and trusted by a score of decorators to deliver, pick up and install furniture pieces in clients' homes, Bevard has been satisfying discriminating decorators and homeowners since opening its doors in 1989.

Helmed by founder Frank Bevard, the company has eight movers, six drivers and six trucks. Although the company veers away from regular house moves, they are willing to do residential jobs for regular clients. Bevard and his team are also specialists in moving fine art and have garnered commissions from auction houses of the ilk of Christie's and Butterfield's. The company does 60 percent residential work, with the remainder of its jobs coming from commercial clients such as Armani, Ralph Lauren, Prudential Realty, William Morris and ICM.

Cost is a flat fee per hour, per team, with a one hour minimum for a two-man team. Bevard works mostly in Beverly Hills, Palm Springs, Newport, the Valley, Santa Barbara and, recently, Las Vegas. Clients laud the firm's responsiveness, reasonable prices and efficient service.

"Always on time." "Been using for years." "The men are always polite, punctual and well-dressed. This professional team always delivers!" "Perfect for smaller projects but need to use bigger company for bigger projects."

Blue Skys Delivery & Installation 🛍   4.5   4   4.5   5
2100 West Hyde Park Boulevard, Los Angeles, CA 90047
(323) 299 - 2640   www.blue-skys.com
Delivery service

"Outstanding," "professional" and "organized" are some of the things we hear about Blue Skys Delivery & Installation. Since opening its doors in 1983, this 25-man company does mostly local moves but can pack and ship long-distance and internationally. Helmed by husband-and-wife team Ava and Michael Kauffman, the company specializes in moving and installation logistics for decorators. The firm serves 75 percent residential and 25 percent commercial clients. From prominent decorators (Thomas Landry, Dell Schmidt, Lafia/Arvin, Diane Johnson) to celebrities (Lionel Ritchie, Lawrence Fishburne, Kareem Abdul-Jabbar) to hotels (Beverly Wilshire, The Four Seasons in LA, Regent Beverly Wilshire, Beverly Hills Hotel) to resorts and Fortune 500 companies, Blue Skys keeps them coming back for more. Pricing for local moves is determined by the hour (starts at $85 per hour) while long-distance and international shipping are priced by weight and/or cubic foot.

Clients love their "hands-on" approach and we hear that though prices are high, they are "perfectly reasonable" for the excellent service.

	Quality	Cost	Value	Recommend?
	+	$	◆	★

"I love that they are a family business. I feel like I'm their only client." "The guys have great personalities. Really makes moving, which is usually a stressful endeavor, a pain-free experience." "Every crew member gave 110 percent." "My installation company of choice."

Designer Dependable Delivery Inc. 💼   4.5   4   4.5   4.5
2429 Forney Street, Los Angeles, CA 90031
(323) 276 - 0502

Remodeling/redecorating storage and re-installation specialists

Working through some of the country's best decorators, the team at Designer Dependable Delivery is praised for taking care of clients when they are between homes, dealing with major home renovations and expertly handling relocations. References tell us the firm's specialty is consolidating furniture, artwork and other items when a remodeling or redecorating project is in progress. When the home is ready, Designer's crew then installs everything. All clients have to do is show up with the clothes on their backs. The team has been seen unpacking and organizing clothing, hanging pictures and even making beds and fluffing duvets. Frequently called upon to pack and ship valuable antiques and fine art, Designer Dependable Delivery does local, cross-country and international moves.

Owner Carlos Velastegui started his business with one truck and a cellphone. Today, his booming firm has sixteen employees and five bobtail trucks. Personalized and discreet service is Designers Dependable Delivery's "claim to fame," and while it is said they are not cheap, customers report they are professional, competitive and well worth the expense for peace of mind at the end of the day. Rates for local moves are calculated on a per-hour basis (with a two-hour minimum) for one truck, while rates for long distance are per project.

"There is nothing they won't do and nowhere they won't go to help us deliver perfectly assembled, on-time turnkey projects to our demanding clientele." "These guys do it all—they pick up, unpack, store, install—I don't have to worry about a thing." "So professional, so willing to go the extra mile." "Carlos makes me feel like I am his only client." "A real find!" "Installations are precise—true experts."

NorthStar Moving Corporation 💼   5   3.5   5   4.5
9120 Mason Avenue, Los Angeles, CA 91311
(800) 275 - 7767   www.northstarmoving.com

Residential and commercial moving and storage

Described as the "guiding light in a sea of moving companies," NorthStar has been showing its clients the way to a painless move since 1994. From packing and moving priceless antiques to delicate computer systems, Katalan and his team have been praised by customers from Los Angeles to San Francisco and every location in between. Giving the team great marks in every category from professionalism to compassion, NorthStar's clients refer the company to friends and colleagues often. The firm serves a heavy celebrity clientele (Angelina Jolie, Kristy Swanson, Diane Keaton, Anthony Hopkins) as well as a healthy roster of production companies and television networks.

Owner and founder Ram Katalan supervises 40 trucks and over 200 employees who specialize in local, intrastate, cross-country and international moves.

NorthStar offers packing and storage services for household furnishings, as well as for fine art and antiques. The firm has a 100,000 square foot storage facility in Chatsworth and a 25,000 square foot branch in San Francisco. Local moves are priced by the hour, with a two-hour minimum, while prices for cross-country, intrastate and international moves are determined by weight (1,000-pound minimum). For those lucky enough to call both coasts home, NorthStar is the exclusive West Coast agent for Moishe's, located in New York City.

"One of the smoothest moves I've ever experienced." "The best $3,000 I have spent." "The evening we moved in, I cooked supper for the two movers. Nothing fancy, but I wanted to show my appreciation." "NorthStar sets the gold standard for which any business should strive." "It is a tribute to the staff and company that not one single item in the 8,000 pounds I had was broken or marred." "One of the funniest guys around!" "The crew moved like a well-oiled machine." "The circumstances surrounding my move were very unhappy, but the NorthStar team made the situation better than it could have been." "Even my dogs appreciated how nice everyone was."

Padded Wagon 💼   4.5   4   4.5   4.5
4329 Bandini Boulevard, Los Angeles, CA 90023
(323) 263 - 4200   www.paddedwagon.com

Residential and commercial moving, fine art, antiques and high-end decorative work

Judging from the list of happy customers, including some of LA's finest decorators and auction houses, Padded Wagon is considered to be an excellent and reliable national moving company. Since 1953, the firm has offered residential and commercial moving services, specializing in the transport of antiques and high-end designer pieces. Padded Wagon also has a crew that can install art, chandeliers and sconces. Described as reliable and responsive, Padded Wagon is praised for being there for "last minute" jobs.

The company has branches in Florida, Chicago, New Jersey, Atlanta and New York City. The Los Angeles branch opened in 2000 and currently has six trucks and twelve employees, which owner Eddie Dowling has placed under the capable supervision of John Gross. Estimates are always done in person. Prices for local moves are per hour, with a two-hour minimum, while interstate moves are priced by weight. The firm can ship internationally, and does so occasionally.

Sources tell us they feel at ease with their belongings in the hands of the Padded Wagon staff. Many speak about the crew's dependability, professionalism and attention to detail. The company's prices are on the higher end of the scale, reflecting the firm's stature as a company that is a cut above general national movers.

"Padded Wagon has been there on more than one occasion to help us out of a bind." "Great service, great movers." "These guys put in a hard day's work and then some." "Responsive and sensitive to clients' belongings."

Wetzel & Sons Moving & Storage Inc. 💼   4.5   3.5   5   4.5
12400 Osborne Street, Pacoima, CA 91331
(310) 859 - 1028   www.wetzelmovingandstorage.com

High-end residential moving and storage

Whether moving a single piece of furniture for one of LA's hottest decorators or an entire household for one of its many repeat customers, the Wetzel team earns high marks for its professionalism and integrity. Sources say the firm makes them feel easy about their moves no matter what the size, with a staff that is friendly and accommodating.

Wetzel & Sons Moving & Storage Inc. is a family-run operation that dates back to 1976. Focusing on high-end residential clients, the firm offers packing and crating services and boasts one of the finest warehouses in the Los Angeles area. Its facilities are so nice, in fact, the company invites prospective clients to come and see the site for themselves. We have been told that Wetzel's prices are on the higher side, but customers say they are willing to pay a premium to be free from anxiety about their move.

"Not only are they good at what they do, they really seem to enjoy it." "Very good customer service." "Installers are very professional." "We trusted them with our very expensive antiques." "Always on time, and extremely careful." "I have used every delivery service in Los Angeles—Wetzel is second to none."

FIRMS WITHOUT PORTFOLIOS

AirSea Packing Group Inc.   4.5   3.5   5   4.5
8515 South La Cienega Boulevard, Inglewood, CA 90301
(310) 649 - 0892 www.airseapacking.com
Packing and shipping of delicate and valuable items

An international star among moving companies, AirSea Packing will get your valuables there in pristine condition, sources say. A private company in business for over 33 years, AirSea specializes in the packing and shipping of art and specialty items worldwide. With a client list that includes private collectors, decorators, commercial customers and museums, this firm's fame has spread worldwide. It currently operates out of London, Paris, New York and Los Angeles.

Consulting services include on-site packing advice, installation, transportation and security. The firm also has a dedicated weekly container service to ship items from Europe to the U.S. and boasts a 20,000 square foot, climate-controlled storage facility that offers the ultimate in protection and security. In addition, custom-designed storage vaults and a viewing gallery make AirSea Packing a "one-stop shopping" experience for your fine art needs. As if these weren't enough, AirSea also assists clients on buying expeditions by offering courier services and having a staff member take a client around to help with the local language and find local shops, dealing with the paperwork and purchase orders—even going so far as to convert currency and process payment for the purchase—and then, of course, shipping the articles anywhere in the world.

We hear the discreet, trustworthy staff members in the Los Angeles office are well-trained in the art of working with the well-heeled and high-profile clients it serves. References say the types of help AirSea Packing offers are expensive, but the "door-to-door" service estimates include everything, and are typically "right on the money."

"Professional and experienced—I wouldn't trust my valuables to anyone else." "Prices are high-end, but then, so is my antique collection." "Very satisfied with the service." "Impeccable customer service."

Bekins Moving & Storage Company   3   3   4   3
717 East Artesian Boulevard, Carson, CA 90746
(310) 357 - 6150 www.bekinsms.com
Local and long distance, commercial and residential moving and storage

Evolving from a horse-and-buggy company founded in the Midwest in the 1890s, Bekins Moving & Storage Company now serves Los Angeles with some of the most high-tech equipment available. This nationwide company handles commercial and residential relocations both within California and across the globe. Storage facilities are also part of Bekins's "good and reasonable" service. While some references report delays, they are quick to add that the company will do everything in its power to rectify the situation.

"Got the job done right." "Price was quite competitive."

Beverly Hills Transfer & Storage   4   4   4   4
15500 South Main Street, Gardena, CA 90248
(310) 532 - 1121   www.beverlyhillstransfer.com
Residential and commercial moving and storage

When Beverly Hills Transfer & Storage built its first office on Beverly Drive in 1935, its six-story building was considered a skyscraper. Times have changed, and so has the company, which now has offices in the San Fernando Valley, downtown Los Angeles, Sacramento, Manville and Beverly Hills, in addition to the corporate headquarters in Gardena. The firm also has a dispatch office in Hartford, Connecticut. One thing is the same: the firm's reputation for outstanding, careful service.

Beverly Hills Transfer was established in 1928 by Fred Mason and is now helmed by Frank Rolapp, whose father joined Mason as partner in 1942. Rolapp, who bought the company nine years ago, now spearheads 130 trucks and 350 employees. The company is known as a highly skilled and large mover for commercial and residential clients. Some sources say they've used Beverly Hills Transfer & Storage for generations, getting referrals from their parents, and passing the company's name on to their children.

Insiders say Beverly Hills Transfer & Storage caters to each individual client. At the time of initial contact a customer is matched to an account coordinator. This "moving buddy" is available to the customer every step of the way, which, we're told, makes things a little easier when preparing for moving day. Pricing for local shipping is by the hour, long distance is by the pound and international shipping is per cubic foot. Projects range from $400 to $1 million. Clients tell us their possessions were handled by the staff as if they were their own, and that prices are reasonable for the high quality of work.

"Efficient and great turnaround." "Frank is friendly, laid-back and extremely professional." "Workers are respectful and punctual." "Great sales team." "Can get pretty busy but they will return phone calls the next day."

Beverly Packing   4   4   4   4
645 North Fairfax Avenue, Los Angeles, CA 90036
(323) 658 - 8365   www.beverlypacking.com
Trade and residential packing, shipping, delivery and storage services

Mike Sarbakhsh was once a dissatisfied addressee, chronically receiving shipments that were damaged and badly packed. In 1981, he decided to take matters in his own hands and started designing special packages for specific items, which led to him opening his own shipping company. The rest, as they say, is history.

Today, Beverly Packing caters specifically to the packing, delivery and transportation needs of the trade. Described by clients as "very good" and a pleasure to deal with, this mid-sized company can do local jobs or handle long-distance projects involving cross-country trips and warehousing. Whether you're moving an antique armoire across town, transporting a shipment of lamps across the country or shipping valuable paintings to Europe, those in the know say you can trust Beverly for the assignment. Beverly Packing is often called to handle the shipping and packing needs of galleries, art dealers, production companies, designers and auction houses such as Bonham's & Butterfield's. Recently, the team at Beverly Packing was commissioned by Fox News to handle all the packing and shipping for their computers for the 2005 Superbowl.

The firm has six bobtail trucks and two larger ones. Each truck usually has one driver and one helper. The company also has a 30,000 square foot storage facility. Sources tell us that while Beverly's services are not inexpensive (minimum projects start at $225 and can go up to $175,000), prices are highly competitive and the dollars are well spent on personalized attention.

"Great service." "I have no reservations recommending this company." "A good source." "Excellent local company." "Always responsive."

Blue Chip Moving & Storage   2.5   2.5   4   3.5
13525 Crenshaw Boulevard, Hawthorne, CA 90250
(323) 463 - 6888   www.bluechipmoving.com
Residential and commercial moving and storage

One of the Los Angeles area's larger Mayflower Transit agents, Blue Chip Moving & Storage offers a wide array of services to its commercial and residential customers. Whether you decide to pack yourself or choose to let the experts at this company assist you, we hear the staff is reliable and has a solid work ethic on the job. If it is storage you need, this firm will be at your front door with a storage container capable of holding an entire room's worth of furniture. You pack it up and lock it up, and Blue Chip will take it away for you, eliminating the need for renting trucks to cart things to a storage facility.

For those interested in knowing exactly where their belongings are at all times, Mayflower, Blue Chip's "parent," offers online tracking of your move. "Techies" report that all you do is enter your order number and your truck's location is identified. For straightforward, simpler moving jobs, clients tell us that team Blue Chip gets the job done in reasonable time and at a decent price.

"The service was better than I expected." "Nice group of hard workers."

Chipman Moving & Storage   3.5   3.5   4   4
2116 East 220th Street, Long Beach, CA 90810
(510) 748 - 8700   www.chipmancorp.com
Residential and commercial moving and storage

In business since 1939, Chipman Moving & Storage has a colorful history. Begun as a one-man operation run out of founder Arthur Chipman's home in 1939, the business expanded when the United States entered World War II. Relocating military personnel across the country, Chipman added more trucks and more employees, eventually adding a warehouse.

Today, Chipman is a major presence in the Southern California moving and storage arena. With over 300 highly trained employees, 200 trucks of all sizes and ten warehouses, this agent for United Van Lines has the ability to move both commercial and residential clients as well as help them with their general storage needs.

Clients say they are treated well by this basic moving firm and the service is good. Since Chipman Moving & Storage is large, it has the manpower to help with the smallest details, from organizing the actual move to providing information on local schools and merchants in your new community. Prices are reported to be within customers' expectations.

"Fast, efficient and professional." "If you are not looking for a boutique operation, this conglomerate is for you."

Chris' Moving Men   **3.5   3.5   4   4.5**
18118 3/4 South Broadway, Gardena, CA 90248
(310) 769 - 0142   www.chrismovingmen.com

Residential and commercial moving, packing and storage services

Since this company opened its doors in 1979, its discriminating clients have been recommending these moving men to friends. Founded by Chris Soderberg, this mid-sized firm has twenty employees and ten trucks. Holding PUC and ICC licenses, the company does local, long-distance and a few international moves. Soderberg and his team take on everything from one bedroom apartments to multi-million-dollar estates. 80 percent of their clientele is residential, and the roster of past clients includes corporate executives, celebrities and well-heeled homeowners. The firm also boasts a 30,000 square foot storage facility.

Cost for local moves is by the hour (the base fee is $79 per hour), while cross-country and international shipping are priced by the pound. Minimum fees per project usually start at $160 to $200 locally and $500 cross-country. Sources tell us the personnel are extremely professional and "careful" about their belongings. We also hear that the reasonable prices are a good value for the efficient service.

"Adheres to deadlines." "Very professional. They seem to have a great system going." "Would definitely hire again."

Elite Transfer   **4.5   3.5   5   4.5**
239 West 146th Street, Gardena, CA 90248
(310) 532 - 4272

Transporters and installers of furniture, antiques and artwork

Working primarily with fine-furniture manufacturers and decorators, the small team at Elite Transfer has developed a reputation for being "expert" handlers, transporters and installers of antiques, furniture and other decorative items. The six-year-old company, which makes both local and national deliveries, also provides storage services to those who are awaiting the construction or redecoration of their homes. Clients say this company does a wonderful job installing artwork and handling furniture and other precious items with great professionalism and care.

Sources say they appreciate Elite Transfer's specialized attention, and they repeatedly compliment the firm's organization and attention to detail. Although Elite is not a typical residential moving company, it has been known to do household moves for its clients, who, we are told, like the service so much they keep coming back.

"We have worked with Elite for five years, and they have never let us down." "Great people to work with—always up-front and honest." "Elite moved us into our first family home. They were very courteous and prompt and took great care with all of our furniture." "The nicest people. I trust them 100 percent." "Their professional and personal service is refreshing." "The best delivery company we've ever worked with."

	Quality	Cost	Value	Recommend?
	✚	$	◆	★

F.Y.I./For Your Interior Installations   4.5   4   4.5   4.5

8581 Santa Monica Boulevard, Suite 472, West Hollywood, CA 90069
(818) 760 - 7377

Delivery and installation for design trade and residences; specialty services

Highly recommended by some of LA's premier decorators and designers, the small team at F.Y.I./For Your Interiors Installations handles design trade installations as well as residential moves. Owners Jeff Pendergrast and Michael Williams specialize in managing the logistics of out-of-state projects that originate in Los Angeles. Clients praise their ability to execute entire jobs flawlessly.

Whether consolidating, delivering and installing furniture and antiques or expediting and managing inventory control, this company is praised for providing services most other companies will not touch. For example, after a move, the team can arrange to have unwanted, leftover items auctioned, saving owners time and effort. F.Y.I. is so thorough, it has been known to take photos of items before and after delivery. Insiders tell us the firm keeps detailed portfolios of each project. Considering the range of exceptional services, prices are described as more than competitive.

"Calm, charming, thorough—they always go the extra mile." "Very accommodating and professional." "Jeff and Michael are personable and knowledgeable." "Great guys—a pleasure to work with." "They always go above and beyond the call of duty." "First-rate service and dependability." "Service with a smile."

Fine Art Shipping   5   4   5   4.5

404 North Oak Street, Inglewood, CA 90302
(310) 677 - 0011   www.fineartship.com

Art handling and installation, specialty delivery service

Specialty moving, indeed. Serving the professional art community since opening its doors in 1982, Fine Art Shipping lives up to its name—and then some. In addition to galleries, museums and collectors, the company caters to the residential moving needs of high-end clients. From transporting a single piece of antique furniture for repair to orchestrating the move of an entire household from one mansion to another, this team, led by owners Ron and Betsy Dorfman, is professional, responsive and, above all, discreet (you won't see the company name splashed all over its trucks).

Some of the services offered by the firm include customized packing and crating of precious items, as well as their storage and delivery. Working with a network of affiliates around the country and the world, Fine Art Shipping can act as brokers, moving shipments in and out of Los Angeles with ease. Clients say they feel confident with their valuable belongings in the hands of Fine Art Shipping. The fact that the company is insured by Lloyd's of London doesn't hurt either. This twenty-man company has four specially equipped bobtail trucks and one climate-controlled truck for shipping museum-quality pieces. Fine Art Shipping also has its own in-house art installers.

Over the years, Fine Art Shipping has earned the trust of its customers by catering to their unique and demanding requests. The company ships locally, cross-country and internationally with projects ranging from $300 to $50,000. While described by some clients as expensive, no one seems to mind writing the check when they receive their delivery on time and intact.

"This company is great—very accommodating." "No complaints! Very sensitive to our needs—friendly and professional." "The staff is very careful." "Ron and Betsy are fabulous—they make shipping and delivery painless."

	Quality	Cost $	Value ◆	Recommend? ★

Gentle Giant Moving & Storage   3.5   2.5   5   3.5

2042 East Maple Avenue, El Segundo, CA 90245
(310) 978 - 2939   www.ggiant.com

Residential and commercial moving and storage

A favorite among top business executives and celebrities alike, Gentle Giant Moving & Storage is praised for taking great care and pride in its work. The company started modestly in 1986 with two men and a truck, and has since blossomed into an operation with a real presence, boasting 50 highly trained employees, fifteen trucks and a storage/office facility spanning 80,000 square feet.

We hear that with all its resources, Gentle Giant has the ability to serve almost any relocation need, no matter how large. Clients are 90 percent residential and the firm can do local and national moves. Prices for local moves are by the hour (with a two-hour minimum) and cost for cross-country moves are determined by weight (with a 1,000-pound minimum).

"What a great staff. I was very impressed." "The price was right on the money." "They were able to handle my difficult move effortlessly, with no problems at all."

Heritage 21st Century Movers   3   2.5   4.5   3

2945 Columbia Street, Torrance, CA 90503
(310) 320 - 1785   www.h21sls.com

Residential and commercial moving and storage

Since 1980, Heritage 21st Century Movers has been satisfying the relocation needs of both residential and commercial clients. An authorized agent for Mayflower Transit, this company's sizable staff can handle projects ranging from basic household moves to jobs involving art, antiques or delicate electronic audio/visual equipment. For those "between homes" or in the midst of a major relocation, the firm boasts a 40,000 square foot warehouse for storage.

Clients tell us the company is reliable and a good choice for basic moving. We've heard their prices are moderate for a friendly team that sources say does "a good day's work."

"Professional staff—they didn't leave me hanging like my previous mover did." "Price was reasonable, and they did a pretty good job, too."

	Quality	Cost	Value	Recommend?
	✚	$	◆	★

Lombardi's Van & Storage

5 3.5 5 5

817 Lake Street, Burbank, CA 91502
(661) 266 - 9681

Residential moving and storage, specialty delivery service

Whether moving to a new home in Los Angeles, Aspen, Palm Beach or New York, clients say they are absolutely thrilled with the attentive service they receive from James Lombardi's small team at Lombardi's Van & Storage. These movers are said to handle household moves with the "patience of saints." In fact, one client admits to having the team move a sofa back and forth across the room for more than two hours until it was situated "just right." Forty percent of Lombardi's business is concentrated on deliveries for decorators and interior designers, who praise the firm's impeccable record. Packing, unpacking and storage are also on the menu at Lombardi's.

Customers tell us they return again and again because Lombardi sees things through to the very last detail. Local moves are priced by the hour and cross-country moves by the pound. With rates coming in at just above standard, Lombardi's is considered a real bargain by sources who appreciate its "consistent quality and professionalism" and its patience in serving a rather demanding clientele.

"James is very involved and caring." "Lombardi's does whatever it takes to get the job done." "We have used them several times, and not one thing has ever been broken. I will never use anyone else again!"

MiniMoves Inc.

4 3.5 4.5 4.5

5525 Peck Road, Arcadia, CA 91006
(800) 300 - 6683 www.minimoves.com

Small residential and commercial moves

This Chicago-based company with operations in New York and Los Angeles comes highly recommended by decorators, antique dealers and homeowners alike. By handling moves of 3,500 pounds or less, MiniMoves is reported to provide service that one could not get from "big job" companies. Known for fair pricing and a strong work ethic, the firm is a good choice for those moving in or out of apartments or for those transporting one or two pieces of furniture.

As a member of the board of the Better Business Bureau, MiniMoves CEO Jack Arslanian makes sure his staff represents his company and industry with professionalism and pride. Established in 1991, the company's service has been recognized by *The Wall Street Journal, Crain's* and ERC Mobility online. And this good-hearted company recently offered the use of its trucks to the Red Cross to pick up and deliver items to benefit tsunami victims. While the moves may be mini, sources tell us the service is big. The company charges by the hour for local moves, with a two hour minimum and charges according to item for cross-country moves.

"Excellent turnaround. Meets deadlines without a hitch." "Great customer service." "Reliable and thorough." "Jack is one of the friendliest people around."

Modern Installations

4.5 3.5 5 4.5

4843 West Pico Boulevard, Los Angeles, CA 90019
(310) 864 - 8341

Specialty pick-up, delivery and storage for the trade

Working almost exclusively on residential projects, this much-admired company's small team has developed quite a reputation with the stars of LA's decorating community. Described as "a true winner," that really cares about the job, this local favorite is said to deliver unsurpassed service and sensitive, outstanding work.

After working for top moving companies in Los Angeles for fourteen years, Daniel Madrigal ventured out on his own in 2000 to form Modern Installations. Madrigal keeps the focus on personal attention by knowing the likes and dislikes of each client. He is also on-site at each move.

Madrigal helms a team of ten employees and has three bobtail trucks in service. The company now has a 5,000 square foot storage facility. The firm only does local moves. Charging by the hour, the firm can handle moving everything from a single sofa to an entire household. Do note that, unlike movers listed in the phone book, Modern Installations usually works through decorators or referrals only.

"Danny is caring and responsive." "They have always done everything possible to accommodate our needs. They can handle urgent deliveries with little notice." "These guys are great!" "Very easy to work with, and they met our deadline." "Danny and his team really take care of us." "My clients appreciate their punctuality, friendliness and respect for the expensive and irreplaceable objects they deliver and install. We love them." "My secret weapon!"

Plycon Van Lines   4.5   4   4.5   4.5
4240 West 190th Street, Suite C, Torrance, CA 90504
(310) 419 - 1200   www.plyconvanlines.com
Residential moving and storage, delivery services to the trade

The list of professional clients who trust the company to transport fine furniture, antiques and other designer pieces reads like a "who's who" of Los Angeles decorators. Because Plycon has seven offices throughout the US, it is able to make deliveries across town or across the country with equal ease. Insiders say the care and efficiency the company exhibits is, like the goods they move, priceless.

A family-run company, Plycon Van Lines has two separate divisions to handle residential and trade customers. The residential side of the 47-year-old company also gets rave reviews. With services ranging from inspecting belongings to carefully wrapping and packing them, Plycon boasts many satisfied customers. The firm can also move cars. While sources say Plycon's prices are not cheap, they are competitive.

"Great team—very cooperative." "I would use Plycon again—they were very accommodating." "I was eight months pregnant on moving day, and the guys would not let me lift a finger."

Precision Packing and Installation   4.5   3.5   5   4.5
4518 Vanowen Street, Burbank, CA 91505
(323) 849 - 2113
Residential and commercial moving and storage; crating, packing, fine art, antiques

Specializing in the transportation, storage, packing and installation of items ranging from art and antiques to furniture, this fifteen-year-old firm is "on speed dial" for many of LA's top decorators. In addition to offering specialized delivery services, Precision is known to perform high-end residential and commercial moves.

The team—led by owner Al Faruzzi, who has an impressive 48 years of experience in the moving business—is said to be meticulous, professional and caring about its work. Clients say the company's prices are worth the cost for the high level of service provided, which may explain why most of the firm's business is repeat. In the final analysis, sources say Precision does exactly what its name promises.

"Precision makes coordinating a renovation easier and smoother than any other company I have used." "A friend referred Al a few years ago, and now I wouldn't think of using another mover." "Al really cares about making his clients happy."

	Quality	Cost	Value	Recommend?
	+	$	◆	★

Rudd's Transfer & Storage   2.5 2.5 4 3.5

1763 Seabright Avenue, Long Beach, CA 90813
(562) 436 - 9709   www.rudds.com

Residential and commercial moving and storage, international shipping

With 81 years of experience in Southern California, Rudd's has built its reputation on being "highly attentive" to its residential and commercial clients. An Atlas Van Lines agent, the company boasts that it can move practically anything anywhere on the planet. Rudd's is also licensed as an international port agent in Long Beach and LA, and can work with forwarding agents to get your belongings where they need to go. In addition, its storage facilities can accommodate your most prized items—even your car. The company's storage facility is 25,000 square feet.

Clients tell us that the Rudd's staff is very professional and takes great care to do a good job. Prices have been described as very competitive for the high quality of work and personalized attention provided.

"They arrived on time and did a really good job." "I have had so many bad experiences with movers. But this time, I was finally happy." "The crew took great care in everything they did."

S&M Moving Systems   3.5 3 4.5 4

12128 Burke Street, Santa Fe Springs, CA 90670
(562) 567 - 2100   www.smmoving.com

Local and long distance moving and storage

Sources tell us this is a solid, reliable company with a good reputation. In business since 1918, S&M Moving Systems boasts one of the largest truck fleets in the United Van Lines network. In addition to its Southern California location, S&M has operations in Northern California, New Mexico, Arizona and Massachusetts and can handle local and long distance moves from all of these areas. Services include both residential and commercial moving, as well as storage.

Crews are said to be well trained, courteous and flexible, and most clients report their moves went as planned with no major problems. We're told that when the inevitable glitches did occur, S&M's staff was more than happy to do whatever possible to fix them. Sources say S&M fits the bill for basic moving needs at a reasonable price.

"Reliable. Always on schedule." "Sometimes hard to get in touch with, but will always return phone calls." "A bargain considering the efficient service."

Hiring Painters & Wallpaperers

Walk into a room painted a beautiful celadon green and immediately your mood changes—you become calmer, more relaxed. By merely changing the color of a space, you can produce a feeling of drama or tranquility. Designers know that painting is one of the quickest, most versatile and cost-effective things you can do to transform a room. But painting can be a messy and hazardous proposition for the novice, so many homeowners opt to hire a professional contractor.

Painting contractors with a wide range of abilities and services abound in the Los Angeles area. Choices range from small start-ups to large established firms, and from straight painters to custom muralists. Depending upon the size of the job and the quality and complexity of the work, there is a painting contractor out there for you.

Where to Look for a Professional

Finding the right painting contractor for your job involves some research. It is very important to check references and ask to see a certificate of insurance. Each contractor should have workmen's compensation and general liability insurance to protect you from job site-related liabilities. Several trade organizations, such as the Painting and Decorating Contractors of America (www.pdca.org), list paint contractors in your area. And of course, *The Franklin Report* offers a range of client-tested choices.

Contracts

Reputable contractors will encourage using a written contract. Your contract should clearly explain the scope of the work to be performed and include a list of the surfaces to be painted, a time schedule for the project, payment procedures and any warranty or guarantee the contractor might offer.

Pricing Systems

When considering price, it is important to note that the cost structure of straight painting is much different than that of decorative work. While some firms do both types of work, your bill will be determined using different factors in each case.

The cost of straight residential painting varies based on such factors as the cost of the materials and the company's overhead costs. You should invite at least three contractors to bid on your paint job, and ask each to submit a detailed written proposal. Painting contractors charge on a per person per day basis, which generally runs in the $400 to $475 range for nonunion jobs (this equates to approximately a 3 on our Cost scale). Union jobs start at about $500 per person per day. The contractor should provide you with an overall cost estimate for the job that is broken down by room. Also ask for a step-by-step plan outlining how the job will be spackled, skimmed and painted. If colors are being matched, ask the painter to apply 24-inch-square samples on the walls.

Decorative painting—which in the case of murals or decorative finishes is often considered "art"—is much more subjective price-wise. This process is usually more involved—there are meetings with the homeowner, decorator and painter to determine a style or theme and to incorporate the decorative work into the overall design plan. Time frames for completing a job are usually longer compared to straight painting. All of these factors contribute to the cost of decorative painting.

When considering the "bottom line" for any painting job, ask for client references. They can provide valuable insight into not only the quality of work and timing, but cost as well.

How Many Painters Will Be in My House?

The size of the crew largely depends upon the scope of the job involved. Some painters listed in this guide are sole proprietors who work on small jobs themselves and subcontract larger jobs—others are larger companies with complete crews. Ask how many men will be working on your job and whether there will be a supervisor or principal on site.

The Elements of a Professional Paint Job

Flat painting a room involves preparing the walls, trim and ceiling surfaces for the paint as well as the paint job itself. To prepare walls, paint crews will do all the taping, plastering, plaster restoration, if needed, and skim coating. This prep work is considered one of the most important elements of a paint job as it provides the foundation for the paint. A primer coat, which prepares the walls for the paint, should be applied to dry walls. Two coats of high-quality paint should be applied to the wall surfaces.

Which Paint?

The quality of the paint is crucial in determining its longevity. Fine quality paint, properly applied, should last for six to seven years. If you or your contractor skimp on the quality of the paint, you may be facing a new paint job a lot sooner than you would like. The two most common types of paints are latex and oil-based paints. Latex paint is water-based and dries quickly, which allows for more than one coat to be applied in a day. Latex paint is better at resisting mildew, easier to clean and lasts longer than alkyd paints, which are oil-based. Alkyd paints are preferred by many painters because they are durable and long lived, but they take longer to dry, have a significant odor and can yellow over time. Most experts agree that oil-based paints are best suited for the doors and trim, and latex paint for the walls and ceilings.

Lead Paint Hazards

The presence of lead paint presents health hazards in many homes. The federal government banned the use of lead paints in 1978. Therefore, if you live in an older home or apartment building, it may contain a layer of lead paint if it was painted prior to that year. When sanding is done in advance of painting, the sanding may cause lead dust to enter the air in your home. Your contractor should provide you with a pamphlet that discusses lead issues in your home. Ask your contractor what measures he takes to ensure that lead particles are eliminated. If you need to have your home inspected or have lead removed, the Environmental Protection Agency (www.epa.gov) issues licenses for companies and professionals who work with lead control, including removal, inspection and risk assessment. Other good resources for more information about lead and asbestos include the American Lung Association (www.lungusa.org), the US Consumer Product Safety Commission (www.cpsc.gov), the American Industrial Hygiene Association (www.aiha.org), the Department of Housing and Urban Development (www.hud.gov) and the Occupational Safety and Health Administration (www.osha.gov).

WALLPAPER

Wallpaper can add depth, texture and visual interest to a room. Floral or striped wallpaper can make even small windowless rooms cheerful. It can also be a costly investment, so it is important to find a qualified, competent professional to install your paper. Finding a wallpaper hanger can be as easy as talking to your paint contractor, as most also provide this service. Depending upon the complexity of the job, it may be appropriate to contact a professional who specializes in wallpaper hanging. One source is the National Guild of Professional Paperhangers (NGPP). For their local chapter local, call (310) 822 - 2287 or visit www.ngpp.org.

Cost for wallpapering is based on a per roll basis with rates averaging about $50 per roll. Most wallpaper is sold in double-roll units, which measure approximately 60 square feet. The price quoted should include trimming the sides of the paper if necessary. Professionals will strip your walls of existing paper and prep it for the new paper for an additional fee. Your wallpaper hanger should calculate the quantity of paper you will need for the room based on the room size as well as the "repeat" pattern on your paper. The larger the repeat, the more paper you will need. The newer vinyl wallpaper comes pre-pasted, while traditional and costlier papers need to be trimmed and pasted with wheat paste.

DECORATIVE FINISHES: THE ART OF IMITATION

Decorative finishes, often called "faux finishes," are used by painters to add depth or to imitate materials such as marble, wood, paper, stone, metal and fabric. These finishes can be elegant, whimsical or dramatic, depending upon the artist and the paint technique utilized. Current trends today include fake wood ("faux bois") paneled libraries, limestone façades and "washed" finishes. When done by a gifted artist, a faux finish can cost more than the material being imitated. Decorative finishes can customize a space with color and texture and dramatically reflect the owner's style.

DECORATIVE PAINTING: A MASTER TRADITION

A wall-sized mural that re-creates a Pompeian gallery . . . majestic Greek columns beside the swimming pool . . . famous storybook characters dancing along the walls of a child's room . . . these enchanting effects are the work of decorative painters.

Decorative painting is an art form that uses techniques that have been passed down by artisans throughout the centuries. Today, decorative painters can come from a variety of backgrounds—some have fine art degrees, many have studied the techniques of the Old Masters in Europe and others have been schooled specifically in decorative painting. These professionals carry forward the legacy of a tradition that was once passed from master to apprentice. Both artists and craftsmen, many decorative painters have a thorough knowledge of specific historical and decorative styles and have the ability to translate this knowledge in a historically accurate artistic rendering. Others, however, are clearly unqualified to be attempting this work.

There are many forms of decorative painting. Some of the most popular include fresco, murals and trompe l'oeil. Over time, techniques and materials have been enhanced and improved, allowing artists and artisans to produce works that have lasted—and will last—for centuries.

When you are considering any decorative painting style, ask to see a portfolio of the artist's work and, if possible, visit a home that has work of a similar nature. Decorative showhouses are also an excellent venue in which to witness the artistry of decorative painting. Many decorative painters use these showcases to demonstrate their talents. If working with an interior designer, consult with him or her on the project and how it will enhance your overall room design. If the designer finds the artist for you, ask how that affects fees. Artists should also provide you with renderings of the work to be produced.

Fees vary widely for decorative painting and are based on many factors, including the scope and scale of the project, degree of difficulty and expertise of the painter. Ask your contractor to provide you with a sample board of the paint technique you desire. Some charge for this service while others include it in the total cost of the project. Decorative finishes can be charged on a per person or on a per day basis, and sometimes a square foot basis, but are usually priced per job.

Decorative painting can be a major investment, but certainly one with exquisite results.

Paint-Choosing Tips

✧ Use oil-based paint for metals and trim; latex for wood and drywall.

✧ High-traffic areas need a durable, easy-to-clean paint job. Use delicate paint applications in light-traffic areas only.

✧ Use flat paint for base coats; gloss to set off trim and doors.

✧ Be alert to the number of coats required. Eggshell paints, for example, take at least one extra coat.

	Quality	Cost	Value	Recommend?
	✚	$	◆	★

PAINTERS & WALLPAPERERS

💼 FIRMS WITH PORTFOLIOS 💼

A Trompe L'oeil 💼   4.5   3.5   5   4.5
255 Huguenot Street, New Rochelle, NY 10801
(646) 785 - 3587   www.atrompeloeil.com

Decorative painting, murals and Italian plaster

Fresh on the American scene (but certainly no stranger to the faux finish world) is Patrick Bancel, a low-key, understated and modest artisan whom clients describe as "a master." Originally from France, Bancel studied and worked alongside icons of the decorative painting world for eighteen years before bringing his company, A Trompe L'oeil, to the United States. Bancel's natural ability has been refined by practical experience like a fine wine, and patrons toast him all over the world. A true artist, Bancel has also put his brush to fine art canvases, some of which hang in galleries across Europe and the U.S.

Bancel studied the Dutch masters and honed his Old-World technique working as assistant director of the famed Van Der Kelen Institute of Painting in Brussels. Today, he works for himself, taking on projects in and around New York and Los Angeles in every imaginable decorative discipline: faux finishes, trompe l'oeil, paintings on canvas, aging, glazing, murals, gold leaf and on and on. Bancel is said to possess the kind of dedication to his craft that is rare in this country, and clients say they are "thrilled" to have found him. The excellent prices seem very reasonable for these works of art.

"His knowledge of Old-World techniques is not often seen anymore. It is a breath of fresh air to see this dedication." "Patrick not only has the pure talent needed for top projects, but his personality and demeanor make you want to work with him again and again." "A real can-do attitude." "Clearly a master at his craft, with great vision and superior skill. He is a pleasure to work with." "My living room has been transformed and enriched beyond my highest expectations." "Patrick is extremely likable, modest and reliable. A real find."

Academi Decorative Art & Design 💼   4.5   4   4.5   4.5
402 Robertson Boulevard, Suite 5, Los Angeles, CA 90048
(310) 368 - 0473

Lifelike decorative painting and design

"Authentic" is the word that best describes the hand-painted work of Academi Decorative Art & Design. Purist Yari Horilczenko can transform an ordinary column into a convincing piece of old marble; or he may paint a hand-finished vaulted ceiling to truly resemble the sky. Sources say a talent for mixing his own paints supports Horilczenko's creativity and marvelous eye. The environmentally conscious Horilczenko is known to use Old-World recipes and techniques. Sources say his lime wash and fresco paints are made with natural earth-ground pigments that give the finished product "a genuine vibrancy" not possible with synthetics.

Prior to transforming homes in LA's celebrated communities, Horilczenko was a skilled artisan working in Australia, and clients around the world rave about this multitalented artist. Often Horilczenko starts with a paintwork job and ends up serving as a consultant on the entire room. Collaborating with some of the best decorators and designers in the business, Horilczenko has adapted ancient and historic methods to the conditions of modern-day interiors and exteriors, creating gorgeous ancient-looking frescoes on some very new walls. Clients say Horilczenko's knack for infusing each project with a unique character justifies the expense.

"Talented, fun to work with and most importantly—innovative." "I am never disappointed." "Yari is wonderful—a brilliant artist with creative vision." "Incredible color sense."

Alan Silverstein Painting   4.5   4   4.5   5

264 South La Cienega Boulevard, Suite 557, Beverly Hills, CA 90211
(310) 470 - 9218   alanthepainter@aol.com

Straight and decorative painting

Alan Silverstein isn't called the "guru" of straight and decorative painting for nothing: He can match a color in five minutes, a talent that's gotten many a decorator out of a bind. With his handpicked crew in tow, Silverstein is up to any challenge, offering an impressive list of services, including glazing, staining, faux finishing, straight interior and exterior painting, and Venetian plaster. After 21 years in the business, Silverstein can take clients' "sketchy" ideas and translate them into a beautiful finished product. He is known to go the extra mile, using an additional coat of paint to give a "luxurious" enamel look or sensing when a color "just isn't quite right" and re-doing it.

The firm is said to be professional, efficient and extremely ethical. Sources say Silverstein believes in building a relationship with a client that will last for many years, not just long enough for the paint to dry. We hear that he returns calls the same day and personally oversees each job. Silverstein also keeps up on the latest paints and techniques, including environmentally friendly products and some European imports. Both decorators and homeowners praise this firm for fair business practices and lovely work, a combination that keeps them coming back year after year. Though prices are described as high, clients say the quality of work combined with the "lower than normal" disturbance and mess is well worth it.

"The attention to detail is amazing." "Alan is just wonderful." "I use Silverstein Painting for everything. They are fabulous." "Crews are neat, professional and talented." "We are so happy with his services. He painted and supervised two huge duplexes. Alan came up with the colors and—va voom! We had new houses."

Associated Painting Co. Inc.   4   3   5   4

2531 Page Drive, Altadena, CA 91001
(626) 794 - 4777   jrieder@pacbell.net

Straight and decorative painting

High-profile clients, contractors and decorators associate this firm with truly professional, reliable and talented painting. Headed by owner Jim Rieder, Associated Painting Co. handles jobs ranging from straight painting projects to more intricate decorative work such as specialty finishes, glazes and furniture-quality cabinet finishes.

Rieder started painting during college to earn some extra cash. Nineteen years later his seasoned company boasts a team of 45, who are described as "so neat they could paint in suits." Though Associated focuses its efforts on multimillion dollar new construction houses, we're told they keep prices down.

"I just tell them what I need, and they are off and running." "Prices are competitive, and the work is very good." "Jim and his crew are professional, meticulous and talented."

	Quality +	Cost $	Value ◆	Recommend? ★

Barr Haus Painting Inc.
22616 Califa Street, Woodland Hills, CA 91367
(818) 703 - 8922   barrhauspainting@hotmail.com

Quality **4.5** Cost **3.5** Value **5** Recommend **4.5**

Straight and decorative painting

Working in some of the most prestigious neighborhoods from Malibu to Beverly Hills, Barr Haus Painting has been beautifying the walls of celebrity clients for twenty years. Often working through top decorators, the company has a stellar reputation for organization, professionalism, mobility and getting the job done "no matter what." Owner Scott Barr has been described as extremely flexible, and is often able to accommodate new jobs at a moment's notice.

In addition to straight painting, the firm does all its own prep work and has a crew that handles special finishes. No job is too big for this staff of twenty—in fact, sometimes it seems like a 20,000 square foot home is just par for the course. Barr is reputed to take pride in the fact that he is willing to "go above and beyond," taking on small jobs with no minimums to help a decorator or homeowner "in a pinch." Time frames for projects depend on the size of home and the number of special finishes. Costs are considered very reasonable for the quality work.

"One of the top firms. They can do straight painting all the way to faux finishes and Venetian plaster." "The service is well worth the expense." "Scott knows his colors and his custom mixing is amazing." "Very detail-oriented and professional."

Brandon Banaga & Associates
1831 Tapo Street, Simi Valley, CA 93063
(805) 527 - 9715   banagapainting@sbcglobal.net

Quality **4** Cost **3.5** Value **4.5** Recommend **4.5**

Straight and decorative painting, faux and antique finishes

We're told this fast-lane firm gets plenty of LA traffic from architects, decorators and the recommendations of happy clients. Brandon Banaga & Associates is said to do "whatever it takes" to get the job done flawlessly. Owner Brandon Banaga is known in the industry for being accommodating and extremely easy to work with. Moreover, many say, he is meticulous when it comes to color coordination.

In business for more than eleven years, we hear Banaga's crew of nine does one of the best straight paint jobs around. But Banaga is also experienced in fancier types of brushwork, including strié, glazing, marbleizing, wood graining and Venetian plaster, which is typically handled by Banaga himself. The good prices have clients flocking to this frequently recommended firm.

"Brandon and his crew are wonderful. Nothing is ever a problem." "I constantly recommend them to friends and colleagues." "They bend over backwards to make sure you are happy."

Chameleon Paintworks
2506 28th Street, Santa Monica, CA 90405
(310) 453 - 4444   www.paintworks.us

Quality **4.5** Cost **4** Value **4.5** Recommend **4.5**

Color consulting and project planning; decorative/straight painting and murals

We hear this firm "adapts like a chameleon" to any painting situation, making it a favorite for grand Hollywood homes. The team at Chameleon Paintworks prides itself on turning clients' wishes into reality through the creative use of surfaces, textures and colors. Owner Joe Nicoletti focuses primarily on design-oriented residential projects, but has also completed high-profile commissions for The Biltmore Hotel and the 2002 MTV and Grammy Awards. Clients applauded Nicoletti's exceptional ability to personalize a customer's home or business.

Trained at New York City's School of Visual Arts and the Fashion Institute of Technology, Nicoletti is praised for his acute visual design sensibility. He is said to have all the tools at his disposal, including straight, decorative and architectural painting, wood finishes, color systems and restoration of architecturally significant homes. We're told that Nicoletti is always looking for a fresh challenge. His new shop in LA will offer in-house interior design and landscape architecture services, along with a full menu of painting options.

Nicoletti prefers to oversee a job from start to finish, including all prep work. Personal attention from the principal comes at a premium, but ultimately clients feel they save money by having Chameleon do the job the right way the first time.

"Chameleon brings a very creative approach to personalizing our space." "They transformed kitchen cabinets, furniture, coffered ceilings, murals, wall finishes— one stop." "Joe has the ability to know what I want and just does it—no stress, no problems." "Really a great company. Joe is talented and really fun."

Charles McLaughlin Marbler-Grainer   5 4 5 5
PO Box 3771, Westlake Village, CA 91359
(805) 529 - 3993 chamcl1@adelphia.net
Artisanal decorative painting, faux finishes, marbling, wood graining

The son of a master painter, Charles McLaughlin is said to have "paint in his blood." References rave about this "major talent" who is "so generous with his time and knowledge. Insiders praise his expressive execution of a wide range of media—Venetian plaster, marbleizing, wood graining, antiquing, gilding and water gilding, among others. Many remark McLaughlin's work style is easygoing and flexible, reflecting the fact that he "genuinely loves what he does."

McLaughlin has been in business in LA for sixteen years. After apprenticing with his father, he studied under another master artisan who introduced him to decorative painting. In addition to focusing on the steady flow of work from prominent LA decorators, he continues his art education, keeping up with the latest trends and techniques in decorative painting. Describing him as expensive, customers say his quality, skill and end results are worth every cent.

"Charles is a superb craftsman and his sense of color sets him apart from others." "His aspiration for perfection is unequaled." "He has transformed a mere house into our home and castle." "One of the best faux finishers I know." "Very easy to work with, always on time and on budget, end product is superb." "Charles is truly second to none in his quality of work, knowledge of the trade, work ethic and personal friendliness." "He aims to please and hits the mark every time."

Color Your World   3.5 2.5 5 4
14720 Valerio Street, Los Angeles, CA 91405
(818) 766 - 5411 www.webuildyourworld.com
Straight and decorative painting

Former set designer and scenic painter Sam Khoram left the movie business by a side door when he started creating murals for the homes of entertainment industry clients in 1989. These days, through his firm Color Your World, Khoram offers murals, faux finishes, Venetian plaster, mosaic tile—and just about any other decorative technique that can be done to a wall, floor or ceiling. His glazing work in particular is described as "really lovely."

Khoram's firm of 25 does everything from basic straight painting jobs to intricate and detailed murals. A second, related Khoram company, We Build Your World, will build and remodel small kitchens and bathrooms. Khoram works on each and every project himself and is said to go above and beyond to get the job done perfectly. Given the level of personalized service and the quality of the work, the moderate rates are considered a bargain.

"Stands by work and returned for touch ups and corrections. Good experience!" *"Completes projects on time."* *"I've hired Sam to carry out many projects for my clients' multimillion-dollar homes and my own personal investment properties. Sam is professional and works well with my clients and staff."*

Daugherty's Painting & Decorating Inc. 4 4 4 4.5
PO Box 522, Malibu, CA 90265
(310) 457 - 8247   www.daughertyspainting.com
Straight and decorative painting

This straight and decorative painting firm is so well-liked that homeowners tell us they are actually sad to see the crew leave. Reputed to be "willing to do anything to make the client happy," Daugherty's Painting & Decorating takes on large and small jobs that range from traditional to exotic. With seventeen years in the business, owner Steve Daugherty has generated a long list of repeat customers, whose good word of mouth keeps the company busy up and down the coast of Southern California.

A real-life Tom Sawyer, Daugherty got his start painting a neighbor's fence at the age of ten. For his second job, he painted his teacher's entire house. These days Daugherty works with some of LA's biggest building contractors and most exclusive decorators. Already masters of straight painting, we hear these workmen are rapidly becoming experts at Venetian plaster. Rates are a little higher but are equal to the higher work quality and clients agree that when you hire this firm, you're getting a crew of professionals who take great pride in their work.

"Steve is great to work with. He always has a great attitude and that filters down to the outstanding crew." *"I love working with them."* *"Simply excellent."*

Erick A. Bloom ▪ 4.5 4 4.5 4.5
12572 Charloma Drive, Tustin, CA 92780
(714) 731 - 1795
Expert installation of wallpaper, fabric and murals

Erick A. Bloom is known as one of the only craftsmen in Los Angeles who can properly hang Zuber wallpaper. Maybe it's the 35 years of experience, or maybe it's the training (Bloom apprenticed under a German paperhanger for several years). Either way, we hear Bloom's work is virtuoso quality. He can expertly hang a priceless mural, and do just as impeccable a job when installing fabric, leather or wallpaper on walls. No wonder clients return to Bloom's firm year after year.

Along with his small staff, Bloom works up and down the West Coast on all kinds of installations, and customers report there is nothing he cannot hang. Sought out by dozens of decorators, often returning to do more than one project for the same designer, Bloom has a thriving referral business. More than one source describes his custom wallpaper jobs as "works of art." For this kind of expertise, those in the know are willing to pay Bloom's high end prices.

"The only man I allow to touch my Zuber." *"So efficient, doesn't rush a job, but certainly does not drag it out."* *"Bloom is expensive, but so is my wallpaper."* *"When I give Erick a project, I can relax and know he will handle it the right way."* *"I trust only him with my valuable and delicate work."*

	Quality	Cost	Value	Recommend?
	+	$	◆	★

Jacqueline Moore Designs

4.5   4   4.5   4.5

1618 Stanford Street, Suite E, Santa Monica, CA 90404
(310) 453 - 9421   www.jacquelinemoore.com

Exquisite period reproduction; hand-painted furniture

Decorators tell us they rush to Jacqueline Moore's shop with their furniture finds, eager to have Moore work her magic on their antique treasures. A specialty hand painter and finisher, Moore can authentically recreate the look of weathered French Provençal or hand-painted chinoiserie. Her faux bois finish and raised gold leaf thrill even the most jaded decorator. She is especially renowned for antique patterns delicately crafted onto furniture, fireplaces, built-in bookcases and woodwork. And we're told her work with Asian scenic painting is nothing short of brilliant.

Born in the UK, Moore graduated with an art history degree from Sheffield College of Art and Design in South Yorkshire. Fifteen years ago, feeling drawn to the Los Angeles lifestyle, she packed her bags and took a chance on the New World. While working as a nanny for a family who owned a furniture company, she landed her first commission—and the rest, as they say, is history. After stints at several other firms, Moore ventured out on her own in the early 1990s. A jaw-dropping list of clients from her first decade includes Hollywood royalty and some of the most extraordinary five-star hotels in the world. *Architectural Digest* and *Art & Antiques* have come calling, too.

Today, assisted by a small staff, Moore painstakingly paints Japanese fishing villages onto Asian lacquer armoires. Her dainty brush can produce a perfect English floral bouquet or Venetian scene—whatever the antique suggests to her. A smaller percentage of Moore's business is concentrated in the reproduction and building of exceptional antique period furniture. Slightly above-average costs are considered a tremendous value, especially since Moore can recreate a bygone era within the timeframe demanded by a twenty-first century patron of the arts.

"Jackie is a true artist, able to create beautiful finishes on almost every piece of furniture." "Her work summons an era no longer with us." "Finishes are absolutely beautiful." "So wonderful to work with."

Jimenez Custom Painting Inc.

5   3.5   5   5

5937 Lemona Avenue, Van Nuys, CA 91411
(818) 908 - 9937   info@jimenezcustompaintinginc.com

Expert straight and decorative painting

"Talent times five"—that's how sources describe Jimenez Custom Painting Inc. The Jimenez brothers—Jorge, Ricky, Carlos, Javier and Jerry—personally run and oversee every project. Known for its highly responsible and meticulous work ethic, this company works with decorators and builders to create "beautiful" painted walls, cabinet finishes and decorative painting projects.

The boys learned the business from their dad before banding together to form the company twelve years ago. Sources say whether your job is small or large, the Jimenez brothers and their staff of sixteen not only have some serious skills, but are polite, friendly and wonderful to work with. Antique wood finishing, marbleizing, wood graining, gold leafing and Venetian plaster are all well within their capable reach. Several clients report that they use Jimenez Custom Painting year after year to maintain their homes, and often recommend them to friends and family. With competitive pricing and extraordinary quality, customers rate this firm a five-star value.

"Not only is their work top quality, but they keep the work area clean and really care about your satisfaction with the results." "These guys have a great attitude— they are team players who work well with my other sub-contractors." "Very meticulous work, but not to the point of being compulsive and over-priced." "Fantastic

decorative finishes—their staining and faux work is beautiful." "They finished my kitchen cabinets so beautifully that the kitchen is now my favorite room in the house." "The best I've ever seen."

LSI/Evan Wilson    4   3.5   4.5   5

2702 Stevens Street, La Crescenta, CA 91214
(818) 957 - 7785   evan@lsi-art.com

Murals, fine art and ornamental painting; historical restorations

When he's not traveling the globe to work on historic building restorations, Evan Wilson can be found closer to home, transforming "generic" Los Angeles mansions into reflections of their owners' personalities. Wilson often works with decorators, architects and general contractors, and he can handle a wide array of requests. His talents range from historic restoration to ornamental, decorative and trompe l'oeil painting. Wilson also does fine art landscapes and portraits. His high-profile clients say his relaxed manner belies his exquisitely detailed work.

In business for seventeen years, Wilson is already a major figure in his field. On any given day, it's not uncommon for him to be at work on a 40,000 square foot mansion painting murals and gold leafing. Though it's difficult to put a price on art, sources say that having Wilson's work gracing their walls is well worth it considering the very good prices.

"We count on him consistently." "A real gentleman." "Evan Wilson is truly amazing—consider yourself lucky if his work is in your home." "His trompe l'oeil is breathtaking."

Miguelangelo & Company    4.5   3.5   5   4.5

56 Watkins Way, Oak View, CA 93022
(805) 649 - 8025   www.miguelangeloandco.com

Decorative painting, Venetian plaster and murals

It may not be at the level of the Sistine Chapel, but the work is awfully good, say fans of Miguelangelo & Company. This young firm has impressed decorators and homeowners alike in the five years it has been operating in Los Angeles. Insiders say owners Miguel Leon and Greg Lee know their Venetian plaster and murals. Clients also trust Miguelangelo & Company to do all types of decorative painting, including complicated faux stonework and "European-aged walls," which require a three-color, hand-rubbed finish and iridescent wash over Venetian plaster.

The firm's two principals bring very different experiences and backgrounds to their partnership. Leon is the artist of the pair, having worked with other LA painting firms for twenty years before going out on his own. We're told he wields his brush with talent and finesse. Lee takes care of the business end of things, drawing on his producing, directing, acting and set design experience. We hear the principals and their staff of ten artists are a "pure joy" to work with. Clients say the team is talented, professional and run by "two of the nicest guys." And you don't have to be a prince or a pope to be able to afford Miguelangelo—their excellent rates strike customers as "more than fair."

"Very talented." "These guys really know what they are doing." "So clean and tidy." "From the second you meet them, they are a pleasure to have around."

	Quality	Cost	Value	Recommend?
	✚	$	◆	★

"This is a really special company." "Integrity, skill and personality plus." "The quote was accurate and the work was excellent and fast." "They kept us informed through the entire process by showing us examples of the stages of the project."

Paulin Paris 🛍️   5   4.5   4.5   5

503 Venice Way, Venice, CA 90291
(310) 569 - 8640   www.paulin-paris.com

Superb high-end decorative painting, sculptures and murals

The spectacular creations of Paulin Paris grace the fashion houses of Dior and Valentino, the Zuber fabric and wallpaper studio, and elite homes around the world. Trained at the Ecole des Beaux Arts, this master takes his inspiration from the gilded past—but creates murals, paintings and sculptures that exude modern allure. But lest you think of Paris as an "artiste," please note that references applaud his willingness to tailor his vision to the client's desires. In fact, insiders roundly praise Paris's ability to approach a project as an artist, but also work alongside the architect and designer.

For over sixteen years, Paris has traveled from his native France to exclusive homes around the globe. He divides his time between studios in New York, Paris and Los Angeles, where he works on murals, paintings and sculptures, and handles five to six big projects per year. An average project takes roughly two months and a hefty investment, but no one's complaining. In fact, Paris's fellow artists at the most elite levels of fashion design are clamoring for his time—a sure indicator of the brilliance of his work.

"I have never seen such beautiful work!" "If you can afford him, you will spend the rest of your life admiring his work." "Paris is extraordinarily talented, and a wonderful person as well."

Real Illusions 🛍️   4   3.5   4.5   4.5

1104 Palms Boulevard, Venice, CA 90291
(310) 452 - 0237   www.realillusionsinc.com

Custom painting, plastering and gilding for walls and fixtures

LA's industry leader in custom hand-applied architectural surface finishes in Venetian plaster and paint is Real Illusions. With seventeen years under its belt, this popular firm boasts a client list that resembles a "who's who" of the architecture and design world. Real Illusions produces almost every kind of decorative work, including faux finishes, murals, gilding, patinas and Venetian plaster. You won't find any sponges or rags at Real Illusions. But the company's innovative techniques, though secret, produce beautiful results. Clients tell us the firm's skill at making the new look old "rivals time itself."

Real Illusion's "skilled and personable" owner, Jo Lesoine, brings a wealth of knowledge to her small firm. Schooled in Europe, Lesoine worked under master artisans before opening her own company. Trade professionals praise her lending library full of hundreds of samples and recipes. Assisting Lesoine with the business and marketing side of things is the capable Darren Franks, director of operations, a former consultant to major corporations. Insiders say this team has the talent and skill to bring ideas to fruition, whether the job is a feature wall in a commercial building or a detailed project in a mansion in the Hollywood Hills.

"They always deliver a fabulous end product with little or no problem." "My clients are always thrilled with their work." "So professional and fun to work with." "Real Illusions makes me, the designer, look like a winner." "In the expensive range, but so worth it." "Creative, organized and great to have in your home." "Lesoine runs a great business." "Imagination along with a good work ethic and very professional."

	Quality	Cost	Value	Recommend?
	✚	$	◆	★

Richard Davis Fine Decorative Painting   4   4   4   4

5421 West Pico Boulevard, Los Angeles, CA 90019
(323) 934 - 6877 www.richarddavisstudio.com

Architectural decorative painting, stenciling and trompe l'oeil

Extremely well known by decorators and architects, Richard Davis is sought after for his years of experience and "fluency" in many genres, including stenciling, wood graining, faux bois and glazing. Sources say Davis excels in an "historical" setting and is brilliant at recreating period styles. His extraordinary trompe l'oeil is said to be done with a degree of excellence that "sets him apart from the crowd."

Davis has been in the business of beautifying spaces since 1983. Trained at New York's School of Visual Arts, Davis worked in galleries, apprenticed for a frame restorer and was mentored by a theatrical painter before going out on his own in Los Angeles. His firm is small, allowing for highly focused, personalized attention. Clients report they can count on Davis from the "consultation" and project development phase all the way through to the final product. They appreciate his willingness to collaborate and his expertise and skill as a craftsman. Costs are typically calculated by the project and are reasonable.

"Richard is a true artist." "His experience is endless. He can do anything, and do it well." "He is able to create subtle and striking wall finishes—he even trompe l'oeil'd a floor—with an expert's sense of color and scale."

Sydney Harbour Paint Company   4   3.5   4.5   4.5

801 Mateo Street, Los Angeles, CA 90021
(213) 228 - 8440 www.sydneyharbourpaints.com

Color consultation and imported paints

"Color guru" Michael Khan, the new owner of Sydney Harbour Paints, has generated quite a buzz among LA's elite architects, interior designers and painters for his custom paints. Khan's boutique shop stocks high-end architectural finished paints, such as French wash, lime wash, distemper wash, wood washes, concrete washes, fresco and acrylics—all water based and all environmentally friendly. Insiders say they appreciate both the breadth and the beauty of Khan's admittedly expensive inventory.

Khan's interest in Old-World paints began during his tenure as a master builder, restoring historical government buildings in his homeland of Australia. Two years ago he jumped at the opportunity to purchase Sydney Harbour Paint Company. Classes are regularly held at the shop to educate the trade as well as the public about paint. Five knowledgeable employees are on staff to assist a vast clientele, but don't wait till the last minute to make your selection—we hear the shop is so popular they can't keep the shelves stocked.

"Michael is supplying a great service." "Always helpful and knows paints." "The shop's selection is primo but they run out quickly."

Wallpaper City    3.5   3   4.5   4.5

1758 Lincoln Boulevard, Santa Monica, CA 90404
(310) 450 - 9946 www.wallpapercity.com

Wallpaper installation, straight and decorative painting, flooring, kitchen/bath design and installation, and upholstery

The gates of Wallpaper City open to reveal a company as diverse as the city it serves. In business for over 36 years, the firm is known for its expertise in straight and decorative painting, wallpaper installation and flooring, but it's also developing a following for its kitchen and bath design/installation—as well as for its upholstery. No wonder some liken Wallpaper City to a boutique Home Depot.

298

	Quality	Cost	Value	Recommend?
	+	$	◆	★

Often called upon to work for decorators and designers in LA, owner Mike Maman and his team of twenty, some of whom have been with Maman for 30 years, are said to be knowledgeable and professional. The company boasts a 7,000 square foot "do-it-all" showroom where clients can browse through 3,000 wallpaper catalogs, get ideas for the planning and execution of their kitchen and bathroom project or select the perfect flooring or upholstery. The excellent staff is on hand to shepherd clients through the experience. Although the company offers a plethora of services, clients report that they are happy in whichever "department" they end up in. Prices are low for the upscale market.

"Mike's willingness to go the extra mile to ensure the quality of his work is uncommon in the industry." "Mike has consistently proven himself to be reliable." "I have come to rely on Wallpaper City for all my wallpaper needs."

FIRMS WITHOUT PORTFOLIOS

Andrew Gray Finishing & Decorative Painting   4   3   5   4
4648 Hollywood Boulevard, Los Angeles, CA 90027
(323) 667 - 0696   www.andrewgrayshowroom.com
Finishing specialist; decorative painting

Homeowners often call Andrew Gray long after the builder is gone to thank him for his choice finishes for cabinets and walls—they're that good. Gray undertakes custom staining and lacquer work, gold or silver leafing projects, as well as Venetian plaster. Clients appreciate his ability to take them through the design process, from sample boards to completion, and appreciate his excellent prices.

Born in the UK, where he trained in antique conservation and restoration, Gray officially opened Andrew Gray Finishing & Decorative Painting in LA twelve years ago. Admirers tell us that his creative gifts and his love of fine furniture are prominently displayed in his showroom, which features a few special lines of furniture and his own handmade pieces.

"Andrew really knows how to get it right." "Such a wonderful craftsman." "Andrew's work has made my home complete. My cabinets are spectacular."

Artistic Designs/Wayne Shaw   4.5   4   4.5   4.5
PO Box 1362, Solvang, CA 93464
(805) 896 - 9799
Decorative painting and finishing

Self-taught artist Wayne Shaw provides a full range of decorative painting services to some of the most prominent interior designers in Southern California. Sources tell us that Shaw is that rarest of left-brain/right-brain combos, described as both "extremely talented and creative" and "very business-like." Shaw keeps the process organized, preparing detailed plans, updating clients on progress and billing steadily to avoid surprises at the end. No wonder he has a following of happy customers who come back again and again.

A small company based near Santa Barbara, Artistic Designs frequently dispatches one of its two crews to Los Angeles. Shaw and his team handle projects that run the gamut: from lime washes, cabinet finishes and Venetian plaster to more unusual jobs, such as metal and rust finishes. Clients compliment Shaw on his expertise and love of color. The firm's prices are competitive given the high quality work and it is said they put "110 percent into each project" and "never cut corners."

"Wayne Shaw and his people did an outstanding job on our home." "So organized—he had every detail covered." "Shaw does fantastic work." "Creative,

professional and great to have working in your home." "His ideas never seem to stop flowing."

Bill Jackson   4.5   4   4.5   4.5
3510 South Barrington Avenue, Los Angeles, CA 90066
(310) 397 - 1708
Straight and decorative painting and finishing

You won't find Bill Jackson in the yellow pages. He doesn't need to be, since he's swamped with referrals. We're told Jackson and his team can handle any painting challenge. From straight painting to decorative effects and full finish, Jackson's work is routinely described as "gorgeous." We hear that this easygoing principal is a dedicated, hardworking professional with over 45 years' experience.

Jackson puts all that experience to work in some of LA's high-profile residences and commercial locations, tending to every job personally. Admirers say that when you turn over your home to Jackson, you're certain to receive the absolute best care. Clients appreciate his diligence and professionalism, and several say they refuse to go elsewhere. Those lucky enough to have discovered Jackson (usually through the best interior designers) say the work of this small and highly personalized company is well worth the expense.

"More than I wanted to pay, but fabulous." "Bill is really great. He is talented, easy to work with and very, very experienced."

Brian Collier Painting   4.5   4.5   4   4.5
2733 Cardwell Place, Los Angeles, CA 90046
(323) 650 - 6638   bmcpainting@adelphia.net
Straight painting and staining

Brian Collier Painting specializes in superior residential straight painting and staining. Known in the industry for its thorough prep work, the firm is praised for its very fine painting. In addition to straight painting, the company can also be counted on to do superb staining work on cabinets, doors, etc. Fans also applaud Collier Painting's expertise in painting large homes.

Collier painted his way though high school and college and firmly committed to the trade over twenty years ago by opening his own firm. Today, he and his crew of 28 work primarily through general contractors, and we're told they've generated quite a healthy "word-of-mouth" client list—despite prices in the "very expensive" range.

"Brian and his crew do very lovely work." "They cost a fortune, but if you want a truly great paint job, they are the ones to call." "Best around. He is fantastic." "Tidy and clean."

C.W. Isley Painting   3.5   2.5   5   4
11184 Orville Street, Culver City, CA 90230
(310) 391 - 3067
Straight painting

Sometimes, all you need is a good, old-fashioned paint job. Whether you're putting a house on the market or moving into a new home, sources say this established firm does a terrific job with the basics. Specializing in straight painting, the crew at C.W. Isley Painting comes highly recommended by architects, builders and real estate agents. We're told the firm enjoys a healthy amount of repeat and referral business.

With 22 years in business, owner Chris Isley is clearly doing a lot of things right, but prospective clients should note that his firm's territory is limited to the west side of LA. In addition to its "super" paint jobs, the Isley team is reported to help out with such tasks as installing baseboards. Clients recommend Isley for top-notch straight painting and friendly service at extremely fair prices.

"These guys are really great. Professional, clean and get the job done on time." *"Not just painters, they helped me with some odds and ends that needed to be taken care of." "You can send him into any house and he is so respectful." "Good value for the money."*

Condimenti Inc.   4.5   3.5   5   4.5
200 South Canyon View Drive, Los Angeles, CA 90049
(310) 576 - 0460

Frescoes, murals, decorative painting

Renaissance to neoclassical, Gothic to Art Nouveau, the European-inspired work of Condimenti Inc. thrills many a hard-to-please client. Insiders praise owner Claudio Sgaravizzi for his astonishing ability to paint in any style the client wishes. Sgaravizzi will even go beyond the artwork on request, taking on faux finishing projects and often lending advice on all aspects of interior design.

A former student of graphic and industrial design and architecture at an art institute in Italy, Sgaravizzi worked in his native land for fifteen years as a graphic artist and art restorer. In 1999, Sgaravizzi made the leap to LA, where he now specializes in classical-style murals and frescoes. While his work is "simply amazing," clients tell us that Sgaravizzi is a delight to work with and a pleasure to have around. The very reasonable prices are described enthusiastically by loyal customers all over LA as "definitely not New York."

"The trompe l'oeil is simply the best." "Claudio has the ability to work in difficult conditions and does a great job while maintaining the most positive attitude." "The work Claudio did for us has become the soul of the house." "He is not only a true master and an artist at his craft, but he is very businesslike. We are pleased with the way he contracts for the work, his thoughtful proposals, his regular billing and the fact that the work is completed on schedule and on budget." "Claudio's painting is fabulous. It is admired by everyone who sees our home."

Demar Feldman Studios   4   3.5   4.5   4.5
241 South Norton Avenue, Los Angeles, CA 90004
(323) 938 - 5826   dfs241@pacbell.net

Faux finishes, trompe l'oeil, decorative art and murals

Anyone who has dined at Spago, visited the Walker Zanger Showroom, or gone people watching at the trendy nightspot Barfly has experienced the stunning decorative work of Demar Feldman Studios. Sources say these magicians can make a brand new home look 100 years old or create a stunning work of trompe l'oeil. Whether you want faux finishing, gilding or wood graining, we hear Demar Feldman has the right people for the job—and over twenty years of experience in LA.

Owner Mimi Feldman's creations are in great demand among Hollywood's A-list celebrities. Demar Feldman Studios is a licensed contractor and carries the required insurance to work in the most fabulous private homes and public spaces. But sources tell us that even "regular" people can take advantage of the "creative

	Quality	Cost	Value	Recommend?
	✚	$	◆	★

wizardry" this diverse company has to offer. Two principals and a staff of ten take care of most projects, but Feldman can "crew up" for large projects, putting together a team of "some of the best talent" around.

We hear that Feldman, who holds a master's degree in fine art from the Otis Art Institute, is "all business" when it comes to helming this well-run firm. Clients say that Feldman is very realistic and up front about costs, so there are no surprises in the end. Moreover, we hear she hasn't raised prices in a decade. With prices holding steady "near the high end of the middle," sources say the firm's services are affordable to the "moderately rich and famous," too.

"Extremely easy to work with." "Flexible and accommodating when changes are needed." "I have worked with many faux finishers and consider Demar Feldman among the best and most professional." "Mimi is very clear about what the job will cost—and sticks to it." "The job was done on time and extremely beautifully."

Galice Inc.   4   4   4   4
3923 West Jefferson Boulevard, Los Angeles, CA 90016
(323) 731 - 8200   catherine@galiceinc.com
Decorative plaster

Catherine Lutz-Holden's company takes its appellation from the trade name of the plaster product it uses in its creations. Specializing in the installation of decorative plaster, Galice is acclaimed for its fine work with four types of finishes: smooth, metallic, textured and weathered. The firm's decorative panels, fitted with exotic elements, such as mother-of-pearl and emeralds, are highly sought after and have been shipped as far as Bora Bora. Closer to home, Galice's work has appeared in boutique hotels, movie studios, corporate offices and the homes of A-list celebrities.

It comes as no surprise, then, that some of Southern California's best decorators swear by this fifteen-year-old firm's service and product selection. Sources tell us the company's installers must go through rigorous training in Galice's trademarked processes before working in the field. Crews are said to be experienced, and easy to work with, and have reportedly been with Holden from the beginning. Costs, which are calculated by the square foot, fall into the reasonable category.

"Efficient and professional service." "I like the results—so do people who visit my home." "The staff really knows what they are doing. I never had a problem." "Galice transformed the look of my home—we absolutely love it."

Garth Benton   5   4.5   4.5   5
2763 Calle Quebracho, Thousand Oaks, CA 91360
(805) 241 - 7448
Museum-quality murals

Fine art connoisseurs insist that Garth Benton creates the kind of exquisite murals that "should be admired and treasured." Insiders say Benton's "never-ending" skills are made manifest by the diversity of his commissions, which are inspired by everything from first-century Roman frescoes to eighteenth-century Chinese wallpaper to Art Deco and Modern designs.

Benton, who has been described as one of the top five muralists in the world, truly executes museum-quality pieces. He has worked on such notable projects as the 1,000-foot mural in the J. Paul Getty Museum in Malibu, and been published in fine art books. Benton studied art at UCLA and Art Center College of Design after being inspired by the work of his cousin, the late Thomas Hart Benton, a teacher of Jackson Pollock and a well-known artist in his own right.

Benton is renowned for his meticulous research, immersing himself in the history of a civilization before he lifts his brush. Benton often paints his murals

Quality	Cost	Value	Recommend?
✚	$	◆	★

on canvas so they can be transported, a detail clients appreciate—especially when they decide to move. Though sources say they "cannot put a price" on these works of art, they willingly write a very large check. *"Benton's work is breathtaking." "In addition to being one of most talented artists of his time, he is a wonderful person—soulful and real." "I am glad to know that this kind of skilled artist still exists." "Garth transports you to another time with his art."*

Jakeway Finishes   4   3   5   4.5
9171 Bidwell Street, Temple City, CA 91780
(626) 253 - 1255   www.jakewayfinishes.com
Decorative painting, murals on canvas, cabinet finishes

The largely self-taught Jim Jakeway delights both decorators and homeowners, who can't decide what tickles them more—his terrific work or his winning personality. Well-versed in all types of decorative painting, from faux finishing and glazing to inlaid hardwood floors and cabinet work, Jakeway also excels at ornamental painting. Turns out this jack-of-all-trades is a whiz at murals, too, which he puts on canvas so owners can take them when they move. Clients adore his children's murals, which they describe as whimsical, fun and "executed with passion."

Jakeway Finishes has been beautifying the homes of high-end clients in the Los Angeles area for a decade, at what are described as less expensive rates. In addition to his great technical talent, Jakeway is said to be personable and easygoing. A true professional, Jakeway "takes a great deal of pride in every project," and will not rest until he meets his own high standards.

"There is rarely a day that passes that we don't notice and appreciate the exceptional talent he brought to our project." "Jim truly appreciated and understood the importance of what we were trying to accomplish in our home." "Jakeway is passionate concerning the quality and integrity of his trade." "His color sense is extraordinary, and he can create great beauty." "His ceiling work is tremendous."

Jean Horihata Design   4.5   4   4.5   4.5
3329 Cahuenga Boulevard West, Los Angeles, CA 90068
(323) 850 - 3246   jhorihata@yahoo.com
Decorative and furniture painting; stenciling and murals

From trompe l'oeil and glazing to murals and elaborate stenciling, Jean Horihata's genius for transforming wall surfaces has earned her a loyal Angeleno base that includes many Hollywood names. Beyond walls, ceilings and floors, Horihata takes on furniture gilding and distressing projects. Clients often stay with Horihata through many projects, enjoying both the results and the process of working with this "easygoing," "delightful" artisan.

A graduate of the Day Studio Workshop in San Francisco, Horihata has been running her decorative painting company in Los Angeles for over twelve years. Insiders say she has a definite "style of her own" that is subtle and traditional, but with a twist. Recent projects include unusual Pompeii-inspired murals. Prices are above average but expected and some love her work so much that as soon as one project ends, they start saving up for the next.

"She has mastered many techniques." "Her stenciled floors are magnificent." "Jean is remarkably talented." "Her ability to conceptualize and her craftsmanship is unmatched." "She and I have worked on projects that resulted in completely new and original approaches." "The creative process is a joy and the final product is exquisite."

	Quality	Cost	Value	Recommend?
	✚	$	◆	★

Michael Foulkrod/Site Unseen   3.5   3   4.5   4
PO Box 461974, Los Angeles, CA 90046
(323) 848 - 9615   www.siteunseenstudio.com
Decorative painting, murals

Sources declare that "if you can dream it up, Michael can paint it." A former fashion model, Michael Foulkrod started working as a decorative painter in New York 23 years ago, working with some of the Big Apple's most established decorators. Since founding Sight Unseen in 1991 in Los Angeles, Foulkrod and his small staff have developed a following of loyal clients who return year after year for his decorative finishes and murals.

Foulkrod, who studied at the Maryland Institute and the Museum School in Boston, is described as highly creative. In addition to its traditional decorative work, the firm has taken on a swimming pool project and painted an aquarium in a private residence. We hear Foulkrod's Venetian plasterwork is some of the best around. Thanks to a typical two-week turnaround and very good fees, sources say LA is going to see a lot more of Site Unseen.

"I have known Michael for years and his murals are spectacular." "Nice work makes up for the artistic temperament." "Michael's creative scope gives him an edge."

Nancy Kintisch   4.5   4   4.5   4
3636 Brunswick Avenue, Los Angeles, CA 90039
(323) 663 - 3930   nakintisch@yahoo.com
Decorative painting, stenciling and murals

As its quirky name suggests, Off-White Castle Studios is not for the traditional or the faint of heart. Owner Nancy Kintisch comes recommended by some of the best-known decorators in the country for her unorthodox designs. Kintisch is "a creative dynamo" who won't hesitate to "go out on a limb." If you have an idea that is set in stone, she's probably not for you, but risk takers who love to try something different rave about Kintisch's experiments in painting. It is said that Kintisch does her best work with creative people who are willing to allow a project to evolve.

After getting her BFA in painting from RISD, Kintisch headed out west and developed a clientele. Today, she is well known throughout Los Angeles for her patterning and stenciling, but she also does "fantastic" murals. Typically hired for her painting skills, Kintisch often becomes involved in interior design and color consultation after she arrives on a project. Her studio sells unique and comfortable furnishings, tiles and textiles in addition to her own decorative painting. Kintisch's work has been featured in magazines such as *Architectural Digest*, *House Beautiful* and *Town & Country*. Prices are unexpectedly reasonable for the "memorable" work that keeps the faithful coming back for more.

"So talented." "She did a custom-made stencil of grasscloth which was nothing short of amazing." "Nancy's coffered ceilings need to be seen to be believed."

NaturalWalls   4   3.5   4.5   4
2376 Ganesha Avenue, Altadena, CA 91001
(626) 398 - 9383   www.naturalwalls.com
Finishing and plastering with organic materials

Using Old-World techniques and natural materials, the artisans at NaturalWalls create what have been described as "rich," "authentic" surfaces. After seven years in the business, principal Scott Nelson is well known in the industry for the quality of his European-style wall treatments and his modern-day faux finishes. Decorators, architects and homeowners gush about the firm's organic materials and the way the color mixing is done from an "artist's palette" rather than from paint store swatches. References call Nelson "an artist rather than a contractor," and he has developed a solid following of both residential and commercial clients.

Nelson supplemented his book learning with apprenticeships with several master craftsmen. Today, working with a crew of three, he does "a phenomenal job" on a wide array of projects, including Venetian and clay plaster. Nelson became intrigued by beautiful wall finishes while traveling across Europe, and developed a technique for using the English Armourcote product to make the structural details of a house appear richer and more sophisticated. Prices are said to be "excellent" for a firm that combines consummate professionalism with the artistic touch.

"The finest faux painter I've seen." "Scott is fantastic—great to have on a project." "One of the most pleasant and down-to-earth artists I have encountered in this business."

Pyramid Plastering Inc.   4   3   5   4.5

14687 Plummer Street, Panorama City, CA 91402
(818) 893 - 4741   www.pyramidplastering.com

Interior and exterior plastering and stucco

A favorite among high-end builders in Los Angeles, Pyramid Plastering provides full-service plaster and stucco for both indoor and outdoor projects. To stay at the top of the pyramid, this firm keeps up with the very latest trends while continuing to practice the state-of-the-art techniques "from the old days." For instance, Pyramid is one of the few remaining practitioners of the dying art of "run plaster molding," a skill that involves building up details from flat walls using only templates and plaster. From standard plastering to cutting-edge custom interior to architectural foam finishing, we hear nothing but high praise for the crew at Pyramid Plastering.

Having accumulated more than 40 years in the plaster and stucco business, the owners of this firm are experts in all aspects of their craft. Whether it's a custom home in Hollywood Hills or a hip new restaurant opened by an A-list celebrity, Pyramid delivers outstanding work at excellent prices for this market. Clients tell us this company is known for understanding and ensuring that the client's vision becomes a reality. Described as "completely customer oriented," Pyramid has a long list of repeat customers who come back for the personalized service, timely work and very fair pricing.

"Pyramid did exactly what we asked for." "Very versatile firm. They are highly professional and ethical." "A very nice company to work with on a project."

R.E. Plumb Painting Co.   4   3   5   4

20749 Parthenia Street, Winnetka, CA 91306
(818) 882 - 3142

Straight and decorative painting, cabinet finishing

Who do architects, interior designers and contractors call when they need a top-shelf straight painter? R.E. Plumb Painting Co., a 34-year veteran of all types of paint jobs around Southern California. We hear owner Dick Plumb gets so many commissions from the great word of mouth, he has to turn clients away.

	Quality	Cost	Value	Recommend?
	+	$	◆	★

Plumb, who was "turned on to paint" while working at his father's paint and hardware store, leads a team of 27 on projects large and small—but almost exclusively in custom-built homes. Beyond the straight painting jobs, Plumb's firm will take on decorative work and cabinet refinishing. Known in the industry for approaching jobs with the "utmost integrity," Plumb delivers an honest day's work for an honest day's pay—a formula that apparently brings happy clients and their friends back again and again for the "excellent quality" and "prices that won't break you."

"Beautiful work." "Professional service and innovative finishes." "Plumb is very skilled in the art of painting. The end result is first class."

Scott Flax Studio   4.5   3.5   5   4.5
1660 Stanford Street, Santa Monica, CA 90404
(310) 829 - 1445   scottflax@aol.com
Commissioned, site-specific painting; architectural colorist

"King of Color" Scott Flax is praised by the decorators, architects and homeowners who hire him to transform architectural spaces with color and light. A "true collaborator," Flax is said to be experienced, knowledgeable, professional and "fun to work with." Coordinating a color palette while overseeing a team of artisans, Flax can "work magic" for his clients, merging his technical know-how with his "refined aesthetic sensibility."

Trained at the Pratt Institute in New York, Flax worked at EverGreene Studios as a decorative painter before heading to LA fifteen years ago. He's been working for well-heeled clients ever since, most recently executing a lot of site-specific painting projects (primarily murals). If he's not working on a special mural, Flax is often hired to act as the "art director" on significant projects. Clients and peers say they love working with Flax and are willing to pay any price for the privilege, but this claim isn't tested by the reasonable Flax, who charges excellent rates.

"Scott's expertise with color made him the right choice." "He approaches each project as he would a painting."

Steve Beattie Painting Inc.   5   4   5   5
1766 West Ridge Road, Los Angeles, CA 90049
(310) 454 - 1786   beattiepainting@aol.com
Flawless straight and decorative painting

It is not unusual to hear the words "make it perfect" on painting jobs run by Steve Beattie, for this is the mantra by which he works. Celebrities and business tycoons call on his team for everything from straight painting work to elaborate decorative finishes. Strié, Venetian plaster, parchment finishes and enamels are just a few of the techniques the company has mastered. Colorists, decorators and homeowners all say, "Consider yourself lucky if Steve Beattie's brushes have touched your walls."

Beattie has been collaborating with some of Southern California's most prestigious high-end builders and designers since 1986, building a reputation for "flawless" painting. Sources tell us Beattie and his staff, most of whom have been with him as long as he has been in business, are extremely talented and have a genuine love for what they do, which leads to great camaraderie on the job. The firm's crews are known in the industry for taking the time to painstakingly prepare walls for paint—which, as any good contractor will attest, is the key to a beautiful job. With every nook and cranny cared for as if it were the centerpiece of the house, Beattie's team really does "make it perfect"—at prices that correspond to the serious attention paid to your walls.

"Huge crews—extremely skilled." "Three-quarters of their time is spent doing the prep, one-quarter of the time is in the painting—especially near the beach

where durability is an issue." "Expensive, but they balance the line between a boutique firm and one that does high volume without losing the quality." "What they do is intense." "I want to keep touching my new enamel—it is like butter!"

The Painted Room   4   3.5   4.5   4.5
13861 Wallabi Avenue, Sylmar, CA 91342
(818) 833 - 9630

Decorative painting, murals, restoration and refinishing, architectural casting

Smart, talented artisans Shelley Mills and Stephen MacDonald specialize in traditional decorative painting, custom finishes for furniture, accessories and walls at The Painted Room. In business since 1989, the firm's expertise extends to trompe l'oeil, murals, faux finishing and furniture restoration. In addition, they will also do architectural casting and sculpture, and design accessories for the home. Sources say that Mills and MacDonald are "very hands-on" and are closely involved in each project.

Mills, who studied at the JFK Center for Museum Studies in Stanford, holds a master's degree in the history of American decorative arts. Previously, she worked in New York at the Brooklyn Museum collaborating on the reinstallation of nineteenth-century period rooms and at the de Young Museum in San Francisco, where she worked in the curatorial department of the American Paintings Collection. Clients and peers report that Mills's historical background brings an element of completeness to a room. MacDonald did custom prop design in the film industry and owned his own furniture refinishing and restoration studio before joining up with Mills. MacDonald is described as "a skilled problem solver" who can handle any situation with "professionalism and finesse." This extremely thoughtful, talented duo is said to produce beautiful results in conjunction with their team of six. Typically commissioned for traditional-style projects, the firm charges prices that are very good. Some of their time these days is spent on the southern tip of Florida where they recently opened a small branch office.

"They are a dream team—talented, and very nice to deal with." "The murals are simply elegant."

Valley Painting Service   4   3.5   4.5   4
14619 Bessemer Street, Van Nuys, CA 91411
(818) 780 - 7553   valleypainting@sbcglobal.net
Straight and decorative painting

Trade professionals and the public alike turn to the 32-year-old Valley Painting Service for excellent straight painting, faux finishes, marbleizing, wood graining and Venetian plaster. Owner Tim O'Brien and his staff of twelve have pleased many a decorator and contractor with their knack for getting it right the first time.

O'Brien painted his way through graduate school and has been enhancing interiors and exteriors of LA's high profile houses ever since. Assisted by his loyal staff, O'Brien works mostly in Southern California, but he will travel for the right job. Valley Painting often employs additional skilled professionals to come by and work on furniture, cabinets, windows, doors and shutters in the firm's on-site controlled environment spray booth. Major paint producers have been known to stop by to test their new products, which gives O'Brien a sneak peek at the latest. The firm charges excellent fees and takes from one to six months to complete a house, depending on the size of the project.

"A large company that can handle anything," "My sprayed doors look so gorgeous."

HIRING A PLUMBER

Whether it's trimming out a kitchen and bath remodel, installing an entire system for a new home, handling a routine repair or maintenance call, or tending to an absolute emergency, you need a plumber you can count on.

Although most plumbers are available for a simple service call, some high-end service providers prefer to limit such calls, especially 24-hour emergency service, to existing customers. This practice ensures that loyal customers will receive the highest level of service and quality with a prompt response.

WHERE DO I START?

Hold on to that plumbing contractor who has proven himself over the course of a major project. Handpicked by your trusty general contractor (GC), he knows the guts of your home better than anyone. Even if you aren't planning a renovation and just need someone to handle more mundane problems, such as leaky faucets, it's worth putting in the effort to build a relationship with a plumber who can offer quality and service, so he'll be there before you're sunk.

If you are starting from scratch, remember some plumbers focus only on larger-scale contract installations and remodels, while others devote their efforts entirely to service and repair. Marry your job to the right plumber. The best first sign is someone answering the phone—not just an answering service—but a live company employee in an actual office. If you can't get hold of someone during business hours, the chances that you'll get a response on a Saturday night when your bath looks like Niagara Falls are slim. A decent high-end plumber shouldn't be spooked by foreign or custom fixtures, or force his standard ones down your throat. And when unfamiliar fixtures are involved, the firm should be willing to call the manufacturer and do its homework to ensure proper installation. The firm should also be able to deliver options at different price points. While plumbing basics haven't changed much in 100 years, the firm should also be up to the latest technology, such as energy-efficient tankless water heaters and sound suppression systems.

Calling references is your last line of defense. For larger jobs, such as kitchen remodels that require coordination between trades, contractors are the best assessors of a firm's performance. For smaller service and maintenance jobs, clients are your best bet. To both you'll want to ask the usual questions about quality of work and whether the project was finished on schedule and on budget. However, because plumbing can be a messy business, respect for surroundings and cleanliness are equally important.

A JOB FOR PROFESSIONALS

You should only consider a full-time licensed professional for your plumbing needs. Though a license is not required in California to perform basic plumbing maintenance work, your service provider must be licensed for any jobs that require the filing of a permit. As always, ask about insurance, including workmen's compensation and liability insurance. Your plumbing professional should always be responsible for obtaining all permits necessary for your job.

ON COST

For larger projects, each plumbing contractor will submit its bid to the GC, who will then incorporate it into the overall bid submitted to the client. Often the GC for your project will bring in a trusted plumber for the job, but you are free to ask your GC to include another plumber in the bidding process, which ensures that bids are competitive. If your renovation is relatively small and a GC is not involved, get several estimates for the proposed work.

For smaller jobs and service calls, which include repair and maintenance, most companies charge an hourly rate ranging between $55 and $80. A 3.5 Cost rating in *The Franklin Report* approximately reflects a $65 rate. However, please remember, a company's standards in relation to product and safety, the depth of its resources and the demand of its customer base can all affect cost on top of hourly rates, and are factored into the rating.

Some companies charge a set, one-time diagnostic fee to produce an estimate, even for smaller jobs, while others will send troubleshooters or technicians to assess the work and come up with a price free of charge. All will work up fixed estimates for larger jobs to be executed in a contract. Fees for contract renovation work are typically higher than fees for new construction per hour and per square foot. In the end, it should come down to the company with the best reputation for quality and service, not just the low bidder.

GUARANTEES AND SERVICE AGREEMENTS

When your equipment is installed, it should come with both a warranty from the manufacturer and a guarantee from the service provider. Be sure to ask about service agreements. Many plumbing professionals will provide regular "checkups" and inspections. It may seem like wasted money at first, but over time these measures can prevent an emergency.

SAVE MONEY BY SAVING TIME

If you inventory the state of your plumbing and think ahead about work that will need to be done, your plumber will be able to work more effectively. Check faucets, drains, radiators and fixtures throughout the house and compile a list. Present this list to the plumber upon arrival so he can prioritize the various tasks and work simultaneously if possible. This way, you won't have to call him in again for another minor repair in a few weeks.

If the plumber will need access to the pipes under your kitchen sink, clear out the area to save billable time. Also put away or protect anything vulnerable to damage. Your plumber will appreciate being able to get to work without having to wade through piles of children's toys or rummage around in a cabinet full of cleaning supplies.

Don't wait until your bathroom is flooded with four inches of water. Develop a good relationship with a plumber now, and you'll never have to flip frantically through a phone book and throw yourself at the mercy of whatever plumber happens to be free.

MORE THAN PIPES

YOUR PLUMBER IS TRAINED TO DO MUCH MORE THAN FIX CLOGGED DRAINS. A FULL-SERVICE PLUMBER CAN:

- ✧ Provide condensation drains for air conditioning units.
- ✧ Install the boiler, lines and radiators necessary for household heat.
- ✧ Install hot water recirculation and water pressure booster pumps.
- ✧ Hook up major appliances (gas stoves, washing machines).
- ✧ Make a gas-meter connection, install gas lines and provide gas shut-off valves.
- ✧ Install storm/slop drains for the kitchen, patio, garage, laundry rooms, greenhouse and roof.

PLUMBERS

Calcoast Plumbing   4   3.5   4.5   4
568 Constitution Avenue, Suite D, Camarillo, CA 93012
(805) 482 - 3420

Plumbing installation and service

We hear that third-generation plumber Cal Miller has the kind of demeanor that makes homeowners, architects and contractors feel like old family friends. They call upon Calcoast's 25 plumbing professionals for high-end remodeling and new construction jobs ranging from $10,000 to $200,000. The firm can handle the most demanding finishes and fixtures and will do its homework on new product. It also designs and installs sound suppression to mute its plumbing systems.

Clients tell us Miller is always available one-on-one. They applaud his ability to move manpower effectively and keep jobs flowing—Miller dispatches a foreman to every job site. Calcoast's ranks are filled with technicians who approach plumbing as a serious profession. Each of them apprentices through a state program, attending school one day a week for four years. Calcoast's upper-end prices reflect Miller's investment in his workers and personal commitment to quality service.

"Calcoast is competitive, meticulous and well organized." "A bigger firm, but reliable and good."

Fred Morrow Plumbing Inc.   5   3.5   5   5
16137 Valerio Street, Van Nuys, CA 91406
(818) 376 - 6538   www.fredmorrowplumbing.com

Expert plumbing installation and service

Since 1976, fourth-generation plumber Fred Morrow has been building a reputation for excellence and honesty. In 29 years in the business, Morrow Plumbing has yet to receive a single complaint against its license. The firm's integrity is so widely heralded that it is frequently brought in as a consultant for arbitration settlements.

The company offers the best in complete plumbing design, installation and maintenance for pipes, water heaters and gas lines. With Fred Morrow's extensive experience in custom residential remodels, service and repair, he's the kind of guy people call when they need to fix other plumbers' less-exacting work. Los Angeles' most discriminating general contractors turn to Morrow to design complex systems for clients who want the latest noise-resistant and energy-efficient technology.

The Morrows were plumbers even before there were plumbers. In the 1800s, Fred Morrow's German-born ancestors became experts in steam fitting and the other trades that would become modern-day plumbing. Morrow himself started out at the age of eight, clearing scrap for his grandfather, a master plumber. Today, Morrow has fifteen employees, many of whom have been with him for years, and

	Quality	Cost	Value	Recommend?
	✚	$	◆	★

still visits jobs regularly—a sign of the diligence for which he earns high marks from references. His team's knowledge and experience set it apart, sources report, while the firm's rates fall in line with standard rates.

"I swear by them." "It has been my pleasure to work with Fred Morrow Plumbing for twenty years." "I have had excellent advice, service and repair. All handled with honesty, integrity and efficiency. They are terrific." "Stands behind his work." "Dealing with Fred Morrow Plumbing is one area of our lives where we can experience complete peace of mind."

Gordon's Plumbing Inc.　　　　3.5　3　4.5　4
1512 Euclid Street, Santa Monica, CA　90404
(310) 394 - 6415
Plumbing installation and service

Second-generation plumber Blake Leiting runs this family owned and operated company with his two sisters, Tammy Leiting and Debbie Sundquist. Started in 1975 by the their father, Gordon, the firm today performs installations in high-end custom homes and offers full service and repair to customers in the Santa Monica, Beverly Hills and San Fernando Valley areas. The firm is 22 employees strong and offers service 24/7. We hear the owners and the staff take great pride in their work, laying out jobs with precision and answering questions with a smile. Gordon's is also noted for its recirculation systems.

"Finally, a plumber who does it right the first time." "The 24-hour service has come in handy more than once."

John K. Keefe Inc.　　　　4　3　5　4.5
9221 West Olympic Boulevard, Beverly Hills, CA　90212
(310) 274 - 9888
Plumbing and HVAC service and repair

This established Beverly Hills firm opened its doors in 1940 and has maintained a sterling reputation. The firm specializes in service, including 24-hour emergency assistance and repairs. Remodeling work is performed for existing customers. John K. Keefe Inc. also provides service and repair on AC and heating systems, serving West LA from Santa Monica to Hancock Park. We hear the firm gives high-ly ethical service at reasonable rates, which include one-way travel time.

Started by John Keefe, who ran the firm until just a couple of years ago, the business was recently acquired by another plumbing contractor with a long history, HL Moe of Glendale, who's been around since 1927. Ron Izuno now heads up the business, blending HL Moe's commercial instincts with Keefe's family feel. Twenty-seven employees, a mixture of long-time Keefe vets and newly acquired Moe experts, uphold the good Keefe name.

McDermott Plumbing　　　　4　3　5　4.5
7861 Alabama Street, Suite 13, Canoga Park, CA　91304
(818) 343 - 1491
Plumbing installation and service

Talk about a lifetime warranty—this plumbing contractor's clients' kids are now clients. McDermott installs, services and repairs generations of residential waterworks around Calabasas and Hidden Hills. Upper-end fixtures and careful installation are hallmarks of this firm, which often works with bathroom marble contractors. Even steam baths are no sweat for McDermott.

Owner Rick Flores runs this small, four-person plumbing shop. Flores has been a part of this firm since 1979 and, usually, you can still find him out on each job. He and his crew are routinely applauded for being especially considerate when

Quality	Cost	Value	Recommend?
+	$	◆	★

altering existing space. Flores's reputation as a fair and honest guy is well-known: when NBC News Channel 4 and the Better Business Bureau produced a local segment on unfair plumbing practices, they chose McDermott to represent the good, honest plumbers. McDermott's rates are standard.

"The whole experience is fair and reasonable—scheduling, pricing, servicing."

Ortega Plumbing   5   4.5   4.5   5

4129 Milton Avenue, Culver City, CA 90232
(310) 505 - 9854
Plumbing installation and service; design specialists

We hear this veteran can execute the most fantastic high-end designs—Louis Ortega once installed glass piping on a beachfront home with floor to ceiling glass walls. Whether it's transparency you desire or more demure options, Ortega lays pipe on custom residentials from 1,500 to 23,000 square feet. The firm's star-studded clientele value its skills with high-end fixtures, while its budgets and timetables keep contractors smitten.

Ortega has worked in the trade since the age of twelve, when he started learning from his uncle on weekends. After tech school and a tour with a plumbing company that focused on large custom homes, Ortega went out on his own. He has kept the firm to a manageable size—only seven technicians—in order to ensure his high-quality standards. Ortega provides up-front and thoughtful assessment of job specs, often devising a better means of installation. His services are considered to be among the very best in his class, and clients can expect to pay higher rates.

"If there ever was a high-end plumber, it's Louis." "His work is amazing. A truly rare artisan in the industry."

Oscar Plumbing & Electric   4.5   4   4.5   4.5

PO Box 6015 , North Hollywood, CA 91602
(818) 506 - 4915
Plumbing installation and service; electrical service

Who said electricity and water don't mix? The only plumber/electrician we've come across, this firm is reputedly stellar in both fields. Started ten years ago by Oscar Garcia, who picked up his multitasking skills in Mexico City, the firm specializes in renovations and additions for high-end residential work.

Garcia's crew of five divides its efforts between plumbing and electric work. Clients employ Oscar Plumbing & Electric for one or both skills—a plus when coordinating kitchen and bath remodels. The firm is quite experienced in handling exotic plumbing fixtures. Clients say that if Garcia comes across an unfamiliar piece of hardware, he'll immediately get on the phone with the manufacturer. Plumbing work includes gas piping, but the firm does not install large appliances. On the electrical front, Oscar is knowledgeable about home automation systems.

Garcia is an involved, hands-on owner. He himself performs all of the installation with his crew. We hear he is a perfectionist and always tries to top his service, job after job. A computerized pricing structure breaks down costs per item or task. While prices fall at the upper end of the range, we're told every penny is returned in service.

"Service was excellent. No problems." "Oscar helped remodel my kitchen and bathroom. His work was spotless."

	Quality	Cost	Value	Recommend?
	+	$	◆	★

Plotke Plumbing

Quality 4 **Cost** 4 **Value** 4 **Recommend?** 5

523 North Larchmont Boulevard, Los Angeles, CA 90004
(323) 463 - 9201

Plumbing installation and service

Tried and true Plotke Plumbing has been laying pipe across Los Angeles since 1959. No job is too daunting for these plucky plumbers—with three trucks on the road, the firm takes on everything from servicing clogged sewers, repairing gas lines, and re-piping high-end kitchens and baths to installing high-efficiency tankless water heaters. Seventy-five percent of Plotke's work is service and repair, and the balance falls to re-pipes and remodels. The firm works within a twenty-mile radius of its West Hollywood location. We hear that word of Plotke's excellence gets around the neighborhood in no time, and it's not uncommon for Plotke technicians to be dispatched to several jobs on the same block in the same day!

In 1987, the firm passed through the hands of original founder Jerry Plotke to longtime Plotke employee Mario Sanchez. Today, his son, Mario Sanchez, Jr., runs the firm with foreign-fixtures expert and new partner Lynn Shirly. Sanchez meets with clients and provides estimates while Shirly supervises quality control in the field. The firm is small, and we're told its crew of four is both highly skilled and client-friendly. The outfit is a family affair: Sanchez's wife keeps order in the office, while his brother runs a branch of Plotke Plumbing down in San Diego.

Clients say someone always picks up the phone at Plotke during office hours and that plumbers remain on call via pager after hours. Customers have even been talked through problems over the phone. We hear the firm sticks to its appointments and will always call ahead if there's a problem. The firm's rates are competitive, while its services blow most of the competition out of the water.

"Bar none, the best." "A great crew. Very conscientious." "I love these guys. They take extra care. Will guarantee their work for a long time." "They can get busy, but there's a reason for that."

Plumbing by Randell 2

Quality 4.5 **Cost** 4 **Value** 4.5 **Recommend?** 5

19030 Arminta Street, Reseda, CA 91335
(818) 993 - 0615

Precision plumbing installation and service

Clients say that there's not a plumbing system in Los Angeles that Randell or Randell can't handle. Partners Randell Press and Randell Haner can do it all—be it a minor repair for a homeowner, a remodel on a luxury condo for an interior designer or design and installation of a brand-new system in a custom 30,000 square foot mega-home for a general contractor. We hear this small firm of six takes a methodical, patient approach to its work, emphasizing precision, not production. Its clients span the San Fernando Valley, Malibu, Beverly Hills, Holmby Hills and Santa Monica areas.

Press mans the office, while Haner works the field. Clients applaud the firm's knowledge of high-end European product and its ability to engineer custom solutions, from noise reduction to radiant systems. Clients love the fact that Randell 2's work proves as sensitive to the architect's intent as to the homeowner's budget. The firm also works as a troubleshooter for Grohe product.

"They were very prompt in responding to my call." "I looked for a while for a plumber for my Pre-War renovation. They turned out to be just the guys." "There are plenty of cheaper plumbers—what you're really paying for is their knowledge base and customized service."

	Quality	Cost	Value	Recommend?
	✚	$	◆	★

Power Plumbing   3   3   4   4

10659 Magnolia Boulevard, North Hollywood, CA 91601
(323) 936 - 4547

Plumbing repair and remodeling

High-caliber Angeleno insiders put forth a powerful argument for using this firm. Licensed and bonded, the firm boasts over twenty years in business, handling repairs and remodels across Los Angeles and the San Fernando Valley. Fees are calculated by the job, not by the hour. Twenty-four-hour emergency service is available to all clients. Work is guaranteed for one year.

"Power Plumbing is exactly what I want in a plumber: responsible, no nonsense."

R.O. Stewart   4   3   5   4.5

1166 Northwestern Avenue, Los Angeles, CA 90029
(323) 469 - 5851

Plumbing remodeling and service

A family-operated business for over 80 years, R.O. Stewart remodels and services plumbing in existing homes. One crew concentrates on remodels, while another is wholly dedicated to service. The firm installs the newest custom systems (low noise and extra pressure), while also repairing "gravity heaters" in older homes and buildings. The firm's expertise in designer and foreign fixtures impresses clients and manufacturers alike, including Grohe, for which it does factory service work. R.O. Stewart is available throughout metropolitan Los Angeles but does most of its work within a fifteen-mile radius of its office.

Brothers Andy and Tony Stewart have now led the firm for more than fifteen years, and the business has been located in the same building since 1920. A number of elite contractors tell us they trust this eight-person firm on the most sensitive jobs, like running pipe through the drilled hole in a $50,000 Ming vase. Clients tell us the Stewarts sell them only what their systems need, and that the firm is always reachable when questions arise. With a reputation built solely on referrals, Stewart's rates still beat those of many plumbers with splashy ads in the Yellow Pages.

"'Creative' and 'plumber' are not two words I usually think of together. But these guys have something special." "It's a real can-do company." "A friend told me about Stewart, and he's been my guy ever since."

Specialty Hardware and Plumbing   4   4   4   4

283 South Robertson Boulevard, Beverly Hills, CA 90211
(310) 659 - 9351   info@specialtyhardware.net

High-end kitchen and bath showroom

The secret cabinet door, drawer hardware and plumbing supply source for Southern California's design and construction bigwigs, this to-the-trade firm provides product for the ambitious outfitting of kitchens and baths. The firm writes the hardware and fixture specs for many elite projects. With over twelve years in the field, owner Jason Crystal knows where to go to procure rare or foreign fixtures. The firm also sells its own line of towel bars and accessories. Specialty's specialty, however, is the design and fabrication of new custom fixtures or reproduction of older models, from tubs to cabinet hardware—a service it will also provide for creative retail clients.

	Quality	Cost	Value	Recommend?
	✚	$	◆	★

Surfside Plumbing and Rooter   4   4   4   4

1917 Roscomare Road, Los Angeles, CA 90077
(866) 321 - 7473   www.surfsideplumbing.com

Plumbing installation and service, sewer cleaning and replacement, HVAC installation and service

If it's "high tide" in your bathroom, the team at Surfside Plumbing can be a life-saver. Covering Los Angeles, Santa Monica, Pacific Palisades, Malibu, Beverly Hills, Brentwood and Bel Air, this firm services anyone's work and guarantees arrival at your home within 45 minutes. Surfside also provides 24-hour emergency service for all callers, not just repeat customers. From sewers to water heaters, disposals to toilets, Surfside services (and installs) all kinds of water systems.

Founded in 1950, Surfside has been family owned and operated ever since. Sources say principal Harry Steininger never loses his cool and always takes the time to explain the problem and how it occurred. Surfside charges by the job, not by the hour, and they provide a complete diagnosis showing the price before they begin work.

"We called Surfside for an emergency toilet replacement. Harry was able to make the replacement without going back to his shop." "Excellent service at a very fair price." "Harry took care of the problem calmly, quickly and with a sense of humor."

Waterworks

8715 Melrose Avenue, West Hollywood, CA 90069
(310) 289 - 5211   www.waterworks.com

Bath design, sales and installation referral

See Waterworks's full report under the heading Kitchen & Bath Design

HIRING A RUG CLEANING, INSTALLATION & REPAIR SERVICE PROVIDER

Does your heirloom Oriental display a record of your adorable yet hard-to-house-train puppy? Did Uncle Mike spill a Bloody Mary on your Persian? Did your cat sharpen his claws on that hidden corner of your needlepoint? Or is your rug just overdue for its regular cleaning (every two to four years, according to The Oriental Rug Importers of America)? Not to worry: rug cleaners and restorers can address every kind of need on every type of rug, from museum-quality handmade rugs to inexpensive carpeting.

GATHERING INFORMATION

When choosing cleaners or restorers, there are many factors to consider. Ask if they perform free, written estimates. If they make house calls, do they charge a travel fee, and do they have free pickup, delivery and reinstallation? Before they quote you a price, you may wish to inquire how they set their rate: by the job, the hour or the size of the rug? Do they require a deposit? Will they arrange a payment plan if you need one? Do they offer discounts for multiple rugs or rooms? It's a good sign if they honor their estimate, even if the job overwhelms their expectations. It's an even better sign if they guarantee perfection, and don't consider the job finished until you are satisfied. Such an assurance (especially in writing) may be more valuable than letters of reference or membership in one of the professional associations, though both of these would add further reassurance of competence.

If your rug is handmade and you think it may be valuable, you may want to get it appraised by a rug-care service before having it cleaned or repaired. If it is valuable, you'll need to consider more expert (and expensive) services. On the other hand, you may also discover that the rug isn't worth nearly as much as you believed, and hence may not warrant lavish attention. Either way, a professional appraisal certifies the value of your belongings in case of mishaps—you may want to inquire beforehand whether liability falls in your court or whether the cleaner/restorer's insurance covers any mishaps. Many rug cleaning and reweaving establishments appraise rugs for insurance, estate sale, tax and charitable donation. Watching appraisers evaluate your rug also allows you to preview their professionalism. If their work instills confidence, hire them for the whole job—if not, you can still use their appraisal (and estimate, if they perform one simultaneously) as a first opinion in approaching another establishment. For complicated (expensive) repair or restoration jobs, ask how long it will take. Often the expert restorers have other jobs they must finish before they can get to yours. If your rug is valuable, it is worth waiting for the best.

If the rug needs repair before cleaning, confirm that the restorer knows the techniques of the tradition in which the rug was made: Navajo yarn-dying and rug-weaving methods differ vastly from those of Iran. Ask to see a portfolio of their previous repair work, which often displays side-by-side "before" and "after" pictures. Inspect how well they match colors, recreate designs, and blend repairs into existing weaves. If your rug is valuable, inquire whether an expert or an apprentice will perform the repair work. Also, see to it that all repair work is included in the estimate, from reweaving holes to remapping worn areas, restoring moth damage to rewrapping seams and re-fringing to re-blocking your rug to its original shape. Particularly thorough rug conservationists will even unravel strands and overcast weaving to blend repairs into the rug's existing texture and design.

CLEANING AND DRYING TECHNIQUES

There are many different cleaning methods, each of which addresses different situations with varying degrees of efficacy and expense. Carpet cleaners typically have mobile operations, and will clean rugs and wall-to-wall carpets in your home with hot "carbonating" systems, steam-cleaning or dry-cleaning. Will they move the furniture to clean under it or do they expect it ready when they arrive? Rug cleaners, on the other hand, usually perform the cleaning at their site. They may expect the rug to be rolled up and waiting for their pickup. Silk rugs, fragile tapestries and textiles with "fugitive" (short-lived) dyes, or bright colors that might "bleed" (run), should be hand-washed—the most delicate and expensive method. Luster cleaning immerses the entire rug in cleaning solutions, and thus achieves a deep clean while minimizing wear on the fabric. Soap washing involves running a vacuum-like machine over the rug; this vigorous method is only for particularly rugged or less-valuable rugs. Discuss in advance what problems the cleaner can and can't fix. For example, excessive wear on a hallway rug will still be there after a cleaning, though it will be much less noticeable. If you are health or environmentally conscious, ask whether the company offers nontoxic cleaners.

Any rug that's washed must also be dried properly to avoid mildew and dry rot. Be sure to ask about the time and drying technique for in-home jobs—you should know beforehand if you need to reroute traffic through the patio for three days. For in-plant jobs, bigger outfits have dry rooms where they control temperature and humidity levels. In the home, drying basically involves not walking on the rug until it is dry, which depends on humidity and other factors. Some businesses also offer stain protectants, which they apply directly to the rug to shield it from future accidents (should the tipsy uncle return). Other companies may take a purist approach, preferring periodic cleaning to chemical protectants.

CARPET AND RUG INSTALLATION

Before the carpet or rug is put down, padding should always be laid first. Padding gives more cushioning for your feet and keeps the rug from sliding, which helps prevent slips, falls and spills. Ask what kind of padding the installer will use, as there are generally different quality and price options.

For wall-to-wall carpeting installation, the most common method is to lay wooden tack strips around the perimeter of the room. The tack strips have pins sticking up that grab the carpet and hold it in place. The tack strips are attached to the floor using small nails, which leave holes in the floor when the carpet is removed. The padding also is usually either nailed or stapled to the floor. If you must cover your nice wood floors (for the kids, maybe), you should discuss with the installer how to minimize the floor damage. Unfortunately, there is not that much that can be done if you want wall-to-wall. Some installers may suggest attaching the carpet with double-faced tape, but most say that this doesn't hold well and the carpet shifts and buckles. If your floor contributes to the value of your apartment, it is simply better to stick with area rugs. Remember to ask whether or not there are any potential extra charges, such as for ripping up existing wall-to-wall carpeting before installing the new one or for disposing of the old carpeting and pads if you don't want to keep them.

Some rug cleaners focus on just stain and odor removal services to meet the needs of pet owners, smokers and families with small children (or just klutzes). Many providers offer stain protection for future spills, which, depending on your lifestyle, may be a sound investment. Other companies specialize in emergency services in case of fire, smoke or water damage, and may even be available round-the-clock. If you're moving, remodeling or otherwise in need of storage, look to the larger outfits for mothproofing and storage services. After storage or in-plant services, many companies will reinstall your rug over appropriate padding.

Rug cleaners and restorers also offer many other services for rugs and other furnishings. Many rug cleaners also clean curtains and upholstered furniture. Some businesses prefer to remove the draperies from the home and wash them at their facilities. In-home carpet cleaners are more likely to clean curtains in the house.

Since curtains, upholstered furniture and rugs dominate most of the space (not to mention the attention) in a room, rug cleaners and restorers emphasize the importance of maintaining these items. Their colors will be clearer, they'll last longer, you'll be inhaling less dust—and your home will look more beautiful.

On Cost

Prices among rug companies vary immensely because each has its own specialties and services. Some rug firms work on standard cleaning and focus on wall-to-wall broadlooms, upholstery and drapery. For this type of cleaning, some charge by the square foot, which could start at $.25 (a 2.5 for cost in *The Franklin Report*) per square foot and could go up to $1 to $1.25 per square foot. Most companies charge $.30 to $.60 per square foot. Then again, some give a flat rate after inspecting the carpet and seeing how much cleaning needs to be done. This usually conforms to their minimum rate, which most companies have. Minimum rates start at $50 and go up to $150 for standard wall-to-wall broadloom cleaning.

Area rugs are a different terrain altogether. Los Angeles has numerous experts and "specialized" firms that only deal with area rug cleaning, repair and restoration—those that work mostly with the rare, the old, the valuable and in most cases, only the handmade ones. Most companies who do standard wall-to-wall cleaning also clean area rugs, but the older and rarer the rug is, the more specialized the cleaning, repair and attention it needs. Pricing for area rug cleaning starts as low as $1 (a 2.5 for cost in *The Franklin Report*) per square foot and could go as high as $3 to $5 per square foot, depending on the amount of cleaning needed and the value of the rug. These firms also have minimum rates, and fees start at $100 minimum up to $700. Then again, if your area rug is not a hundred years old and requires only regular cleaning or minimal repairs, you could end up paying a standard $50 to $100 per job or $1.25 to $2 per square foot.

Don't Let the Rug Be Pulled Out From Under You!

❖ Get several bids. Prices among competent cleaners can vary quite a bit.

❖ When you have an estimate, ask if it's binding. Ask what factors might cause it to become higher (or lower) when the job is actually done.

❖ Is there a minimum charge for a house call? If the cost of cleaning your rug is below the minimum you might want to have them perform another service (such as clean or stain-proof another rug, piece of furniture or curtains) at the same time.

❖ Once in your house, the rug cleaner will often do another rug for much less money, especially if paid in cash.

❖ Some of the larger, more commercial cleaners offer regular specials. Get on the mailing list to receive updates. If you're not in a hurry, wait for a sale.

Rugs — Cleaning, Installation & Repair

■ FIRMS WITH PORTFOLIOS ■

Coat Carpet & Fabric Protection 🛍   5   3.5   5   5
269 South Beverly Drive, Suite 171, Beverly Hills, CA 90212
(310) 286 - 9651
Cleaning and protection for carpets, area rugs, upholstery and window treatments

The secret to Coat Carpet & Fabric's success lies with a special protective sealant, developed by owner Jeff Bradley 26 years ago with a friend in Houston, Texas. Unlike common water-based protectants, such as Scotchgard, Bradley's formula is polymer-based and lasts for three washings before wearing off. Sources say the sealant's amazing resilience is one big reason why they keep coming back to Coat.

Described by insiders as a "treasured secret," this mid-sized, seventeen-year-old company provides maintenance programs for both residential and commercial clients in Beverly Hills, Bel Air, Brentwood and Pacific Palisades. Satisfied customers have been known to fly Coat's specialists out to second homes in New York and San Diego. Notable commercial clients include the Southwestern University School of Law and Fox Family Network. Bradley and his team have also been responsible for protecting all fabrics, carpets and upholstery for the Association League's Designer Showhouses and *House Beautiful's* Celebrity Showhouses since 1999. The company is an associate member of ASID.

The firm cleans all types of area rugs and carpets (including sisal and seagrass), upholstery, fabric walls and drapery treatments—and all cleaning is done on-site. Pricing for carpets is determined by the square foot, furnishings by the piece and fabric walls by the linear foot. Slightly above-average prices are described as a great value by clients who appreciate Coat's unique ability to protect their prized rugs and carpets from spills and stains.

Niagara Carpet & Cleaning Systems Inc. 🛍   5   3   5   5
10755 Sherman Way, Suite 3, Sun Valley, CA 91352
(818) 503 - 9447   www.niagaracarpetcleaning.com
Area rug, carpet and upholstery cleaning, repair and restoration

One of Los Angeles's best-kept secrets, Niagara Carpet & Cleaning Systems is considered by high-end dealers, manufacturers, designers, architects and homeowners to be one of the region's preeminent area rug and carpet cleaners. The bulk of the firm's business is subcontracting for dealers who can't fit the slow and meticulous task of cleaning and repair into their schedules. The firm favors the kind of regular maintenance that really does keep your floor "so clean you can eat off of it."

In business for 25 years, Niagara is managed by its founder, Tom Tarpinian. The company cleans, repairs and restores all types of antique and modern area rugs and tapestries, wall-to-wall carpets, upholstery and wall coverings. We hear that this firm is one of the few that specializes in cleaning sisal, seagrass and jute rugs. Fabric protection, block sizing and flood damage control are just a few of the additional services these skilled workers provide. The licensed, bonded and insured company is a member of ASID and The Coat & Fabric Institute. Every member of its ten-person staff has passed all courses and exams required by the Institute of Inspection, Cleaning & Restoration Certification. Insiders tell us that the workers of Niagara are very skilled and knowledgeable.

With a primarily residential clientele, Niagara serves West LA, Pasadena, West Hollywood, Bel Air and Marina del Rey. Depending on the job, cleaning is done on-site or in Niagara's plant. There is an extra charge for pickup and delivery. Pricing is usually per square foot and estimates are free, as is the moving of furniture when necessary. Customers say they don't mind the real world prices because the efficient and dependable service is well worth the cost. Some sources are satisfied enough to insist they won't use anyone else.

"Very hands-on." "The only company I recommend. Good follow-up." "I've been depending on them for years." "Punctual and efficient." "Always my first choice."

FIRMS WITHOUT PORTFOLIOS

AAA 1 Carpet & Upholstery Care   4   2.5   5   4
13127 Hartland Street, North Hollywood, CA 91605
(310) 451 - 3411 www.aaa1carpetcare.com

Area rug, carpet and upholstery cleaning and repair; hardwood floor maintenance and refinishing

As an acknowledged, acclaimed authority in the carpet cleaning industry, AAA 1 Carpet has been satisfying residential and commercial clients ever since it opened doors in 1979. Established and managed by Daniel Gonzales, the company cleans and repairs area rugs, wall-to-wall carpets, upholstery and fabric walls. The firm's many services also include cleaning, refinishing, sanding and repairing hardwood floors.

Clients appreciate the company's 24-hour emergency service, established specifically for water or flood damage. Cleaning is usually done on-site, but AAA 1 also has cleaning and repair capabilities in its plant. The eight-person firm charges by the square foot, gives free estimates and will pick up and deliver for free. AAA 1 will also move furniture, if necessary, at no extra cost.

Reliable, easygoing, punctual and organized are how clients refer to workers at this company. While some say they do a "reasonably good job," others tell us they are "efficient and thorough" and that they "know exactly what to do." All agree, however, that the company's excellent work ethic and moderate prices keep them coming back for more.

"Always solid work. They get the job done." "They finish on time. Always available." "I have no problem leaving them in the house unattended. They are honest and reliable."

Ace Rug & Furniture Cleaning Co.   4.5   3   5   4.5
9054 Santa Monica Boulevard, Los Angeles, CA 90069
(310) 273 - 9631 www.acerugcleaners.com

Area rug, carpet, upholstery and furniture cleaning and repair

A true legend in the industry, Ace Rug & Furniture Cleaning Co. has been cleaning, repairing and installing wall-to-wall carpets and area rugs for the last 51 years. This residential and commercial firm is also an ace at cleaning drapes, furniture, upholstery and fabric, including silk, Haitian cotton, leather and suede.

Ace takes great pride in the Turbo 400, its unique and powerful extraction cleaning system (the firm claims the process removes 90 percent of dirt and residue). Since the Turbo 400 uses a minimum of moisture and a crystallized foam, carpets dry faster than with typical steam process systems. Building on its tradition of innovation, Ace also works with the specialized Bonnett Method, a non-toxic solvent option that has been a great success with finicky fabrics and their equally discerning owners. Diana Elkins helms a staff of 25 that serves clients in Beverly Hills, Brentwood, Santa Monica, the San Fernando Valley, Burbank, Pasadena and prominent stores along Rodeo Drive. Illustrious clients include the Beverly Hills Hotel, the Bel-Air Hotel, the Park Hotel, Le Mondrian and UCLA. Pricing is usually by the square foot and the workers will move furniture at no extra charge. Ace recently acquired a brand-new plant in downtown LA where they have free pickups and delivery for area rugs.

Sources tell us Ace Rug is professional, punctual, efficient and diligent. The firm has a minimum fee to do a project. With its "moderate to standard" prices and customer-oriented service, this carpet-cleaning legend aces the test of its demanding clientele.

"I trust them completely." "Honest. Good about explaining things." "They've been around a long time. Knowledgeable about their work." "Courteous workmen. Accomplishes task with minimum mess."

Amadi Carpets Inc.   4.5   2.5   5   4
408 North Robertson Boulevard, West Hollywood, CA 90048
(310) 659 - 5353   www.amadicarpets.com
Area rug cleaning, installation, repair, restoration and retail

Selling, cleaning and restoring Persian, Aubusson, Indian, Oriental and Tibetan area rugs is a family affair for Zabi Ahmadi and his five brothers, second-generation rug tradesmen from Afghanistan. Together, they also own a manufacturing company in Afghanistan that produces the fine rugs for which their country is known, in customized original and antique designs. The seven-year-old company sells an extensive collection of antique and modern area rugs, tapestries, kilims and needlepoints, both in Afghanistan and Los Angeles. Their showroom, a popular destination for many LA decorators, is open to the public.

Insiders say Ahmadi's workmen are quiet and efficient, and that the company's rug selection is among the best in the city. Though Amadi Carpets primarily serves residential and commercial clients in Beverly Hills, Brentwood, Bel Air and San Diego, it has been known to do installations and repairs as far away as New York and Pittsburgh. Pricing is by the square foot with free estimates, pickup, delivery and moving of furniture—when necessary. When it comes to luxurious, finely woven Afghan rugs, Ahmadi is at the top of insiders' lists.

"Splendid work ethic." "Very good knowledge of carpets." "Always delivers on time. Reliable." "Friendly and personable." "Pleasant and easy to work with." "Beautiful custom work."

Anacapa Window & Carpet Cleaning
3920 Inglewood Boulevard, Suite 5, Los Angeles, CA 90066
(310) 398 - 3214
Residential and commercial window and carpet cleaning

See Anacapa Window & Carpet Cleaning's full report under the heading Window Washers

	Quality	Cost	Value	Recommend?
	✚	$	◆	★

Ariana Rugs Inc.

| | 4 | 3 | 5 | 4.5 |

8408 Melrose Place, Los Angeles, CA 90069
(323) 653 - 2424   www.arianarugs.com

Area rug cleaning, repair, restoration, retail and wholesale

Boasting an extensive collection of Aubussons, Oriental, Indian and Persian area rugs, as well as kilims, needlepoints and tapestries, Ariana Rugs' inventory rivals that of any firm in Los Angeles. Ariana was established in 1990 by Ahmad Ahmadi and his brother Alex, who grew up working in their family's rug business in Afghanistan. Today, the Ahmadis have three showrooms in Southern California, and their rugs are carried exclusively by prominent showrooms in Chicago and San Francisco. Ariana Rugs serves residential and commercial clients throughout the LA area and as far away as San Diego. The firm's latest showroom opened in 2002 in Redondo Beach.

Though primarily a dealer, the company also cleans, repairs and restores. It also designs custom rugs. Pricing is by the job and there is an extra charge for pickup and delivery. Clients say the reasonable prices are a good deal for Ariana's third-generation master craftsmanship.

Bobcat Carpet & Fabric Care

| | 4 | 2.5 | 5 | 4.5 |

11630 Tennessee Avenue, Los Angeles, CA 90405
(310) 478 - 4438   www.bobcatcarpetcare.com

Area rug, carpet, upholstery and textile cleaning and repair

Decorators, homeowners, rug dealers and textile manufacturers run toward this Bobcat. We hear Bobcat Carpet & Fabric Care is the place to call for all rug and carpet cleaning, repair and protection needs. Founded in 1977 by Al Casas and his wife, Vicky, this family-owned business cleans on-site or in its plant. Al holds certificates from the Institute of Inspection and Restoration Certification (IICRC) and the Association of Specialists in Cleaning and Restoration (ASCR) and clients value his restoration expertise.

The firm deals primarily with residential clients but does a bit of high-end commercial and museum work. The twenty-person firm serves most of West LA, some parts of San Diego, Palm Springs and Santa Barbara, and has done projects in New York and Las Vegas. Hourly rates apply for repair work, while cleaning charges are generally determined by the square foot. There is a minimum fee required per project but moving of light furniture and touch-ups are free.

References enthuse about Bobcat's high-quality cleaning and repair services. Customers also love the fact that the company will go the extra mile to help out a client. When one client's home flooded, Bobcat was there at 5:30 a.m. to save the fine rugs. Customers tell us they appreciate the moderate prices for competent service, reliability and promptness that they feel are worth every penny.

"Good follow-ups." "Customer-oriented." "Very good at what they do. A joy to work with."

Decorative Carpets Inc.

| | 4.5 | 3 | 5 | 4 |

8900 Melrose Avenue, Los Angeles, CA 90069
(310) 859 - 6333   www.decorativecarpets.com

Area rug retail, installation and custom design

One of Los Angeles's oldest purveyors of fine rugs, Decorative Carpets has been a preferred source for decorators, dealers, hoteliers and discriminating private clients for 50 years. Founded by Lou Sugarman, the company's tradition of excellence is now maintained by his son George, who studied Carpet Technology and Design at Kidderminster College in England.

Though Decorative Carpets sells and installs area rugs, its real forte is custom designing them. The company's showroom features a wide selection of Sugarman's creations, all of which are hand-tufted in Thailand. Licensed, bonded and insured, this company of twenty has customers in Beverly Hills, Bel Air, Malibu, Pasadena—and in all corners of the globe. Commercial clients include many of the highest of the high-end: The Four Seasons, The Peninsula, Dior and Shutters on the Beach, to name a few. Pricing is generally per square foot, and while there is no minimum charge for a project, there is an extra fee for pickup and delivery.

Everything at Decorative Carpets is top of the line—including its knowledgeable, professional, courteous customer service. Or should we say, almost everything. Prices are considered quite reasonable, which makes clients consider Decorative's beautiful custom rugs an extremely good deal.

"They stand behind their work. Knowledgeable about the market and what's out there." "They work to please. Accommodating." "Not stingy on samples." "Have been using them for years. We are extremely comfortable with them. They won't let us down."

Drakes Quality Carpet & Upholstery Services

| | 4 | 2.5 | 4.5 | 5 |

PO Box 241045, Los Angeles, CA 90024
(310) 915 - 0134   www.drakescarpetcleaning.com
Area rug, carpet and upholstery cleaning, installation and repair

Highly recommended by insiders, Drakes is well known for cleaning, repairing and installing wall-to-wall carpets. The company, which also cleans leather, chenille, upholstery and area rugs, specializes in spot-cleaning pet stains. Drakes also has a maintenance program for the routine cleaning of wall-to-wall carpets that is designed to fit each patron's needs. Cleaning is done on-site or in the company's plant.

Established in 1998 by Diana Drake, the firm is licensed, insured and certified by the Institute of Inspection, Cleaning and Restoration Certification (IICRC). Drakes is located in West LA but serves clients in most of LA County, San Fernando Valley, Orange County, Ventura County, Northern San Diego County and the entire Palm Springs area. Cleaning is priced by the square foot while repair is priced by the hour. Pickup, delivery, estimates and moving of some furniture are free of charge.

Sources praise the efficient and customer-oriented service Drakes provides. We hear that the company's follow-up skills, professional demeanor, flexibility and moderate prices make them one of the most reputable carpet cleaning businesses in Los Angeles.

"The least expensive carpet cleaner I've had." "Fabulous job on spots and stains." "I love their billing system. Customer service is amazing and they work around my schedule." "I was very impressed and have referred them to several people." "Very professional. Took time to explain things to me." "Gets the job done quickly and without fuss." "Diana is such a pleasure to work with."

J.H. Minassian & Company

| | 5 | 4 | 4.5 | 4 |

8687 Melrose Avenue, Suite B139, Los Angeles, CA 90069
(310) 657 - 7000   www.jhminassian.com
Area rug retail, cleaning, repair, restoration and custom design; antique rug specialists

This company's name is all over the place: from design magazines to decorator's rolodexes to homeowner's cell phones. Since 1905, J.H. Minassian & Company has been known in Los Angeles as a prominent vendor of elegant rugs. Like the makers of its beautiful antique rugs, the firm believes in quality over quantity. Though primarily a dealer, the company will also repair, clean, install and restore area rugs. Its extensive collection includes Persian, Oriental, Aubusson and Indian area rugs, as well as kilims, needlepoints and tapestries. If none of these satisfy, the firm will custom-design a handmade rug to your specifications.

David Soleimani and his sons, Jacob and Jonathan, oversee a crew of twelve service and sales employees. Insiders report the firm serves a "heavy Hollywood clientele" as well as other high-end interior decorators, architects, dealers, collectors and homeowners. Licensed, bonded and insured, the business serves most of the greater LA area, as well as clients from Italy, France, London, New York, Australia and as far away as Korea. Pricing is generally per rug. Like a jeweller on Oscar night, the firm even "lends" clients rugs to try out in their homes with no obligation to buy.

We hear that, though the firm is very busy and prices are high, its exquisite inventory makes J.H. Minassian the only choice for many of its loyal clients.

"Wonderful people to work with." "Knowledgeable about the business." "Hard to talk to due to their busy schedule, but otherwise efficient and courteous."

Lawrence of La Brea 4.5 3.5 4.5 4
671 South La Brea Avenue, Los Angeles, CA 90036
(800) 242 - 6554   www.lawrenceoflabrea.com
Area rug cleaning, repair, restoration and retail

Its quirky name and respected services make this firm a standout among its peers along La Brea Avenue. Sources say Lawrence of La Brea continues to win fans among many of Los Angeles's high-end collectors, interior decorators, architects and homeowners. Mainly a dealer of fine antique and modern rugs, the firm also does cleaning, repair, restoration and installation of area rugs.

Established in 1999 and managed by David Nourafshan, the firm stocks a splendid array of antique Chinese, Tibetan and Persian rugs, antique and custom-made Turkish kilims, French tapestries and Aubussons. The company also locates and appraises rare rugs for clients at no extra cost. Lawrence of La Brea also manufactures modern area rugs in their recently expanded plants in India and Pakistan.

Cleaning can be done on-site or in the company's plant, and there is a special 24-hour emergency service for water damage. Services are usually priced by the square foot and restoration and repair by the hour. Workers are willing to move furniture for on-site jobs—for others, pickup and delivery are free. There is, however, a charge for a written appraisal on antique rugs or tapestries.

Licensed, bonded and insured, the company has a crew of fourteen full-time employees, including eight full-time weavers. The business primarily serves West LA and some areas around Orange County. The firm is also a member in good standing of the Better Business Bureau, ASID and the Interior Business Association (IBA). Sources tell us you don't have to be a desert prince to get the royal treatment from the customer-oriented, efficient and punctual staff.

"Fantastic. One of our favorite stops." "You are treated like a king while in the showroom. Very friendly." "One of our favorites for mid-market goods and custom Tibetan orders." "Reputable. Very accommodating." "Can produce any design imaginable."

Melrose Carpet 4 3 4 5
7951 Melrose Avenue, Los Angeles, CA 90046
(323) 653 - 4653   www.melrosecarpet.com
Area rug and carpet retail, installation, repair and design; window treatments

"Excellent," "innovative" and "fresh" are some of the adjectives used by clients to describe Melrose Carpet. The firm is reported to be one of the city's favorite rug and carpet sources. Established in 1965 by Isaac Noviam, who learned the trade under the tutelage of his father, Amir, Melrose Carpet restores, repairs and installs area rugs and window treatments. It also installs wall-to-wall carpets, hardwood, cork, rubber, tile and vinyl floors. A family-owned company, it is one of Los Angeles's biggest suppliers of sisal and seagrass rugs. Its showroom, which is open to the public, houses an impressive rug inventory.

With a full-time staff of 25, Melrose Carpet, now helmed by Isaac's sister, Janet, is licensed, bonded, insured and a member of The Chamber of Commerce and the World Floor Coverings Association. Dealing primarily with residential clients in Beverly Hills, Brentwood, West Hollywood and San Francisco, the company works with designers, contractors and architects. Installation and retail are usually priced by the square yard or by the square foot. Restoration and repair are by the hour. Estimates are free, but there is a charge for pickup and delivery as well as for moving furniture. This full-service, good-value firm comes highly recommended by clients and is a requisite stop on any search for seagrass or sisal rugs.

Sources tell us Melrose's selection is extensive, its workmen efficient and the sales staff very professional and knowledgeable. We're told follow-up appointments don't fall by the wayside and deadlines are met effortlessly. Prices are reasonable and many agree the service is excellent.

"Innovative." "Cutting-edge selections." "Definitely customer-service oriented. Constantly updating their products." "Responsive. Great on follow-ups."

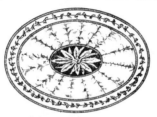

Thomas Rug Cleaning Company   4   2   5   4
3000 Riverside Drive, Los Angeles, CA 90039
(323) 660 - 7388
Area rug cleaning, repair and restoration

As a boy growing up in Armenia, Hagop Torkomian learned the history of rugs and how to care for them from the old woman who lived next door. Though he went on to study electrical engineering, he never forgot those early lessons. In 1974, after several years in Lebanon, where he learned to repair carpets, Torkomian moved to America to work with one of Los Angeles's most prominent dealers. In 1979, he founded Thomas Rug Cleaning Co.

Today the firm sells, repairs, restores and cleans all types of antique and contemporary area rugs, tapestries, needlepoints and kilims. It also sells and cleans sisal and seagrass floor coverings. Thomas Rug's amiable service is reported to be a favorite among well-heeled homeowners, architects and designers, and the firm has twelve full-time employees to serve its clients. It is a testament to his excellent reputation that many of LA's top rug dealers send out their cleaning and repair jobs to Torkomian's shop.

Thomas Rug Cleaning works on both commercial and residential projects, charging by the square foot for cleaning and by the hour for repair. There is a minimum charge for each project. Estimates are free and so is pickup, delivery and moving of furniture. We hear this company is reliable and efficient. Sources say the firm's moderate prices and terrific service make it a first choice for repeat business.

"Trustworthy and reliable." "Cleans like a dream." "Will go out of their way to please." "My first and only choice."

HIRING A SECURITY SYSTEM
SERVICE PROVIDER

Some of us turn on the TV set when leaving the house and consider it a security measure. Of course, with an American home burglarized once every eleven seconds, it could also be considered hospitality. In fact, security systems, the first centrally controlled, integrated systems to make it into most homes, are merging with the fire/life-safety and convenience/lifestyle versions now forming the backbone of home automation. So, if you really think "Three's Company" reruns will frighten potential burglars (and you may have a point), you can program your TV's routine—along with the rest of your security system's functions—over your cell phone or the Internet while vacationing halfway around the world. Now if only you could get the vacuum cleaner to pick up your mail.

Like their A/V brethren, security system service providers are marketing themselves as one-stop shopping for your home's central nervous system. No one company may be best at everything yet, but security is a safe place to start smartening up your home.

A HOST OF HIGH-TECH OPTIONS

Options once reserved for technophiles, super-villains, museums or celebrities have become available to anyone. Closed circuit television (CCTV) can now be fed through your TV or computer and can be monitored online, allowing you to eyeball for trouble from virtually anywhere. Card Access Control is another viable option on pricier security systems. This feature lets you arm or disable security settings with the simple swipe of a magnetic card key about the size of a driver's license. Sensors can be installed that detect motion, temperature change, smoke and carbon monoxide, fluctuation of sound waves, broken glass or breached barriers. When tripped, they transmit the disruption to a central control panel, which in turn relays the home location and the point of alarm to the monitoring company. The monitoring company immediately attempts to contact the homeowner (unless specifically instructed to call authorities right away) to verify that a break-in has occurred. If there is no response, or the respondent fails to give the proper secret password, the police or fire department is notified. In addition, some monitoring companies will dispatch their own personnel to check out the situation, either from the street or, if keys are provided, inside the home itself.

The explosion of cellular and wireless technology promises further protection options and convenience to homeowners. Teamed with battery packs in the event of power failure, communication is fully safeguarded. Wireless modular components (touch-pads) can be placed in convenient locations by homeowners themselves. (This is great for renters, too, who can take the wireless system with them when they move.) Alarm warnings range from the sound of a voice calmly repeating "fire" or the crazed, vicious barks of a pack of Rottweilers to sudden illumination of all the lights in your home as if it were Dodger Stadium.

All of these functions are managed through a central control panel, traditionally a keypad and display. But as this industry charges toward the home-automation front, touch screens or PC platforms are increasingly becoming the way to go, which makes it much easier to program and manage your systems. You can keep tabs on alarm history and security status or play back the sequence of lights you turn on and off while driving home from work—and doing it all remotely via computer or cell phone.

For the celebrity glitterati crowd there are high-end options like safe rooms and bodyguard services. For the right price, you can be as safe as a Saudi Prince or an American senator. However, cost and inconvenience are so prohibitive as to limit these services to the unlucky celebrities who really need them.

Choosing the right system is as much about the logistical characteristics of your location (i.e. apartment vs. house, rural vs. urban) and budget as it is about the degree of system integration you want in your home. Options range from an "I'm Protected" warning sticker on a window to a virtual HAL 5000. How sophisticated do you want to get? How intrusive? A homeowner's personal circumstances and susceptibility must also be considered.

On Cost

The cost of any security system depends upon the number of devices, the sophistication of the control unit, the degree of integration, the term and service of the monitoring and whether or not the technology is wireless. Basically, cost reflects the time and material for installation plus the monitoring agreement.

Monitoring agreements vary from month-to-month contracts to long-term commitments of up to five years. At the end of the term, the monitoring agreement should be automatically renewable, with a ceiling for rate hikes spelled out in the contract. Payment can be made on a monthly, quarterly or annual basis. If you break your contract, you may be held responsible for as much as 90 percent of the unexpired term, but most high-end security firms will let it go to avoid ill will or tarnishing their reputation. If you sell your home, however, you should be able to transfer your monitoring agreement over to the new owners.

It is important to know the parameters of your monitoring agreement before you sign it. Many people are involved in your security, and awkward mistakes will cost you time and could cause system malfunction. Security providers allow a familiarization period in which no signal is acted upon. Use this time wisely. Once you're up and running, you may be charged by both the monitoring company and the city for false alarms that waste their time. They will also charge you to reprogram controls. Be absolutely sure you're comfortable with the system setup and its use before signing the agreement. Warranties should cover parts and labor for one year, and you can opt for a maintenance agreement that covers such extras as emergency service.

After you invest in a security system, check with your homeowner's insurance company. You may be able to get a reduction in your insurance rate.

Getting Plugged In

Finally, your security system provider may need an installation permit, and certain components and installation methods may need to comply with local regulations. As the homeowner, you must provide permanent electrical access and a permanent telephone connection.

What to Consider When Choosing a Security System

✧   Do you own or rent?
✧   Is it a house or an apartment?
✧   How many entrances and windows does the house have?
✧   Are there children or pets in the home?
✧   How often are you around?
✧   Who has access while you're away (housekeeper, etc.)?
✧   Is the neighborhood crowded or isolated?

	Quality	Cost	Value	Recommend?
	✚	$	◆	★

Security Systems Design & Installation

ADT Security   3   3   4   3.5
5400 West Rosecrans Avenue, Hawthorne, CA 90250
(800) 238 - 4459   www.adt.com
Home security systems and monitoring; fire detection equipment

For more than 125 years, ADT has been helping to secure and monitor homes and businesses in Los Angeles. A well-known national security firm, ADT installs and maintains burglary, fire, flood and carbon monoxide detection systems.

Clients describe ADT as "serious security" and praise the efficiency and quality of the service. Sources tell us the systems are reasonably priced, but caution that clients shouldn't forget the ongoing monthly fees. The company offers its own alarm monitoring services and is reputed to have an excellent service staff. However, some say ADT can make the average client feel "lost in the shuffle" of a massive, if time-tested, organization.

Advanced Security Concepts   4.5   4.5   4   5
16116 Dickens Street, Encino, CA 91436
(818) 990 - 3957   www.ascsecuritysite.com
Highly trained personal security guards, safe rooms and home security systems

To those for whom home security is a major concern, Advance Security Concepts offers some serious options. Principal Oded Krascinsky made his name training armed personal security for celebrities and corporate tycoons. Krascinsky has more than thirteen years' experience in the protection business, guarding diplomats from Israel, athletes and Hollywood notables. He also served in the Israeli army and the Secret Service. Today, he designs custom residential security systems and safe rooms of the highest order.

Krascinsky started Advanced Security Concepts in 1999 with a focus on guards, but he soon branched out into technical service when clients asked him to consult on their home security systems. Today, Krascinsky has four certified system installers on staff, in addition to eight security guards and bodyguards who undergo training every six months in a number of life-saving techniques. Upon request, Advanced will provide guards to monitor a residential security system from a security room on-site. Sources say Advanced provides very high-end security at high-end prices.

"This is serious protection for serious clients."

Bonded Electric Construction
4284 Sawtelle Boulevard, Los Angeles, CA 90066
(310) 636 - 1060   www.bondedelectric.com
Electrical installation and service

See Bonded Electric Construction's full report under the heading Electricians

	Quality	Cost	Value	Recommend?
	+	$	◆	★

Brink's Home Security

4	3.5	4.5	4

3607 West Pacific Avenue, Burbank, CA 91505
(800) 334 - 9750   www.brinkshomesecurity.com

Large and small-scale home security systems

Whether you want a standard burglar alarm or a more advanced 24-hour monitoring system with fire and carbon monoxide detectors, Brink's can provide it. One of the largest home security companies in the US, Brink's Home Security was founded in 1983 as an offshoot to its 140-year-old armored car delivery service. Today, Brink's Home Security monitors home security systems for more than 700,000 customers in more than 98 cities across North America.

Although some say Brink's huge organization can overwhelm clients, making them feel lost in the crowd, others say they appreciate the advantages of a big firm (like 24-hour phone support). Brink's offers a number of services for the average small household at reasonable prices, but is not known for designing highly customized security systems. The firm does boast its own monitoring facilities, and all of the company's installers are certified by the National Burglar and Fire Alarm Association.

Current Technologies

3.5	3.5	4	4

18423 Walker Basin Road, Caliente, CA 93518
(866) 460 - 8324

Service-oriented home security systems

Owner John Zullo focuses exclusively on residential security systems, allowing him to stay current with the latest technology. Current can custom-design security systems of up to 255 zones with any combination of CCTV surveillance systems, fire alarms, burglar alarms and card-access control. Zullo will also set up telephone networks and hardwire your house for cable or DSL Internet connections.

Most of Current's clients are in Pacific Palisades, Beverly Hills and Bel Air, but this small, three-person firm will take on jobs across the San Fernando Valley. We're told that Current favors NAPCO burglar alarms and sells a variety of surveillance equipment at mid-range prices. Zullo also offers third-party monitoring and a one-year warranty on parts and labor. After a Current system has been installed, which usually takes about four days, Zullo walks the customer through a thorough instruction process. Customers appreciate the attention, and the fact that one of Zullo's staff will respond almost immediately to service calls.

"John really takes the time to make sure the client knows how to use their system."

Eagle Alarms Company

4.5	3	5	5

14358 Magnolia Boulevard, Sherman Oaks, CA 91423
(800) 946 - 5200

Design/installation of home security, A/V, computer and telephone systems

Since 1994, owner Haroon Azari's eagle eye has been searching out state-of-the-art home alarm and monitoring systems—and earning him the trust of many discriminating LA residents. Billed as one-stop shopping for all low-voltage electrical services, Eagle Alarms installs home security systems, telephone and computer networks, and large A/V systems, including screening rooms. Eagle also provides CCTV surveillance systems, and cable and ethernet. Eagle Alarms primarily uses DSC products for its security systems and Panasonic products for its telephone networks.

Respected by the area's high-end architects and general contractors, Azari has been known to integrate a complex security system into the home and train its users in a matter of two days. However, clients are quick to note that Azari and his staff take the time to ensure that they feel comfortable using their system. With a lightning-quick response time and no fines for false alarms to third-party monitors, Azari runs a very customer-friendly firm. Clients say the company's fees are quite reasonable, and often lower than those of other custom-security providers. Many say that Eagle's ability to provide numerous services saves them time and money.

"Haroon is a wonderful man. He gets right down to work, but never loses the personal touch." "He'll even give you his pager number, just in case you ever need him."

H&H Security Systems Inc.   5   4   5   5
12449 Chandler Boulevard, Valley Village, CA 91607
(818) 985 - 4142
High-end home security systems and surveillance

Mike Hill carries on the tradition of extraordinary service started by his father, Ernest, in 1969. High-end contractors often recommend this "top-notch" firm for its 24-hour service. The firm offers CCTV surveillance, fire alarm systems and card-access control. We hear that Hill primarily uses NAPCO brands for control equipment. For card access, he uses Continental exclusively. The company is one of the few that will hold premise keys for clients, which means that Hill will personally show up and secure a property if the police are called in to investigate.

H&H's protection net extends across San Fernando Valley, Beverly Hills, Santa Monica and Malibu. The firm has a devoted staff of four, all of whom have undergone training and background checks. Clients say Hill's systems are user-friendly and extraordinary, but they say the company's most significant asset is its devotion to the vanishing art of customer service. Hill simply will not leave a project until both he and the client are perfectly comfortable with the system's ease of use. H&H's hourly fees are on the higher end, but sources tell us higher rates are justified by Hill's professionalism and a solid two-year warranty on parts and labor.

"Mike's so genuinely concerned with the customer, it's like he's another family member." "His thorough training of the client is the key element of his services, no doubt about it." "He's friendly, talkative and a pleasure to deal with."

Highlander Security and Telecom   4   3   5   4.5
4650 Dulin Road, Suite 211, Fallbrook, CA 92028
(877) 877 - 1927
Comprehensive home security and surveillance systems

Highlander Security and Telecom installs high-end systems for a most discriminating clientele. Led by owner Steve McClain, the company offers services ranging from custom residential security systems and telephone networks to hardwiring home office computer networks. McClain works closely with interior designers, architects and general contractors, who generate more than half of his annual commissions. The firm is the exclusive subcontractor for one of the area's best A/V system designers, and implements security systems for some of LA's most recognizable Hollywood names.

McClain started the firm in 1991, following in the footsteps of his father, who spent 35 years in the business. Today, the two work together, offering 24-hour service, CCTV surveillance, fire alarms, burglar alarms and hi-tech card-access control security systems. The company also offers in-house monitoring systems—a rarity for a small security firm. Highlander has an extensive coverage area ranging from Ventura County to the Mexican border. We're told the eight-person staff responds almost immediately to service calls. Despite taking on more than twenty large projects each year, Highlander is lauded for its highly personalized service. It offers very reasonable rates and a competitive warranty on parts and service.

"Steve is an honest man who got great training from one of the best in the business." "They can do it all, and they do it without an attitude."

Home Automator Inc.
1060 Aviation Boulevard, Hermosa Beach, CA 90254
(310) 379 - 2222

A/V, home automation, security systems

See Home Automator Inc.'s full report under the heading Audio/Video Design & Installation

Home Tech Inc.
7661 Densmore Avenue, Suite 1, Van Nuys, CA 91406
(818) 781 - 0976 www.htssystems.com

A/V systems, computer systems, security systems and telephone networks

See Home Tech Inc.'s full report under the heading Audio/Video Design & Installation

Pro-Tech Systems Inc.   4.5   4   4.5   4.5
4827 Top Circle, Simi Valley, CA 93063
(805) 522 - 1659 www.pro-techsystems.com

Service-oriented home security systems and safe rooms

Pro-Tech Systems has a single focus: designing and installing the highest-end security systems and safe rooms for some of Hollywood's biggest names. The company provides 24-hour service, CCTV surveillance systems, fire alarm systems, telephone network installation and third-party home monitoring services. By providing individualized attention, Pro-Tech's staff has earned accolades from insiders and clients alike for their professionalism and patience in training home-owners to use their systems.

Founded in 1978 by Paul Ott, the company acquires the majority of its projects through relationships with general contractors, working largely on the west side. Half of Pro-Tech's six employees are certified installers, including Ott's two sons. Sources say that knowing the company is family-run puts clients at ease. We are told the company's hourly rates are on the high end, but the services rendered combined with Pro-Tech's reliability makes them worthwhile. Pro-Tech offers a one-year warranty on parts and labor.

"They really walk you through the whole process, and there aren't a whole lot of companies that will take that kind of time."

	Quality	Cost	Value	Recommend?
	✚	$	◆	★

Protection One Inc.
3.5   3   4.5   4

14801 Califa Street, Van Nuys, CA 91411
(800) 438 - 4357   www.protectionone.com

Standard home security systems

One of the largest monitored security companies in the country, Protection One serves more than 1.3 million people across North America. With more than 60 offices, numerous call centers and a staff of 2,300, it's easy to see why some say personalized service is not this company's strong suit. For those who are seeking solid security systems without all the bells and whistles (literally), Protection One is a safe bet. The company has branch offices in Van Nuys, and potential clients are invited to stop in for a consultation about its modestly priced services.

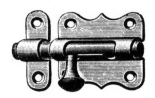

San Marino Security Systems
5   3.5   5   5

2384 Huntington Drive, San Marino, CA 91108
(626) 285 - 7778   www.sanmarinosecurity.com

Customer-oriented home security systems

References say this firm is quick to respond to service calls, never charges for them and provides a full five-year warranty on its parts and service. And if those aren't enough reasons to make San Marino Security Systems a great choice, owner Phil Raacke's thirteen years of experience as a police sergeant and his staff of friendly technicians are the clinchers. San Marino secures the vast majority of its commissions from homeowners' word-of-mouth referrals, although some work does come from high-end architects and decorators.

San Marino provides 24-hour service on its systems, which can include CCTV systems, fire alarms, burglar alarms, home-automation systems and card-access control. With a staff of fourteen, this large security company boasts ten certified installers. San Marino's service area is mainly limited to the San Gabriel Valley, but it will take on projects in LA's exclusive enclaves. The firm can set up security systems in homes ranging from 800 to 24,000 square feet. Sources say it's hard to believe San Marino charges reasonable flat rates, considering the firm's celebrity clientele and unparalleled customer service.

"No charge for service calls? How can you beat that?" "Phil is a man I respect for his integrity and his talent."

Theatre Design Concepts
1660 Corinth Avenue, Los Angeles, CA 90025
(310) 479 - 3568   www.tdc4av.com

A/V systems, specialists in home theaters, home automation, security systems

See Theatre Design Concepts's full report under the heading Audio/Video Design & Installation

	Quality	Cost	Value	Recommend?
	✚	$	◆	★

Vital Services

| | 5 | 3 | 5 | 5 |

6457 East Westwood Street, Moorpark, CA 93021
(805) 529 - 1949   www.vitalservices.com

Large-scale commercial and home security systems

Vital Services understands the serious nature of its business and performs its tasks with all the gravity they deserve. Insiders say Vince Nigro is one of the most respected men in the security industry, and for good reason. Since 1991, Nigro has provided cutting-edge security systems to some of LA's most exclusive (and reclusive) neighborhoods. But Nigro also helped to draft the language for California's strict security guidelines, which dictate background checks for all employees installing home security systems.

Only twenty percent of Nigro's commissions are residential. Nigro will accept projects from clients seeking high-end custom protection, but the majority of his work comes by referral from some of the city's most sought after general contractors. When he does take on residential jobs, he covers everything from the creation of safe rooms to installing CCTV surveillance both indoors and out and card-access controls. Remote monitoring is offered through a third-party provider at very competitive rates. With a substantial staff of fourteen, all of whom are certified installers, Nigro is known as a consummate professional. Despite his busy schedule, we hear that he really takes the time to explain a system to the homeowner. Prices are extremely competitive in terms of hourly rates, falling below many of LA's other high-end security providers.

"There's no doubt about it, Vince is one of the most knowledgeable men in the business." "I have the highest respect for him—you won't find a man or a company that has more integrity, not to mention incredibly reliable services and products." "He can put a system together that would make Fort Knox look like an easy break."

Hiring a Swimming Pool
Service Provider

There's nothing like a cool dip on a hot summer day. So why should building a swimming pool be stressful? Here's a primer on how to find a pool professional who won't leave you high and dry.

Dipping Your Toe in

Most swimming pools today are made of concrete and finished with a material called gunite. Those constructed of fiberglass present an alternative of lesser quality. The classic rectangular, aqua-blue swimming pool still exists, but the options today are as varied as your imagination. For example, the texture and color of the gunite finish can affect the hue of the water, and consequently the character of the pool. Grays create a deep blue quarry feel, while whites speckled with flakes of color create a sparkling effect, not unlike that of crushed sea shells in beach sand. A popular contemporary design is the "natural look." Free-formed and employing rock or faux rock, these pools blend into the landscaped surroundings. Another popular swimming pool is the "vanishing edge" pool which has an edge that appears to drop off into the surrounding area. Also known as "negative edge" pools, these can be quite stunning when framed by a Hollywood Hills view.

After choosing a style, another consideration should be how you intend to use the pool. If you're a swimmer, a pool long enough for legitimate laps is a must. However, if there are going to be a lot of young children using the pool, depth can become an issue. Do you like to float aimlessly into little nooks or pull half-gainers off the diving board? "Power Pools" with their slides and other waterpark amenities are an increasingly popular form of entertainment for Southern California families with children.

Making the Plunge

Swimming pools are certainly not cheap, but if you're savvy about materials and design, your pool professional can help you get the most for your money. In-ground concrete and gunite pools range anywhere from $35,000 to over $1 million. Cost is determined by the complexity of the design and quality of the materials. Significant amounts of engineering, often required for hillside or beachside construction, will increase costs considerably. Although fiberglass swimming pools, which range from $25,000 to $50,000, represent a less expensive alternative, in-ground concrete pools wear better, last longer and are, quite simply, more attractive. Other costs to consider are the pool deck (which can consist of concrete pavers, poured concrete, tile, stone or even sod), housing or camouflage of the mechanical equipment and fencing with a self-closing gate (often a code requirement).

Pool contractors typically perform all the work themselves. This work includes site excavation, concrete work, irrigation plumbing, mechanical and electrical work, tile and stone work and putting in the gunite overlay. Because much of the most complicated work is encased in concrete and buried under a deck (we are talking water here), an incompetent installation can be a disaster—and expensive and dirty to fix. Landscaping firms, which often coordinate with pool professionals, are a good source for recommendations. Your pool should complement its environment, so it's always important to have a landscape architect, architect, general contractor and pool professional who can talk to one another.

CERTIFICATION ASSOCIATIONS & SAFETY

It is essential that the company you choose to build your pool be a member of the National Spa and Pool Institute (NSPI) or Association of Pool and Spa Professionals (APSP). Members of these organizations are kept well informed of not only the technical side of pool construction, but also the current state and national safety requirements for pool construction. Warranties should be long term. In the state of California, any contracting job—including swimming pool construction that costs $500 or more—must be done by someone who has a valid contractor's license from the Contractors' State License Board. This means that the individual must pass a written exam.

While swimming pools can be an incredible form of entertainment, they are also an enormous responsibility and potential safety hazard if used improperly. A dependable, respected swimming pool company can not only inform you of your aesthetic options, but also can talk to you about safety options, such as fences to surround your pool area and pool alarms.

WHAT ABOUT SAFETY?

✧ Aesthetics are no excuse for leaving your pool unprotected. There are many types of pool fences on the market that will detract very little from the overall appearance of your pool and backyard.

✧ Ask your pool builder about pool alarms. Alarms can alert you if someone or something unexpectedly enters the water.

✧ There is no substitute for adequate supervision. Be aware of who is near your pool at all times. If a child is in the water, always have a "spotter" near by.

✧ Consider one of the many types of pool covers that block access to the water, keeping pets and children safe.

✧ Don't tempt children—keep toys away from the pool so they don't wander close to the water unsupervised.

SWIMMING POOL
CONSTRUCTION & MAINTENANCE

FIRMS WITH PORTFOLIOS

All Phase Construction
6737-B Variel Avenue, Suite B, Canoga Park, CA 91303
(818) 340 - 2095   www.allphaseconstruction.com
Landscape design/build and swimming pool design
  See All Phase Construction's full report under the heading Landscape Architects/Designers

Aquatic Technology Pool & Spa   4.5   5   3.5   5
PO Box 130, Morgan Hill, CA 95038
(408) 776 - 8220   www.aquatictechnology.com
Swimming pool design/build, specializing in challenging locations

  Paul Benedetti, owner of Aquatic Technology, has a reputation for being able to design pools in the most challenging spaces, including hillsides and rooftops. Considered one of the premiere pool designers in California, Benedetti is a lifelong nature lover and swimmer. He established his company in 1993 with the goal of improving the pool industry. The firm specializes in using luxury materials, such as tumbled marble and glass tiles. An industry leader, the Silicon Valley-based company will take on projects throughout the United States, including Los Angeles. Benedetti has one full-time employee and uses subcontractors for construction. We hear that he's phenomenal at coordinating projects and is always on-site and available to his clients.

  Aquatic is also adept at incorporating and installing fiberoptic lighting. Benedetti has even created his own fiberoptic fixtures for fountains. The company takes on six to eight projects a year—top-of-the-line costs range from $100,000 to $1.1 million. Benedetti offers a three-year shallow-end to deep-end warranty along with the standard five-year equipment warranty and ten-year structural warranty. Tours of selected prior projects are available by appointment.

  "In selecting a contractor to build our infinity edge cliff-side pool and spa we interviewed five different companies. Only Paul was able to immediately gain our confidence with both his knowledge and ability to turn our fuzzy ideas into a real design." "Paul is a very innovative and creative individual who has the client's best interests in mind, trying to deliver an outstanding project in the time and budget allotted." "If I have any problems, Paul is here immediately, even at 8 PM" "High-quality work." "Very knowledgeable and responsive to our needs." "Good follow-up." "Someone I would recommend if money was not an issue."

	Quality	Cost	Value	Recommend?
	+	$	◆	★

Patricia Benner Landscape Design 📷
135 North Orange Drive, Los Angeles, CA 90036
(323) 933 - 1091   www.benner-design.com

Classical gardens and swimming pool design with a California twist

See Patricia Benner Landscape Design's full report under the heading Landscape Architects/Designers

FIRMS WITHOUT PORTFOLIOS

A. Lee Shelbourne and Associates
15904 Strathern Street, Suite 24, Van Nuys, CA 91406
(310) 854 - 1916   www.gardens-pools.com

Landscape design/build and swimming pool design

See A. Lee Shelbourne and Associates's full report under the heading Landscape Architects/Designers

Ahern Construction Corporation   4   4   4   4
860 Hampshire Road, Suite J, Westlake Village, CA 91361
(818) 707 - 2800   www.ahernconstruction.com

Unique swimming pool design/build

We hear Tim Ahern's unusual pools are some of the coolest in the Los Angeles area. Ahern, whom clients call a "capable guy," has been in business since 1978. He is highly regarded among his peers not only for his pool designs, but also for his waterslides, waterfalls, caves and stamped concrete. Sources say that Ahern works closely with clients throughout the entire design and construction process. The firm offers the latest advances in pool technology, including 3-D artistic renderings of your future pool and computerized remote control systems.

All Valley Pool & Spa   🗁   🗁   🗁   🗁
16800 Los Alamos Street, Granada Hills, CA 91344
(818) 243 - 5415

Swimming pool design

Atlas Swimming Pool Company   3.5   3.5   4   4
5401 West Pico Boulevard, Los Angeles, CA 90019
(323) 938 - 9090   atlasswimpools@aol.com

Swimming pool design/build

Jerry Dobkin, owner of Atlas Swimming Pool company, has been working in the pool industry since the 1960s. With a strong repeat clientele, the firm specializes in both new pool construction and major renovations of existing pools. We hear that Dobkin and his team are able to give an old pool a much needed facelift, installing hard wire remote systems and creating a pool fit for a king. Insiders comment that Atlas runs a "very tight ship." Clients say that Dobkin personally oversees every project and never takes on more than he can handle. Most of the firm's projects are in Beverly Hills and Studio City, but larger jobs have taken them to Malibu. Prices range between $50,000 and $200,000.

Avanti Pools Inc.   4   3   5   4

8138 Orion Avenue, Van Nuys, CA 91406
(818) 501 - 3759   www.avantipoolsandspas.com

Swimming pool design/build

Insiders call Bernard Zimmering a "sincere and honest guy" whose pools are some of the finest in Los Angeles. Since 2000, Zimmering has been leading his own team of ten in the design and construction of about 50 pools a year. Sources say Avanti Pools works closely with landscape designers and architects, creating pools that perfectly fit clients' needs. The firm offers special design features, such as waterfalls, fiberoptic lighting, colored plaster, tile inlay and negative edges.

Zimmering learned the pool construction business from his parents, who started their company in 1963. All that experience translates into very high quality, but clients say Avanti's prices are relatively low. Pools from Avanti start at $25,000 to $50,000. There is a structural warranty for as long as the customer owns the pool. The company is a member of the National Spa and Pool Institute (NSPI).

Babcock Pools Inc.   ▭   ▭   ▭   ▭

5169 Douglas Fir Road, Suite 3, Calabasas, CA 91302
(818) 991 - 9989

Swimming pool design/build

David Tisherman's Visuals Inc.   5   5   5   5

504 6th Street, Manhattan Beach, CA 90266
(310) 379 - 6700   www.tisherman.com

Luxury swimming pool design/build

David Tisherman's "visuals" are serious works of art, report Los Angeles' top architects and designers. Tisherman, who is said to "set the gold standard in the industry," is recognized for his expertise in complex structural designs, such as cantilevered pools off mountainsides. His designs are described as elegant, sleek and imaginative.

Tisherman designs and builds approximately twenty pools per year. His offices in California and New Jersey field calls from clients as far away as St. Croix and Acapulco. But while all acknowledge that Tisherman's pools are the crème de la crème, even those with unlimited means have been known to balk at his prices, which can start at $150,000.

Tisherman was educated at Harvard and the Art Center School of Design in Pasadena. He is a principal founder of Genesis 3 Design Group, a training academy that seeks to raise standards of aquatic design and construction. Tisherman's work has appeared on the cover of *Architectural Digest, House & Garden* and the *Robb Report*, reconfirming its status as a true luxury good. Tisherman has a second office in Marlton, New Jersey.

"David's projects are typically a no-compromise, very high-end, difficult process. He's the best pool builder I work with." "An incredible designer with a great eye for detail and craftsmanship. Thinks highly of himself, but delivers." "Simply the best, most knowledgeable water feature and pool contractor I've ever dealt with. On top of it all he's a great person." "David's creative ability surpasses the competition. His construction and attention to detail are fabulous."

	Quality	Cost $	Value ◆	Recommend? ★

Derian Quality Pools Inc.   4   3.5   4.5   4
PO Box 1352, Moorpark, CA 93020
(805) 529 - 6677   www.derianqualitypools.com

Resort-inspired swimming pool design/build

Sources tell us that stepping into a Derian pool is like slipping into a finely tailored suit. Each pool is designed and built to clients' exacting specifications. We hear that Derian's pool designs are inspired by the sexy, playful and vibrant aesthetic of Tuscan and Mexican resorts. Clients praise the firm for giving them European pool design with Angeleno attitude.

Principals Billy Derian and Kerri McCoy have been in the industry for almost 30 years and employ more than 130 people. While most of Derian's projects are in Beverly Hills, Pacific Palisades and Malibu, the firm also offers nationwide design and consulting. A pool from Derian starts at $60,000. The company offers a lifetime structural warranty, a testament to the reportedly high quality of craftsmanship and construction.

"They finished the job on time and on budget. Excellent client communications." "Very pleased with how Derian figured out our spa leak after many years and lots of money spent on another company." "Not the cheapest, but very good. Great engineering capabilities." "Kerri made sure that all work was completed in a timely and professional manner. Any problems were corrected without issue or additional charges. Excellent job!"

Earth Patterns/Holdenwater   4.5   4   4.5   5
729 East Chapman Avenue, Fullerton, CA 92831
(714) 626 - 0333   www.waterarchitecture.com

Integrated swimming pool design/build and landscape architecture

Sources say Mark Holden is one of the best in both the swimming pool design and landscape architecture fields. For fifteen years, Holden has been designing and building some of the premium outdoor spaces in Southern California. Highly respected by his peers, Holden understands the importance of the structure and durability of a pool. In fact, he's so confident of the final product that he guarantees his work indefinitely. Insiders say that what separates Holden from others is his ability to not only deliver a phenomenal product, but also to coordinate with subcontractors and establish good lines of communication with clients.

Due to the complexity and size of Holden's projects, he takes on only a few annually. In addition to designing and building the actual pool, Holden also will design the hardscape and landscape area around the pool. We hear that in his spare time, this water guru teaches at Cal Poly/Pomona and has written articles for the pool industry in *Watershapes* magazine. A pool shell from Holden can range anywhere from $25,000 to $800,000. According to clients, it's money well spent.

"Excellent workmanship." "Reliable, easy to work with, phenomenal follow-through." "They absolutely stand behind their work."

Environmental Aesthetics, Inc.   4   4.5   3.5   4
18401 Burbank Boulevard, Suite 122, Tarzana, CA 91356
(818) 881 - 9000   www.rockwork.com

Custom man-made rock formations; pool design/build

Homeowners in search of swimming pools that scream "fun in the sun" say Environmental Aesthetics is the company to call. Specializing in man-made rock formations for pools, waterslides and waterfalls, the firm creates playscapes that are waterparks in miniature. With a client reference list that includes some of the biggest stars in Hollywood, this firm is not for the client who wants something understated.

	Quality	Cost	Value	Recommend?
	+	$	◆	★

Insiders say that Ken Macaire, founder of Environmental Aesthetics, has an unbelievable talent for making man-made rock look natural. Macaire is a seasoned veteran who has been in the landscape and pool industry since the 1970s. His boulder pools and lagoons have been featured in *House & Garden, The Wall Street Journal* and the *Los Angeles Times.*

Garden View Landscape Nursery & Pools

70 East Montecito Avenue, Sierra Madre, CA 91024
(626) 355 - 3541   www.garden-view.com
Landscape and swimming pool design/build

See Garden View Landscape Nursery & Pools' full report under the heading Landscape Architects/Designers

Jeff Kerber Pool Plastering Inc.   3.5   3.5   4   4

10841 Fremont Avenue, Ontario, CA 91762
(800) 560 - 7946   www.jeffkerber.com
Swimming pool plastering for existing pools

Sources say that Jeff Kerber can replaster an old, weathered pool and make it sparkle like new. Although Kerber established his firm in 1989, his family has been in the pool plastering business since the 1950s, and he learned the plastering trade at the ripe old age of ten.

This eager-to-please firm offers six types of surfaces in more than 50 colors. In addition to plastering, Kerber also does decking, tile and masonry. For homeowners who want to avoid the expense of building a new pool, we hear that Kerber is the man to call. The firm's impressive portfolio includes commercial projects such as the Ritz-Carlton in Pasadena and the Carlton in Beverly Hills.

Jeff Schatz Construction

21071 Wave View Drive, Topanga, CA 90290
(310) 455 - 2874
Renovations and additions

See Jeff Schatz Construction's full report under the heading Contractors and Builders

John Crystal Pools Inc.   3.5   3.5   4   4

18419 Napa Street, Suite B, Northridge, CA 91325
(818) 885 - 0004   www.johncrystalpools.com
Swimming pool design/build

Landscape architects around the greater Los Angeles area say that John Crystal is "definitely a wonderful pool contractor to include in *The Franklin Report.*" For over 21 years, John Crystal, along with his staff, have been building and remodeling pools of the highest quality. References say that Crystal's impeccable communication skills have made his company one of the most successful pool companies in the LA area. The firm's in-house staff can do everything from the pool design, plumbing and tiling to the actual installation of the equipment.

"I have used John for swimming pool projects and have always been happy with the end result."

Min Yoshida Custom Pools   ▱   ▱   ▱   ▱

2749 Colby Avenue, Los Angeles, CA 90064
(310) 473 - 4449
High-end residential swimming pool design

Nick Williams & Associates Inc.
18751 Ventura Boulevard, Suite 200, Tarzana, CA 91356
(818) 996 - 4010   www.nickwilliamsdesigns.com
Natural landscape design and swimming pool design

See Nick Williams & Associates Inc.'s full report under the heading Landscape Architects/Designers

Questar Pools and Spas Inc.   5   5   4   5
28942 Welcome View, Escondido, CA 92026
(760) 751 - 2507   www.questarpools.com
Award-winning swimming pool design; "vanishing edge" specialists

Skip Phillips, owner of Questar, has earned a stellar international reputation that few pool designers can match. Industry leaders say that Phillips' sound construction and amazing technical knowledge make him one of the true elite. A former president of the National Spa and Pool Institute (NSPI) and the winner of more than 60 design awards, Phillips creates designs that insiders say are not only stunning in appearance, but also extremely durable. Phillips specializes in "vanishing edge pools" and has even created a vanishing edge design package that is used by hundreds of pool builders around the country.

Since 1981, Phillips has been designing, consulting and constructing pools around the globe. Despite the firm's small staff of five, Phillips manages more than 50 projects at a time. The company subcontracts out all aspects of the construction process. However, we hear that Phillips manages his crews like the expert that he is, ensuring that the final product mirrors the initial design concept. Swimming pools from Questar start at $100,000 and have been known to reach as high as $800,000—even so, we hear these designs exceed clients' expectations.

"There is a lot more to his designs than you can see." "Our pool is a real conversation piece." "Skip is not a pool salesman, he is an excellent pool designer." "Great response time and rapid turnaround."

Rock Designs Pools and Waterscapes Inc.   4   4   4   4
21739 Ambar Drive, Woodland Hills, CA 91364
(818) 340 - 7978   www.rockdesigns.com
Custom man-made rock formations; pool design/build

For those who like their poolside drinks on the rocks, we hear this is a good firm to call. Owner Bill Brooks will design new waterscapes or remodel existing pools all around the Los Angeles area. Designs incorporate the rugged texture of boulder-scapes and sculpted rock concrete decks, as well as bucolic water spills and waterfalls. Difficult sites are no problem for this rock-solid firm.

Rock Designs has completed projects for Brad Pitt, Garry Shandling, Aaron Spelling and many other showbiz luminaries. In addition to residential projects, the company has created rock designs for zoos and resorts. The firm does most of its work in West LA and the West Valley, but will travel if the project is tempting enough.

"Brooks is a great guy for any waterscape work that you need to do." "I use him all the time."

Wilson Custom Construction
6914 Canby Avenue, Reseda, CA 91335
(818) 996 - 7036   deanwcc@aol.com
Residential renovation, pools and landscaping

See Wilson Custom Construction's full report under the heading Contractors and Builders

HIRING A TILE, MARBLE & STONE SERVICE PROVIDER

With California's indoor/outdoor lifestyle, tile, marble and stone promise the perfect all-weather surface. Marble kitchen counters make beautiful surfaces on which to work. Granite brings a dramatic flair to the bathroom, and carefully placed stones give a fireplace earthy, Old World charm. Colorful, artistic tiles can brightly define the style of a kitchen, be it Spanish, French, or Scandinavian. These materials come in a staggering range of types, qualities, shapes and colors. Tiles, for example, range in size from five-eighths of an inch square to one square foot and up. Marble comes in tile form or in slabs—pieces of stone larger than 24 inches square—which can be cut in various sizes and shapes to fit the area.

WHERE DO I START?

Your choice of tile depends on your specific needs. For example, if you are selecting tiles for a high-traffic area like an entryway or kitchen, you'll want durable tiles that will not show wear and tear. If you are tiling your kitchen, you might consider a durable stone, such as granite, or a ceramic tile that is easy to clean and maintain. Smaller tiles tend to be used for decorative purposes because they are more laborious to install and harder to clean, while the larger tiles are used for more practical purposes, such as covering a floor. Remember, each kind of tile has its advantages and drawbacks. The installer that you choose should be able to help you explore what kind of tile will work best for you. Also keep in mind that the installer you choose should specialize in installing the type of tile you pick. For example, the process for installing delicate glass tiles is not always the same as installing ceramic tiles.

Tiles, either man-made or natural, can be as plain as classic bathroom-white ceramic or as intricate as hand-painted/embossed pieces from Portugal. Man-made tiles are generally porcelain or ceramic and are durable and resistant to stains. Some manufacturers rate ceramic tile on a scale from 1 to 4+, from least to most durable. Porcelain is considered more durable than ceramic because porcelain is not glazed. Note that porcelain is actually a form of ceramic, but is fired at such high temperatures that it is more dense than the material labeled ceramic. Porcelain is vitreous, or glass-like—water cannot penetrate it—and this is one reason why porcelain is stronger than ceramic. Because of the firing process that ceramic tile undergoes, the color as well as the shape of the tile is permanent.

NATURAL TILE AND STONE

Most natural tiles—such as marble, granite, limestone and slate—will last forever. That doesn't mean they will look like new forever. Marble is one of the most classic, desired and expensive stones, and because it scratches and stains easily it must be sealed after installation. Even after the marble is sealed, it will still be more vulnerable to scratching than other stone, such as granite, so be prepared to care for and maintain a marble installation. There are many types of seals to choose from: a matte seal preserves the stone's natural color or texture, a glossy seal makes the stone appear shiny and smooth and gives it a more formal appearance, and a color enhancement sealer brings out the stone's colors and beauty.

Like marble, granite is a natural stone that comes in both tiles and slabs. Granite is one of the strongest stones, but it also needs to be sealed after professional installation. Granite is more impervious to stains than marble, and also less expensive.

In general, marble and granite slabs are more expensive than tile because the slabs are customized and take more of the installer's time. Slabs are commonly used for areas such as countertops and around fireplaces. Installing slabs requires different skills than installing tile, which is why you should ask a potential installer if he normally installs tile or slab.

ON COST

With the exception of the hand-painted variety, tile is generally priced per square foot. This simplifies price comparisons of tiles that differ greatly in size or shape: once you know how many square feet you need for your area, it's easy to calculate the difference in total cost between tile choices. Basic ceramic and porcelain tiles range from $2 to $20 per square foot. Hand-painted tiles can cost anywhere from $8 to $150 each.

On the whole, stone tiles, such as marble and granite, are more expensive than their ceramic counterparts. The price of marble and granite depends on color and type. Natural stone is quarried all over the world, and a particularly desirable origin can make it more expensive. Some stone is easier to find and is not considered as rare as other types of stone. Like ceramic tiles, natural stone tiles are priced per square foot. Marble and granite slab, however, is priced per project because there are so many variables in slab work. The price depends on the edges, customization and amount of work that goes into the actual installation. Slabs also have to be cut to fit the area precisely. The pricing of slab work depends on how difficult the stone was to get and how large the slab is. The larger the slab, the more expensive it is going to be to transport.

Tile and stone installers generally charge per project. The more custom work they have to do, such as edges and corners, the more expensive the project. Also, note that more artistic tile installation, such as creating mosaics, is much more expensive. Hiring a larger company can be cheaper because much of the work can be done in-house, and the company can buy in bulk to save on materials. Also, installers will not have to be subcontracted and the materials will often be in stock. If you order from a smaller company and they do not keep a particular, expensive tile in stock, the price could be higher than from a larger company. With any installer, tile or marble that has to be ordered can significantly delay your project.

WHO INSTALLS THE TILE, MARBLE AND STONE?

Some of the service providers in this guide use their own installers and some subcontract the work out. If you choose a company that uses installers that are not in-house, make sure that the company has used them before and ask for references. Some companies also keep a list of installers that they use on a regular basis.

QUALIFICATIONS

No professional certification is required to install tile, marble and stone, but there are other ways of screening potential installers. For example, they should have a business license and, ideally, a general contractor's license. An excellent way to evaluate a potential installer is to ask for references, speak to them, and look at photographs of previous installations. Membership in professional organizations may also confer credibility to this service provider. These associations can offer general information as well as answer some of your simple questions about tile and marble installation. The main professional associations to contact for information are The Marble Institute of America (614-228-6194), Ceramic Tiles Distributors Association (CTDA) (800-938-2832), The Tile Council of America (864-646-8453) and the Ceramic Tile Institute of America (805-371-TILE).

Whether you decide to install simple ceramic tile in your shower or rare marble in your living room, the entire process will go more smoothly with a basic understanding of these special materials as provided above.

DECORATIVE IDEAS

✧ For tile in the kitchen or high-traffic areas, consider a darker grout for easier upkeep and a more formal appearance.

✧ Install tile mosaics around kitchen windows, add a tile inlay to your floors and walls or scatter tiles with a thematic print (herbs for a kitchen or shells for the shower).

✧ Use a stone or tile molding to crown your master bathroom or mix marble countertops with a ceramic tile backsplash.

✧ For the children's bathroom, use hand-painted tiles in favorite colors to make washing more fun or give the playroom some pizzazz with a bright tile chair-rail or "homemade" mosaic.

✧ Too traditional? Exotic stones, such as quartzite, slate and alabaster, can offer a unique alternative to other natural surfaces and are just as functional!

✧ Don't overlook the nouveau! Some of the latest metallic and glass tiles are made to refract light, giving a glimmer to the dullest spaces.

TILE, MARBLE & STONE

🛍 FIRMS WITH PORTFOLIOS 🛍

Tile With Style 🛍   4.5   3.5   5   5
1800 South Robertson Boulevard, Suite 33, Los Angeles, CA 90035
(310) 287 - 2420   tilewithstyleinc@yahoo.com
Custom Tile Installation

In the case of this stylish specialist in ceramic, stone, mosaic and glass tile installation, there's plenty of substance beneath the flash. Satisfied clients in the Palisades, Santa Monica and Beverly Hills praise the solid work of Andy Geller and his twenty-plus tile setters, many of whom are third-generation practitioners of the trade. Clients say the firm's expertise is nicely complemented by quick response time and amazing follow-through.

Established three years ago, Tile With Style is an offshoot of Geller's wife's greatgrandfather's company, which has been around since 1906. Working with both retail clients and the trade, the firm gets 98 percent of its customers from word of mouth. Projects range anywhere from $1,500 for a kitchen backsplash to $80,000 for major installations. References rave that this mid-priced company always stands behind its work and that its dedicated customer service exceeds that of many competitors.

"Andy has great taste and is a great help as I restore my vintage apartment buildings." "The only company I would ever use for tile installation." "Andy worked great with my decorator." "A great communicator." "Worked on both my homes. Most importantly he shows up on time." "His workers are clean and friendly. Would and have referred him to friends and family." "Finally, nice to work with a contractor that returns my calls promptly." "We always recommend him to friends. His client service and responsiveness is second to none—promptly returns calls and gives his clients exactly what they want."

FIRMS WITHOUT PORTFOLIOS

Ann Sacks Tile & Stone Inc.   5   5   4   5
8483 Melrose Avenue, West Hollywood, CA 90069
(323) 658 - 8884   www.annsacks.com
Cutting-edge handcrafted tile and stone design and retail

An industry leader in tile and stone, Ann Sacks' design is always "on the leading edge of the creative and the adventurous." Specializing in handcrafted tile, limestone slab, antique stone and custom terra cotta mosaics, this nationwide company offers an ever-changing selection of products in its showroom. Also on display are exclusive tile collections by designers Barbara Barry and Rebecca Gore, and a selection of luxury plumbing products and bathroom fixtures.

A division of Kohler, Ann Sacks stores can be found in sixteen prime locations across the continental United States, including Los Angeles, Manhattan, Chicago, San Francisco, Denver, Dallas, Portland and Seattle. The Los Angeles showroom

	Quality	Cost	Value	Recommend?
	✚	$	◆	★

has been open for fourteen years and can recommend a number of quality installers of its product lines. Sources say Ann Sacks never fails to impress, but you can expect to pay dearly to stay on the avant garde.

"I don't know how they do it, but they are always ahead of the next wave of style." "Always helpful, but quite costly." "I do not buy the basic stuff here due to the expense, but they inspire my designs."

California Art Tile   4.5   4   4.5   4.5
8687 Melrose Avenue, Suite B447, West Hollywood, CA 90069
(310) 659 - 2614   www.californiaarttile.com
Rare tile designs by local artisans; supervised installation

Even veteran trade and design professionals get excited about California Art Tile's showroom in the Pacific Design Center. Owner Brian Flynn procures his intriguing and hard-to-find tile products from a network of local artisans. A number of Los Angeles' best decorators rely on California Art Tile, which has been in the vanguard of ceramic art and architectural tile since 1985.

California Art Tile can be found in settings ranging from courtyard fountains to hotel bathrooms—and not just in the Golden State. Flynn also distributes his goods to other unaffiliated (but certainly savvy) showrooms around the United States. Clients tell us they are as pleased with the firm's service—which includes design and supervision of installation—as they are with its fabulous tiles.

"Accommodating, knowledgeable." "They're easy to deal with, and trustworthy."

Chiarini Marble & Stone   4   3   5   5
830 East Washington Avenue, Santa Ana, CA 92701
(714) 547 - 5466   www.chiarini-marble.com
Marble and stone fabrication and installation; fireplaces

Area architects recommend Chiarini Marble & Stone for custom manufactured limestone, marble and granite. The firm specializes in tumbling and distressing. In addition to producing fine product for floors, kitchens and baths, Chiarini provides a selection of fireplace mantels and facades in styles from French to Tudor.

Established over a half century ago by George Chiarini, Sr., the firm remains family owned and operated in the hands of his two sons, George and Richard. Chiarini Marble & Stone accommodates both commercial and residential clientele, working closely with customers from design through completion.

Countertops by Olive Mill   3.5   3.5   4   4
4247 East La Palma Avenue, Anaheim, CA 92807
(714) 528 - 3789   www.olivemill.com
Granite and solid surface countertop design and manufacture

Clients say Countertops by Olive Mill is top drawer. With more than 25 years of experience fabricating solid surfaces, Olive Mill has an encyclopedic knowledge of kitchen countertops. In addition to granite, the firm offers a wide selection of Corian, Zodiac and Caesarstone options.

The company facilitates installation via a professional roster of subcontractors. Clients compliment Olive Mill's handholding from concept through completion, saying the staff is very attuned to their needs.

"When I compared their prices, they were less expensive than Home Expo." "They told me their goal was to deliver the very finest craftsmanship, but they do price accordingly." "The dollars spent were worth every penny." "Throughout the process of remodeling my kitchen, I must have visited their showroom a dozen times. The staff is extremely knowledgeable, patient and low pressure."

	Quality ➕	Cost 💲	Value ◆	Recommend? ★

Country Floors
4.5   4.5   4   5

8735 Melrose Avenue, West Hollywood, CA 90069
(310) 657 - 0510   www.countryfloors.com

Handmade and imported tile retail

Country Floors is known as an industry leader in mostly traditional, very high-quality tiles. In business for more than 40 years, the firm has beautiful showroom locations across the United States, where customers can browse a wide variety of handmade and imported tiles—including Country Floors' own popular private label line of Mediterranean and French floral tiles.

References report the showroom staff is uneven but say the product is worth it. Although Country Floors does not perform its own installations, references say the firm's outsourced installers are dedicated and exacting.

"I was amazed at the large selection of tiles in the showroom." "They were all I needed for the entire house—from bath to kitchen to front hall." "I got some great ideas for my kitchen floor." "Everyone at the store was helpful and pleasant." "The salespeople are not particularly client-friendly, but it is worth the struggle for the product. Send the architect to deal with them." "They sent my curtain fabric to Italy and had artisans paint tile columns to cover the ugly gas pipe in my kitchen. They turned a liability into a gorgeous asset." "They are amazing . . . uniquely interesting."

Craig Cullen
📁   📁   📁   📁

27077 Sea Vista Drive, Malibu, CA 90265
(310) 457 - 9991

Tile and stone installation

Exquisite Surfaces
5   4.5   4.5   5

731 North La Cienega Boulevard, Los Angeles, CA 90069
(310) 659 - 4580   www.xsurfaces.com

Imported European marble and stone; antique fireplace specialists

This company's exquisite marble and natural stone have won over many of the design community's most celebrated practitioners. The experts salute Exquisite Surfaces as the best in the field when it comes to restoring, salvaging and integrating antique fireplaces into new houses. The company imports many of its pieces from France and Italy. Clients tell us that the firm's 6,000 square foot showroom—filled with antique terracotta tiles, antique marble fireplaces and French limestone countertops—is "not to be believed."

Owner Paula Nataf started Exquisite Surfaces in 1997 after coming to the United States from France. She now runs the business with her two sons, overseeing 25 employees. While Nataf calls Los Angeles her home, the firm's stellar reputation has brought it work in New York, Florida, Colorado and Arizona.

The company tackles twenty to thirty large projects annually, with hard-surface budgets averaging $200,000. However, the firm will also take on smaller jobs in the $10,000+ range. For European elegance and sumptuous marble and limestone, the best in the business say you can't do better than Exquisite Surfaces.

	Quality	Cost	Value	Recommend?
	+	**$**	**◆**	**★**

"Faced with importing many materials, they manage to maintain quality and timely deliveries which is much appreciated from our end." "Superb and unique vintage European limestone fireplaces." "Paula has come through with flying colors on every occasion. She is the pearl of La Cienega Boulevard." "Great showroom staffed by intelligent and helpful salespeople." "Their follow-up is outstanding and they are very conscientious with customer service." "They use an antiquing process on their limestone that is the best I have seen in the United States." "Paula has a great eye and understands the vernacular in which we work."

Guy Sebban Tile and Marble 4 4 4 5

5706 Wish Avenue, Encino, CA 91316
(818) 996 - 4634   sebban97@aol.com
Marble and stone fabrication and installation

Sources report that Guy Sebban fabricates and installs marble and stone for a number of the town's top celebrities and designers. Sebban, who mastered his trade in his native France, has been in business for 28 years and will do anything from simple countertops to ornate fireplaces. Clients are charmed by his French accent—and by the attention he pays to their projects.

A good deal of the firm's work is concentrated in Bel Air, Pacific Palisades and Malibu. Sebban's project budgets fall anywhere between $5,000 and $200,000, and while the cost is squarely high end, the quality is roundly praised.

"Excellent and above average workmanship." "Great customer service." "He returned my phone call almost immediately."

Holiday Carpet & Floor Covering Company

505 North La Cienega Boulevard, Los Angeles, CA 90048
(310) 657 - 1301
All types of flooring retail, design and installation

See Holiday Carpet & Floor Covering Company's full report under the heading Flooring

Joanie O'Hara Schecter Marble Specialist 4 3 5 5

17352 Sunset Boulevard, Suite 105D, Pacific Palisades, CA 90272
(310) 459 - 6778   www.marblespecialist.com
Tile, marble and stone design coordination

Joanie O'Hara Schecter has been coordinating the design and installation of tile, marble and stone for more than two decades. Clients say she demonstrates a keen knowledge of natural stone products and is up on the latest trends. Schecter is praised for her reassuring patience in guiding clients through the selection and installation process. Going beyond just floors, Schecter is an all-around marble specialist who knows just where to find the best reproductions of antique Italian mantels. Schecter counts architects, designers and retail customers among her clientele.

While Schecter does not have a showroom, we hear she can show off plenty of exotic and innovative samples at her office. Prices are based on a reasonable hourly rate plus the cost of material and are in line with the firm's highly regarded service.

"My husband and I had the good fortune of meeting Joanie through the introduction of our friends and her former clients in Los Angeles. She was the best thing to happen to us." "Knowledgeable and patient in a difficult field." "Joanie found materials for us that we hadn't been able to locate anywhere else, and for the best price." "She created unique and elegant designs for the limestone floors

and fireplace facings throughout our house, as well as the marble in the master bath." "Supervised the work superbly."

Laird Plumleigh   4   4   4   4
1111 Urania Avenue, Encinitas, CA 92024
(760) 436 - 1831   www.lairdplumleigh.com

Ceramic tile design and manufacture

Just like the ancient alchemists, this firm prides itself on turning dross, boring surfaces to gold. There's no magic to producing fine finished ceramic tile; Laird Plumleigh, formerly Alchemie Studio, just has the necessary dedication to create the best in ram-pressed, decorative and field tile. The firm is also heralded for its complex matte glazes, sculptural landscape tiles, fountain components and fireplace façades.

Former ceramics teacher Laird Plumleigh and his artisans have been creating art for over 26 years. Plumleigh works with both retail and trade customers. The company welcomes prospective clients by appointment to its studio, where they will find hundreds of "absolutely breathtaking" designs and moldings. The firm offers a set price list based on square footage. Plumleigh and his team charge hourly for custom designs.

"Great tiles for mosaics."

Lodestar Statements in Stone   5   4   5   5
231 East 58th Street, New York, NY 10022
(212) 755 - 1818   mr.lodestar@aol.com

Semiprecious stone and tile mosaic design and installation

Like ancient mariners who looked to the stars for guidance, clients trust Lodestar Statements in Stone to lead them to masterful Byzantine and Florentine mosaic work. The firm designs and creates stunning mosaics for tabletops, decorative floors and murals, working in semiprecious stones, such as onyx, malachite, sodalite and quartzite.

Commissions come from private clients as well as from some of the world's most elegant hotels and restaurants. Although the firm's showroom is located in New York City, West Coast clients say principal Stewart Ritwo is more than happy to mail his design portfolio. Works are produced in New York City and shipped anywhere.

The type of stone, intricacy of design and panel size informs the cost of a Lodestar project, which clients admit requires a certain caliber budget. Indeed, more than a few of Ritwo's most ardent admirers have been known to stretch their intended budgets to accommodate Lodestar's magnificent work.

Mosaix   4.5   5   3.5   4
13208 Saticoy Street, North Hollywood, CA 91605
(818) 765 - 3778

Innovative tile mosaics

This firm creates "original," "stunning" mosaics on floors, countertops and furniture. Principal Merle Sheridan's computer-generated patterns are first etched into limestone. Then, each piece is colored by hand. The unusual process generates a truly unique look, which has earned Sheridan's original pieces a featured spot at the Pasadena Showhouse. Sources say this extraordinary work comes at extraordinary prices.

"His work is more like a piece of art. Breathtaking." "A true artisan. If only I had half of his talent."

	Quality	Cost	Value	Recommend?
	✚	$	◆	★

Renaissance Marble Inc.   3.5   3.5   4   4

8818 Bradley Avenue, Sun Valley, CA 91352
(818) 504 - 0100   www.renaissancemarbleinc.com

Custom-cut natural stone installation

Renaissance man Athens Bordokas and his staff have been earning kudos for their installation of high-end custom-cut natural stone for almost two decades. Although the firm's clientele is concentrated in Beverly Hills and Pacific Palisades, its fine craftsmanship has been sent as far away as Taiwan and Hawaii.

The firm gives free estimates and is said by clients to exhibit a thoroughly professional attitude toward projects.   Bordokas's confidence in his finished product translates into a one-year guarantee of the firm's work. Upper-end costs are calculated based on the complexity of the detail and the quality of stone used.

"A great company for custom work. Athens is one of LA's real talents."

Serena Marble & Granite Inc.   4   3   5   4.5

10325 Glenoaks Boulevard, Pacoima, CA 91331
(818) 834 - 8544   www.serenamarble.com

Marble, granite and stone fabrication and installation

A trusted resource for a varied roster of industry professionals and homeowners, this firm specializes in the fabrication and installation of marble, granite and all types of natural stone. With more than twelve years at the helm of Serena Marble, owner Jayme Lim has expertise in all manner of stonework applications, including interior and exterior wall veneer, floor paving, soffits, arches, elevator cabs, walls, countertops and fireplaces. Lim is said to freely share his knowledge with clients, who appreciate his skills, smarts and service.

"Fun guy and very good." *"Jayme stands behind his work."* *"You get more than you pay for."* *"Excellent quality and consistently on time."* *"Fair and ethical business practices."*

Solistone Inc.   4   4   4   4

11030 Weaver Avenue, South El Monte, CA 91733
(626) 575 - 0154   www.solistone.com

Rare imported stone; kitchen and bath design

All that glitters comes through Solistone's hands at one time or another. Insiders say Solistone imports and distributes some of the most unique, precious and rare paving and decorative stone in the United States. Products span the globe: porphyry from Italy and Argentina, granite from China, decorative pebbles from the South Pacific, and Islamic and Moorish tiles. All can be accessed by appointment at the firm's 2,000 square foot showroom.

Soli Beshart opened his firm's doors in 1998. It's a favorite of clients in and around Brentwood and Pacific Palisades. In addition to selling tiles and stones, Solistone also offers a kitchen and bath design service.

"As someone who works with many tile companies, I would recommend Solistone to anyone." "Soli is definitely one of the best guys around."

Sunset Tile & Marble   3.5   4   3.5   4
2245 25th Street, Santa Monica, CA 90401
(310) 396 - 6271

Tile and marble installation

Contractors say Sunset Tile & Marble is a great secret source when it comes to tile, marble and terrazzo. Paul Lee started the firm in 1983 and has been steadily gaining fans ever since for his exacting installation work. Projects range from less than $100,000 up to $2 million for both commercial and residential clientele.

The Marble Shop/Rubin   5   5   4   5
Marble & Granite Inc.
7124 Radford Avenue, North Hollywood, CA 91605
(818) 764 - 4777

Marble and stone fabrication and installation

Bigger may just be better in the case of The Marble Shop. The firm's huge 57,000 square foot fabrication facility allows it to produce almost any kind of cut-to-size, waterjet design or edge detail job. The Marble Shop's stable of 60 employees also enables it to take on a number of large jobs simultaneously.

Family owned and operated since 1997, The Marble Shop was founded by Shuki Rubin. A native of Israel, Rubin first settled in New York City before resettling in Los Angeles. With the help of his sister Keren and brother Ofer, Rubin established what sources call one of the most successful marble and stone fabrication and installation companies in the entire LA area.

Ninety percent of the projects are high-end residential, the other ten percent commercial. Although the company will do smaller jobs, projects average $200,000 to $2 million. While Rubin's big-time budgets leave some out in the cold, those who choose to go with The Marble Shop speak warmly of its extraordinary products and exceptional customer service.

"The Marble Shop is a very tightly run and organized company." "Client communication and relationships are established early on." "The follow-through—with the required scope of work and estimates—is always timely and well presented."

Walker & Zanger West Coast Ltd.   4   4   4   4
8750 Melrose Avenue, West Hollywood, CA 90069
(310) 659 - 1234   www.walkerzanger.com

Ceramic and natural stone tile retail and project management

Since its inception in 1952, Walker & Zanger has enjoyed a solid reputation coast to coast for stocking exceptional ceramic and natural stone tiles. We're told high-end residences aren't the only ones using this veteran firm—clients also include such prestigious commercial projects as the Bellagio Hotel & Casino in Las Vegas and the Kimbell Art Museum in Fort Worth, Texas. References say Walker & Zanger's beautiful showrooms and well-informed sales staff are nicely complemented by project managers who oversee the installation process.

"Despite the mammoth size of the company, I always feel like I am their only client."

Whalen Tile Inc.

| | 4.5 | 4.5 | 4 | 5 |

PO Box 69577, West Hollywood, CA 90069
(310) 657 - 7802

Ceramic tile installation specialist

Angeleno interior designers and architects swear by Steve Whalen, a 25-year veteran of the tile business. Often described as the best installer in town, Whalen also gets recruited for especially tricky installations. We hear his expertise extends to setting the most intricate custom mosaic murals. Whalen's upper-end installation fees range from $3,000 to $100,000 and are estimated on a per project basis.

"The best installer in Los Angeles!"

Zeolla Marble Company Inc.

| | 3.5 | 3.5 | 4 | 4 |

5327 Vanalden Avenue, Tarzana, CA 91356
(818) 344 - 3219

Tile, marble and stone fabrication

This family-operated tile and stone fabricator has been serving high-end designers and contractors for more than 40 years. Zeolla keeps busy in both high-end residential and commercial projects, its work stirring up positive word-of-mouth buzz.

"Zeolla Marble Company is by far the best quality of work I have ever seen." *"High quality and fine craftsmanship combined with two generations of high-end service define this company."* *"Great work and very nice people."*

Hiring an Upholstery & Window Treatment Service Provider

Did you inherit a gorgeous set of French 1940s chairs that need reupholstering? Would you like to transform your aging—yet amazingly comfortable—armchair into a spectacular piece that matches your sofa and decor? Or are you ready to buy a complete set of custom-upholstered furniture for your living room? Whether you are thinking about the design and construction of your piece or which fabric to choose, upholstery and window treatment experts are the professionals to call.

Many high-end upholsterers and drapers who do specialized work deal exclusively with the trade (decorators and architects), and not the public at large, which is noted in our reviews. Also, many of these service providers focus on custom work—creating a piece from scratch rather than from a line of showroom choices. Usually the decorators provide sketches or pictures to point the artisans in the right direction, and fabrics are provided by the customer.

What Type of Upholstery Service Do I Need?

Your three basic choices are custom upholstery fabrication, reupholstery and custom slipcovers. You may not need a completely new piece of furniture. Depending on the condition of your frame and webbing, you may choose to reupholster or have custom-made slipcovers as a less-expensive alternative. A favorite decorator trick is to use a Crate & Barrel frame and upgrade the fillings to create a well-priced custom piece.

To help narrow down the service you need, determine how the furniture will be used. Is it a seating piece that is frequently used by the family and guests (and pets), or a more stylized piece that is located in a less frequently used space? If it will receive heavy use, you'll choose springs and cushioning that will stand up to this treatment as well as a fabric that is durable and easy to clean.

Know Your Upholstery Construction

FRAMES: The frame is the skeleton of your piece, determining the sturdiness as well as overall appearance of the object. The best frames are made of kiln-dried hardwood, preferably premium alder maple. Oak and ash are less expensive, but decent options. Pine will fall apart very quickly. Kiln drying removes moisture and sap from the wood, which could cause the frame to warp or bend. When assembling the frame, the ideal method involves using dowels and cornerblocks. This is more costly than using nails and glue but will greatly increase the quality and add years to the life of your piece. Tacks are the preferred method for attaching fabric to the frame, although staple guns are sometimes used. Staple guns should never be used in constructing a quality frame, however.

SPRINGS: The main function of springs is to support the furniture's cushioning. The two basic spring systems for upholstered furniture are round coil springs (like a slinky) and flat, continuous, S-shaped, "no-sag" coils. Most fine, traditional pieces use hand-tied steel spring coils, in which coils are tied by hand in eight places around the diameter of the spring ("8-way, hand-tied").

S-shaped continuous or zig-zag coils are sometimes used in contemporary pieces for a flatter look, but do not provide the same support as spring coils. S-shaped springs can become lumpy or uneven over time, and put much more pressure on the frame since they are attached directly to it. Therefore, if you are using S-coils, the frame must be built very sturdily so it won't break apart over time.

In very high-quality cushion construction, the springs are then individually wrapped, encased in foam, and covered in a down and feather mixture (see below for details). This is all encased in a muslin bag to contain the fluff before being covered with fabric. This combination provides firmness and helps the cushion to hold its shape. The ultimate upholstery houses also put down in the arms and backs of their pieces, but this generally adds about 30 percent to the price.

CUSHIONS: These come in two types—attached and loose. In attached construction, fiber or down and feather are wrapped around a foam core and placed over the spring system, which is then covered with fabric. Loose cushions resemble big pillows that are easily fluffed, moved or turned over to prevent signs of wear. Both types of cushions can be stuffed with a wide variety of fillings, from luxurious pure goose down and down blends to synthetic foam.

Down is the ultimate cushion filling and comes at a premium price. The typical down-feather blend consists of 50 percent goose down and 50 percent duck feathers, and is used for very high-end custom upholstery. The ultimate puff look is 100 percent goose down, which offers almost no support and must be fluffed by the housekeeper once a day to look right and remain comfortable. Because of the high level of maintenance and much higher cost required for goose down, many consumers prefer to go with a combination of 50/50 down and feather over a foam core. Upon request, however, most of the houses reviewed below can deliver whatever the customer prefers. A lesser-quality cushion is 25 percent goose down and 75 percent duck feathers, which is harder and should cost less. All Dacron foam is the least costly alternative, and is not generally found in high quality work.

FABRICS: The possibilities are endless when choosing upholstery fabric. With so many options, you can narrow your search by exploring a few basic issues. Prices vary widely, from $10 to well over $400 per yard. The most important issue is how the piece will be used. Do you need a super durable fabric that can withstand daily use? Or is it a not-to-be-touched showpiece? Some fabrics are simply stronger than others. Ease of cleaning should also be considered. Pieces in the family room or children's bedroom may attract more dirt. Darker, more durable fabric that withstands frequent cleaning would be appropriate for this furniture. Upholsterers handle the issue of fabric in a variety of ways. Some have catalogs and swatches from which you can choose—but most ask you to bring in your own fabric, better known as COM (customer's own material).

Keep in mind that the ease or difficulty of working with a particular fabric will affect the price of the job. Thicker fabrics, velvets and horsehairs can be more difficult to edge properly. Also, you will need more yards of fabric with a large repeat or pattern, so the upholsterer can match the design perfectly at the seams—a key factor in separating fine quality from hoi polloi work.

WHAT TO LOOK FOR IN QUALITY WORK

When viewing the work of an upholstery professional in the workroom or at someone's home, keep the following points in mind:

❖ Check all the seams for pattern matching and a perfectly centered and balanced design on any cushions or surfaces. This can be particularly important with more intricate patterns.

❖ Are the sofa skirts lined? Is the cushion of the slipper chair invisibly secured with clips, as it should be? Is the welt or trim tightly stitched?

❖ Ask what percentage of the seams are hand sewn. In the

finest workrooms, all the curtain trims, leading edges and hems are completely hand done. Some even do the curtain basting and sofa seams entirely by hand.

✧ Check to see if any of the seams pucker, such as those along the arm of a sofa or on the back of a club chair. Seams and welts should be perfectly smooth, unless you are looking for that Old World, hand-sewn look. Slight needle marks on the edges are fine if the pieces are actually done by hand (and the ultimate look for the sofa connoisseur), but wavy edges are unacceptable.

On Cost

As with any specialized custom work, upholstery prices vary significantly based upon the quality aspects discussed above. To choose the appropriate expense level, you should assess the application. A chair in your four-year-old's room will probably not require the same quality of fabric or workmanship as a sofa in your living room where you entertain regularly. Most decorators separate the "public" (living room, dining room) vs. "private" (bedrooms, playrooms) with two different price points.

For the high-quality work reviewed above, sofas are generally $450 to $650 per foot for attached cushion, and an additional $25 per foot for loose cushions. This means a high-quality, eight-foot sofa is $3,000 to $6,000 before the cost of the fabric, and receives a 4 rating in the reviews of *The Franklin Report*. Of course, you can get a $1,000 sofa at a retail store including fabric, and this may be very appropriate for many circumstances, but is not of the same genus.

Window Treatments

From a simple minimalist panel to a layer-upon-layer, elaborate design, many elements come together to make a window treatment. Carefully selected shades, sheers, curtains and valances may be held together with various trims, chords, brackets and hardware—and possibly finished off with decorative finials. Some upholstery and window treatment professionals also do hard window treatments, which include all types of shades, laminated shades (roller shades, covered in your choice of fabric) and blinds, custom made in your choice of materials to coordinate with your curtains.

Where Do I Start?

To help you decide on the perfect window treatment for your room, many shops can work miracles with photos and magazine clippings. Once you've settled on a basic design (perhaps with the help of your decorator or examples from your upholsterer), measurements are taken. Most high-quality service providers will come to your home and measure as part of the cost. Less expensive workrooms or retail stores will charge a fee to take measurements, which may or may not be applied to the order. Ask about the costs before asking for a home visit.

It is highly recommended that you do not take the measurements—lest you be held responsible when they are an inch off. Most window treatments, for example, take up wall space as well as cover your window—which is not obvious. Will you have finials that may add extra yardage on each side of the window? Will your drapes actually open and close or just be decorative? All of these factors will need to be considered when measuring and drawing up the plans.

Window Treatment Fabric and Construction

As with custom furniture upholstery, fabric choices for window treatments are endless. As with upholsterers, retail window treatment shops will provide you with a choice of fabrics and custom workrooms will require you to provide your own

(COM). Some retail stores will charge you extra if you provide your own fabric. In addition to selecting a fabric for color, texture and print, consider how easy it will be to clean. Curtains and windowsills in the city are vulnerable to dust, dirt, grime and soot, whereas the elements are a bit more forgiving in the suburbs.

Most window treatments require more than one layer of fabric. For the most luxurious look, with excellent volume, curtains have a three-layer construction: fabric, a lining of silk or Dacron and interlining. The interlining is commonly made of flannel, which not only provides heft and a bit of structure, but also a measure of soundproofing. The ultimate interlining is bump—a special, hard to get super-thick flannel from England. If you're looking for a lighter, airy look, a lining will be sufficient.

ON COST

High-quality, mostly hand-sewn curtains are expensive. A three-layer construction, with lining and interlining, will be significantly more expensive to produce than a single or two-layer construction. For an eight-foot window with a double fabric panel trim on each side and a box-pleat valance, the fabrication can cost about $1,100 to $1,400, before fabric and trim costs, considered a 4 in *The Franklin Report*. This includes lining and interlining provided by the workroom, home measuring and installation.

TIPS ON CARING FOR UPHOLSTERED FURNITURE

GENERAL CARE

❖ Ask your upholsterer or fabric supplier exactly how to care for your new fabric.

❖ Vacuum often to get rid of dirt particles that cause abrasion and wear.

❖ Don't allow pets on fine fabrics—their body oils rub off onto the fabric and are tough to remove.

❖ Protect fabric-covered pieces from the sun—if not in use—to avoid fading and deterioration.

❖ Turn over loose cushions every week for even wear.

❖ Beware of sitting on upholstered furniture while wearing blue jeans or other fabric-dyed clothing—the color may "bleed" onto the fabric.

❖ Do not set newspapers or magazines onto upholstered furniture, as the ink may also bleed onto the fabric.

❖ Regular professional cleaning is ideal.

SPILLS

❖ Immediately after the spill, blot (don't rub) the area with a clean cloth. Dried spills are more difficult to remove.

❖ Carefully follow the instructions on the cleaning product (don't wing it).

❖ If you use water for cleaning, be sure it is distilled.

❖ Choose a hidden area on the fabric to pretest the cleaner for color fastness before applying to the spill.

❖ Avoid making a small spill larger by working lightly, blotting out from the center. To avoid rings, 'feather' the edges by dampening the edge of the spill irregularly and blotting quickly.

❖ Using a small fan or blow dryer (on low setting), quickly dry the cleaned area.

UPHOLSTERY & WINDOW TREATMENTS
SERVICE PROVIDERS

 FIRMS WITH PORTFOLIOS 💼

Alexander Muller Custom 💼   **4.5**   **4**   **4.5**   **4.5**
Upholstered Furniture
8273 San Fernando Road, Sun Valley, CA 91352
(818) 504 - 1785

Trade only—Boutique custom upholstery

Citing his extraordinary skills and magnificent attention to detail, insiders turn to Alexander Muller when reworking older pieces of furniture. Several of the city's top decorators depend on Muller's expertise. Known for his professionalism, Muller does what he says he will do and does it on time.

Hired in the 1960s as a "guy Friday" for Radford & Sons, Muller soaked up all he could before venturing out on his own in 1972. Legendary interior designer Tony Duquette was among his early high-profile clients. Today, Muller maintains a staff of three, preferring to keep his business small, personalized and truly "custom." Working closely with his team, Muller creates upholstered pieces and slipcovers that are described by decorators as "truly singular in construction" and "simply wonderful pieces." Considering the level of individualized attention Muller provides, prices are viewed as well worth it.

"Expert craftsman." "Alex did wonders for some of my older pieces." "Right on schedule." "Beautiful work, and reasonable prices."

Brambila's Drapery Inc. 💼   **4.5**   **4.5**   **4**   **4.5**
5018-20 West Venice Boulevard, Los Angeles, CA 90019
(323) 939 - 8312   www.brambilasdrapery.com

Retail and trade—Custom upholstery and window treatments

Sources tell us they have Brambila's on "speed dial" for "one-stop" custom upholstery and window treatments. Top-tier decorators wax poetic about the firm's wall upholstery and tented ceilings, while residential clients talk about Brambila's "marvelous" ability to re-create a piece from a photograph. The company builds and installs its custom upholstery and window treatments, and they offer a great selection of hardware.

Since 1990, Juan Brambila has been running the family business. Along the way, Brambila has been involved with some unique jobs—from private jets and yachts to first, second and third homes for some of LA's best and brightest.

Brambila says his staff of twenty has done virtually everything imaginable with furniture, bedding and draperies. Although the company deals primarily with decorators, its small showroom is open to retail clients, who can view works in progress and get ideas for their own projects. All who know the company say it is run with such pride, skill and professionalism that they don't even mind the considerable expense.

"Simply wonderful." "Everything is available here—truly one-stop." "A fantastic source." "Great work for the money." "I was so impressed with the suede walls—they were done perfectly."

Castle Draperies & Interiors 🛍 4 3.5 4.5 4.5

23287 Ventura Boulevard, Woodland Hills, CA 91364
(818) 883 - 7273   www.castledraperies.com

Retail and trade—Custom window treatments and upholstery

We hear this firm's exceptional window treatments and upholstery really make clients feel like a man's home is his castle. Elegant drapes and custom shades are delivered with great care being paid to the customer's experience. It's no wonder that Southern California retail clients (along with a few select decorators) flock to this 50-year-old establishment.

Owner David Moles joined the business in 1975 after marrying into the family. Coming in with a degree in business, Moles started as an installer. After mastering installation, he quickly taught himself how to sew and make drapes. Sources report that the efficient Moles is great to work with, and that his relatively small but effective staff of six can handle up to 40 jobs at the same time. Window treatments and shades constitute the bulk of the business, supplemented by custom upholstered furniture, walls, headboards and pillows, all at mid-range prices. Delivery takes approximately four weeks.

"We have worked with Castle Draperies & Interiors on four separate occasions as well as referred them to friends. They've exceeded expectations every time." "A true professional." "Outstanding work. He always knows what looks best—always!" "A pleasure to work with."

Classic Design/Raoul Benassaya 🛍 5 5 4 5

19771 Magellan Drive, Torrance, CA 90502
(310) 324 - 1600   www.classicdesignla.com

Retail and trade—Hand-sewn custom upholstery and window treatments

Classic Design is the kind of place that triggers exclamation points. "The absolute epitome of excellence!" "The industry standard bearer!" And one question mark: "How can they take so long?" Raoul Benassaya, the founder of Classic Design is happy to answer that last point. It's because the firm will only do a job one way—the right way—which to Benassaya means 100 percent hand-sewn, much of it done by his own fingers.

Described by the finest decorators in LA as a true artisan, Benassaya got his start as a fourteen-year-old apprentice in France. (Benassaya's son Julien, who works alongside his father, is the sixth generation of the family to enter the trade.) Benassaya founded Classic in LA in 1986 and grew the firm into the 25-member, 30,000 square foot establishment it is today. Doing both traditional and contemporary custom work, the firm specializes in the reupholstery and restoration of modern 1950s and 1960s Knoll and Herman Miller pieces. The firm is equally adept at providing antique restoration, custom beds, slipcovers and leather working. The firm's extraordinary reputation has earned it some plum commercial commissions. For the J.P. Getty Center Galleries, Classic was called upon to make 190 chairs and all the benches in collaboration with Richard Meier, and to create the gallery's wall upholstery with Thierry Despont.

Many of Classic's custom designs are said to have an East Coast sensibility, "equalling the quality of the highest caliber guys in New York, at about two-thirds the cost." While the stated delivery time is eight weeks, no item this fine is released before its time.

"If I can afford the time and the cost for the client, they are definitely my first choice." "A minimum of twelve weeks, sometimes many, many months, but totally worth it." "He will interview you, not the other way around." "Before they will start on a restoration, weeks of research is done in the library." "No stitch is visible." "You have to go down there to make sure Raoul is working on your piece and no one else's." "Not to be taken lightly. Serious quality at a serious price."

Creative Draperies of California

5	4.5	4.5	4.5

6926 Valjean Avenue, Van Nuys, CA 91406
(818) 779 - 2171

Trade only—Expert custom window treatments

Creative Draperies has built a stellar reputation on getting it right the first time. Partners Chris Farinella and Michael Danon ask a bevy of questions before even one thread is stitched to make sure they understand a designer's vision precisely. All visions are welcome—at Creative, we're told, "nothing is impossible." The firm's resumé includes successful (and complicated) installations of custom drapery treatments, fabric Roman shades and woven reed shades.

Farinella and Danon, who established the firm in 1983, have 65 years of drapery experience between them. Assisted by a staff of ten, the partners manage every detail. All treatments are pre-mounted in the workroom for a review before being delivered to the home. Designers compliment the firm for going the extra mile at each stage of the process. Its 7,500 square foot facility and showroom displays samples of their work as well as custom wrought iron and wood hardware. With quality this good, it's no wonder that Creative's products have been installed in fine homes throughout the world. Whether the design is simple or elaborate, Creative's couture styling and finishing set its pieces apart, both in terms of price and result.

"I know that there will never be a pucker." "We have used them more times than I can remember, and nothing has ever gone back." "Chris and Mike are straight shooters, and a pleasure."

Contempo Floor Coverings Inc.

902 South Barrington Avenue, Los Angeles, CA 90049
(310) 826 - 8063   www.contempofloorcoverings.com

All types of flooring retail and installation, plus upholstery and window treatments

See Contempo Floor Coverings Inc.'s full report under the heading Flooring

Douglas Wright & Associates

4.5	4.5	4	5

5976 West Pico Boulevard, Los Angeles, CA 90035
(323) 931 - 6578   curtainworkroom@sbcglobal.net

Trade only—Custom drapery and upholstery

This mid-sized shop has a big reputation, counting some of LA's most exclusive decorators and architects among its clients. Known for its gorgeous high-end draperies, Douglas Wright & Associates recently added custom upholstery to a list of offerings that includes slipcovers, headboards, screens, hand-fabricated drapery hardware and upholstered walls. The vast majority of the work is painstakingly done by hand.

Former journeyman Douglas Wright designed draperies with independent workrooms for 25 years before opening his own shop in 1998. Ten capable craftspeople work primarily on drapes and ancillary projects, with a smattering of upholstered pieces. Upholstery is delivered in six to eight weeks with prices falling at the high end. Drapery is more reasonably priced and takes five to seven weeks.

"Top of the line." "Doug is so intelligent and personable." "The hand-forged iron hardware is amazing. They can do anything." "The best decorators in town have found these guys. When the word gets out, they're going to be swamped."

Embroidery Palace Inc.   5   3.5   5   5

8815 Dorrington Avenue, West Hollywood, CA 90048
(310) 273 - 8003   www.floriocollection.com

Trade only—Fine Old-World custom embroidery

The opulent art of embroidery is the specialty of Janet Rodriguez's to-the-trade firm, whose luxurious stitching is in demand for extraordinary residential and hotel projects. Embroidery Palace has created elaborate bed valances, sewn family crests into chairbacks and left its imprint on beautiful Roman shades, drapery panels, upholstery fabrics, slipcovers and headboards. There are gorgeous pillows and, of course, elegant bedding to match.

Inspired by her visits to the historic palaces of Europe, Rodriguez came home to LA and started embroidering everything in her own house. Friends were amazed—and just like that, a business was formed. Today, her work can be seen in luxury hotels such as The Four Seasons, St. Regis, W and Viceroy. The town's most celebrated decorators commission everything from the most elaborate continental designs to bumblebees and seashells for the kids' rooms.

Rodriguez and partner designer Joanna Poitier have created a line of embroidered silk taffeta and linen drapery panels, along with a new furniture collection of embroidered leather upholstery, chinoiserie chairs and tables. The new product lines are available at showrooms across the country, but the custom business remains based in LA. Custom work is priced by the design and the size, and delivery can take from two to eight weeks.

"She can do 200 lampshades in the most reliable fashion." "We have used Janet time and time again to give that distinguishing edge to our work." "She is so well priced compared to the New York alternatives, and she can make it happen perfectly though the fax and phone." "Janet is so incredibly nice and open to any possibilities." "The Old World brought to LA."

Fredericka Marx/Patricia Pignatello   4.5   4   4.5   4.5

1846 South Wilton Place, Los Angeles, CA 90019
(323) 732 - 4651

Retail and trade—Fine custom window treatments and upholstery

Delighted clients say they return "year after year" to this mother-daughter firm noted for its "beautiful construction" of everything from window treatments to upholstery to luxurious bedding. Daughter Fredericka Marx and mother Patricia Pignatello are renowned for their ability to realize a designer's concept and their "exceptionally high standards for fabric and installation." Customers can relax and let their capable hands take over. Measurements are taken twice for every project, and either Marx or Pignatello supervises each installation, often, we hear, over coffee and conversation.

Pignatello has logged over 45 years in the industry, and Marx has an interior design degree from the Art Institute of Seattle. Together, they run a creative, professional company with a workroom of seven employees. Marx is often involved in several stages of the project, from selecting fabric to consulting on styling. We hear she's quite a "dynamo," getting things done efficiently and beautifully. The firm prides itself on on-time delivery.

An A-list Beverly Hills design clientele keeps the shop hopping, but Marx and Pignatello are more than happy to take on business from the general public. Sources tell us they appreciate the duo's candor. While Marx and Pignatello will ultimately do whatever the client desires, they're candid about what they think is not right—often saving customers valuable time and money.

"Fredericka and Pat do the finest work imaginable with superb Old-World crafts-manship and attention to detail." "Marx does whatever it takes to make a project perfect." "Not shy—she will tell it like it is." "Not only am I thrilled with their work but everyone who sees it wants to know who did it." "A hidden jewel." "They accomplished the impossible in our home, making our ten-foot-high sliding doors appear to be beautiful French doors with curved tops."

Jacoby Drapery   4   3   5   4.5

23616 Strathern Street, West Hills, CA 91304
(818) 999 - 3468   www.jacobycompany.com

Retail and trade—Custom window treatments and upholstery

From top-of-the-line draperies to Roman shades, these window treatment specialists lay out a veritable smorgasbord of options for the public and decorators alike. Husband-and-wife team Gary and Cory Jacoby offer a huge variety of window treatments, along with headboards, comforters and accessories. The firm also carries the Hunter Douglas collection of blinds and shades. For "straightforward," "basic, well-crafted" work, clients say Jacoby Drapery is a sure bet.

Cory is the creative half of the team, interpreting sketches and working directly with customers to realize their visions. Gary handles production and installation of every project. The firm serves homeowners and many corporate clients at excellent prices, charging a fee of $65 per hour for on-site work. Delivery is said to be fast, as long as the size of the project is not overwhelming.

"A terrific team." "Organized and extremely professional." "Gary and Cory were instrumental in the actual design."

PK Robles & Company   4   3.5   4.5   4.5

756 North La Cienega Boulevard, Los Angeles, CA 90069
(310) 855 - 9888   www.pkrobles.com

Trade only—Fine custom upholstery and furniture

Key industry players flock to PK Robles & Company, where "they will make any piece of furniture you want," and everything is of artisanal quality. Selling exclusively to the trade, the company focuses on three major areas: custom uphol-stered furniture, custom exposed wood furniture (e.g., carved chairs, tables and armoires), custom wood stains and exotic finishes. Whether it's one chair for a homeowner or 200 for a hospitality client, a celebrity mansion or a prestigious pub-lic space, the company takes great pride in its workmanship and professionalism.

Following in the footsteps of her father, second-generation owner Patricia Robles-Ruiz leads the 54-year-old firm with her sister Jooj Moacanin. Sources appreciate that Robles-Ruiz and her staff engage in true collaboration rather than "just taking orders." We hear the firm's artisans can wonderfully re-create any style using photos, sketches or even just the client's "verbal concepts." It is a testament to the firm's fine work that the company is often asked to create the prototypes for production furniture houses. Many are happy to wait the standard eight to ten weeks for this kind of quality at excellent prices. The company just moved to the renowned Rituals Designer showroom near the Pacific Design Center.

"They created a beautiful 1930s grand salon chair and ottoman with custom pillows to match our color scheme and design. The chair is a work of art, and the showpiece of our room." "Very professional, delivered when promised." "Great

style at a good price." "Patricia is extremely professional, and quite a hard worker." "They can manufacture any design."

Posse LLC 🛍   4.5   4   4.5   5

5853 Washington Boulevard, Culver City, CA 90230
(323) 930 - 9699   flaniganc@aol.com

Trade only—Custom upholstery made the old-fashioned way

Carl and Constance Posse's smallish shop has made quite a splash since it opened in 2001. This husband-and-wife team has wooed some very elite decorators by making upholstery the old-fashioned way, with mostly coil springs and 50/50 down. About 90 percent of the work is done by hand, and down is used in most of the chair backs—something not often found in LA. All pieces are made with extreme care and precision.

The firm arrived with a distinguished pedigree: Constance managed Barbara Barry's office for five years, while Carl had worked briefly at JF Chen, and for three years at the now-defunct James Jennings. Today, they lead a crew of eight through the stages of superior furniture production and handholding. Clients rave about the biweekly status reports, which are faxed to them, tracking the progress of their projects. A standard (eight-foot coil) down sofa is well priced for premium product and will be delivered in four to six weeks (or, one week in a pinch). Considering the average prices, regulars say, the craftsmanship is extraordinary.

"Couture pieces at very fair pricing." "Carl and Constance are an absolute pleasure to work with." "While they are clearly on a learning curve, they have a great eye and will happily correct any issues." "Their welts are the smallest in town." "We switched to them because of the better service, excellent quality and the good pricing."

Roth Draperies 🛍   4.5   4   4.5   5

506 South San Vicente Boulevard, Los Angeles, CA 90048
(323) 655 - 5162   tjr1@earthlink.net

Trade only—Exceptional custom window treatments

Catering exclusively to the trade, Roth Draperies keeps designers coming back for more with its seasoned Old-World craftsmanship, tremendous selection and charming owner. We hear Tom Roth's "wonderful demeanor" is surpassed only by his uncanny ability to "ask all the right questions." Those in the know say that Roth Draperies will take care of any and all window treatment needs—from exquisitely finished drapes to exceptional custom hardware.

With more than 40 years in the window treatment business, Roth Draperies is a fixture of the high-end market. Assisted by a staff of six, Roth has fulfilled commissions in LA, New York, Bermuda and beyond. High-end residential jobs are on Roth's schedule alongside haute couture commercial projects. Prices are described as standard for high-quality work, with wait times of four to six weeks.

"Amazing Old-World skill." "One of the finest firms I have ever used." "Tom and his staff are remarkable." "His hand-sewn work is lovely." "My first and only choice for clients who can pay the prices and appreciate the quality of work."

Villa Savoia Inc. 🛍   4.5   4.5   4   5

9052 Santa Monica Boulevard, West Hollywood, CA 90069
(310) 860 - 8978   www.villasavoiainc.com

Artisanal custom embroidery

For one-of-a-kind masterpieces, LA's hottest designers seek out Michael Savoia's one-man firm. A master of delicate embroidery and hand beading, Savoia puts his unique stamp on draperies, upholstered furniture, pillows and tablecloths.

We hear Savoia is a true artisan, whose list of specialties includes embroidery over applique with chenille chain stitch and three-thread cording. With work this fine, it's no surprise that clients are "very high profile."

Before launching his own business, Savoia had worked in the offices of Donghia and Mimi London, and dabbled in design work. Two years ago Savoia, who holds a masters in weaving and textile design from Edinburgh State University in Pennsylvania, started crafting mainly European and American patterns out of his tiny showroom. A nineteenth-century hand-guide machine does most of the stitching, but decorators say Savoia can be found frequently sewing smocking by hand himself. We're told that Savoia's inventive mind enjoys a challenge, and when a customer recently asked him to re-create a piece of seventeenth-century Greek embroidery, he was happy to oblige.

Projects are taken and completed on a first-come, first-serve basis, depending on complexity. Prices fall at the high end of the range, with 50 percent paid up front, but the regular clients of Villa Savoia stand ready to pay a premium for high-end boutique embroidery.

"Savoia's embroideries are a work of art, and he is the best artisan around. I use him exclusively to embroider all my clients' draperies." "A great craftsman and a great human being."

FIRMS WITHOUT PORTFOLIOS

A. Rudin   3.5   3.5   4   4
8687 Melrose Avenue, Suite G172, Los Angeles, CA 90069
(310) 659 - 2388
Trade only—High-volume custom upholstery

Trade professionals turn to A. Rudin for its reliably "excellent" upholstery work. This large, family owned and operated organization consistently delivers the goods—and even if some say it's a little on the commercial side, they keep coming back for more.

Established in 1912 by Morris Rudin, the firm is led today by his son, Arnold. One hundred employees strong, Rudin can accommodate hospitality and office building jobs in addition to high-end residential projects. The company's Pacific Design Center showroom displays over 60 furniture samples and 200 fabrics. The firm will do both modern and traditional work, usually with a 25/75 between goose down and feathers. Lead times are eight to ten weeks and costs are reasonable for the elite market.

"They are very flexible about what they can do." "Dependable and straightforward." "Staff is terrific."

Anton's Decorator Workroom   4   4   4   4.5
323 South La Brea Avenue, Los Angeles, CA 90036
(323) 937 - 0484
Trade only—Custom window treatments

Owner Teresa Iizuka perpetuates the 54-year-old "Anton tradition" of high-quality, custom window treatments to the trade. Flowing draperies, motorized curtains—whatever a designer needs, Anton will make it precisely and creatively.

Iizuka fell in love with design and pattern-making while studying for an MBA in international finance. Her "passion for fashion" eventually pulled her away from the corporate world, and twenty years ago she bought Anton's and began a new career. Sources say Iizuka runs an ethical, professional firm and has great instincts for what looks good.

Anton's staff of nine is reputed to do excellent work in any style, from sleek and modern to embellished and frilly. Time frames typically run from four to six weeks. While prices are described as high end, the work is considered to be truly "expert."

"Teresa is dynamite—so great at what she does." "Anton's can do anything. That is why I go back year after year." "Their abilities are endless." "Teresa is really fun to work with."

Avon Quilting   4.5   3.5   5   4.5
8313 Beverly Boulevard, Los Angeles, CA 90048
(323) 651 - 3448

Trade only—Third-generation fabric quilting specialists

Royalty rely on this third-generation firm to provide the very best custom quilted bedding and linens. Brothers Mark and Gary Raby uphold the exacting standard set by their grandfather in 1947 and sustained by their mother before them. Decorators and other upholstery workrooms commission work from the Raby brothers, including quilting, finished bedspreads, duvet covers, pillows, dust ruffles, hand-tied comforters, bolsters, headboards, upholstered sleigh beds and tablecloths.

Avon takes on a variety of assignments, from unique items for high-end residences to outfitting rooms in Las Vegas hotels. Depending on orders, the staff can expand to up to twelve employees. The average job takes four to six weeks and prices are said to be good for the value. A high level of repeat business testifies to the trade's satisfaction with these quilting experts.

"They are always there for me." "I've had a relationship with them for twenty years and counting." "They have all the equipment to handle any job." "The De Angelis of quilting."

Best Class Upholstery   4   3   5   4
2934 West Pico Boulevard, Los Angeles, CA 90006
(323) 731 - 6678

Trade only—Custom upholstery and drapes

We hear this small upholstery and drapery shop is among the best in its class. Insiders say owner Jaime Chan lovingly tends to fine antiques, traditional pieces, modern and contemporary furniture, and draperies. Catering to the trade, Best Class's work can be found in high-end homes from Beverly Hills to San Francisco to Seattle.

The self-taught Chan founded Best Class in 1996 with a focus on personalized service. Still working with a staff of just two, Chan gives full attention to each piece and reportedly takes his craft very seriously: he will only deliver merchandise when it's perfect (usually about four to six weeks). Accustomed to working with all types of fabric, Chan especially likes to create in chenille, leather and silk. The final product is said to be well priced and "exceptionally handsome."

	Quality	Cost	Value	Recommend?
	➕	💲	◆	★

"A great craftsman." "Chan really gets into the work and so does his staff." "They deliver beautiful furniture for my clients." "Easy to work with."

Bobrosky Company   4.5   3.5   5   4.5
3363 La Cienega Place, Los Angeles, CA 90016
(310) 842 - 8054
Trade only—Custom upholstery

At Bobrosky Company, meticulous craftsmen create and restore upholstered works of art. Antiques are confidently returned to their glorious original condition, and custom pieces are produced with great assurance. It's not surprising that many of LA's more established traditional decorators have been relying on the firm since 1959.

Founder Bryan Bobrosky asked Duane Longworth to buy the company from him in 2003. Sources say Longworth rose to the challenge and has upheld the good Bobrosky name while expanding into selected new areas such as slipcovers. Currently seven employees work on between twenty to forty pieces at any given time. All work is performed in-house, including the making of the frames and the filling of down cushions. Lead times of eight to twelve weeks are common, but Bobrosky's trade clientele is willing to wait for his exquisite, detailed work and excellent rates for the quality received.

Carl's Custom Lamps & Shades   5   4.5   4.5   5
8334 Beverly Boulevard, Los Angeles, CA 90048
(323) 651 - 5825
Retail and trade—Unique custom lamp and shade design

A guiding light in the industry, this firm offers world-class, unparalleled lamp and shade designs. For 47 years, Carl's Custom Lamps and Shades has catered to a high-end retail and trade clientele, who applaud the firm's craftsmanship and professionalism. So beautiful that they ought to be in pictures, Carl's lamps tend to be featured in about six to ten movies a year. But this firm is no prima donna—customers tell us they love how the staff make them feel "so at home."

As far as creativity is concerned, the sky's the limit. Bring in almost any item "from the traditional to the outrageous" and owner Carl Freedman and his team can make it into a lamp. Shades are either hand sewn or laminated, using the client's pick of silks, cottons and vintage fabrics. We hear that Freedman is as pleased to see a person come through the door with a simple lamp project as to see one of the LA stylemakers who depend on him. Carl's can accommodate jobs large and small, from basic items that are reasonably priced to over-the-top works of art. A straightforward job takes about two weeks—more complex jobs are welcome, but they take a bit more time.

"Carl can do anything and everything." "So talented, I wouldn't go anywhere else." "Very accommodating—especially when I need things yesterday." "They know everybody."

Danny's Custom Upholstery   3.5   3.5   4   4
629 North Almont Drive, West Hollywood, CA 90069
(310) 278 - 6923
Trade only—Custom upholstery

For 27 years, the trade has relied on Danny's Custom Upholstery for solid, personalized work. Whether it's his own line of custom-upholstered furniture or pieces commissioned by decorators, owner Danny Canon is personally involved with the creation of every item. We hear Canon's seven-member staff can handle projects both large and small, basic and intricate—and all are beautifully styled.

Sources say Canon's experience seems virtually endless and that he can work in any style. Insiders single out his French-inspired pieces as particularly noteworthy. Designers have come to trust the likable Canon to do all manner of upholstery jobs with "wonderful taste" and professionalism.

"Danny is a nice guy and delivers high-end, great looking sofas." "Better than most in the business." "He'll make special effort to speed up the process when time is a big factor."

Design Decor   4.5   4   4.5   4.5

822 Arroyo Street, San Fernando, CA 91340
(818) 837 - 1985
Trade only—Hand-crafted custom upholstery

For some of the absolute "cream of the crop" LA decorators, only Design Decor's superb hand-crafted upholstery will do. Priding himself on exquisite quality and consummate professionalism, Juan Munoz of Design Decor works tirelessly to assure that every last item is flawless. Munoz uses only the finest materials and personally attends to each project and makes every cut himself. No wonder insiders say Munoz makes it "perfect every time."

Munoz originally learned upholstering from his father but perfected his craft under the watchful eye of Rose Tarlow. In Design Decor's twenty-plus years of business, Munoz has earned a reputation for uncompromising excellence and the finest workmanship. The firm uses maple as the standard wood for frames as opposed to alder. Pristine traditional pieces are completed alongside immaculate leather restorations from the mid-twentieth century. Munoz's firm usually works on ten projects at one time. Prices are said to be high and waits can be on the longer side, but clients are delighted by the couture beauty of the pieces.

"Absolutely fantastic. I couldn't be more pleased." "Juan is so accommodating and yet he has a clear viewpoint." "He goes above and beyond to make sure that everything is just so." "A perfectionist." "The best of the best in LA." "Beautiful couture work."

Diamond Foam & Fabric   3   2.5   4.5   4.5

611 South La Brea Avenue, Los Angeles, CA 90036
(323) 931 - 8148   www.diamondfoamandfabrics.com
Fabric and custom pillow emporium

Both Hollywood stars and homemaker hobbyists frequent Diamond Foam & Fabric's massive showroom, where an extraordinary collection of over 10,000 designer, retail and original fabrics are piled to the ceiling. If you can manage to choose from this astonishing array of options, Diamond Foam can turn any fabric into the pillow of your dreams—and within two weeks. Interior designers and entertainment industry set decorators tell us they can't decide what they love more: the incredible selection or the quick turnaround.

Jason Asch, Diamond Foam's indefatigable owner, got hooked on the fabric business while working at the company the summer after graduating from college. Twenty-three years later, he's still incredibly enthusiastic about sharing his vast knowledge of fabrics and design with clients. Customers appreciate the firm's friendly, accommodating attitude. A small, efficient group, headed by Earl Johnson, can make most any pillow or cushion that a customer sees in a magazine or brings in as a sketch. Most requested are classic throw pillows, window seats, outdoor furniture cushions and chair pads with a simple welt, sometimes embellished with decorative trims. The firm stocks a wide range of fill, from Dacron fiber to Japanese fiber to goose down combinations. Prices are considered an extremely good value.

"Jason is a whirlwind of design creativity and verve." "The foam shop is fast and effective." "If they don't have it at Diamond, it's not available."

Fine Draperies   4.5   3.5   5   4.5

5939 Kester Avenue, Van Nuys, CA 91411
(818) 989 - 5567 finedrapes@sbcglobal.net

Trade only—Custom drapery and upholstery

Traditional, impeccably professional and blessed with a sterling reputation, Fine Draperies is a commanding presence on the LA design scene. Owner Mark Horwitz is praised for his seamless grace in handling clients' aesthetic and practical concerns and is said to inspire other designers with his knowledge. Styles range from conservatively tailored to truly sublime, all flawlessly executed. Elite decorators in LA and beyond turn to Fine Draperies with confidence, calling Horwitz's work "nothing short of spectacular."

After owning a family apparel business in South Africa, Horwitz opened his LA custom upholstery and window treatment firm ten years ago. He heads up a team of nineteen that is said to be extremely attentive to every client who steps through the door. Perhaps they are taking their cues from Horwitz, who has been known to "lose sleep" over getting the job just right. Having rapidly developed a following of clients who "absolutely adore" working with him, Horwitz (who is a licensed contractor) is said to be "on the way up." Fine Draperies work now hangs in some of the finest homes in LA and in the windows of a number of boutique hotels across the country. Customers are pleasantly surprised to receive a fair bill for an extraordinary product.

"Here's how much I like his work: he just custom-made all the drapes on a 15,000 square foot house I'm decorating, and now I'm using him for three other projects." "Considering how busy the shop is, he manages to deliver a first-class product every time." "Always, always first-rate. That's why I work with him exclusively." "I can always depend on Mark to understand my vision right away."

First Stop Drapes/Design Works   4.5   4   4.5   4.5

1371 West 24th Street, Los Angeles, CA 90007
(310) 271 - 4317

Retail and trade—Personalized custom upholstery and window treatments

We're told this firm is the first stop for a number of extraordinary decorators, who like to score fabulous drapes at slightly less fabulous prices. First Stop Drapes/Design Works offers high-end custom window treatments, upholstery and a host of accessories such as pillows, bedskirts and headboards. Owner Octavio Godoy has been known to travel the world for his trade clients, who appreciate his twenty-plus years of experience and attentive service.

Sources say Godoy always knows "where you are coming from." He is praised for being able to take a simple sketch or photo and reproduce "exactly" what the customer wants. Godoy's seven-year-old, retail-friendly shop is a small, family-run affair with seven on staff and a sincere commitment to its clients. Decorators sigh over the kind of personalized attention "you just can't get" at some of the bigger workrooms. Godoy and crew take on just three projects at one time and progress "at a good pace." Though the prices aren't cheap by any means, the high level of workmanship makes First Stop an excellent value in the industry.

"Better than some of the more famous companies—and cheaper." "Outstanding range of services." "Octavio is my secret source." "Amazing attention to detail." "The pieces came out beautifully, way beyond my expectations."

	Quality	Cost	Value	Recommend?
	✚	$	◆	★

Interior Custom Upholstery   3.5   3.5   4   4.5
2312 South Robertson Boulevard, Los Angeles, CA 90034
(310) 558 - 0417

Trade only—Custom upholstery

For fast, efficient reupholstering, designers from all over LA head to Interior Custom Upholstery. Owner Pablo Chavez leads this fifteen-person firm in both reupholstering and the creation of new custom furniture.

In business for over twenty years, Interior Custom Upholstery is known for good work at fair prices. Prospective clients can check out the firm's work in its small showroom. Interior's staff is described as detail-oriented, professional and positive.

"Pablo is such a wonderful find." "Quick, beautiful and well priced." "They're great about timing."

Irma Cristiani Interiors   4.5   4   4.5   4.5
8910 Melrose Avenue, Los Angeles, CA 90069
(310) 276 - 3486

Luxurious custom window treatments

Known for her fabulous Italian sense of style, Irma Cristiani delivers gorgeous window treatments that "have been impressing clients for over 35 years." High-end decorators can't get enough of her signature opulent draperies, whose beautiful cut literally causes people to stare. When searching for the trappings of la dolce vita upholstery projects (soft goods and intricate window treatments) designers trust Cristiani to oversee every detail, from sketch to installation.

Sources say Cristiani's understanding of traditional European finery allows her to effortlessly create in the grand style. Often the secret lies in Cristiani's wonderful details. Typically the firm keeps eight to nine artisans on hand, but the workshop can "crew up" for larger projects, or to accommodate tight schedules. We hear the price is expensive for the "stunning quality" and worth it.

"An extraordinary craftsperson." "Years of experience are evident in the final product." "Clear, honest—and willing to do whatever it takes." "Does a lot of work for clients looking for over-the-top." "Working with 100 yards of Fortuny does not faze Irma."

JC Upholstery   4   3.5   4.5   4
9556 West Pico Boulevard, Los Angeles, CA 90035
(310) 275 - 5760

Retail and trade—Custom upholstery

We hear this firm's keen eye for detail makes it stand out from the crowd. Retail and trade clients alike say that owners Jaime and Christina Dongo know when a piece is right or wrong and won't let an item leave the shop until it's just right.

In addition to upholstered furniture, JC Upholstery will do headboards, slipcovers and whatever else a client can conjure up. Jaime focuses on crafting each piece, while Christina manages service and quality control. Collaborating with some of LA's top decorators, the two manage to wow regulars with their productivity, usually handling five projects at once. Sources say you can expect to wait six to eight weeks for your order.

"Jaime and Christina are fast, friendly and honest. They have never let us down!" "We have worked with JC for many years on numerous projects and they are superb." "I was more than thrilled with the results."

	Quality	Cost	Value	Recommend?
	✚	$	◆	★

JJ Custom   4.5   3.5   5   4.5

641 North La Peer Drive, Los Angeles, CA 90069
(310) 276 - 4126   jjcustominc@earthlink.net

Trade only—Custom upholstery

The "old-guard of LA upholstery," JJ Custom is valued by top-tier LA decorators for its years of experience with the classic California style. This firm's track record of excellent quality, versatile skills and dependable production goes back to 1965. The to-the-trade company crafts high-end upholstery in its own frame shop and masterfully fabricates pillows, bedding and some case goods, including tables and mirrors.

JJ Custom is truly a family affair, with Gerald Jebejian running the business with his wife, two daughters, and son-in-law. The company boasts 35 employees and an impressive 2,400 -square foot showroom, whose 50 items serve as inspiration to its designer clientele. We're told that JJ Custom's workroom primarily uses "arc" or "continuous" springs with extra-sturdy premium alder frames. The firm's outstanding custom pieces fall within the "good" price range and are generally delivered in twelve weeks.

"They specialize in more transitional pieces and are very comfortable with the larger California feel." "These guys are pros—I know it will get done and it will get done right."

Lloyd's Custom Upholstery   5   4.5   4.5   4.5

8550 Melrose Avenue, Los Angeles, CA 90069
(310) 652 - 0725   www.lloydscustomfurniture.com

Retail and trade—Distinguished custom upholstery

Serving select retail customers and mostly the trade, Anthony Kafesjian is a well-known and well-loved character in the industry. Deeply rooted in the eighteenth century, Anthony defines the word Luddite: not only does he shun computers and faxes, but he uses only "real" carbon paper for orders. This love for Old-World traditions is reflected in the exceptional quality of his upholstery work and custom built furniture.

Kafesjian's father, Lloyd, learned the trade from his fellow Turkish upholsters in Chicago. Opening the family firm in the Windy City in 1933, Lloyd moved the business to LA in 1969. Today, the firm has twenty employees. Anthony, a math major with a B.S. from UCLA (did he use an abacus?) is said to bring an outstanding sense of proportion to the firm's painstaking work. Before any commissions are accepted, a face-to-face is required and the estimate is sent via snail mail. As an extra precaution, all complicated pieces are tested in muslin on site. Work is delivered in six to eight weeks.

This distinguished firm also charges distinguished prices well above standard. Decorators tend to use the firm for their client's very best pieces, but not for the kids' rooms. Having worked with Kafesjian for over thirty years, many customers feel a deep loyalty to the firm and enjoy periodically stepping back in time to visit it.

"The style is similar to George Smith, but much better." "Anthony makes sure everything is perfect and comfortable to him. This means a lot since he is 6'6" tall." "The quality is amazing, but Anthony likes to do it his way." "An established master of the craft."

M&L Upholstery   4   3   5   4
4316 West Jefferson Boulevard, Los Angeles, CA 90016
(323) 732 - 0804

Trade only—Custom upholstery

This small "diamond in the rough" has quite a pedigree: its two founders, Martin Sonis and Leopoldo Basurto, worked seventeen years apiece at the top-of-the-line Lloyd's Custom Upholstery before striking out on their own in 1997. Since then, M&L has become "a secret source" for a couple of well-known LA interior designers, who turn to the firm for custom furniture, upholstered walls and bedding. We're told that M&L "can recreate just about anything" simply by looking at a picture or drawing. Fans of this small shop see it as a great place to get an excellent value on top-quality work.

"No frills and very small. But less expensive than some of the other guys—and will do exactly what I want."

Monte Allen Interiors   4   3.5   4.5   4.5
2326 South Centinela Avenue, West Los Angeles, CA 90064
(310) 207 - 7676   www.monteallen.com

Trade only—Custom upholstery

Autographed glossies signed by the likes of Sharon Stone, Nicole Kidman and Sting decorate Monte Allen's 7,000 square foot showroom—evidence that this firm has captured the hearts of some of the top designers in LA and their celebrity clientele. Whether it's reupholstery or custom slipcovers for existing furniture or making something from scratch, this long-cherished firm is applauded for living up to its Hollywood legend.

Owner Esa Yia-Soininmaki apprenticed for industry icon Monte Allen in the early eighties, before Allen retired. With his teacher's blessing, the Finnish artisan took over the Monte Allen name and its loyal clientele. Today, Yia-Soininmaki oversees 50 employees, but we hear he still manages to give the personal touch to each custom piece that comes through the shop. Working with 30 to 40 clients at one time, the firm nevertheless manages a turnaround of eight weeks for a custom job and three to four weeks for a slipcover or reupholstery. The firm's workshop-turned-showroom in West LA also displays its own line of furniture and case goods.

"I can depend on the finished piece to look good." "I don't have to visit the shop during the process because I can totally trust Esa to get it." "Why would I go anywhere else? They're quick, valuable and lots of fun to boot."

Nancy Stanley Waud Fine Linens   5   4.5   4.5   5
8918 Burton Way, Suite 4, Beverly Hills, CA 90211
(310) 273 - 3690   nstanleywaud@earthlink.net

Trade only—Exquisite custom embroidery

Time and again, we're told that Nancy Stanley Waud linens are the finest in Los Angeles. Decorators going for the ultimate look and homeowners who verge on the obsessive all say that no one can compare. Waud is commended for her "exquisite" designs, attention to detail, and high-quality materials and stitching. Additionally, clients appreciate her innate ability to suggest the appropriate weight, color and texture for the look they are trying to achieve. Not surprisingly, this does not come cheap and it takes a while, but the customers are unanimously pleased.

Everything is custom, often derived from the endless collection of samples seen in the studio. Almost anything can be fabricated and embroidered by the firm, including dust ruffles, duvets, tablecloths, dressing table skirts, headboards, pillows, and bed and bath linens. The legend goes that the firm was started in 1983, after Waud worked for a furniture manufacturer who got more requests for her pillows than for the furniture.

Prices vary considerably based on the intricacy of the design and thread count. Lead times are typically four to six weeks. Decorators can send Waud fabric memos from the job and Waud will send back design concepts and thread suggestions. Often entire houses are done all in one shot. We're told the company ships a product only after it has been carefully inspected and perfectly ironed.

"The designs are both whimsical and sophisticated, sometimes in the same pattern." "Parish Hadley would use no one else, and had boxes and boxes shipped to New York regularly." "Once you've seen her stuff you'll never go back."

O'Shea Custom   4.5   4.5   4   4.5

7640 Gloria Avenue, Unit B, Van Nuys, CA 91406
(818) 988 - 2313

Trade only—Custom window treatments and upholstery

LA designers depend on O'Shea Custom for elaborate window treatments and innovative modern hand-stitched designs. With per window costs ranking among the highest in the industry, decorators don't go to the shop for run-of-the-mill projects. This is a source for insiders who need complex pieces of extraordinary quality, from upholstered furniture and window treatments to headboards, upholstered beds, bedding, motorized curtains and roller shades.

Owners Mary and Brian O'Shea actually met in a skyscraper penthouse doing high-end interior work. Brian was the carpenter and Mary (a former costume designer) was doing the couture curtains. The couple established O'Shea Custom in 1985 and remain the heart and soul of the operation, which has just one part-time employee. Their boutique shop accepts only a handful of "expensive and selective" jobs.

The O'Sheas themselves measure every window and supervise every job, and their personal guarantee stands behind every product. Everything is of the highest quality. Bump is used for interlining, which is even thicker than the finest felt, and all work is hand-sewn. Even something as small as a custom pillow is done to stunning perfection. At O'Shea's, both quality and prices run quite high. Curtains are delivered in six to twelve weeks.

"Clear and focused." "Excellent quality." "The expense is not necessary all the time, but for really interesting, difficult work, we use the O'Sheas."

Paul Ferrante Inc.   5   4.5   4.5   5

8464 Melrose Place, Los Angeles, CA 90069
(323) 653 - 4142   pfshop@earthlink.net

Trade only—Distinctive antique furniture and reproductions; custom lamps and shades

Designers speak in superlatives when recommending Paul Ferrante. Some say the firm has "no equal in the industry," while others say simply, "My one and only." This company, renowned for its discerning taste, resides at the top of nearly everyone's list, thanks to its exquisite antique and reproduction furnishings and its extensive collection of custom lamps and shades. Clients cannot say enough about the superior customer service and attention to detail that is at the heart of what they do.

Founded over 40 years ago by Paul Ferrante, who was soon joined by Tommy Raynor, the firm originally focused on the very best European antiques. Today, its refined reproductions have became as coveted as its antiques. The business is a family affair—Tommy's sister Grace serves as general manager and her two daughters ably handle sales and the business side. A sampling of the firm's masterful work is on view at the showroom listed above and a new annex across the street, as well as at the Pacific Design Center in LA and at design centers across the country.

"They do business the old-fashioned way, both in terms of product and in terms of customer service." "If it is not right or the end user has any issues, Ferrante will work with you to find the best solution." "They absolutely stand behind their products." "Tommy has the best eye in LA." "Ferrante treats all its customers with respect, whether you are purchasing an item for $50 or $500,000." "This is my favorite shop and I love working with Ferrante."

Preferred Window Coverings Inc. 3.5 3.5 4 4
14821 1/2 Oxnard Street, Van Nuys, CA 91411
(818) 783 - 9100
Trade only—Custom window treatments

When it comes to smart, stylish drapes, Gregg Taylor has positively amazed clients with what he can accomplish in a timely fashion. Recognized for his crisp, clean, classic designs, Taylor "really can do anything—and do it well," say the designers and architects who know his work.

Taylor established his firm in 1981 and has a hand in most of the measuring, engineering and cutting. Draperies, Roman shades, valances and shutters are his specialties, and he will do bedding as well. Designs are often spare and streamlined. He juggles many projects at one time, and additional workers are hired as the job requires, with Taylor directing the flow. We hear that Taylor places a strong emphasis on customer service. Depending upon the details, prices are in the real-world range.

"I have used Gregg for sixteen years, and he just inherently understands where I want to go." "Nothing is ever overdone."

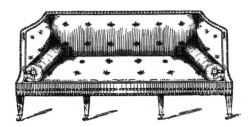

Raymond Gorini 4 4 4 4.5
750 North Kings Road, Suite 116, Los Angeles, CA 90069
(323) 655 - 6281
Trade only—Custom window treatments and wall upholstery

A trade-only clientele applauds the work done by Raymond Gorini and his small staff. Specializing in window treatments, the firm also "does a lovely job" on wall upholstery and bedding, our sources report. Gorini is known in the industry for handmade projects and does all of the installations himself, putting his personal stamp of quality on every commission. References state that he is extremely flexible and patient throughout the process.

With 25 years of experience in the field, Raymond Gorini has overseen his own operation for the past fourteen, catering to some of LA's favorite decorators and their celebrity clients. Prices are described as reasonable for the high quality work and time frames of four to eight weeks can be expected, depending on the level of detail requested. Customers say they are both happy to wait and to pay for Gorini's easygoing excellence.

"He can handle the finest eighteenth-century work with grace." "Such a joy to work with." "Raymond knows exactly what I want, and executes it flawlessly." "He is easygoing—you can change a pleat along the way, no problem." "I love the wall upholstery."

Residence   4   4   4   4.5
4464 West Adams Boulevard, Los Angeles, CA 90016
(323) 731 - 9991

Trade only—Custom upholstery

This well-established, large firm originally owned by Lindsay Shuford was recently taken over by a Newcomer—Frank Newcomer, that is, who has reportedly "taken the ball and run with it." With his "terrific personality," Newcomer has no trouble fraternizing with the firm's celebrity clientele, and we hear he's carefully maintaining Residence's reputation for excellence.

Newcomer worked as a writer in the movie business for 25 years before moving to LA in search of a new vocation. He took up Residence two years ago and reports he couldn't be happier with his choice. Newcomer has spent a great deal of time learning the ins and outs of the business, and insiders say he's an amazingly quick study. He's kept the preexisting staff of 40 artisans on to upholster and build custom furniture, along with recliners for screening rooms, headboards and bed sets. The staff are described as easy to work with and always professional.

Located in an industrial part of town, Residence's 1,800 square foot showroom isn't glamorous, but that doesn't stop hip interior designers from dropping by to see the goods. Residence utilizes a special duck down mixture, which gives its upholstery a softer, plush feeling and lasts longer than most fill. The firm's 8-way hand-tiered spring frames are solid wood with machine grain, and everything is cut to match. Prices are reasonable, delivery is said to be speedy, and Residence can also execute metal furniture within six to eight weeks. Decorators in a hurry can count on Residence as a "swift" ally in their race against time.

"Outstanding service and great follow-through." "Even when my clients have a change of heart (about firmness, softness, stitching, etc.), they will accommodate." "Frank and his staff bailed me out of a challenging situation where I needed 100+ pieces of upholstery in a compressed time frame. They are the best."

Ricardo Ramos   4   3.5   4.5   4.5
5421 Cartwright Avenue, North Hollywood, CA 91601
(818) 761 - 9246

Trade only—Custom window treatments and upholstery

A secret source of several top decorators, Ricardo Ramos is known in the industry for his "remarkable" hand-finished draperies and Roman shades. In some mystical way, Ramos takes vague sketches and drawings and translates them into "exactly what the client wanted." Window treatments, upholstered headboards, canopy beds and pillows are handled by this small boutique firm. Insiders say Ramos is a talented professional who has a "wonderful way about him." Working primarily in the LA area, Ramos will nevertheless go wherever the customer resides, in the past tending to a sizable project in Saudi Arabia.

In the business for over sixteen years, Ramos struck out on his own six years ago and has since developed a following of loyal fans who will only use him. When you hire this firm, you are hiring the owner, since Ramos oversees all work and does the installations himself. Prices for draperies and upholstery are in the reasonable range, and timeframes generally run between three and four weeks.

"Very small and very personalized." "His work is absolutely luxurious." "I found Ricardo last year and will never use anyone else, he is that good." "One of the nicest people in the industry." "In a word: stunning."

Santa Cruz Design   3.5   3   4.5   4
5217 Venice Boulevard, Los Angeles, CA 90019
(323) 938 - 3878

Trade only—Custom window treatments and reupholstery

Santa Cruz Design is known for creating custom-made draperies, pillows and bedding for the trade, but owner Carlos Hurtado's small, skilled team will also tackle reupholstery projects. Reports indicate that this firm works best when in close communication with the decorator or designer.

Hurtado has been in the drapery/upholstery business for over twenty years. He hung up his own shingle more than thirteen years ago, and there are many clients who have been with him since he opened. Loyal fans tell us they like the personalized service and the fact that Santa Cruz will come back a year later (at no charge) to fix anything that goes awry. Prices are very good and we hear that work takes about three to four weeks.

"They haven't raised their prices in years." "Good, solid work at more than fair prices."

Style and Comfort   3.5   3   4.5   4
5312 West 8th Street, Los Angeles, CA 90036
(323) 936 - 3120

Trade only—Custom upholstery, furniture and window treatments

Few upholsterers combine the virtues of fine hand-sewn work and expedited delivery, which is why Style and Comfort earns high marks from the trade. This small eleven-year-old firm manages to achieve a turnaround time of two to three weeks, with results that are said to be "very good."

Led by owner Luis Salazar, this firm specializes in custom-made upholstered furniture, but has been known to take on window treatment projects and recently started building frames. We hear that Salazar and his team work best when you supply the drawings and fabric samples. Sources say this company is "eager to please" and works hard to satisfy its clients. Reasonable prices look even better in light of the fact that Style and Comfort's regular turnaround is faster than some firms' express service.

"We love Luis at Style & Comfort." "A mom-and-pop shop that always comes through for us in time and at a good price." "For simple and straightforward reupholstery, they can't be beat."

The Silk Trading Company   3.5   3   4.5   4.5
360 South La Brea Avenue, Los Angeles, CA 90036
(323) 954 - 2283 www.silktrading.com

Retail and trade—Sophisticated, modern, luxurious fabrics, drapery and upholstery

Affordable, accessible luxury is how The Silk Trading Company bills itself, and clients agree. Known by many as a purveyor of fine silk and textiles by the yard, the company has broken new ground into custom upholstery, custom drapery and a highly successful ready-to-wear drapery line called "Drapery Out-of-a-Box." Described as luxurious, classically derived and consistently well crafted, the firm's recently developed signature style is reflected in these products. Of course, the key differentiating factor here is cost (much less since you do it yourself) and availability (immediate gratification). Clients include both homeowners and decorators looking for that perfect shade of dupioni.

Owners Andie and Warren Kay began Silk Trading in the early 1990s after international careers in opera singing and clothing design and marketing, respectively. Coming from London to LA, they opened a 600 square foot shop in Santa Monica. Today, they boast 8,000 square feet on La Brea and five additional, substantially sized showrooms throughout the United States, including a very large showroom in the basement of ABC Carpet in NYC. The firm's reputation gains momentum every year due to its ever-widening array of quality products and, now, services. About 30 pieces are available for upholstery in the furniture line, which may be covered in either Silk Trading fabrics (done 80 percent of the time) or your own choice of materials (COM). Drapery and reupholstery services may be done only with the company's fabrics. Orders take from four to ten weeks.

Prices vary but approximate wholesale—a welcome concept for homeowners. There is also a relatively small but growing interior design service. For a modest $500 fee, a well-trained staff decorator will visit your home or help you choose among the resources of the entire ABC store at a ten percent discount.

"Fashionable, but not trendy." "Their silks are regularly used interchangeably with the best available in the D&D and are about 30 percent less expensive." "The sales staff in the basement of the D&D could not be nicer and really know the product line." "It was so easy—they came, they measured, they installed. No muss, no fuss." "The reupholstery service was very well managed. Once I chose one of their fabrics, they came the next day, took away my sofa and it reappeared five weeks later looking brand-new."

Ty-Teck Interiors   4.5   4   4.5   4.5
7277 Santa Monica Boulevard, Los Angeles, CA 90046
(323) 876 - 8220

Trade only—Intricate custom upholstery, wall upholstery and window treatments

For elaborate draping in the finest historical traditions, decorators trust Ian Tyson, a craftsman with an impeccable pedigree. Working for Charles Hammonds in London, Tyson's training ground included many of the English royal palaces and the Saudi Royal Trust estates. Tyson went on to Jules Edlin, the notable New York wall upholstery firm, where he worked on coveted commissions such as the gallery walls of the Metropolitan Museum of Art and commissions for Mark Hampton. By the time Tyson opened Ty-Teck's doors in LA in 1989, he had years of elite experience under his belt.

Assisted by seven employees, Tyson now serves LA designers and their impressive clientele. His firm does about three-quarters of its work in custom upholstery, using all the Old-World methods. Decorators trust him to execute their most complex designs. A great deal of the work is hand sewn, and bump is often used for interlining. Famous clients include the Sultan of Brunei and Vernah Harrah of Harrah's Casinos. The firm is said to be fluent in a wide range of styles—from Persian, Asian, Texan and Italian to (of course) Californian.

Ty-Teck does a rendering of every room that must be approved by the client before work begins. Upholstery and drapery costs are expensive, with work taking about four to eight weeks.

"They can do the really tricky and complicated treatments that I would not trust to anyone else." "His Edwardian draperies are amazing." "Ian is just so interesting and fun to work with."

	Quality	Cost	Value	Recommend?

Valley Drapery & Upholstery   4   4   4   4

16616 Schoenborn Street, North Hills, CA 91343
(818) 892 - 7744   vdrapery@aol.com

Trade only—Custom upholstery and window treatments

Run like "a well-oiled machine," the large firm of Valley Drapery & Upholstery creates custom furniture, window treatments and soft goods for a solid repeat-business clientele. Sources say they return—project after project—for the consistently excellent work. Though the staff is 60 members strong, loyal clients tell us Valley Drapery offers the attentive, personalized service of a family business. Customers say there is always a knowledgeable voice on the other end of the phone line, and an installer is never far away in case of an "emergency."

In business since 1985, brothers Michael and David Sewitz came on the scene by purchasing a custom soft goods company. At the request of their decorator clients, they soon expanded into custom upholstered furniture and window treatments. The firm is said to be diligent about meeting schedules and deadlines—standard turnaround is three to four weeks. Prices for both upholstery and window treatments are standard for the industry.

"They take deadlines very seriously, and I appreciate that." "Very big operation, but they certainly don't treat you like a stranger."

Zambrano Custom Furniture   4.5   4   4.5   5

1115 Lillian Way, Los Angeles, CA 90038
(323) 461 - 3055

Trade only—Expert custom upholstered furniture

A perennial favorite of some of the most recognizable names in interior design, Bob Zambrano and his team are known in the industry for their Old-World methods of building first-rate custom furniture. We hear that Zambrano, who's been in the business since high school, personally attends to every detail from his desk in the center of the workshop.

For over thirty years, this firm has been growing a reputation for fine service and fabulous furniture in Los Angeles and around the world. We hear Zambrano & Co. can do anything, including exotic exposed wood pieces. The twelve-member firm also handles some of Barbara Barry's work, including prototypes for her Baker furniture line.

Six to eight weeks is the typical wait for a piece by Zambrano. Prices start at standard but can climb to extremes, depending on the project. This veteran firm gets high marks from clients for friendly, personalized customer service and for its extraordinary product.

"Bob is a true expert at what he does." "Their workroom is so clean you can eat off the floor." "The key to a good sofa is the cushions, and Zambrano's are perfection." "He is extremely organized and gets things done when he says he will." "I never feel like a number. Bob gives the most personalized service."

Hiring a Window Washer

There are too many magnificent views in LA to allow an Angeleno to accept a grimy window. Window washing may seem like a straightforward project, but because residences come in a variety of shapes, sizes and conditions, there are many variables for your service provider to deal with. You'll want to review your situation with the cleaning service before somebody shows up to do the actual washing.

Do Your Homework

Before you contact any window washers, take stock of your windows. How many do you have? Are they storm windows, dormer windows or French doors? Do you have window guards or grates? How many? Do the windows open in, slide up and down, or tip out? Are they old or new? Are they dirty enough that they'll need to be power-washed or scraped? If you live in a high-rise condo or loft building, are there hooks outside the windows to which the washer can connect himself and his equipment? If so, are they all secure? Taking these factors into consideration, the service provider should be able to give you a rough "guesstimate" over the phone. If you omit any information, the work may end up costing more than the original quote once somebody shows up to give you a formal estimate.

It's customary for window washers to provide a free estimate, but you may want to confirm this on the phone with the service provider too. Once your windows are inspected, you should receive a written estimate. Getting the estimate in writing will help prevent unexpected charges later. For example, a service provider could claim that the job was more involved than expected, and try to charge a higher fee after the work is done.

What Should I Expect?

You'll want to ask the service provider a few questions before signing any contracts. Inquire about the length of time the company has been in business (the longer, the better), where most of its customers are located and whether they can provide references. The references will help you get an idea of how reliable the provider is: how long it takes to schedule an appointment, if it gets the work done on time and thoroughly, and if its workers clean up after themselves. Most of the window washers listed didn't vary enormously—you might have to wait longer for an appointment with one company than another, but all have received good reviews from customers.

Be sure that your service provider is fully insured and can show proof of workmen's compensation and liability insurance. If it does not have this coverage, you may be responsible for any accidents that happen on your property. There is no specific license or certification for window cleaning companies other than filing to operate as a business with the Department of Labor.

On Cost

There are three general methods of pricing: per window, per job or per hour, with an estimate of the time necessary to complete the job. In addition, some companies have minimums and/or charge for estimates. The most common method of pricing is a basic rate per window, taking window size into account. It is a good idea to inquire about a discount if you have a large job (20 or more windows). Many vendors will negotiate a better price if there is a substantial amount of work to be done. For a basic 6-over-6 window (a window that has two frames that slide up or down, each with six separate panes) with no window guards, paint or unusual amounts of dirt, you can expect a price range from $5 to $15 per window, with the majority of vendors charging $8 to $10. However, factors like location, type of window (Do you have thermal panes, storm windows, etc.?), accessibility (Are the windows hard to reach? Do you have hooks or crevices for the window washer to secure himself to?) and amount of dirt should be considered and discussed, since these might affect the final estimate.

PREPARING FOR WINDOW-WASHING DAY

Once you have set up an appointment, clear a path to the windows to prevent mishaps. Move that antique table with the priceless lamp. Remove objects that may obstruct access to sills and benches. Draw back your curtains and window treatments. A service provider should show the utmost respect for your home and protect your carpets and walls from drips and spills. If it makes you more comfortable, schedule free time for yourself on window-washing day so you can keep an eye on the process.

CLEANING CALENDAR

A professional window cleaning twice a year is usually sufficient, but if your residence is especially exposed to the elements of city life, you may need more frequent cleanings. Summer is generally the busiest time of the year for the window washing industry in Los Angeles. Be sure to call well in advance if you want your windows cleaned at peak times.

SOMETHING EXTRA

Window cleaners often offer a variety of other services, from cleaning screens and blinds to waxing and sanding floors. They might pressure-wash canopies, awnings, sidewalks, garages and greenhouses or do heavy-duty cleaning of gutters, carpets, upholstery and appliances. Some also offer basic handyman services, house painting and clean-up after renovations. If you are pleased with the company, consider using it for other household projects. Now that you can see through your windows again, you might notice all kinds of things.

TIPS FOR WASHING WINDOWS
BETWEEN PROFESSIONAL SERVICE CALLS

- ✧ Never wash windows in the bright sunlight. They'll dry too fast and carry a streaky residue.
- ✧ Use a squeegee instead of paper towels.
- ✧ For best results, skip the store-bought spray cleaner and use a mixture of one cup white vinegar diluted with a gallon of warm water.
- ✧ Sponge the cleaning solution onto the window then drag the squeegee across the glass. Wipe the squeegee blade with a damp cloth after each swipe.
- ✧ For extra shine, rub window glass with a clean blackboard eraser after cleaning.
- ✧ If you absolutely *don't* do windows, share these tips with your housekeeper.

	Quality	Cost	Value	Recommend?
	+	**$**	**◆**	**★**

WINDOW WASHERS

🛍 FIRMS WITH PORTFOLIOS 🛍

Dave The Window Washer 🛍   4.5   2.5   5   5
1800 South Robertson Boulevard, Suite 129, Los Angeles, CA 90035
(310) 454 - 6780   www.windowwasher.com

Residential/commercial window washing; carpet, upholstery and gutter cleaning

Dave The Window Washer sounds like the name of a band, and in fact, founder Dan Rastorfer is a rock musician who took up window washing as a day job back in 1985. These days, Rastorfer has a lot of loyal fans in Pacific Palisades, Malibu, Silver Lake, Beverly Hills, Hollywood and San Diego. Licensed, bonded and insured, Rastorfer's firm is a member of the International Window Cleaning Association and the Scaffolding Industry Association.

The company serves residential, commercial and industrial clients, specializing in high-rises. Aside from window washing, the firm offers carpet and upholstery cleaning, pressure and steam cleaning, trash chute cleaning, gutter cleaning, screen repair and graffiti removal. The firm charges per job based on a free estimate that takes into account the number and accessibility of windows and the job's location.

Sources report that Rastorfer is a man of his word who does his work "with integrity and professionalism." His workers are described as organized, prompt and courteous. With great word of mouth and a cool name, Dave the Window Washer has no trouble getting bookings.

"The most reputable guy I know." "No need to look anywhere else." "He does what he says at the price he says and in the time he says." "Book this guy early, as he can get pretty busy."

Paul's Professional Window Washing 🛍   5   4.5   4.5   5
2707 Foothill Boulevard, La Crescenta, CA 91214
(818) 249 - 7917   www.paulsprowindow.com

Residential/commercial window washing; gutter and glass cleaning; post-construction clean-up

Since opening its doors in 1981, Paul's Professional Window Washing has been acquiring a growing list of residential and commercial clients. Founded by Paul Dutton, who started doing window washing part-time in college, this licensed, bonded and insured company makes windows shine all over the west side. Paul's Professional also offers services such as power washing, exterior house washing, gutter cleaning, blind cleaning, post-construction cleanup, glass restoration, and chandelier and mirror cleaning. The firm's full-service screen repair section can do work on site or back at headquarters.

Dutton served on the board of the International Window Cleaning Association for three years and is regarded among his peers and clients as a very "astute businessman." A frequent contributor to the industry's trade journal, Dutton is also a consultant and speaker for various seminars on window washing. In 2004, the business was awarded an honorary Mayor's Award from the local Chamber Of Commerce.

Paul's Professional Window Washing charges per job, based on a free estimate. Though prices are at the high end of the range, the "prompt," "courteous," "efficient" service is widely considered to be worth it.

"Goes out of the way to do something extra." "Extremely thorough. Very good at what they do." "A bit more expensive than most, but he delivers excellent results." "Paul is always on top of things." "A pleasure to have around."

FIRMS WITHOUT PORTFOLIOS

Ace Window Cleaning Service — 3.5 3 4.5 4
1088 South Fairfax, Los Angeles, CA 90019
(323) 857 - 1860
Residential/commercial window washing

Ace Window Cleaning was established in 1988 by Cortez Hayes, who grew up in the window washing business. Today, this licensed and insured family firm serves residential and commercial buildings of up to three stories, primarily in Beverly Hills, Santa Monica and Pacific Palisades.

Pricing is per job, based on a free estimate that factors in size, number and location of windows. With four full-time employees, the firm also provides janitorial services.

Amaidzing — 4 2.5 5 5
14717 Archwood Street, Van Nuys, CA 91405
(310) 278 - 1878   www.amaidzing.com
Residential/commercial window washing; housekeeping services

Founded and operated by firm CEO Kelli McAllister, Amaidzing not only cleans windows, screens and blinds, but also provides weekly, monthly or occasional maid and housekeeping services to a residential and commercial clientele. Now in its fourth year, the company charges a flat fee of $26 per cleaner/per hour with a one-hour minimum.

References say only good things about this company, and we hear that the Amaidzing crews are prompt, reliable and organized. Insiders appreciate the company's flexible scheduling—Amaidzing can send over a crew on the same day it receives a call.

"The crews are very good." "Organized. There is always professional and pleasant supervision." "Prompt." "Stays on top of things."

Anacapa Window & Carpet Cleaning — 3.5 2 5 4.5
3920 Inglewood Boulevard, Suite 5, Los Angeles, CA 90066
(310) 398 - 3214
Residential/commercial window washing; carpet cleaning

Dan Mullen has been a one-man band since 1988. For his westside residential and commercial clients, Mullen will wash windows and clean upholstery or carpets. Mullen also does pressure washing. All services are performed on site, and customers say this solo act gets the job done quickly and efficiently.

Mullen works in Bel Air, Culver City, Santa Monica, Marina del Rey and surrounding areas. There is a flat hourly rate to clean windows and carpets. Prices are described as moderate, and in light of Mullen's brisk service, the firm is considered a good value.

"Dan is a quiet and efficient man." "He gets the job done with minimal mess."

	Quality	Cost	Value	Recommend?
	✚	$	◆	★

Expert Window Cleaning   3   2.5   4.5   4

8832 Sylmar Avenue, Panorama City, CA 91402
(818) 830 - 0971

Residential/commercial window washing; janitorial services; post-construction cleanup

"A neighborhood favorite" in a neighborhood that encompasses the greater part of LA, Expert Window Cleaning earns kudos for its excellent work ethic, reliability and thoroughness. The firm is owned and managed by founder Art Gutierrez, who supervises most of the work—when he's not doing it himself. Expert will wash windows in buildings of up to twelve stories. The firm also provides plenty of other services, including power washing, high-power steam cleaning, gutter cleaning, chandelier cleaning, janitorial services and post-construction cleanup.

The firm serves residential and commercial clients in most of Los Angeles, as well as some parts in the San Fernando Valley and Orange County. Pricing is usually per hour, per person, or occasionally by the job, based on a free estimate. A family business with three full-time employees, Expert is a member in good standing of the International Window Cleaning Association, and its staff has passed the Scaffold Industry Association exam.

"I can count on Art at a moment's notice." "Very detailed. I have been using them years!"

GI Cleaning Service Inc.   4   2.5   5   5

4735 Oakwood Avenue, Suite 7, Los Angeles, CA 90004
(323) 460 - 6491   www.gicleaningservice.com

Residential/commercial window washing; carpet & floor cleaning; janitorial services

At GI Cleaning Service, the workers really dress the part. Sporting military fatigues from head-to-toe and toting walkie-talkies, these well-regarded troops are said to wash windows and clean floors with veteran precision and thoroughness.

Rene Williams established the firm in 1996 after retiring from the army. Today, GI Cleaning serves prominent residential and commercial customers around Beverly Hills, Pacific Palisades, Malibu and Santa Monica. The company charges a flat fee per hour, per person. Licensed, bonded and insured, the company also provides carpet cleaning, janitorial and housekeeping services, pressure washing, gutter cleaning, marble cleaning and post-construction cleanup. The firm holds a double A rating from The Better Business Bureau. GI Cleaning was also named Best Cleaning Service for 2003 by *LA Weekly* magazine.

Patrons tell us GI's workers are very knowledgeable and efficient. We hear the staff always finishes the job on time. Customers salute GI's combination of high quality and competitive rates.

"Prompt. Military precision." "Very organized." "Exceptional, especially when motivated." "Bring in the troops!" "I'd trust no one else."

	Quality ✚	Cost $	Value ◆	Recommend? ★

Harbor Window Cleaning   4   2.5   5   5

8648 Harrison Way, Buena Park, CA 90620
(310) 379 - 5791

Residential/commercial window washing

Harbor Window Cleaning has been keeping clients' homes shipshape for the past 30 years. Owner Mike Steele worked at his uncle's window washing business before venturing out on his own; today, his firm serves residential and commercial clients around Los Angeles and the South Bay. In addition to windows, Harbor will also handle building maintenance and cleaning.

References praise Steele and his team as dependable, trustworthy and diligent. Insiders say Steele is always on top of things and does most of the work himself. Steele charges per job based on a free estimate, and we hear that his moderate prices and good work ethic keep clients coming back for more.

"A nice, all-American man. Presents himself very well and does his work with integrity." "Gets along well with everyone. Very easy to work with." "Efficient, thorough and dependable."

Inside Out Window Cleaning Inc.   4   2.5   5   5

605 West Huntington Drive, Suite 615, Monrovia, CA 91016
(800) 369 - 3674   www.insideoutwindowcleaning.com

Residential/commercial window washing

Clients can't say enough good things about Inside Out Window Cleaning. We hear this large firm's workers are efficient, clean and organized. Husband-and-wife team Jim and Susan Holder are very hands-on managers, making sure their 45 full-time employees deliver impeccable window washing to their residential and commercial clients.

Commercial project rates are determined by measuring each pane and charging by the square foot, while residential clients are given a flat rate fee (with a minimum charge). The moderate prices are said to be a good value for the outstanding service.

Established in 1985 and incorporated in 1991, Inside Out works in West LA, Santa Monica, Brentwood and San Marino. Not only is the firm a member of the International Window Cleaning Association (IWCA), but Jim also served on the Association's board in 1999.

"I have been working with them for twenty years. I'm very satisfied with their work." "One of the best." "Gets the job done." "Can get quite busy so scheduling might be a bit difficult." "Excellent work ethic."

Mahogany Cleaning Services   3.5   2   5   5

269 South Beverly Drive, Suite 260, Beverly Hills, CA 90212
(323) 293 - 1885

Residential/commercial window washing; janitorial services

Along with window washing, janitorial and cleaning services, Mahogany Cleaning Services also offers pressure washing and awning cleaning to its clientele in West LA, Santa Monica and Malibu. Established in 1999 by Victoria Archie, this family business is licensed, bonded and insured. Though the firm does some commercial work, it primarily serves residential clients on the west side.

Customers tell us that Archie and her crew are competent, fast and organized. Pricing is by the job with a flat minimum fee. Mahogany's moderate prices are considered by many to be a good value for the efficient service they provide.

"A very nice lady. Great with follow-ups." "Knows what she is doing." "Hands-on businesswoman."

	Quality	Cost	Value	Recommend?
	+	**$**	**◆**	**★**

Milliken Window Washing   5   2   5   5

1318 North Formosa Avenue, Los Angeles, CA 90046
(323) 876 - 4579

Residential/commercial window washing; gutter and glass cleaning

What started out as a side job for former musician Mike Milliken is now a full-fledged business with a healthy audience. Milliken's one-man firm washes windows for a primarily residential clientele. (Milliken does serve a small number of commercial customers, but he will not do high-rise jobs.) In addition to window washing, Milliken also does gutter cleaning, skylight and chandelier cleaning, as well as glass restoration.

References praise this "polite young man" for his professionalism and attention to detail. Clients clearly appreciate the zest he shows for his work. Milliken typically works in Pacific Palisades, Beverly Hills, Hollywood and the San Fernando Valley, doing most projects by himself and only subcontracting workers for very large jobs. Some say that since Milliken usually works alone, scheduling can be a bit of a challenge—however, the fabulous, surprisingly inexpensive service is definitely worth the wait.

"You can put him in your house and leave—his honesty is unquestionable." "I sometimes need to nudge him to hike up his prices—he is too nice." "There's nobody quite like Mike."

Mr. Window Cleaning   4.5   2.5   5   5

15155 Chaumont Street, Lake Elsinore, CA 92530
(877) 679 - 4636   www.mrwindow.net

Residential/commercial window washing; glass and gutter cleaning; post-construction cleanup

With only a hundred dollars in his pocket, Garry Jalowka bought his first squeegee and ladder. After getting his first client, Jalowka officially established Mr. Window Cleaning in 1993. The rest, as they say, is history. Mr. Window's client list multiplied exponentially, transforming a one-man operation into a full-fledged window cleaning company with more than a dozen employees. Today, Jalowka's company provides services for residential, commercial and industrial customers in high-rise buildings up to 30 stories and will roll out a national franchise by 2006.

Mr. Window usually charges by the window and serves customers in Los Angeles, Orange County, San Bernardino County, Riverside County, Culver City, San Diego—and as far away as Nevada and Arizona. Licensed, bonded and insured, the firm is a member of the International Window Cleaning Association, where Jalowka served on the board, and the Power Washers of North America. His workers have passed the exams of the International Window Cleaning Certification Institute, which trains window washers with an emphasis on safety measures. Mr. Window also provides awning and gutter cleaning, pressure washing, house washing, bird control, chandelier cleaning, glass restoration, window tinting, screen repairs, as well as post-construction cleanup.

We hear that Jalowka and his team are efficient, prompt and "the friendliest people around." References appreciate the high quality of Mr. Window's work and the very reasonable prices.

"Great people to work with. Excellent job." "Very friendly. Customer-oriented workers." "Reliable and thorough." "Never had a bad experience with them."

	Quality	Cost	Value	Recommend?

Sunrise Window Cleaners Inc.   4.5   2.5   5   5

PO Box 9172, North Hollywood, CA 91609
(818) 769 - 9000

Residential/commercial window washing; general outdoor cleaning

Zane Britt grew up in the New York window washing business, but he chose the sunset coast when he founded Sunrise Window Cleaners in 1977. Today Sunrise serves residential and commercial window washing clients in West LA and Orange County. Britt's eighteen-man crew also provides such services as power washing, awning and sidewalk cleaning, graffiti removal and descaling of water deposits on glass.

Licensed, bonded and insured, the company is a member of the Building Owners and Managers Association, the International Window Cleaning Association and the Scaffold Association. Loyal clients report that the team at Sunrise is very professional, prompt and efficient. The customer-oriented service make this company a favorite among LA's well-heeled residents, and the moderate prices don't hurt either.

"Excellent work ethic. Good sense of humor." "They fix any problems that arise." "Professional. Britt will go out of his way to make clients happy."

The Master Cleaner Inc.   3.5   2.5   5   5

PO Box 24, Canoga Park, CA 91396
(818) 704 - 3927   www.gwindowcleaning.com

Residential/commercial window washing; janitorial services and general cleaning; post-construction cleanup

References agree: This company's truly a master of its trade. Established in 1997 by George Barrera, The Master Cleaner serves residential and commercial clients in Beverly Hills, the San Fernando Valley, Malibu, Pacific Palisades, Ventura County and San Bernardino County. This family firm offers window cleaning, pressure washing, janitorial cleaning, awning and sidewalk washing, and gutter cleaning—as well as "very detailed" post-construction cleanup.

We hear Barrera and his team are very thorough, efficient and courteous. They are especially noted for adhering to deadlines. Sources also say that this firm's workers go out of their way to give something extra, and that Barrera can be counted on during emergencies. The Master Cleaner is licensed, bonded and insured, and calculates its moderate rates per job, based on a flat fee.

"They will stay as long as it takes." "George stays on top of things." "Efficient service at competitive prices." "Pays attention to detail." "After construction was finished, my house was unlivable. After George came, everything—from windows to floors—sparkled."

The Window Guys ... LA   4   2.5   5   4.5

311 North Robertson Boulevard, Suite 771, Beverly Hills, CA 90211
(213) 324 - 2192   www.thewindowguysla.com

Residential/commercial window washing

No, "The Window Guys ... LA" is not a new sitcom. Founded in 1998 by Lou Martin, The Window Guys was incorporated in January 2002. These days it serves residential and commercial clients in West Hollywood, Santa Monica, Newport, Laguna del Rey, Beverly Hills, Laguna Beach and Pacific Palisades—and even some clients in Las Vegas. Window washing is the main attraction, but the firm also offers such services as power washing and awning cleaning.

Pricing is usually per window, but Martin also offers special packages for clients requiring regular maintenance programs. Clients praise the staff's excellent, professional work ethic. We hear that moderate prices keep The Window Guys' contented audience coming back for more episodes.

"Clean and fast." "Professionals. Been using them for more than five years."
"Responsive and will accommodate even at short notice."

D

E

F

G

W

Z

THE FRANKLIN REPORT.
The Insider's Guide to Home Services

INSTRUCTIONS: To contribute to a service provider's review, fill out the form below and **fax** it back to us at **212-744-3546** or mail to 201 East 69th Street, Suite 14J, New York, NY 10021. Or you may complete a reference on our website, www.franklinreport.com. Please make sure that you give us a contact e-mail address and a phone number. While all information will remain anonymous, our editorial staff may need to reach you to confirm the information.

Thank you.

FILL-IN REFERENCE REPORT FORM

Client Name:

Client E-mail: Client Phone:

Service Provider Company Name:

Company Contact: Company Phone:

Service (i.e. plumbing):

Company Address:

PLEASE RATE THE PROVIDER ON EACH OF THE FOLLOWING:

QUALITY OF WORK: ❏ Highest Imaginable   ❏ Outstanding   ❏ Strong
❏ Moderate   ❏ Adequate   ❏ Poor

COST: ❏ Over the Top   ❏ Expensive   ❏ Reasonable   ❏ Moderate
❏ Inexpensive   ❏ Bargain

VALUE: ❏ Extraordinary Value, Worth Every Penny   ❏ Good Value
❏ Mediocre Value   ❏ Poor Value   ❏ Horrible Value   ❏ Unconscionable

RECOMMENDATION: ❏ My First and Only Choice   ❏ On My Short List, Would
Recommend to a Friend   ❏ Very Satisfied, Might Hire Again   ❏ Have Reservations
❏ Not Pleased, Would Not Hire Again   ❏ Will Never Talk to Again

COMMENTS:

_____

_____

_____

_____

_____

_____

_____

_____

THE FRANKLIN REPORT.
The Insider's Guide to Home Services

INSTRUCTIONS: To contribute to a service provider's review, fill out the form below and **fax** it back to us at **212-744-3546** or mail to 201 East 69th Street, Suite 14J, New York, NY 10021. Or you may complete a reference on our website, www.franklinreport.com. Please make sure that you give us a contact e-mail address and a phone number. While all information will remain anonymous, our editorial staff may need to reach you to confirm the information.

Thank you.

FILL-IN REFERENCE REPORT FORM

Client Name:

Client E-mail: _____ Client Phone:

Service Provider Company Name:

Company Contact: _____ Company Phone:

Service (i.e. plumbing):

Company Address:

PLEASE RATE THE PROVIDER ON EACH OF THE FOLLOWING:

QUALITY OF WORK: ❑ Highest Imaginable ❑ Outstanding ❑ Strong ❑ Moderate ❑ Adequate ❑ Poor

COST: ❑ Over the Top ❑ Expensive ❑ Reasonable ❑ Moderate ❑ Inexpensive ❑ Bargain

VALUE: ❑ Extraordinary Value, Worth Every Penny ❑ Good Value ❑ Mediocre Value ❑ Poor Value ❑ Horrible Value ❑ Unconscionable

RECOMMENDATION: ❑ My First and Only Choice ❑ On My Short List, Would Recommend to a Friend ❑ Very Satisfied, Might Hire Again ❑ Have Reservations ❑ Not Pleased, Would Not Hire Again ❑ Will Never Talk to Again

COMMENTS:

_____

_____

_____

_____

_____

_____

_____

_____

NOTES

NOTES